ACTEX Academic Series

Models for Quantifying Risk

Sixth Edition

Stephen J. Camilli, ASA
Ian Duncan, FSA, FIA, FCIA, MAAA
Richard L. London, FSA

ACTEX Publications, Inc.
Winsted, CT

Requests for permission should be addressed to
ACTEX Publications
P.O. Box 974
Winsted, CT 06098

Manufactured in the United States of America

10 9 8 7 6 5 4 3 2 1

Cover design by Jeff Melaragno

Library of Congress Cataloging-in-Publication Data

London, Richard L.
Models for quantifying risk / by Richard L. London, FSA; Ian Duncan, FSA, FIA, FCIA, MAAA; Stephen J. Camilli, ASA. -- 6th edition.
pages cm
Revised edition of: Models for quantifying risk, Fifth edition, by Robin J. Cunningham, Thomas N. Herzog, Richard L. London, published in 2012.
Includes bibliographical references and index.
ISBN 978-1-62542-347-4 (alk. paper)
1. Insurance--Mathematics. 2. Risk management. 3. Financial risk. I. Duncan, Ian G., 1950- II. Camilli, Stephen J., 1976- III. Cunningham, Robin J., 1965- Models for quantifying risk. IV. Title.
HG8781.C86 2014
368'.0120151--dc23

2014018664

ISBN 978-1-62542-347-4

General and Historical Preface

The analysis and management of financial risk is the fundamental subject matter of the discipline of actuarial science, and is therefore the basic work of the actuary. In order to manage financial risk, by use of insurance schemes or any other risk management technique, the actuary must first have a framework for quantifying the magnitude of the risk itself. This is achieved by using mathematical models that are appropriate for each particular type of risk under consideration. Since risk is, almost by definition, probabilistic, it follows that the appropriate models will also be probabilistic, or stochastic, in nature.

This textbook, appropriately entitled *Models for Quantifying Risk*, addresses the major types of financial risk analyzed by actuaries, and presents a variety of stochastic models for the actuary to use in undertaking this analysis. It is designed to be appropriate for a two-semester university course in basic actuarial science for third-year or fourth-year undergraduate students or entry-level graduate students. It is also intended to be an appropriate text for use by candidates in preparing for Exam MLC of the Society of Actuaries or Exam LC of the Casualty Actuarial Society.

One way to manage financial risk is to *insure* it, which basically means that a second party, generally an insurance company, is paid a fee to assume the risk from the party initially facing it. Historically the work of actuaries was largely confined to the management of risk within an insurance context, so much so, in fact, that actuaries were thought of as "insurance mathematicians" and actuarial science was thought of as "insurance math." Although the insurance context remains a primary environment for the actuarial management of risk, it is by no means any longer the only one.

However, in recognition of the insurance context as the original setting for actuarial analysis and management of financial risk, we have chosen to make liberal use of insurance terminology and notation to describe many of the risk quantification models presented in this text. The reader should always keep in mind, however, that this frequent reference to an insurance context does not reduce the applicability of the models to risk management situations in which no use of insurance is involved.

The text is written in a manner that assumes each reader has a strong background in calculus, linear algebra, the theory of compound interest, and probability. (A familiarity with statistics is not presumed.)

Models for Quantifying Risk has appeared in five earlier editions. In each of those editions, important authorship contributions were made by Robin J. Cunningham, Ph.D., and Thomas N. Herzog, Ph.D., ASA. ACTEX Publications wishes to express its appreciation to these former co-authors for their lasting contributions to the text.

In addition to the former co-authors, many academic and industry actuaries contributed review services to the first five editions.

The original manuscript was thoroughly reviewed by Bryan V. Hearsey, ASA, of Lebanon Valley College and by Esther Portnoy, FSA, of University of Illinois. Portions of the manuscript were also reviewed by Warren R. Luckner, FSA, and his graduate student Luis Gutierrez at University of Nebraska-Lincoln. Kristen S. Moore, ASA, used an earlier draft as a supplemental text in her courses at University of Michigan. Thorough reviews of the original edition were also conducted by James W. Daniel, ASA, of University of Texas, Professor Jacques Labelle, Ph.D., of Université du Québec à Montréal, and a committee appointed by the Society of Actuaries.

Special thanks goes to the students enrolled in Math 287-288 at University of Connecticut during the 2004-05 academic year, where the original text was classroom-tested, and to graduate student Xiumei Song, who developed the spreadsheet-based material presented in Appendix A.

A number of revisions in the Second Edition were also reviewed by Professors Daniel and Hearsey; Third Edition revisions were reviewed by Professors Samuel A. Broverman, ASA (University of Toronto), Matthew J. Hassett, ASA (Arizona State University), and Warren R. Luckner, FSA (University of Nebraska-Lincoln). All of these academic colleagues made a number of useful comments that have contributed to an improved published text.

Three new applied topics were brought into the Fifth Edition, to meet changes made in the Exam MLC curriculum effective with the May 2012 exam administration. They were contributed by actuaries with considerable experience in their respective fields, and we wish to acknowledge their valuable contributions. They include Ronald Gebhardtsbauer, FSA (Penn State University) for the pension material in Section 14.5, Ximing Yao, FSA (Hartford Life) for the universal life material in Chapter 16, and Chunhua (Amy) Meng, FSA (Yindga Taihe Life) for the material on variable annuities. (This topic has subsequently been removed from the text.)

The new material added to the Fifth Edition was also reviewed by Professor Luckner, as well as by Tracey J. Polsgrove, FSA (John Hancock USA), Link Richardson, FSA (American General Life), Arthur W. Anderson, ASA, EA (The Arthur W. Anderson Group), Cheryl Ann Breindel, FSA (Hartford Life), Douglas J. Jangraw, FSA (Massachusetts Mutual Life), Robert W. Beal, FSA (Milliman Portland), Andrew C. Boyer, FSA (Milliman Windsor), and Matthew Blanchette, FSA (Forethought Group).

SIXTH EDITION PREFACE

This latest edition of *Models for Quantifying Risk* has been revised from the prior edition by a new team of co-authors. There are three major areas of revision.

(1) Early in 2013, the Society of Actuaries announced that Exam MLC would be changed from an all multiple choice exam to one that will be 40% multiple choice and 60% written answer, beginning with the April 2014 exam administration. Accordingly, we have revised our textbook by introducing a number of examples intended to introduce our readers to this new type of Exam MLC question.

(2) Effective for the April 2014 exam, SOA has published an eight-page study note entitled "Notation and Terminology Used on Exam MLC." The purpose of the study note is to inform exam candidates that some notation and terminology used on the exam could be different from that used in certain exam-preparation textbooks, particularly those written by authors oriented to actuarial theory and practice in countries outside of North America. *Our readers should be aware that the Sixth Edition of Models for Quantifying Risk uses notation and terminology that conforms totally to that to be used on the exam.* Exam candidates using this text will have no need to be concerned with the SOA study note.

(3) The presentation of several important Exam MLC topics has been expanded and improved in the new edition. These include the topics of (a) universal life insurance, (b) multi-state model representation of various actuarial models, (c) Thiele's differential equation for the fully continuous reserve, and its approximate solution via Euler's method, and (d) profit analysis and testing, including the notion of the distribution of some of that profit back to the insureds as policyholder dividends under participating insurance contracts. Our expanded treatment of topic (d) has resulted in placing it in its own chapter (Chapter 17).

The current edition of *Models for Quantifying Risk* is organized into three sections.

The first, consisting of Chapters 1-4, presents a review of interest theory, probability, and Markov Chains in Chapters 1-3, respectively. The content of these chapters is very much needed as background to later material. They are included in the text for readers needing a comprehensive review of the topics. For those requiring an original textbook on any of these topics, we recommend either Broverman [5] or Kellison [15] for interest theory, Hassett and Stewart [12] for probability, and Ross [22] for Markov Chains. Chapter 4 presents a brief introduction to the life insurance industry and its products.

The second section, made up of Chapters 5-14, addresses the topic of survival-contingent payment models, traditionally referred to as *life contingencies*. The survival model is presented in Chapters 5 and 6, in both its parametric and tabular contexts. The standard set of single-life, single-decrement actuarial topics are then covered in Chapters 7-11, including contingent payment models (with emphasis on their standard life insurance applications), contingent annuities (life annuities), annual funding schemes (annual premiums), including their m^{thly} and continuous variations, and contingent contract reserves. Extensions to the multi-life cases of joint and last-survivor are presented in Chapter 12 and multiple-decrement models are covered in Chapters 13 and 14.

The third section, consisting of Chapters 15-17, contains three special topics. Chapter 15 deals with the topic of variable interest rates, Chapter 16 addresses the modern insurance product known as Universal Life, and Chapter 17 discusses the important topic of profit analysis and profit distribution to policyholders under participating insurance contracts.

The writing team would like to thank the folks at ACTEX Publications for their contributions to this edition. Gail A. Hall, FSA, served as the project editor, and reviewed a number of the expanded new edition topics. Marilyn J. Baleshiski and Garrett Doherty did the typesetting and graphic arts, and Jeff Melaragno designed the text's cover.

Xiaofeng (Felicia) Lai, a graduate student in the Actuarial Science Program at University of Connecticut, reviewed the entire Sixth Edition manuscript, working all of the new written-answer question examples, and made a number of valuable suggestions.

Finally, a very special acknowledgment is in order. When the Society of Actuaries published its textbook *Actuarial Mathematics* in the mid-1980s, Professor Geoffrey Crofts, FSA, then at University of Hartford, made the observation that the authors' use of the generic symbol Z as the present value random variable for *all* insurance models and the generic symbol Y as the present value random variable for *all* annuity models was confusing. He suggested that the present value random variable symbols be expanded to identify more characteristics of the models to which each related, following the principle that the present value random variable be notated in a manner consistent with the standard International Actuarial Notation used for its expected value. Thus one should use, for example, $\bar{Z}_{x:\overline{n}|}$ in the case of the continuous endowment insurance model and ${}_{n|}\ddot{Y}_x$ in the case of the n-year deferred annuity-due model, whose expected values are denoted $\bar{A}_{x:\overline{n}|}$ and ${}_{n|}\ddot{a}_x$, respectively. Professor Crofts' notation has been adopted throughout our textbook, and we wish to thank him for suggesting this very useful idea to us.

Stephen J. Camilli, ASA
Winsted, Connecticut

Ian G. Duncan, FSA, MAAA
Santa Barbara, California

Richard L. London, FSA
Storrs, Connecticut

TABLE OF CONTENTS

CHAPTER THREE: REVIEW OF MARKOV CHAINS 33

CHAPTER FOUR: CHARACTERISTICS OF INSURANCE AND PENSIONS 47

PART TWO: MODELS FOR SURVIVAL-CONTINGENT RISKS

CHAPTER FIVE: SURVIVAL MODELS (CONTINUOUS PARAMETRIC CONTEXT) 59

PART ONE

REVIEW AND BACKGROUND MATERIAL

The first section of this text presents three sets of mathematical tools, namely interest theory, probability, and Markov Chains, that will be needed to develop, understand, and analyze the various risk quantification models included later in the text.

With respect to these three tool sets, the text assumes that the reader has already completed a standard university course in each topic, or has otherwise already learned this material at a sufficient level. Accordingly, the presentation of these topics (in Chapters 1, 2, and 3, respectively) will be in the nature of a review.

Note that the mathematical tools of calculus and linear algebra are also deemed to be prerequisite skills for a study of this text, but no specific review of them is included.

The fourth chapter in this section presents a brief overview of the life insurance industry and its most basic collection of products.

CHAPTER ONE

REVIEW OF INTEREST THEORY

Many of the risk quantification models considered in this text are ultimately based on a blend of concepts of probability and the theory of interest. In this chapter we review the basic concepts and notation of interest theory. As stated in the Sixth Edition Preface, a prior familiarity with this material is assumed, so that it can be presented as a review without including derivations. Note that only the *compound interest* model is included.

1.1 INTEREST MEASURES

Interest theory usually begins with the concept of the *accumulation function*, denoted $a(t)$, which gives the accumulated value, at time $t \geq 0$, of a unit of money invested at time $t = 0$. Under compound interest, the accumulation function has the exponential form

$$a(t) = (1+i)^t, \tag{1.1}$$

for $t \geq 0$, where i is a parameter of the function. This is illustrated in Figure 1.1.

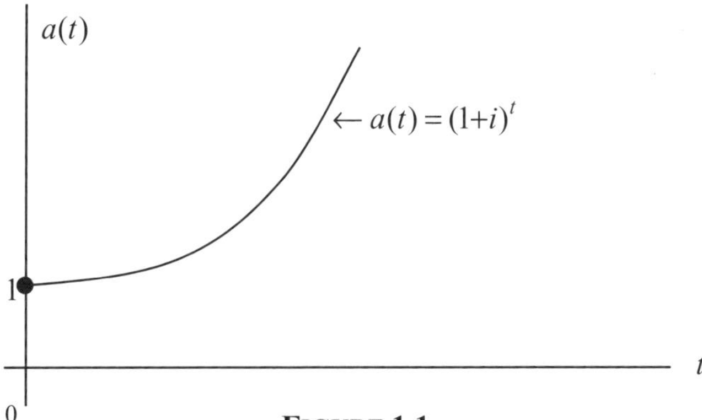

FIGURE 1.1

For the nth time interval, which runs from $t = n-1$ to $t = n$, the *effective rate of interest* is defined as

$$i_n = \frac{a(n)-a(n-1)}{a(n-1)} = \frac{(1+i)^n-(1+i)^{n-1}}{(1+i)^{n-1}} = i. \tag{1.2}$$

Thus we recall that under compound interest the effective periodic interest rate is a constant equal to the parameter in the exponential form of the accumulation function.

For the nth time interval the *effective rate of discount* is defined to be

$$d_n = \frac{a(n)-a(n-1)}{a(n)} = \frac{(1+i)^n-(1+i)^{n-1}}{(1+i)^n} = \frac{i}{1+i} = d. \tag{1.3}$$

Thus we find that the effective periodic discount rate is also a constant, and is a simple function of the parameter of the accumulation function (which is also the effective rate of interest). Solving Equation (1.3) for i we find

$$i = \frac{d}{1-d}. \tag{1.4}$$

The compound interest *discount factor* over one time interval is defined to be

$$v = \frac{1}{1+i}. \tag{1.5}$$

Taking Equations (1.3) and (1.5) together we observe the relationship

$$d = \frac{i}{1+i} = iv. \tag{1.6}$$

Next observe that Equation (1.4) tells us that $d = i(1-d)$ and Equation (1.6) tells us that $d = iv$, so together we have

$$v = 1-d \tag{1.7}$$

and therefore

$$d = 1-v. \tag{1.8}$$

This leads to $d = 1-\frac{1}{1+i}$. Multiplying both sides by $1+i$ then leads to $d+id = 1+i-1$, and finally to the relationship

$$id = i-d. \tag{1.9}$$

An instantaneous measure of interest, known as the *force of interest*, is defined by

$$\delta_t = \frac{a'(t)}{a(t)} = \frac{d}{dt}\ln a(t), \tag{1.10a}$$

which, under compound interest, becomes

$$\delta_t = \ln(1+i) = \delta, \tag{1.10b}$$

a constant function of time. Alternatively we can write

$$(1+i) = e^{\delta} \tag{1.11a}$$

and, in light of Equation (1.5),

$$v = e^{-\delta}. \tag{1.11b}$$

Integrating both sides of Equation (1.10a) with respect to t, between the limits 0 to n, results in the relationship

$$a(n) = e^{\int_0^n \delta_t\, dt}. \tag{1.12a}$$

Under compound interest, with $\delta_t = \delta$, a constant, and $a(n) = (1+i)^n$, Equation (1.12a) then becomes

$$(1+i)^n = e^{n\delta}, \tag{1.12b}$$

as already established by Equation (1.11a). Taking the reciprocals of both sides of Equation (1.12b) gives

$$(1+i)^{-n} = v^n = e^{-n\delta}, \tag{1.12c}$$

as already established by Equation (1.11b).

The reader will recall that the *effective period* (also called the *compounding period* or the *conversion period*) for a rate of compound interest (or discount) is a very important parameter. (An effective *annual* rate of 2% is very different from an effective *monthly* rate of 2%.) Thus we always describe an effective rate by both its numerical value and its period of effectiveness. This leads to the notion of the *equivalence of rates* with different effective periods. For example, an effective annual rate of

$$i = (1.02)^{12} - 1 = .26824$$

is equivalent to an effective monthly rate of 2%, and an effective quarterly rate of

$$i = (1.06)^{1/4} - 1 = .01467$$

is equivalent to an effective annual rate of 6%.

For rates with an effective period of less than one year, such as effective monthly, quarterly, or semiannual rates, we have adopted the notational convention of expressing the *annualized value* of the effective periodic rate. This annualized value is called the *nominal annual rate*. Thus, for example, an effective quarterly rate of 2% is stated as a nominal annual rate of 8%, an effective monthly rate of 1% is stated as a nominal annual rate of 12%, and an effective semiannual rate of 5% is stated as a nominal annual rate of 10%. The notation $i^{(4)} = .08$, $i^{(12)} = .12$, and $i^{(2)} = .10$, respectively, is used. Note that the number in the parentheses is the number of compounding (or effective) periods in a year. The same concept of nominal rate notation also applies to effective rates of discount.

1.2 LEVEL ANNUITY FUNCTIONS

In this section we review the terminology and notation used with level payment annuities-certain, evaluated at a constant rate of compound interest per payment period.

1.2.1 ANNUITY-IMMEDIATE

A *unit annuity-immediate* is one for which the unit payments are made at the *ends* of the respective payment periods, as illustrated in Figure 1.2.

FIGURE 1.2

The *present value* of the annuity, denoted $a_{\overline{n}|}$, is measured at time 0 and is given by

$$a_{\overline{n}|} = v+v^2+\cdots+v^n = \frac{1-v^n}{i}. \tag{1.13}$$

The *accumulated value* of the annuity, denoted $s_{\overline{n}|}$, is measured at time n and is given by

$$s_{\overline{n}|} = (1+i)^{n-1}+(1+i)^{n-2}+\cdots+(1+i)+1 = \frac{(1+i)^n-1}{i}. \tag{1.14}$$

From Equations (1.13) and (1.14) together we can see that

$$a_{\overline{n}|} = v^n \cdot s_{\overline{n}|}, \tag{1.15a}$$

$$s_{\overline{n}|} = (1+i)^n \cdot a_{\overline{n}|}, \tag{1.15b}$$

and

$$\frac{1}{a_{\overline{n}|}} = \frac{1}{s_{\overline{n}|}}+i. \tag{1.16}$$

In the limiting case, as $n \rightarrow \infty$, we have the notion of the *unit perpetuity-immediate*, with present value given by

$$a_{\overline{\infty}|} = v+v^2+\cdots = \frac{1}{i}. \tag{1.17}$$

1.2.2 ANNUITY-DUE

A *unit annuity-due* is one for which the unit payments are made at the *beginnings* of the respective payment periods, as illustrated in Figure 1.3.

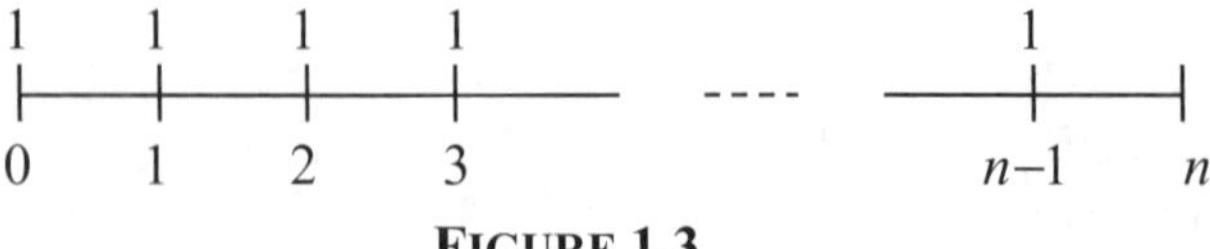

FIGURE 1.3

The present value of the annuity, denoted $\ddot{a}_{\overline{n}|}$, is measured at time 0 and is given by

$$\ddot{a}_{\overline{n}|} = 1+v+v^2+\cdots+v^{n-1} = \frac{1-v^n}{d}. \tag{1.18}$$

The accumulated value, denoted $\ddot{s}_{\overline{n}|}$, is measured at time n and is given by

$$\ddot{s}_{\overline{n}|} = (1+i)^n + (1+i)^{n-1} + \cdots + (1+i) = \frac{(1+i)^n - 1}{d}. \tag{1.19}$$

From Equations (1.18) and (1.19) together we can see that

$$\ddot{a}_{\overline{n}|} = v^n \cdot \ddot{s}_{\overline{n}|}, \tag{1.20a}$$

$$\ddot{s}_{\overline{n}|} = (1+i)^n \cdot \ddot{a}_{\overline{n}|}, \tag{1.20b}$$

and

$$\frac{1}{\ddot{a}_{\overline{n}|}} = \frac{1}{\ddot{s}_{\overline{n}|}} + d. \tag{1.21}$$

In the limiting case, as $n \to \infty$, we have the notion of the *unit perpetuity-due*, with present value given by

$$\ddot{a}_{\overline{\infty}|} = 1 + v + v^2 + \cdots = \frac{1}{d}. \tag{1.22}$$

From Equations (1.13) and (1.18) we can see that

$$\ddot{a}_{\overline{n}|} = (1+i) \cdot a_{\overline{n}|} \tag{1.23}$$

and, conversely,

$$a_{\overline{n}|} = v \cdot \ddot{a}_{\overline{n}|}. \tag{1.24}$$

Similarly, from Equations (1.14) and (1.19) we can see that

$$\ddot{s}_{\overline{n}|} = (1+i) \cdot s_{\overline{n}|} \tag{1.25}$$

and, conversely,

$$s_{\overline{n}|} = v \cdot \ddot{s}_{\overline{n}|}. \tag{1.26}$$

1.2.3 CONTINUOUS ANNUITY

Consider the theoretical notion of an annuity paying one unit of money per year, but split into an infinitely large number of payments of infinitely small size each. Clearly the payments are so "close together" that we interpret the unit as being paid *continuously* over the year. Suppose this arrangement continues for n consecutive years.

The present value of this *unit continuous annuity*, denoted $\bar{a}_{\overline{n}|}$, is measured at time 0 and is given by

$$\bar{a}_{\overline{n}|} = \int_0^n v^t\,dt = \frac{1-v^n}{\delta}. \tag{1.27}$$

The accumulated value, denoted $\bar{s}_{\overline{n}|}$, is measured at time n and is given by

$$\bar{s}_{\overline{n}|} = \int_0^n (1+i)^{n-t}\,dt = \frac{(1+i)^n-1}{\delta}. \tag{1.28}$$

From Equations (1.27) and (1.28) together we can see that

$$\bar{a}_{\overline{n}|} = v^n \cdot \bar{s}_{\overline{n}|}, \tag{1.29a}$$

$$\bar{s}_{\overline{n}|} = (1+i)^n \cdot \bar{a}_{\overline{n}|}, \tag{1.29b}$$

and

$$\frac{1}{\bar{a}_{\overline{n}|}} = \frac{1}{\bar{s}_{\overline{n}|}} + \delta. \tag{1.30}$$

In the limiting case, as $n \to \infty$, we have the notion of the *unit continuous perpetuity*, with present value given by

$$\bar{a}_{\overline{\infty}|} = \int_0^\infty v^t\,dt = \frac{1}{\delta}. \tag{1.31}$$

From Equations (1.27), (1.18), and (1.13) together we can see that

$$\bar{a}_{\overline{n}|} = \frac{d}{\delta} \cdot \ddot{a}_{\overline{n}|} = \frac{i}{\delta} \cdot a_{\overline{n}|}. \tag{1.32}$$

Similarly, from Equations (1.28), (1.19), and (1.14) together we can see that

$$\bar{s}_{\overline{n}|} = \frac{d}{\delta} \cdot \ddot{s}_{\overline{n}|} = \frac{i}{\delta} \cdot s_{\overline{n}|}. \tag{1.33}$$

1.3 NON-LEVEL ANNUITY FUNCTIONS

Often we encounter a sequence of annuity payments that is not level, but that varies in a regular pattern. Here we will consider both arithmetic and geometric patterns of variation.

1.3.1 ANNUITIES-IMMEDIATE

Consider the *unit increasing annuity-immediate* with the arithmetic pattern of payments illustrated in Figure 1.4.

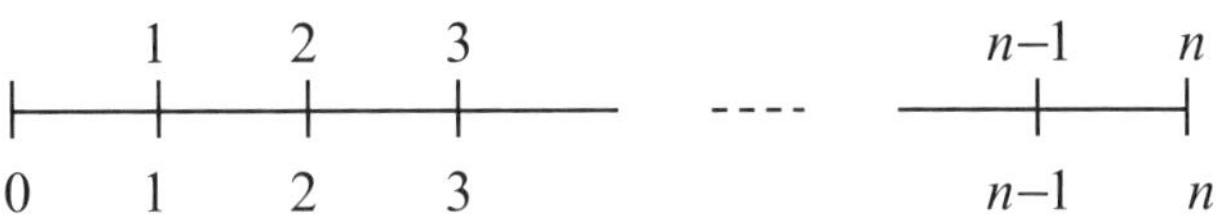

FIGURE 1.4

The present value of the annuity, denoted $(Ia)_{\overline{n}|}$, is measured at time 0 and is given by

$$(Ia)_{\overline{n}|} = v+2v^2+3v^3+\cdots+nv^n = \frac{\ddot{a}_{\overline{n}|}-nv^n}{i}. \tag{1.34}$$

The accumulated value of this annuity, denoted $(Is)_{\overline{n}|}$, is measured at time n and is given by

$$(Is)_{\overline{n}|} = (1+i)^{n-1}+2(1+i)^{n-2}+\cdots+(n-1)(1+i)+n = \frac{\ddot{s}_{\overline{n}|}-n}{i}. \tag{1.35}$$

From Equations (1.34) and (1.35) together it is clear that

$$(Ia)_{\overline{n}|} = v^n \cdot (Is)_{\overline{n}|} \tag{1.36a}$$

and

$$(Is)_{\overline{n}|} = (1+i)^n \cdot (Ia)_{\overline{n}|}. \tag{1.36b}$$

In the limiting case, as $n \to \infty$, we have the notion of the *unit increasing perpetuity-immediate*, with present value given by

$$(Ia)_{\overline{\infty}|} = \frac{1}{id}. \tag{1.37}$$

The *unit decreasing annuity-immediate* has the arithmetic payment pattern illustrated in Figure 1.5.

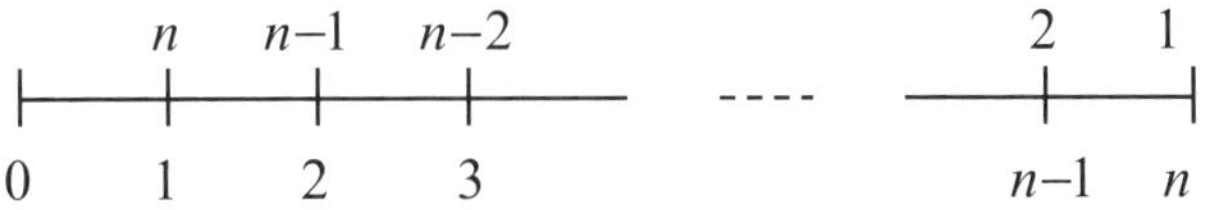

FIGURE 1.5

The present value of this annuity, denoted $(Da)_{\overline{n}|}$, is measured at time 0 and is given by

$$(Da)_{\overline{n}|} = nv+(n-1)v^2+(n-2)v^3+\cdots+2v^{n-1}+v^n = \frac{n-a_{\overline{n}|}}{i}. \tag{1.38}$$

The accumulated value of this annuity, denoted $(Ds)_{\overline{n}|}$, is measured at time n and is given by

$$(Ds)_{\overline{n}|} = n(1+i)^{n-1}+(n-1)(1+i)^{n-2}+\cdots+2(1+i)+1 = \frac{n(1+i)^n-s_{\overline{n}|}}{i}. \tag{1.39}$$

From Equations (1.38) and (1.39) together it is clear that

$$(Da)_{\overline{n}|} = v^n \cdot (Ds)_{\overline{n}|} \tag{1.40a}$$

and

$$(Ds)_{\overline{n}|} = (1+i)^n \cdot (Da)_{\overline{n}|}. \tag{1.40b}$$

The notion of a perpetuity does not apply in the decreasing case.

Annuities-immediate increasing or decreasing in a *geometric* pattern are handled by first principles. If the initial payment (made at time $t=1$) is one unit of money, and each subsequent payment is r times the previous payment, then the annuity has a geometrically increasing payment pattern if $r>1$ and a geometrically decreasing payment pattern if $r<1$. (If $r=1$ the annuity is level, as reviewed in Section 1.2.) The geometric annuity-immediate is illustrated in Figure 1.6.

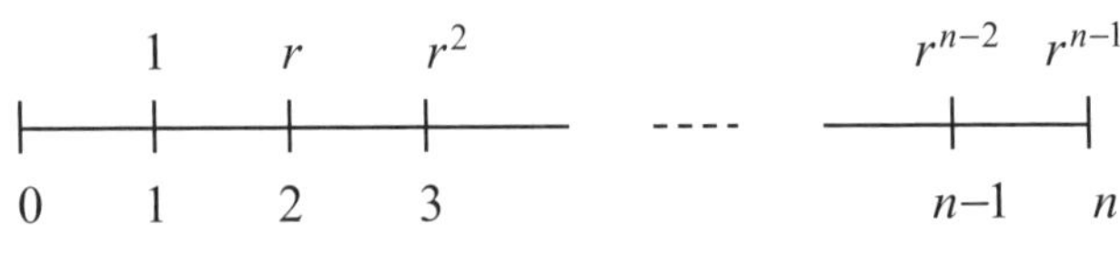

FIGURE 1.6

The present value of this annuity at time 0 is

$$\begin{aligned} PV &= v + rv^2 + r^2v^3 + \cdots + r^{n-2}v^{n-1} + r^{n-1}v^n \\ &= v\left[1+(rv)+(rv)^2+\cdots+(rv)^{n-1}\right] = v\left[\frac{1-(rv)^n}{1-(rv)}\right]. \end{aligned} \tag{1.41}$$

The present value will exist for a *geometrically increasing perpetuity* if the growth rate in the payments is less than the interest rate used to discount the future payments (i.e., if $r<1+i$). Since $r<1$ in the decreasing case, the present value of the decreasing perpetuity will always exist.

The accumulated value of the annuity at time n is most easily found by the now-familiar relationship $AV = PV(1+i)^n$. Note that we have no standard actuarial symbol for the present and accumulated values of these annuities.

1.3.2 ANNUITIES-DUE

The arithmetic unit increasing, arithmetic unit decreasing, and geometric increasing or decreasing annuities reviewed in Section 1.3.1 all have their annuity-due counterparts, with payments made at the beginnings of the respective periods instead of the ends. The following symbols and formulas should now be well understood:

$$(I\ddot{a})_{\overline{n}|} = \frac{\ddot{a}_{\overline{n}|} - nv^n}{d} \tag{1.42}$$

$$(I\ddot{s})_{\overline{n}|} = \frac{\ddot{s}_{\overline{n}|} - n}{d} \tag{1.43}$$

$$(D\ddot{a})_{\overline{n}|} = \frac{n - a_{\overline{n}|}}{d} \tag{1.44}$$

$$(D\ddot{s})_{\overline{n}|} = \frac{n(1+i)^n - s_{\overline{n}|}}{d} \tag{1.45}$$

$$(I\ddot{a})_{\overline{\infty}|} = \frac{1}{d^2} \tag{1.46}$$

In all cases the annuity-due function is simply $(1+i)$ times the corresponding annuity-immediate function.

In the geometric case, we have the payment pattern illustrated in Figure 1.7.

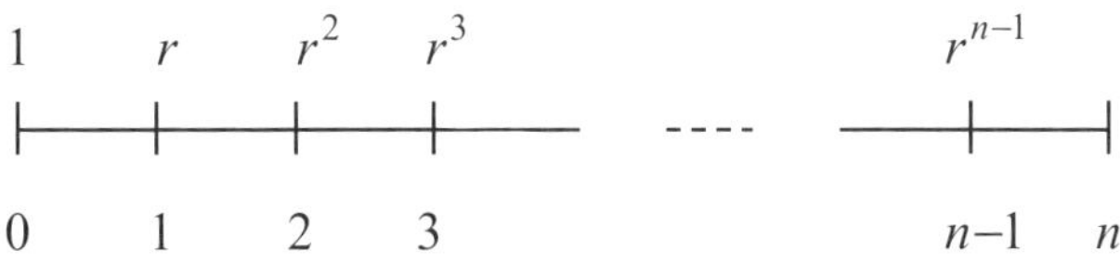

FIGURE 1.7

The present value of this annuity at time 0 is

$$\begin{aligned} PV &= 1 + rv + r^2v^2 + \cdots + r^{n-1}v^{n-1} \\ &= \frac{1-(rv)^n}{1-(rv)} \\ &= \frac{1-\left(\frac{r}{1+i}\right)^n}{1-\left(\frac{r}{1+i}\right)} \\ &= \frac{1-(1+i')^{-n}}{1-(1+i')^{-1}}, \end{aligned} \tag{1.47}$$

which is $\ddot{a}_{\overline{n}|}$ at rate $i' = \frac{1+i}{r} - 1$. The accumulated value at time n is the present value times $(1+i)^n$. Clearly Equations (1.41) and (1.47) together show the now-familiar result that the present value of the annuity-due is always $(1+i)$ times the present value of the corresponding annuity-immediate, since both annuities have the same cash flows but each payment is one year earlier under the annuity-due. Again the present value will exist for a perpetuity-due provided $r < 1+i$.

1.3.3 CONTINUOUS ANNUITIES

Now we return to the theoretical notion of an annuity payable continuously, introduced in Section 1.2.3, this time with a non-level payment pattern. We will look at two subcases of this idea.

First we consider the unit increasing annuity, illustrated in the immediate form in Figure 1.4. Instead of making the payments of $1,2,\cdots,n$ at the ends of each time interval, we think of them as being made continuously over their respective intervals, as illustrated in Figure 1.8.

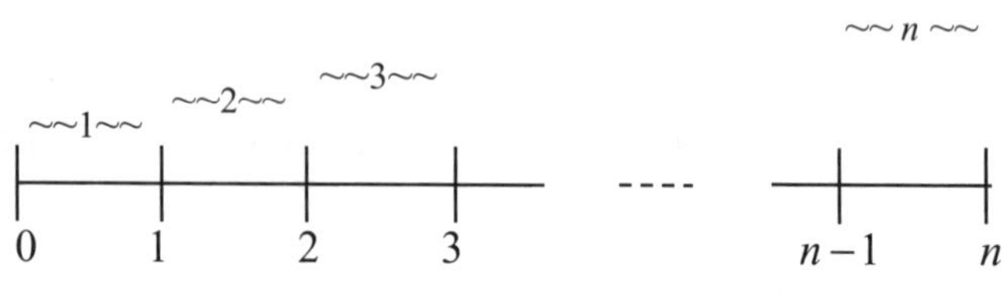

FIGURE 1.8

The present value at time 0 of this step-pattern set of continuous payments can be easily found. We observe that the equivalent value at $t=1$ of the continuous payment in the first interval only is $\bar{s}_{\overline{1}|}$, the equivalent value at $t=2$ of the continuous payment in the second interval only is therefore $2\cdot\bar{s}_{\overline{1}|}$, and so on. The equivalent value at $t=n$ of the continuous payment in the last interval only is $n\cdot\bar{s}_{\overline{1}|}$. Then the present value at time 0 of the entire continuous payment, which is denoted by $(I\bar{a})_{\overline{n}|}$, is

$$(I\bar{a})_{\overline{n}|} = \bar{s}_{\overline{1}|}\cdot v+2\cdot\bar{s}_{\overline{1}|}\cdot v^2+\cdots+n\cdot\bar{s}_{\overline{1}|}\cdot v^n = \bar{s}_{\overline{1}|}\cdot(Ia)_{\overline{n}|}, \tag{1.48a}$$

from Equation (1.34). Since

$$\bar{s}_{\overline{1}|} = \frac{(1+i)^1-1}{\delta} = \frac{i}{\delta},$$

Equation (1.48a) is often written as

$$(I\bar{a})_{\overline{n}|} = \frac{i}{\delta}\cdot(Ia)_{\overline{n}|}. \tag{1.48b}$$

The accumulated value at time n then follows as

$$(I\bar{s})_{\overline{n}|} = (1+i)^n\cdot(I\bar{a})_{\overline{n}|} = \frac{i}{\delta}\cdot(Is)_{\overline{n}|}, \tag{1.49}$$

from Equation (1.36b).

Similarly, we can consider the unit decreasing annuity, illustrated in Figure 1.5, in continuous form as well. Here we would have

$$(D\bar{a})_{\overline{n|}} = n \cdot \bar{s}_{\overline{1|}} \cdot v + (n-1) \cdot \bar{s}_{\overline{1|}} \cdot v^2 + \cdots + \bar{s}_{\overline{1|}} \cdot v^n$$

$$= \bar{s}_{\overline{1|}} \cdot (Da)_{\overline{n|}} = \frac{i}{\delta} \cdot (Da)_{\overline{n|}} \tag{1.50}$$

for the present value at time 0, and

$$(D\bar{s})_{\overline{n|}} = \frac{i}{\delta} \cdot (Ds)_{\overline{n|}} \tag{1.51}$$

for the accumulated value at time n.

The second subcase of non-level payment annuities in continuous form is the case for which the payment varies continuously, rather than in the step function pattern considered above.

In general, suppose payment is being made at time t at rate $r(t)$, so that the differential payment made at time t is $r(t) \cdot dt$. The present value at time 0 of this differential payment is then $v^t \cdot r(t) \cdot dt$, and the entire present value is given by

$$PV = \int_0^n r(t) \cdot v^t \, dt. \tag{1.52}$$

Note that we have no standard actuarial symbol for the general case present value. An important special case is the one with $r(t) = t$, so that payment at time t is being made at a rate equal to the time elapsed since time 0. In this case the present value is denoted $(\bar{I}\,\bar{a})_{\overline{n|}}$, and is given by

$$(\bar{I}\,\bar{a})_{\overline{n|}} = \int_0^n t \cdot v^t \, dt = \frac{\bar{a}_{\overline{n|}} - nv^n}{\delta}, \tag{1.53}$$

upon evaluation of the integral using integration by parts. The accumulated value at time n is given by

$$(\bar{I}\,\bar{s})_{\overline{n|}} = \frac{\bar{s}_{\overline{n|}} - n}{\delta}, \tag{1.54}$$

since, in general, the accumulated value is always the present value multiplied by $(1+i)^n$.

1.4 EQUATION OF VALUE

The final item for the reader to review from a prior study of interest theory is the notion of an *equation of value* and its associated *yield rate*.

Suppose we have a series of payments going from Party A to Party B at known points of time, and another series coming back from Party B to Party A at other known points of time. Each series of payments is called a *cash flow*. Note that a cash flow could consist of only one payment. An example of this is illustrated in Figure 1.9.

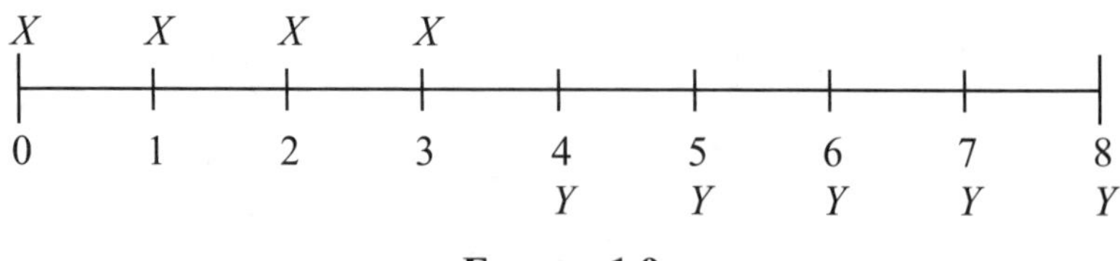

FIGURE 1.9

The cash flow represented by the four X's goes from Party A (say a depositor) to Party B (say a bank) at the times indicated, and the cash flow represented by the five Y's comes back from the bank to the depositor at the times indicated. We can write an equation of value at time 3, for example, as

$$X \cdot s_{\overline{4}|i} = Y \cdot a_{\overline{5}|i}, \tag{1.55}$$

where i is the periodic effective rate of interest that balances the equation. When viewed as an investment transaction by the depositor, we say that i is the investor's yield rate on the transaction.

Under compound interest it does not matter what point of time is selected at which to write the equation of value; the same value of i will satisfy the equation in any case. Often the choice is made to write the equation as of time 0. Then we would have

$$X + X \cdot v + X \cdot v^2 + X \cdot v^3 = Y \cdot v^4 + Y \cdot v^5 + Y \cdot v^6 + Y \cdot v^7 + Y \cdot v^8, \tag{1.56}$$

where v is based on effective interest rate i. Finally, it is often common to write the equation of value as

$$X\left[1+v+v^2+v^3\right] - Y\left[v^4+v^5+v^6+v^7+v^8\right] = 0. \tag{1.57}$$

It is again clear that the same value of i will result from any of Equations (1.55), (1.56), or (1.57). Of course these equations do not lead to closed form expressions for i; rather they must be solved for i numerically using computer software or a sophisticated pocket calculator.

In our work with actuarial models for the quantification of risk throughout this text, we will occasionally encounter the concept of equation of value on either an aggregate or an expected value basis. This review of the equation of value at interest only will help prepare the reader for understanding more complex encounters with the concept when they arise.

CHAPTER TWO

REVIEW OF PROBABILITY

The second basic ingredient for constructing actuarial models for quantifying risk, along with interest theory, is that of basic mathematical probability. Again we are assuming that the reader has completed at least one full semester in calculus-based probability at the university level, so that most of the material contained in this chapter will be somewhat familiar. For several selected topics (see, in particular, Section 2.7), we are less sure that the reader will have this prior familiarity and we will present those topics in greater detail.

Specialized applications of basic probability concepts to various actuarial models are considered throughout the text. Extensions of probability theory that are needed for these specialized applications, which would not normally be covered in a basic probability course, will be introduced as needed in the later chapters.

The most basic concepts of probability are not included in this review; the reader should refer to any standard probability textbook if a review of these concepts is needed.[1] Among the basic concepts not reviewed here are the notion of the probability of an event, negation, union, intersection, mutual exclusion, the general addition rule, conditional probability, independence, the general multiplication rule, the law of total probability, and Bayes' Theorem.

2.1 RANDOM VARIABLES AND THEIR DISTRIBUTIONS

The concept of the *random variable* is the foundation for most of the material presented in this text. Levels of risk can be quantitatively represented by random variables, and understanding the properties of these random variables then allows us to analyze and manage the risk so represented. In this section of this introductory chapter we review basic aspects of random variables and their properties.

2.1.1 DISCRETE RANDOM VARIABLES

A random variable, denoted X, is said to be *discrete* if it can take on only a finite (or countably infinite) number of different values. Each value it can take on is called an *outcome* of the random variable. The set of all possible outcomes is called the *domain*, or *support*, of the random variable.[2] We let x denote a particular value in the domain.

Associated with each value of x is a probability value for the random variable taking on that particular outcome. The probability value is a function of the value of the outcome, denoted

[1] For those needing a good probability text, we recommend Hassett and Stewart's *Probability for Risk Management* [12].

[2] Technically, we should say the domain (or support) of the random variable's probability function, but the shorter phrase "domain of the random variable" is often used.

$p(x)$, and is called, appropriately, the *probability function* (PF). That is, $p(x)$ gives the probability of the event $X = x$. (In some textbooks $p(x)$ is called the *probability mass function*.) The set of all probability values constitutes the *distribution* of the random variable. It is necessarily true that

$$\sum_x p(x) = 1, \tag{2.1}$$

where the summation is taken over all values of x in the domain with non-zero probability.

The *expected value* of the random variable, denoted $E[X]$, is a weighted average of all values in the domain, using the associated probability values as weights. Thus we have

$$E[X] = \sum_x x \cdot p(x), \tag{2.2}$$

where the summation is again taken over all values of x with non-zero probability. The expected value is also called the *mean of the random variable* or the *mean of the distribution*. (The expected value exists only if the sum converges.)

The expected value is a special case of the more general idea of finding the weighted average of a function of the random variable, again using the associated probability values as the weights. If $g(X)$ is any real function of the random variable X, then it can be shown that

$$E[g(X)] = \sum_x g(x) \cdot p(x) \tag{2.3}$$

gives the expected value of the function of the random variable. Note that the mean of the random variable is simply the special case that results when $g(X) = X$.

An important special case is $g(X) = X^k$, and $E[g(X)] = E[X^k]$ is called the kth *moment* of the random variable. (Note that the mean is therefore the *first moment* of the random variable.) Another special case is $g(X) = (X - E[X])^2$, where the expected value of $g(X)$ is called the *variance* of the random variable and is denoted by $Var(X)$. That is,

$$Var(X) = E[(X - E[X])^2] = \sum_x (x - E[X])^2 \cdot p(x). \tag{2.4a}$$

The reader will recall that an equivalent expression for $Var(X)$ is

$$Var(X) = E[X^2] - (E[X])^2, \tag{2.4b}$$

a form often more convenient for calculating $Var(X)$ than is Equation (2.4a). The positive square root of the variance is called the *standard deviation* of X, denoted $SD(X)$.

The moments of a random variable can be generated from a function called, appropriately, the *moment generating function* (MGF), and denoted by $M_X(t)$, provided it exists. It is defined as

$$M_X(t) = E[e^{tX}] = \sum_x e^{tx} \cdot p(x). \tag{2.5}$$

We recognize that this is just another example of finding the expected value of a particular function of the random variable; in this case the function is $g(X) = e^{tX}$. Note that $M_X(t)$ is a function of *t*, with the subscript *X* merely reminding us of what the random variable is for which $M_X(t)$ is the MGF.

The reader will recall that the moments are then obtained from the MGF by differentiating $M_X(t)$ with respect to *t* and evaluating at $t=0$. The first derivative evaluated at $t=0$ produces the first moment, the second derivative so evaluated gives the second moment, and so on. In general,

$$E[X^k] = \frac{d^k}{dt^k} M_X(t)\bigg|_{t=0} = M_X^{(k)}(0) \tag{2.6}$$

gives the kth moment of the random variable *X*.

Several other characteristics of the random variable are also important.

The *mode* of the distribution is the value of *x* at which the greatest amount of probability is located (i.e., the value of *x* that maximizes $p(x)$). Note that several values of *x* could be tied for the greatest amount, in which case the distribution would have several modes.

The *cumulative distribution function* (CDF) of the random variable, denoted $F(x)$, gives the accumulated amount of probability at all values of the random variable less than or equal to *x*. That is,

$$F(x) = Pr(X \le x) = \sum_{y \le x} p(y), \tag{2.7}$$

where the summation is taken over all values of *y* less than or equal to *x*.

The value of *x* for which $F(x) = r$ is called the $100r^{th}$ *percentile* of the distribution. It is the value in the domain of *X* for which the probability of being less than or equal to that value is *r*, and the probability of being greater than that value is therefore $1-r$. In particular, when $r = .50$ we are speaking of the value of *x* for which half the probability lies below (or at) that value and half lies above that value. The value of *x* in this case is called the *median* of the distribution.[3]

[3] The median (or any other percentile) in a discrete distribution is not always clear. For example, if $p(0) = \frac{1}{3}$ and $p(1) = \frac{2}{3}$, then what is the median? Clearly there is no unique value of *x* for which $F(x) = .50$. Either we would say the median does not exist, or we would adopt a definition to resolve the question in each case.

2.1.2 CONTINUOUS RANDOM VARIABLES

A random variable is said to be *continuous* if it can take on any value within a defined interval (or the union of several disjoint intervals) on the real number axis. If this set of possible values, again called the domain or support of the random variable,[4] includes all values between, say, a and b, then we would define the domain as $a<x<b$. If the domain were all non-negative real values of x we would write $x \geq 0$, and if it were all real values of x we would write $-\infty<x<\infty$. Note that the defined values of x could be in several disjoint intervals, so the domain would then be the union of these disjoint intervals. For example, the domain could be all x satisfying $a<x<b$ or $c<x<d$.

Associated with each possible value of x is an amount of *probability density*, given as a function of x by the *probability density function* (PDF), denoted by $f(x)$. Together the PDF and the domain define the distribution of the random variable. It is necessarily true that

$$\int_x f(x)\,dx = 1, \tag{2.8}$$

where the integral is taken over all values of x in the domain.

Analogous with the discrete case, we again consider the weighted average of a function of the random variable, which is the expected value of that function, this time using the density as the weight associated with each value of x. Thus it can be shown that

$$E[g(x)] = \int_x g(x)\cdot f(x)\,dx. \tag{2.9}$$

The same special cases apply here as in the discrete case. For $g(X)=X$ we have

$$E[X] = \int_x x\cdot f(x)\,dx \tag{2.10}$$

as the expected value (or first moment) of the random variable. For $g(X)=X^k$ in general we have

$$E[X^k] = \int_x x^k\cdot f(x)\,dx \tag{2.11}$$

as the kth moment. As before, the variance is given by

$$Var(X) = E[(X-E[X])^2] = \int_x (x-E[X])^2\cdot f(x)\,dx \tag{2.12}$$

and the moment generating function is given by

[4] As in the discrete case of Section 2.1.1, the phrase "domain (or support) of the density function of the random variable" is more technically correct, but the briefer phrase "domain of the random variable" is often used.

$$M_X(t) \;=\; E[e^{tX}] \;=\; \int_x e^{tx} \cdot f(x)\,dx. \tag{2.13}$$

The mode of the distribution is the value of x associated with the greatest amount of probability density, so it can be described as the value of x that maximizes the density function. If several values of x have the same maximum density, then the distribution has more than one mode.

As in the discrete case, the cumulative distribution function (CDF) of the random variable X is defined by $F(x) = Pr(X \leq x)$. It follows that

$$F(x) \;=\; \int_{-\infty}^{x} f(y)\,dy, \tag{2.14a}$$

and, conversely,

$$f(x) \;=\; \frac{d}{dx}F(x). \tag{2.14b}$$

Just as in the discrete case, the $100r^{th}$ percentile of the distribution is the value of x for which $F(x) = r$, and, in particular, the median of the distribution is the value of x for which $F(x) = .50$.

2.1.3 MIXED RANDOM VARIABLES

On occasion we encounter a random variable that is discrete in one part of its domain and continuous in the rest of the domain. Such random variables are said to have *mixed distributions*. For example, suppose there is a finite probability associated with each of the outcomes $X = a$ and $X = b$, denoted $p(a)$ and $p(b)$, respectively, and a probability density associated with all values of x on the open interval between a and b. Then it would follow that

$$p(a) + \int_a^b f(x)\,dx + p(b) \;=\; 1. \tag{2.15}$$

The kth moment of the mixed random variable X would be found as

$$E[X^k] \;=\; a^k \cdot p(a) + \int_a^b x^k \cdot f(x)\,dx + b^k \cdot p(b). \tag{2.16}$$

Mixed random variables appear quite often in actuarial models, particularly in connection with insurance coverages involving a deductible, or a policy maximum, or both.[5]

2.1.4 MORE ON MOMENTS OF RANDOM VARIABLES

Earlier in this section we reviewed the basic idea of the kth moment of a random variable, denoted by $E[X^k]$. This type of moment is called the kth *raw moment of X*, or the kth *moment about the origin*.

[5] These topics are discussed in Kellison and London [16].

By contrast, the quantity $E[(X-\mu)^k]$ is called the kth *central moment of X*, or the kth *moment about the mean*, where $\mu = E[X]$. In particular, the second central moment, denoted by $E[(X-\mu)^2]$, gives the variance of the distribution of *X*, which is denoted by $Var(X)$ or sometimes by σ^2. Recall that the positive square root of the variance is called the standard deviation, and is denoted by $SD(X)$ or sometimes by σ.

The ratio of the standard deviation to the mean of a random variable is called the *coefficient of variation*, and is denoted by $CV(X)$. Thus we have

$$CV(X) = \frac{\sigma}{\mu}, \tag{2.17}$$

for $\mu \neq 0$. It measures the degree of spread of a random variable relative to its mean.

The *skewness* of a distribution measures its symmetry, or lack thereof. It is defined by

$$\gamma_3 = \frac{E[(X-\mu)^3]}{\sigma^3}, \tag{2.18}$$

the ratio of the third central moment to the cube of the standard deviation. A distribution that is symmetric, such as the normal, will have a skewness measure of zero. A positively skewed distribution will have a right hand tail and a negatively skewed distribution will have a left hand tail.

The extent to which a distribution is peaked or flat is measured by its *kurtosis,* which is defined by

$$\gamma_4 = \frac{E[(X-\mu)^4]}{\sigma^4}, \tag{2.19}$$

the ratio of the fourth central moment to the square of the variance (or the fourth power of the standard deviation). The kurtosis of a normal distribution has a value of 3, so the kurtosis of any other distribution will indicate its degree of peakedness or flatness relative to a normal distribution with equal variance.

It is well known (see Equation (2.4b)) that the second central moment (the variance) is equal to the second raw moment minus the first raw moment (the mean) squared. Similar relationships hold for the higher central moments as well. For example, for the third central moment we have

$$\begin{aligned} E[(X-\mu)^3] &= E[X^3 - 3X^2\mu + 3X\mu^2 - \mu^3] \\ &= E[X^3] - 3\cdot E[X^2]\cdot E[X] + 3\cdot E[X]\cdot(E[X])^2 - (E[X])^3 \\ &= E[X^3] - 3\cdot E[X^2]\cdot E[X] + 2(E[X])^3. \end{aligned} \tag{2.20}$$

2.2 SURVEY OF PARTICULAR DISCRETE DISTRIBUTIONS

In this section we will review five standard discrete distributions with which the reader should be familiar. They are included here simply as a convenient reference.

2.2.1 THE DISCRETE UNIFORM DISTRIBUTION

If there are n discrete values in the domain of a random variable X, denoted $x_1, x_2, \cdots, x_n$, for which an equal amount of probability is associated with each value, then X is said to have a *discrete uniform distribution*. Its probability function is therefore

$$p(x_i) = \frac{1}{n}, \tag{2.21}$$

for all x_i. Its first moment is

$$E[X] = \sum_{i=1}^{n} x_i \cdot p(x_i) = \frac{1}{n} \cdot \sum_{i=1}^{n} x_i, \tag{2.22a}$$

and its second moment is

$$E[X^2] = \sum_{i=1}^{n} x_i^2 \cdot p(x_i) = \frac{1}{n} \cdot \sum_{i=1}^{n} x_i^2. \tag{2.22b}$$

In the special case where $x_i = i$, for $i = 1, 2, \cdots, n$, then we have

$$E[X] = \frac{n+1}{2} \tag{2.23a}$$

and

$$E[X^2] = \frac{(n+1)(2n+1)}{6}, \tag{2.23b}$$

so that

$$Var(X) = E[X^2] - (E[X])^2 = \frac{n^2-1}{12}. \tag{2.24}$$

The moment generating function in the special case is

$$M_X(t) = E[e^{tX}] = \frac{e^t(1-e^{nt})}{n(1-e^t)}. \tag{2.25}$$

2.2.2 THE BINOMIAL DISTRIBUTION

Recall the binomial (or Bernoulli) model, in which we find the concept of repeated independent trials with each trial ending in either success of failure. The probability of success on a single trial, denoted p, is constant over all trials. The random variable X, denoting the number of successes out of n independent trials, is said to have a *binomial distribution*. The probability function is

$$p(x) = \binom{n}{x} p^x (1-p)^{n-x}, \tag{2.26}$$

for $x = 0, 1, 2, \cdots, n$, the expected value is

$$E[X] = np, \tag{2.27}$$

the variance is

$$Var(X) = np(1-p), \tag{2.28}$$

and the moment generating function is

$$M_X(t) = (q+pe^t)^n, \tag{2.29}$$

where $q = 1-p$.

2.2.3 THE NEGATIVE BINOMIAL DISTRIBUTION

Note that in the binomial distribution the random variable was the number of successes out of a fixed number of trials, n, where n is a fixed parameter of the distribution. In the *negative binomial distribution* the number of successes, denoted r, is a fixed parameter of the distribution and the random variable X represents the number of failures that occur before the rth success is obtained.[6] The probability function is

$$p(x) = \binom{x+r-1}{r-1} p^r (1-p)^x, \tag{2.30}$$

for $x = 0, 1, 2, \cdots$, the expected value is

$$E[X] = \frac{rq}{p}, \tag{2.31}$$

the variance is

$$Var(X) = \frac{rq}{p^2}, \tag{2.32}$$

and the moment generating function is

[6] Note that if the number of failures, denoted X, is random, then the total number of *trials* needed to obtain r successes, denoted Y, is also random, since we would have $Y = X+r$. Some textbooks (see, for example, Hassett and Stewart [12]), discuss both the "X-meaning" and the "Y-meaning" of the negative binomial distribution.

$$M_X(t) = \left(\frac{p}{1-qe^t}\right)^r, \tag{2.33}$$

where, in all cases, $q = 1-p$.

Note that the description of the negative binomial distribution given here would require that the parameter r be a nonnegative integer. When we consider the important use of the negative binomial random variable as a model for the number of insurance claims, we will see that the requirement of an integer value for r can be relaxed.[7]

2.2.4 THE GEOMETRIC DISTRIBUTION

The *geometric distribution* is simply the special case of the negative binomial with $r = 1$. The random variable, X, now denotes the number of failures that occur before the first success is obtained.[8] Its probability function is

$$p(x) = p(1-p)^x, \tag{2.30a}$$

for $x = 0,1,2,\cdots$, the expected value is

$$E[X] = \frac{q}{p}, \tag{2.31a}$$

the variance is

$$Var(X) = \frac{q}{p^2}, \tag{2.32a}$$

and the moment generating function is

$$M_X(t) = \frac{p}{1-qe^t}, \tag{2.33a}$$

where $q = 1-p$ in all cases.

2.2.5 THE POISSON DISTRIBUTION

The *Poisson distribution* is a one-parameter discrete distribution with probability function given by

$$p(x) = \frac{e^{-\lambda}\lambda^x}{x!}, \tag{2.34}$$

for $x = 0,1,2,\cdots$, where $\lambda > 0$. Its expected value is

---

[7] See Chapter 3 of Kellison and London [16].

[8] As with the negative binomial, some textbooks define the geometric random variable to be the number of trials, Y, needed to obtain the first success. In that case the probability function is $p(y) = p(1-p)^{y-1}$, for $y = 1,2,\cdots$.

$$E[X] = \lambda, \tag{2.35}$$

its variance is also

$$Var(X) = \lambda, \tag{2.36}$$

and its moment generating function is

$$M_X(t) = e^{\lambda(e^t-1)}. \tag{2.37}$$

The Poisson distribution has several delightful properties that make it a convenient one to use in various actuarial and other stochastic applications.

2.3 SURVEY OF PARTICULAR CONTINUOUS DISTRIBUTIONS

In this section we review four standard continuous probability distributions with which the reader should be familiar from a prior study of probability. Additional continuous distributions are introduced later in the text as survival distributions (see Chapter 5).

2.3.1 THE CONTINUOUS UNIFORM DISTRIBUTION

As its name suggests, the *uniform distribution* is characterized by a constant probability density at all points in its domain. If the random variable is defined on the interval $a < X < b$, and if the density function is constant, then it follows that the density function must be

$$f(x) = \frac{1}{b-a}, \tag{2.38}$$

for $a < x < b$. That is, the constant density function is the reciprocal of the length of the interval on which the random variable is defined. The mean of the uniform distribution is

$$E[X] = \frac{a+b}{2}, \tag{2.39}$$

the variance is

$$Var(X) = \frac{(b-a)^2}{12}, \tag{2.40}$$

the moment generating function is

$$M_X(t) = \frac{e^{bt}-e^{at}}{t(b-a)}, \tag{2.41}$$

for $t \neq 0$, and the cumulative distribution function is

$$F(x) = \frac{x-a}{b-a}. \tag{2.42}$$

As a consequence of the constant density function, the median is the same as the mean and there is no mode since all points have the same probability density.

2.3.2 THE NORMAL DISTRIBUTION

The *normal distribution* will have frequent use in our models for quantifying risk. For now the reader should recall that the density function for this distribution is based on the two parameters μ and σ, where $\sigma > 0$, which are also the mean and standard deviation, respectively, of the distribution. Specifically,

$$f(x) = \frac{1}{\sigma \cdot \sqrt{2\pi}} e^{-\frac{1}{2}\left(\frac{x-\mu}{\sigma}\right)^2}, \tag{2.43a}$$

for $-\infty < x < \infty$, where, as mentioned,

$$E[X] = \mu \tag{2.44}$$

and

$$Var(X) = \sigma^2. \tag{2.45}$$

The moment generating function is

$$M_X(t) = e^{\mu t + \sigma^2 t^2/2}. \tag{2.46}$$

An extremely important property of the normal distribution is that any linear transformation of the random variable will also have a normal distribution. In particular, the random variable Z derived from the normal random variable X by the linear transformation

$$Z = \frac{X - \mu}{\sigma} \tag{2.47}$$

will have a normal distribution with mean

$$E[Z] = \frac{1}{\sigma} \cdot E[X] - \frac{\mu}{\sigma} = 0, \tag{2.48}$$

since $E[X] = \mu$, and variance

$$Var(Z) = \frac{Var(X)}{\sigma^2} = 1, \tag{2.49}$$

since $Var(X) = \sigma^2$ and $Var(\mu/\sigma) = 0$. The random variable Z is called the *unit normal random variable* or the *standard normal random variable*. Its probability density function

$$f(x) = \frac{1}{\sqrt{2\pi}} e^{-x^2/2} \tag{2.43b}$$

does not have a closed form antiderivative, so probability values are not found by analytical integration of $f(x)$. Rather, values of the cumulative distribution function $F_Z(z)$ are determined by approximate integration and stored in a table for look-up as needed. Probability values for the normal random variable X are likewise looked up in the table of standard values after making the appropriate linear transformation. A modern alternative to table look-up is that values can be determined by numerical integration using appropriate computer software or even a pocket calculator.

2.3.3 THE EXPONENTIAL DISTRIBUTION

Another standard continuous distribution with some convenient properties is the one-parameter *exponential distribution*. It is defined over all positive values of x by the density function

$$f(x) = \beta \cdot e^{-\beta x}, \tag{2.50a}$$

for $x > 0$ and $\beta > 0$. The expected value is

$$E[X] = \frac{1}{\beta}, \tag{2.51}$$

the variance is

$$Var(X) = \frac{1}{\beta^2}, \tag{2.52}$$

the moment generating function is

$$M_X(t) = \frac{\beta}{\beta - t}, \tag{2.53}$$

for $t < \beta$, and the cumulative distribution function is

$$F(x) = 1 - e^{-\beta x}. \tag{2.54}$$

(The reader should note that some textbooks prefer the notation

$$f(x) = \frac{1}{\theta} \cdot e^{-x/\theta}, \tag{2.50b}$$

so that $E[X] = \theta, Var(X) = \theta^2$, and $M_X(t) = (1-\theta t)^{-1}$.)

Properties of the exponential distribution that make it suitable as a survival distribution in certain cases will be explored in Chapter 5.

2.3.4 THE GAMMA DISTRIBUTION

The two-parameter *gamma distribution* is defined by the density function

$$f(x) = \frac{\beta^{\alpha}}{\Gamma(\alpha)} \cdot x^{\alpha-1} e^{-\beta x}, \tag{2.55}$$

for $x > 0, \alpha > 0,$ and $\beta > 0,$ where $\Gamma(\alpha)$ is the *gamma function* defined by

$$\Gamma(\alpha) = \int_0^{\infty} x^{\alpha-1} e^{-x}\, dx. \tag{2.56}$$

By substituting $\alpha = 1$ into the gamma density given by Equation (2.55), and noting that $\Gamma(1) = 1,$ we obtain the exponential density given by Equation (2.50a). Thus the exponential is a special case of the gamma with $\alpha = 1$. The mean of the gamma distribution is

$$E[X] = \frac{\alpha}{\beta}, \tag{2.57a}$$

the variance is

$$Var(X) = \frac{\alpha}{\beta^2}, \tag{2.57b}$$

and the moment generating function is

$$M_X(t) = \left(\frac{\beta}{\beta - t}\right)^{\alpha}, \tag{2.57c}$$

for $t < \beta$. The cumulative distribution function is given by

$$F(x) = \int_0^x f(y)\, dy = \frac{\beta^{\alpha}}{\Gamma(\alpha)} \int_0^x y^{\alpha-1} e^{-\beta y}\, dy. \tag{2.58a}$$

If we let $\beta y = t,$ so $y = t / \beta$ and $dy = \frac{1}{\beta} \cdot dt,$ then the integral becomes

$$\begin{aligned} F(x) &= \frac{1}{\Gamma(\alpha)} \int_0^{\beta x} \beta^{\alpha} \left(\frac{t}{\beta}\right)^{\alpha-1} \cdot e^{-t} \cdot \frac{1}{\beta} \cdot dt \\ &= \frac{1}{\Gamma(\alpha)} \int_0^{\beta x} t^{\alpha-1} e^{-t}\, dt \\ &= \Gamma(\alpha; \beta x), \end{aligned} \tag{2.58b}$$

where $\Gamma(\alpha; \beta x)$ is the *incomplete gamma function* defined by

$$\Gamma(\alpha; x) = \frac{1}{\Gamma(\alpha)} \int_0^x t^{\alpha-1} e^{-t}\, dt. \tag{2.59}$$

2.4 MULTIVARIATE PROBABILITY

Whenever two or more random variables are involved in the same model we find ourselves dealing with a case of *multivariate probability*. In this section we will review the fundamental aspects of multivariate probability, including the interrelationships among the *joint*, *marginal*, and *conditional distributions*, in both the discrete and continuous cases.

One of the most important aspects of multivariate probability is the process for finding the unconditional mean and variance of a random variable from the associated conditional means and variances. The formulas relating the unconditional and conditional means and variances are given by the *double expectation theorem*. Although this is a result with which the reader might be familiar from prior study, it has so many important applications in actuarial science that we wish to review it in some detail at this time. We will do this by example, separately for the discrete and continuous cases. An example does not establish the general result, of course; for that purpose the reader is referred to Section 7.4 of Ross [21].

2.4.1 THE DISCRETE CASE

We illustrate the key components of discrete multivariate probability with a numerical example. Suppose the discrete random variable X can assume the values $x = 0,1,2$ and the discrete random variable Y can assume the values $y = 1,2$. Let X and Y have the joint distribution given by the following table, and let $p(x,y)$ denote the joint probability function.

Y \ X	0	1	2
1	.10	.20	.30
2	.10	.10	.20

The marginal distribution of X is given by

$$Pr(X=0) = .10+.10 = .20,$$

$$Pr(X=1) = .20+.10 = .30,$$

and

$$Pr(X=2) = .30+.20 = .50.$$

The moments of X can be calculated directly from the marginal distribution. We have

$$E[X] = (0)(.20)+(1)(.30)+(2)(.50) = 1.30,$$

$$E[X^2] = (0)(.20)+(1)(.30)+(4)(.50) = 2.30,$$

and

$$Var(X) = 2.30-(1.30)^2 = .61.$$

Now we consider an alternative, but longer (at least this time), way to find $E[X]$ and $Var(X)$. First we find the marginal distribution of Y as

$$Pr(Y{=}1) \;=\; .10+.20+.30 \;=\; .60$$

and

$$Pr(Y{=}2) \;=\; .10+.10+.20 \;=\; .40.$$

Next we find both conditional distributions for X, one given Y=1 and the other given Y=2. We have

$$Pr(X{=}0\,|\,Y{=}1) \;=\; \frac{.10}{.60} \;=\; \frac{1}{6},$$

$$\Pr(X{=}1\,|\,Y{=}1) \;=\; \frac{.20}{.60} \;=\; \frac{2}{6},$$

and

$$\Pr(X{=}2\,|\,Y{=}1) \;=\; \frac{.30}{.60} \;=\; \frac{3}{6}.$$

From this conditional distribution we find the conditional moments of X, given Y=1. We have

$$E[X\,|\,Y{=}1] \;=\; (0)\left(\frac{1}{6}\right)+(1)\left(\frac{2}{6}\right)+(2)\left(\frac{3}{6}\right) \;=\; \frac{8}{6},$$

$$E[X^2\,|\,Y{=}1] \;=\; (0)\left(\frac{1}{6}\right)+(1)\left(\frac{2}{6}\right)+(4)\left(\frac{3}{6}\right) \;=\; \frac{14}{6},$$

and

$$Var(X\,|\,Y{=}1) \;=\; \frac{14}{6}-\left(\frac{8}{6}\right)^2 \;=\; \frac{20}{36}.$$

Similarly we find the conditional distribution

$$\Pr(X{=}0\,|\,Y{=}2) \;=\; \frac{.10}{.40} \;=\; \frac{1}{4},$$

$$\Pr(X{=}1\,|\,Y{=}2) \;=\; \frac{.10}{.40} \;=\; \frac{1}{4},$$

and

$$\Pr(X{=}2\,|\,Y{=}2) \;=\; \frac{.20}{.40} \;=\; \frac{2}{4},$$

and its associated conditional moments

$$E[X\,|\,Y{=}2] \;=\; (0)\left(\frac{1}{4}\right)+(1)\left(\frac{1}{4}\right)+(2)\left(\frac{2}{4}\right) \;=\; \frac{5}{4},$$

$$E[X^2\,|\,Y{=}2] \;=\; (0)\left(\frac{1}{4}\right)+(1)\left(\frac{1}{4}\right)+(4)\left(\frac{2}{4}\right) \;=\; \frac{9}{4},$$

and

$$Var(X\,|\,Y{=}2) \;=\; \frac{9}{4}-\left(\frac{5}{4}\right)^2 \;=\; \frac{11}{16}.$$

We now come to the key part of the operation. We recognize that the conditional expected value of X, denoted $E_X[X \mid Y]$, is a random variable because it is a function of the random variable Y. It can take on the two possible values $\frac{8}{6}$ and $\frac{5}{4}$, and does so with probability .60 and .40, respectively, the probabilities associated with the two possible values of Y. We can find the moments of this random variable as

$$E_Y[E_X[X \mid Y]] = \left(\frac{8}{6}\right)(.60) + \left(\frac{5}{4}\right)(.40) = \frac{13}{10},$$

$$E_Y[(E_X[X \mid Y])^2] = \left(\frac{8}{6}\right)^2 \cdot (.60) + \left(\frac{5}{4}\right)^2 \cdot (.40) = \frac{203}{120},$$

and

$$Var_Y(E_X[X \mid Y]) = \frac{203}{120} - \left(\frac{13}{10}\right)^2 = \frac{1}{600}.$$

Similarly the conditional variance of X given Y, denoted $Var_X(X \mid Y)$, is a random variable because it too is a function of Y. Its two possible values are $\frac{20}{36}$ and $\frac{11}{16}$, so its expected value is

$$E_Y[Var_X(X \mid Y)] = \left(\frac{20}{36}\right)(.60) + \left(\frac{11}{16}\right)(.40) = \frac{73}{120}.$$

Finally we observe that

$$E_Y\left[E_X[X \mid Y]\right] = \frac{13}{10} = E[X],$$

which states that the expected value of the conditional expectation is the unconditional expected value of X. This constitutes the first part of the double expectation theorem. The second part states that

$$E_Y[Var_X(X \mid Y)] + Var_Y(E_X[X \mid Y]) = \frac{73}{120} + \frac{1}{600} = \frac{366}{600} = \frac{61}{100} = Var(X),$$

which says that the expected value of the conditional variance plus the variance of the conditional expectation is the unconditional variance of X.

2.4.2 THE CONTINUOUS CASE

Multivariate probability in the continuous case is handled more compactly than in the discrete case. We cannot list all possible pairs of (x, y) in the continuous joint domain; instead we specify the joint density at the point (x, y) in the form of a joint density function denoted $f(x, y)$. Recall that the marginal density of X is then found by integrating the joint density over all values of Y, and the marginal density of Y is found by integrating the joint density over all values of X. The conditional density of X, given Y, is then found by dividing the joint density by the marginal density of Y, and, similarly, the conditional density of Y, given X, is found by dividing the joint density by the marginal density of X. These basic relationships are illustrated in the following example.

Let the continuous random variable X have a uniform distribution on the interval $0 < x < 12$, and let the continuous random variable Y have a conditional distribution, given $X = x$, that is uniform on the interval $0 < y < x$. We seek the unconditional expected value and variance of Y.

We could, of course, proceed by first finding the marginal distribution of Y and then finding the unconditional expected value and variance of Y directly from this marginal distribution. Since X is uniform we have $f_X(x) = \frac{1}{12}$, and since Y is conditionally uniform we have $f_{Y|X}(y \mid x) = \frac{1}{x}$. Then the joint density is $f(x, y) = \frac{1}{12x}$, and the marginal density of Y is

$$f_Y(y) = \int_y^{12} f(x, y)\, dx = \int_y^{12} \left(\frac{1}{12x}\right) dx = \frac{1}{12}[\ln 12 - \ln y].$$

To then find the first and second moments of Y directly from the marginal density of Y is a bit of a calculus challenge. Instead, we will find the unconditional expected value and variance of Y from its conditional moments by using the double expectation theorem. We have, since Y is conditionally uniform, $E_Y[Y \mid X] = \frac{X}{2}$ and $Var_Y(Y \mid X) = \frac{X^2}{12}$. Then, directly from the double expectation theorem, we have

$$E[Y] = E_X\left[E_Y[Y \mid X]\right] = E_X\left[\frac{X}{2}\right] = \frac{1}{2} \cdot E[X] = 3,$$

since, being uniform on $0 < x < 12$, we have $E[X] = 6$. Similarly,

$$\begin{aligned} Var(Y) &= E_X[Var_Y(Y \mid X)] + Var_X(E_Y[Y \mid X]) \\ &= E_X\left[\frac{X^2}{12}\right] + Var_X\left(\frac{X}{2}\right) \\ &= \frac{1}{12} \cdot E[X^2] + \frac{1}{4} \cdot Var(X) = \left(\frac{1}{12}\right)(48) + \left(\frac{1}{4}\right)(12) = 7, \end{aligned}$$

since $Var(X) = 12$ and $E[X^2] = Var(X) + (E[X])^2 = 48$.

In the discrete case example, presented in Section 2.4.1, the unconditional mean and variance were found more easily from the marginal distribution than via the double expectation theorem. In this continuous example, however, the opposite is true; the mean and variance of Y are found more easily via the double expectation theorem than from the marginal distribution of Y. The double expectation theorem will have several applications throughout this text.

CHAPTER THREE

REVIEW OF MARKOV CHAINS

Throughout this text we will present a number of actuarial models in the form of *multi-state models*. The underlying mathematics of multi-state models is that of the *Markov Chain*,[1] which is, in turn, a special case of a *stochastic process*. In this chapter we provide an abbreviated review of several varieties of Markov Chains, to the extent necessary to understand their use in analyzing the multi-state models presented throughout the text. Readers requiring a more thorough study of Markov Chains are referred to Ross [22].

A stochastic process arises when a random variable is indexed over time, with the distribution of that random variable depending on the time at which it is considered. For example, suppose the discrete random variable X can take on only the integer values 1, 2, 3, or 4, but the probability that $X=3$, for example, depends on time. Because the associated probability values vary over time, even if the domain of $x=\{1,2,3,4\}$ remains fixed, it is necessary to notate the name of the random variable to indicate the time point at which its several probability values are being considered.

There are two sub-cases to consider. If the random variable might be considered at *any* point of time on the real number axis, we denote the random variable at time t by $X(t)$, for $t \geq 0$, and refer to this model as a *continuous-time* stochastic process. On the other hand, if the random variable is considered, or observed, only at the discrete time points $n=0,1,2,\cdots$, then we denote the random variable at time n by X_n, for $n=0,1,2,\cdots$, and refer to the model as a *discrete-time* stochastic process.

A stochastic process can also be classified as *homogeneous* or *non-homogeneous*. Rather than define these terms for stochastic processes in general, we will define them specifically for Markov Chains, the only type of stochastic process considered further in this chapter. The discrete-time process is presented in Section 3.1 and the continuous-time process in Section 3.2.

3.1 DISCRETE-TIME MARKOV CHAINS

For a discrete-time Markov Chain, we begin by defining a model consisting of $m+1$ *states*, denoted $0,1,\cdots,m$, where $m \geq 1$. The process moves at random among these states. This is illustrated in the following diagram, with $m=2$.

---

[1] Named for the noted Russian mathematician A. A. Markov.

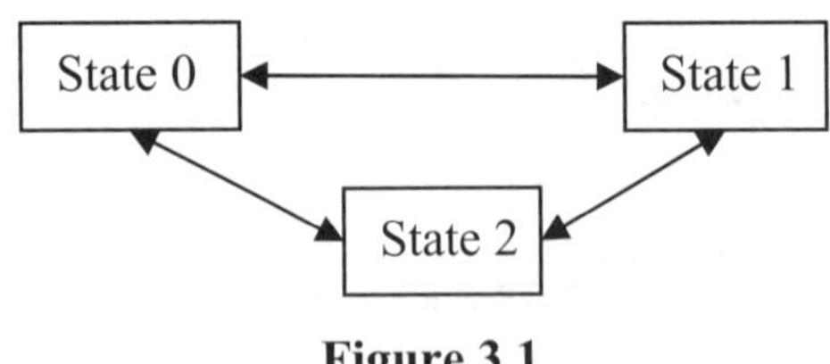

Figure 3.1

The model illustrated in Figure 3.1 involves three states. The arrows indicate that movement is possible from any state to any other state. (When that is so, we say that each state *communicates* with each other state.)[2] The random variable X_n takes on the numerical value of the state in which the process is located at time *n*, for $n = 0, 1, 2, \cdots$, so the possible values of X_n are $\{0, 1, \cdots, m\}$. In other words, if $X_n = i$ we say the process is in State *i* at time *n*. In the three-state model of Figure 3.1, the event notated as $X_3 = 2$, for example, is the event that the process is in State 2 at time 3.

The initial state of the process at time 0 must be specified. In nearly all of the applications of Markov Chains to actuarial models presented in this text, the process will begin in State 0, with the meaning of State 0 defined in each case. Thus we would have $X_0 = 0$ in these applications.

3.1.1 TRANSITION PROBABILITIES

The basic building block of a Markov Chain is the conditional probability that the process will be in State *j* at time $n+1$, given that it is in State *i* at time *n*, including the possibility that $j = i$. For a Markov Chain stochastic process, the probability of being in State *j* at time $n+1$ depends *only* on which state the process is in at time *n*. It does not matter which states the process was in at any times earlier than time *n*. (For this reason, a Markov Chain is sometimes called a *memoryless* stochastic process.) After moving to a new state, we can completely forget where we were in the past. In fact, it is this property of memorylessness that distinguishes a Markov Chain from more general stochastic processes. In mathematical notation, this conditional probability is written as $Pr[X_{n+1} = j \mid X_n = i]$ and is called a *transition probability*.

Figure 3.2

If the transition probability of moving from State *i* to State *j* remains constant over time (i.e., does not depend on the value of *n*), the process is said to be *homogeneous*, and if the transition probability varies with *n* the process is said to be *non-homogeneous*. (The non-homogeneous case is discussed in Section 3.1.5.)

[2] In nearly all of the Markov Chain models encountered throughout this text we will find considerable restriction on the ability of all states to communicate with each other.

The homogeneous transition probability described above is denoted by p^{ij}, so we have

$$p^{ij} = Pr[X_{n+1} = j \mid X_n = i], \tag{3.1}$$

where *i* and *j* can be any of $0,1,\cdots,m$, and $n = 0,1,2,\cdots$. Because the homogeneous transition probability is constant over time, the value of *n* need not be included in its notation. (See Section 3.1.5 for the alternative case.)

Given that the process is in State *i* at some discrete time point, it must be in *some* state at the next discrete time point (including possibly State *i* itself), so it follows that

$$\sum_{j=0}^{m} p^{ij} = 1. \tag{3.2}$$

If $p^{ii} \neq 0$, then it is possible to remain in State *i* over the next time interval, whereas $p^{ii} = 0$ would imply that remaining in State *i* is not possible. (The latter property does not tend to hold in most Markov Chain models encountered in practice.) Further, if $p^{ii} = 1$, then it is not possible to move from State *i* to another state. In this case we say that State *i* is an *absorbing state*, a property that we regularly encounter in the models considered later in the text.[3]

The entire set of p^{ij} transition probabilities for all (i,j) is contained in the *transition probability matrix* **P**, defined as

$$\mathbf{P} = \begin{vmatrix} p^{00} & p^{01} & \cdots & p^{0m} \\ p^{10} & p^{11} & \cdots & p^{1m} \\ \vdots & \vdots & \vdots & \vdots \\ p^{m0} & p^{m1} & \cdots & p^{mm} \end{vmatrix}. \tag{3.3}$$

For example, consider the transition probability matrix

$$\mathbf{P} = \begin{vmatrix} .80 & .20 & 0 \\ .30 & .60 & .10 \\ 0 & 0 & 1 \end{vmatrix}.$$

The associated Markov Chain has three states, which we call States 0, 1, and 2.[4] The probability of moving from State 1 to State 0, for example, is given by $p^{10} = .30$. The fact that $p^{02} = 0$ tells us that it is not possible to move directly from State 0 to State 2, for some reason. The val-

---

[3] Nearly all of our applications will involve a person covered by some type of insurance contract. The process moves into its final state when the person dies, and then never leaves that state. This will be our most common example of an absorbing state.

[4] Some textbooks prefer to identify the states in a three-state process as States 1, 2, and 3. The labeling of the states is arbitrary, of course, but some prefer to begin with State 1 so that the notation used in the matrix **P** is consistent with that used in matrix algebra. When we begin with State 0, then the upper left entry in matrix **P** would be denoted p^{00}, whereas it is usually denoted p_{11} in matrix algebra as the element in the first row and first column. Notwithstanding the convenience of starting the matrix with p_{11}, we use the more common Markov Chain notation of starting with State 0. Our notation also conforms with that used on Society of Actuaries Exam MLC.

ue $p^{22} = 1$ tells us that State 2 is an absorbing state. Because the process is homogeneous, the same transition probability values apply over all discrete intervals on the time axis.

3.1.2 STATE VECTOR

As described above, at time n the discrete-time Markov Chain process is located in one of m+1 possible states. We denote the probability of the process being in State i at time n by π_{in}, for $i = 0, 1, \cdots, m$, and we represent the set of all such probabilities in a row vector denoted $\boldsymbol{\pi}_n$. That is,

$$\boldsymbol{\pi}_n = (\pi_{0n}, \pi_{1n}, \cdots, \pi_{mn}), \tag{3.4}$$

where

$$\sum_{i=0}^{m} \pi_{in} = 1. \tag{3.5}$$

The vector $\boldsymbol{\pi}_n$ is called the *state vector at time n*. The elements of $\boldsymbol{\pi}_n$ define the *state of the process* at time n by giving the probabilities of the process being in each of the possible states.

Now suppose it is *known* that the process is in State i at time n. Conditional on this knowledge, the value of π_{in} would be 1 and the value of each π_{jn}, for $j \neq i$, would be 0. For example, if a 3-state process is known to be in State 1 at time n, then the time n state vector would be $\boldsymbol{\pi}_n = (0, 1, 0)$.

The time n+1 state vector can be determined from the time n state vector as

$$\boldsymbol{\pi}_{n+1} = \boldsymbol{\pi}_n \cdot \mathbf{P}, \tag{3.6a}$$

where $\mathbf{P}$ is the transition probability matrix defined by Equation (3.3). For our 3-state process known to be in State 1 at time n, we have

$$\boldsymbol{\pi}_{n+1} = (0, 1, 0) \cdot \begin{vmatrix} p^{00} & p^{01} & p^{02} \\ p^{10} & p^{11} & p^{12} \\ p^{20} & p^{21} & p^{22} \end{vmatrix} = (p^{10}, p^{11}, p^{12}).$$

This result was to be expected, since the second row of $\mathbf{P}$ gives, in order, the probabilities for being in States 0, 1, 2 at time $n+1$, given that the process is in State 1 at time n.[5]

3.1.3 PROBABILITIES OVER MULTIPLE STEPS

Again consider the 3-state process of Section 3.1.2, known to be in State 1 at time n. What are the probabilities for being in each of States 0, 1, 2 at time $n+2$? These probability values are contained in $\boldsymbol{\pi}_{n+2}$, the time $n+2$ state vector. Since the process is homogeneous, the

[5] In this text we presume that the reader has had a standard semester course in linear algebra, and understands basic concepts such as the multiplication of a row vector times a matrix.

same set of transition probabilities, contained in the matrix **P**, apply as the process moves from $n+1$ to $n+2$ as applied when the process moved from n to $n+1$. Thus we have

$$\boldsymbol{\pi}_{n+2} = \boldsymbol{\pi}_{n+1} \cdot \mathbf{P}. \tag{3.6b}$$

Substituting for $\boldsymbol{\pi}_{n+1}$ from Equation (3.6a) we have

$$\boldsymbol{\pi}_{n+2} = \boldsymbol{\pi}_n \cdot \mathbf{P} \cdot \mathbf{P} = \boldsymbol{\pi}_n \cdot \mathbf{P}^2. \tag{3.6c}$$

With $\boldsymbol{\pi}_n = (0, 1, 0)$ to reflect the known state of the process at time n, we see that the elements in the time $n+2$ state vector are the same as the elements in the second row of the matrix $\mathbf{P}^2 = \mathbf{P} \cdot \mathbf{P}$.

This result is easily generalized from two steps to r steps.

Figure 3.3

To find ${}_r p^{ij} = Pr[X_{n+r} = j \mid X_n = i]$, the probability that a process known to be in State i at time n will be in State j at time $n+r$ (i.e., after r discrete time intervals), we calculate

$$\boldsymbol{\pi}_{n+r} = \boldsymbol{\pi}_n \cdot \mathbf{P}^r. \tag{3.6d}$$

Since $\boldsymbol{\pi}_n$ contains the element $\pi_{in} = 1$ and all other elements equal to zero, it follows that the elements of the vector $\boldsymbol{\pi}_{n+r}$ are the same as those in the $(i+1)^{st}$ row of the matrix $\mathbf{P}^r$. The value of ${}_r p^{ij} = Pr[X_{n+r} = j \mid X_n = i]$ is found in the $(j+1)^{st}$ column of the $(i+1)^{st}$ row of $\mathbf{P}^r$.

3.1.4 PROPERTIES OF HOMOGENEOUS DISCRETE-TIME MARKOV CHAINS

As a result of having the same set of transition probabilities apply over each successive time interval, the homogeneous model has a number of properties that are mathematically interesting. However, we will find with our presentation of various actuarial models as discrete-time Markov Chains throughout the text that the homogeneous model is not a realistic one to adopt, and we will instead make use of the non-homogeneous model to be described further in Section 3.1.5. Because we will make very little use of the homogeneous model from here on, we will not present its further properties in this chapter. The reader interested in reviewing these properties is referred to Chapter 4 of Ross [22].

3.1.5 THE NON-HOMOGENEOUS DISCRETE-TIME MODEL

All of the results developed thus far were based on the property that the set of transition probabilities, summarized in the matrix **P**, remains constant over successive steps in the process. Recall that a Markov Chain with this property is said to be homogeneous.

Now we generalize the process to the case where the transition probabilities need not be the same over successive intervals. We let p_k^{ij}, for $k=0,1,2,\cdots$, denote the probability that a process in State i at time k will be in State j at time $k+1$. That is, p_k^{ij} represents the probability of moving from State i to State j over the $(k+1)^{st}$ discrete time interval of the process. The set of p_k^{ij} probabilities for all i and j is summarized in the matrix of transition probabilities over the $(k+1)^{st}$ interval, which we denote by $\mathbf{P}^{(k)}$. (Note that, for example, $\mathbf{P}^{(3)}$ denotes the matrix of transition probabilities *over the fourth interval in the process*, whereas $\mathbf{P}^3 = \mathbf{P}\cdot\mathbf{P}\cdot\mathbf{P}$ denotes the matrix of transition probabilities *over any three intervals* in a homogeneous process.) For the multiple-step probability, we define

$$_r p_n^{ij} = Pr[X_{n+r}=j \,|\, X_n=i]. \tag{3.7a}$$

A Markov process allowing for different matrices of transition probabilities over different intervals in the process is called a *non-homogeneous* process. It is this version of the Markov Chain that we will use to represent many of the actuarial models encountered later in the text.

In the non-homogeneous case, the state of the process at time n (defined in Section 3.1.2 in the homogeneous case) is given by

$$\boldsymbol{\pi}_n = \boldsymbol{\pi}_0 \cdot \mathbf{P}^{(0)} \cdot \mathbf{P}^{(1)} \cdot \;\cdots\; \cdot \mathbf{P}^{(n-1)}, \tag{3.8}$$

where $\boldsymbol{\pi}_0$ denotes the (known) initial state of the process at time 0, when the process first begins.

For example, we consider a simple two-state model with transition probabilities given by

$$\mathbf{P}^{(0)} = \begin{vmatrix} .60 & .40 \\ .70 & .30 \end{vmatrix}$$

over the first interval of the process, and

$$\mathbf{P}^{(1)} = \begin{vmatrix} .50 & .50 \\ .80 & .20 \end{vmatrix}$$

for the second interval of the process. If the process is known to begin in State 1 at time 0, what is the probability that the process will be in State 0 at time 2?

The desired probability, which we have denoted by $_2 p_0^{10}$, is given by the element π_{01} in the state vector $\boldsymbol{\pi}_2$. We have

$$\begin{aligned} \boldsymbol{\pi}_2 &= \boldsymbol{\pi}_0 \cdot \mathbf{P}^{(0)} \cdot \mathbf{P}^{(1)} \\ &= (0,1) \cdot \begin{vmatrix} .60 & .40 \\ .70 & .30 \end{vmatrix} \cdot \begin{vmatrix} .50 & .50 \\ .80 & .20 \end{vmatrix} = (.70,.30) \cdot \begin{vmatrix} .50 & .50 \\ .80 & .20 \end{vmatrix} = (.59,.41), \end{aligned}$$

so the answer is $\pi_{01} = {}_2p_0^{10} = .59$. Note that here we first multiplied $\boldsymbol{\pi_0}$ times $\mathbf{P}^{(0)}$, and then multiplied the resulting $\boldsymbol{\pi}_1$ vector times $\mathbf{P}^{(1)}$, rather than multiplying $\mathbf{P}^{(0)}$ times $\mathbf{P}^{(1)}$. The answer is the same either way, of course, but with fewer calculations in the approach shown.

The non-homogeneous version of the discrete-time Markov Chain will be used to represent a number of the actuarial models considered throughout this text. The reason why the model needs to be non-homogeneous, rather than homogeneous, will be easily understood as the examples arise.

3.1.6 PROBABILITY OF REMAINING IN STATE *i*

Consider the general probability value ${}_rp_n^{ij}$, given by Equation (3.7a), with $j=i$. In this case we have

$$ {}_rp_n^{ii} = Pr[X_{n+r}=i \,|\, X_n=i], \tag{3.7b} $$

and it denotes the probability of the process being in State i at time $n+r$, given that it is in State i at time n. There are two subcases contained in this event, namely that the process *never left* State i between n and $n+r$, or that it did leave State i but returned by time $n+r$.

The first subcase plays a special role later in the text when we represent certain actuarial models in the multi-state context. Because of this, we will find it useful to define the special symbol ${}_rp_n^{\overline{ii}}$ to denote the probability that a general discrete-time Markov process, known to be in State i at time n, does not leave State i prior to time $n+r$. Since the event of "never leaving" is a subset of the event whose probability is given by ${}_rp_n^{ii}$, it follows that

$$ {}_rp_n^{\overline{ii}} \le {}_rp_n^{ii}. \tag{3.9} $$

As we shall see later in the text, some models include the feature that State i, once left, can never be reentered. When this restriction holds, then it follows that

$$ {}_rp_n^{\overline{ii}} = {}_rp_n^{ii}. \tag{3.10} $$

A simple example of this is the two-state model defined in Chapter 5, where a person is either alive or dead. If State i is the alive state, then once the process leaves State i it can never return to it.

3.1.7 APPLICATION TO MULTI-STATE MODELS

In most of the applications of Markov Chains to multi-state models considered in this text, the process will begin at time 0, so the general probability functions ${}_rp_n^{ij}$, ${}_rp_n^{ii}$, and ${}_rp_n^{\overline{ii}}$ would appear as ${}_rp_0^{ij}$, ${}_rp_0^{ii}$, and ${}_rp_0^{\overline{ii}}$.

However, it will generally be the case that the model will apply to a person covered by some form of insurance contract, with the person being age x at time 0 when the process begins. With the understanding that the process begins at time 0, it is not necessary to place the zero in the subscript of the probability function. But, in a non-homogeneous model, the numerical value of the probability function ${}_rp_0^{ij}$ will be different for different values of the age x, so we should include the age of the person to whom the probability function applies in its notational structure.

Therefore we define the general probability function ${}_rp_x^{ij}$ to denote the probability that a person who is in State i at time 0 at age x will be in State j at time r, at which time the person would be age $x+r$. Now the general probability function defined by Equation (3.7a) will henceforth be written as

$${}_rp_x^{ij} = Pr[X_r = j \mid X_0 = i], \tag{3.7c}$$

reflecting the facts that the process begins at time 0 for a person age x at that time. Furthermore, as already stated, in most applications we will find $i=0$.

The more specific functions ${}_rp_x^{ii}$ and ${}_rp_x^{\overline{ii}}$ would be similarly defined. The logic of this notation will become clearer as applications of this theory unfold later in the text.

3.1.8 TRANSITION ONLY AT FIXED TIME POINTS

Recall that a discrete-time process is one that is observed only at the discrete time points $n = 0, 1, \cdots$. Some writers define a discrete-time process as one for which transition can *occur* only at the several discrete time points, but this is not correct. If the person is observed to be in State i at discrete time n, and in State j at discrete time $n+1$, it does not matter where within the interval $(n, n+1]$ the transition to State j actually occurred.

As we shall see in Chapter 5, a simple application of this idea is the case where State 0 denotes a person being alive and State 1 denotes the person being dead. Then p_x^{01} is the probability that a person in State 0 (alive) at age x will be in State 1 (dead) by age $x+1$. The person does not have to die (i.e., transition from State 0 to State 1) at *precisely* time 1 (age $x+1$) in order to satisfy the probability.

Nonetheless, we will encounter circumstances where transitions do indeed occur only at fixed discrete time points. These models are certainly discrete-time models, and should be viewed as special cases of the more general discrete-time model.

3.2 CONTINUOUS-TIME MARKOV CHAINS

We again consider a model consisting of m+1 states, and let $X(t)$ denote the discrete random variable with possible values $\{0,1,\cdots,m\}$ that indicates the state in which the process is located at time t, for any $t \geq 0$, so that $X(t)=i$ denotes the event that the process is in State

i at time t. The process is said to be a *continuous-time process* because it can be observed at any time t on the real number axis, notwithstanding the fact that $X(t)$ itself is a discrete random variable. As in the discrete-time case, the initial state of the process at time 0 is necessarily known. In nearly all of our applications later in this text, the process will necessarily begin in State 0 at time 0 so we will have $X(0)=0$. As explained in Section 3.1.7, we also assume that the process begins at time 0.

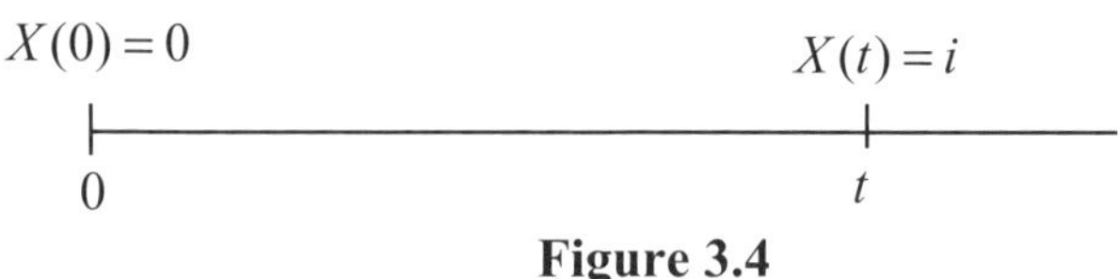

Figure 3.4

Analogous to the non-homogeneous discrete-time probability ${}_r p_x^{ij} = Pr[X_r = j \mid X_0 = i]$, the probability that a non-homogeneous process known to be in State i at time 0 will be in State j after r time intervals, we now consider

$${}_t p_x^{ij} = Pr\left[X(t)=j \mid X(0)=i\right], \tag{3.11}$$

the conditional probability that a continuous-time process will be in State j at time t, given that it is in State i at time 0, for a person who is age x at time 0. To be a continuous-time Markov Chain, the process must possess the memoryless property mentioned for the discrete-time case in Section 3.1.1. That is, the conditional probability of Equation (3.11) depends *only* on being in State i at time 0, and does not depend on the path it followed to reach State i nor the length of time it had been in State i prior to time 0.

As with the discrete-time process discussed earlier, the continuous-time process can be either *homogeneous*[6] or *non-homogeneous*. We will find that the actuarial models represented as Markov Chains throughout this text will usually be of the non-homogeneous type, as they will be a more realistic representation of the circumstance. (See Section 3.2.1 for the definition of a continuous-time homogeneous process.)

As mentioned in Section 3.1.6 in the discrete-time case, we also need to distinguish here between ${}_t p_x^{ii}$, the probability of being in State i at time t for a process (or a person) known to be in State i at time 0 at age x, and its subset probability ${}_t p_x^{\overline{ii}}$, the probability of this person remaining in State i continuously from time 0 to time t.

3.2.1 FORCES OF TRANSITION

For the discrete-time model of Section 3.1, the basic building blocks were the transition probabilities summarized in the matrix $\mathbf{P}$ (in the homogeneous case) or the sequence of matrices $\mathbf{P}^{(k)}$ (in the non-homogeneous case). Then all conditional probability values of the general form $Pr[X_{n+r}=j \mid X_n=i]$, for all i, j, n, and r, can be determined from the known state vector $\boldsymbol{\pi}_n$ and the appropriate matrices.

[6] Some textbooks refer to a continuous-time homogeneous process as a *stationary* process.

For the continuous-time model, with the process observed for all values of t, the basic building blocks are *instantaneous* measures of transition at a point of time, called *forces of transition.*[7] This is a very important point: in the discrete-time case, the process is measured (or observed) only over discrete time intervals, so the event of transition is modeled by probability values over such intervals; in the continuous-time case, the process is measured (or observed) continuously, so the event of transition is modeled by instantaneous rates of transition (which we call forces of transition) rather than by probability values.

In the non-homogeneous case, we might denote the function giving the force of transition from State i to State j at general time s by μ_s^{ij}, where $i \neq j$. However, as explained in Section 3.1.7, the force of transition function at time s will depend on the age of the associated person at time s. If the person is age x at time 0, then the person is age $x+s$ at time s. Therefore, for a process known to be in State i at time s, for a person who is then age $x+s$, we let μ_{x+s}^{ij} denote the force of transitioning to State j at that time. Since this force is needed at all values of s, we recognize that μ_{x+s}^{ij} is a *force of transition function*. We define

$$\mu_{x+s}^{i} = \sum_{j=0}^{i-1} \mu_{x+s}^{ij} + \sum_{j=i+1}^{m} \mu_{x+s}^{ij} \tag{3.12}$$

to be the *total force of transition* out of State i at time s. Note that μ_{x+s}^{i} is the sum of the μ_{x+s}^{ij} over all j *except* $j = i$. For completeness, we could define μ_{x+s}^{ii} as the *force of remaining* in State i at time s.[8] Then the entire set of μ_{x+s}^{ij} forces, including the ones with $j = i$, can be summarized in the *matrix of transition forces* $\mathbf{M}(s)$, where

$$\mathbf{M}(s) = \begin{vmatrix} \mu_{x+s}^{00} & \mu_{x+s}^{01} & \cdots & \mu_{x+s}^{0m} \\ \mu_{x+s}^{10} & \mu_{x+s}^{11} & \cdots & \mu_{x+s}^{1m} \\ \vdots & \vdots & \vdots & \vdots \\ \mu_{x+s}^{m0} & \mu_{x+s}^{m1} & \cdots & \mu_{x+s}^{mm} \end{vmatrix}. \tag{3.13}$$

In the homogeneous case, the force of transition μ_{x+s}^{ij} would be a constant function of s, and therefore denoted simply as μ^{ij}. As stated earlier for the discrete-time process, the homogeneous case has many mathematically interesting properties,[9] but is not appropriate for representing the actuarial models considered later in the text. For this reason, we consider only the non-homogeneous case from here on.

---

[7] These instantaneous measures are analogous to the familiar *force of interest* (see Section 1.1) and the *hazard rate*, or *force of failure*, to be introduced in Section 5.1.4 and used extensively with actuarial models.

[8] The value of μ_{x+s}^{ii} is seldom used in the development that follows.

[9] For example, with a constant force of transition in a continuous-time Markov model, the random variable for the waiting time until the next transition would have an exponential distribution.

3.2.2 FORMULAS FOR ${}_tp_x^{ij} = Pr\left[X(t)=j \mid X(0)=i\right]$

In the non-homogeneous continuous-time process, we begin with the set of force of transition functions μ_{x+s}^{ij}, for $s>0$. We now consider the question of how to determine values of ${}_tp_x^{ij}$ from the set of force of transition functions.

The derivation of an equation for determining ${}_tp_x^{ij}$ starts with an expression for the derivative of ${}_tp_x^{ij}$, with respect to t, known as *Kolmogorov's Forward Equation.*[10] This differential equation, whose derivation we present in Appendix B, is

$$\frac{d}{dt}\,{}_tp_x^{ij} = \sum_{k\neq j}\left({}_tp_x^{ik}\cdot\mu_{x+t}^{kj} - {}_tp_x^{ij}\cdot\mu_{x+t}^{jk}\right). \tag{3.14a}$$

Because the term ${}_tp_x^{ij}$ appearing after the minus sign in Equation (3.14a) does not involve k, we can rewrite Equation (3.14a) as

$$\frac{d}{dt}\,{}_tp_x^{ij} = \sum_{k\neq j}\left({}_tp_x^{ik}\cdot\mu_{x+t}^{kj}\right) - {}_tp_x^{ij}\cdot\mu_{x+t}^{j}, \tag{3.14b}$$

where we have substituted μ_{x+t}^{j} for $\sum_{k\neq j}\mu_{x+t}^{jk}$, by Equation (3.12).

For example, consider a three-state model, where all states communicate with each other. If the process is in State $i=0$ for a person age x at time 0, then ${}_tp_x^{01}$ is the probability of the process being in State $j=1$ at time t. In Equation (3.14b), k takes on only the values 0 and 2. We have

$$\frac{d}{dt}\,{}_tp_x^{01} = {}_tp_x^{00}\cdot\mu_{x+t}^{01} + {}_tp_x^{02}\cdot\mu_{x+t}^{21} - {}_tp_x^{01}\cdot\mu_{x+t}^{1}. \tag{3.15}$$

For the actuarial models considered in this text, the idea of all states communicating with each other will never hold since there will always be at least one absorbing state. This characteristic will simplify the applicable Kolmogorov equation.

The simplest model, that of one life and one decrement which we encounter first in Chapter 5, has only two states, States 0 and 1. In this model, transition from State 0 to State 1 is possible, but the converse is not. Then with $i=0$ and $j=1$ in Equation (3.14a), k takes on only the value $k=0$ so we have

$$\begin{aligned}\frac{d}{dt}\,{}_tp_x^{01} &= {}_tp_x^{00}\cdot\mu_{x+t}^{01} - {}_tp_x^{01}\cdot\mu_{x+t}^{10}\\ &= {}_tp_x^{00}\cdot\mu_{x+t}^{01},\end{aligned} \tag{3.16}$$

[10] Named for another great Russian mathematician, A.N. Kolmogorov.

since $\mu_{x+s}^{10}=0$ for all s. (In Exercise 5-22 the reader is asked to solve this equation for ${}_{n}p_{x}^{01}$.)

In Section 14.4.2, we encounter a model with States 0, 1, and 2, where transition is possible only from State 0 to State 1, State 0 to State 2, or State 1 to State 2. This means that $\mu_{x+s}^{10}=\mu_{x+s}^{20}=\mu_{x+s}^{21}=0$ for all s, and the meaningful values of ${}_{t}p_{x}^{ij}$ are ${}_{t}p_{x}^{00}$, ${}_{t}p_{x}^{01}$, ${}_{t}p_{x}^{02}$, ${}_{t}p_{x}^{11}$, and ${}_{t}p_{x}^{12}$. For ${}_{t}p_{x}^{01}$, for example, Equation (3.14a) simplifies to

$$\frac{d}{dt}\,{}_{t}p_{x}^{01} = {}_{t}p_{x}^{00}\cdot\mu_{x+t}^{01}-{}_{t}p_{x}^{01}\cdot\mu_{x+t}^{12}. \tag{3.17}$$

We will solve this differential equation for ${}_{n}p_{x}^{01}$ in Example 14.9, and for other ij combinations in the Chapter 14 exercises.

3.3 PAYMENTS

In nearly all of the actuarial models encountered in this text, we will be interested in the notion of a payment made when the process transitions from one state to another and also the notion of a sequence of payments made while the process remains in a particular state. We first encounter the former idea in Chapter 7 and the latter idea in Chapter 8.

In the discrete case, suppose a payment is to be made at time r because the process transitioned from State i to State j during the discrete time interval $(r-1,r]$. If the process is known to be in State h at time 0, for a person age x at that time, then the probability of being in State i at time $r-1$ is ${}_{r-1}p_{x}^{hi}$. The conditional probability of being in State j at time r, given in State i at time $r-1$, is p_{x+r-1}^{ij}. Then the overall probability of payment being made at time r is ${}_{r-1}p_{x}^{hi}\cdot p_{x+r-1}^{ij}$.

In the continuous case, suppose a payment is to be made at time t because the process transitions from State i to State j at precise time t. If the process is known to be in State h at time 0, for a person age x at that time, then the density for transition from State i to State j at time t is ${}_{t}p_{x}^{hi}\cdot\mu_{x+t}^{ij}$.

The second notion of payment made *while in* a particular state, rather than upon transition from one state to another, is easier to formulate. Again assume a discrete process is known to be in State h at time 0, for a person age x at that time, and suppose a payment will be made at time r if the process is in State i at that time. The probability of this event is simply ${}_{r}p_{x}^{hi}$, which is therefore the probability of payment.

In the continuous case, again the probability of payment is the same as the probability of being in State i at time t, given a person in State h at age x at time 0, which is ${}_{t}p_{x}^{hi}$.

Because the payments are *contingent* on events that are not certain to occur, the value of the payments is determined in a probabilistic, rather than deterministic, framework. The meaning of this is explained in the chapters that follow.

3.4 EXERCISES

3.1 Discrete-Time Markov Chains

3-1 A discrete-time Markov process has only two states, denoted as State 0 and State 1. A person is age x at time 0, and is located in State 0. We are given the age-specific one-year transition probability values

$$p_{x+k}^{00} = .70 + \frac{.10}{k+1}$$

and

$$p_{x+k}^{11} = .60 + \frac{.20}{k+1}.$$

(a) Find the value of p_{x+1}^{01}.

(b) Find the value of p_{x+2}^{10}.

(c) Find the value of $Pr[X_3 = 0 \mid X_1 = 0]$.

(d) Is this process homogeneous or non-homogeneous? Why?

3-2 A certain animal species can be classified as thriving (State 0), endangered (State 1), or extinct (State 2). Movement among states is governed by a non-homogeneous Markov process defined by the following transition probability matrices:

$$\mathbf{P}^{(0)} = \begin{bmatrix} .85 & .15 & 0 \\ 0 & .70 & .30 \\ 0 & 0 & 1 \end{bmatrix}, \qquad \mathbf{P}^{(1)} = \begin{bmatrix} .90 & .10 & 0 \\ .10 & .70 & .20 \\ 0 & 0 & 1 \end{bmatrix},$$

$$\mathbf{P}^{(2)} = \begin{bmatrix} .95 & .05 & 0 \\ .20 & .70 & .10 \\ 0 & 0 & 1 \end{bmatrix}, \qquad \mathbf{P}^{(k)} = \begin{bmatrix} .95 & .05 & 0 \\ .50 & .50 & 0 \\ 0 & 0 & 1 \end{bmatrix},$$

where $k = 3, 4, 5, \cdots$.

(a) If the species is thriving at time n, is it possible for it to be extinct at time $n+1$? Why?

(b) If the species is endangered at time 0, is it more or less likely to become thriving within one time interval as it remains endangered?

(c) If the species is endangered at $t = 0$, what is the probability that it will ever become extinct?

3.2 Continuous-Time Markov Chains

3-3 A four-state Markov process, with states denoted as States 0,1,2,3, begins in State 0 at time 0 for a person age x at time 0. The process can transition only from State 0 to one of States 1, 2, or 3. (This is the standard multiple-decrement model presented in Section 14.4.1.) The forces of transition are $\mu_{x+t}^{01}=.30$, $\mu_{x+t}^{02}=.50$, and $\mu_{x+t}^{03}=.70$, all for $t\geq 0$.

(a) Is this process homogeneous or non-homogeneous? Why?

(b) Solve the Kolmogorov Forward Equation for ${}_rp_x^{00}$.

(c) Calculate the value of $Pr\left[X(1)=2\,|\,X(0)=0\right]$.

3.3 Payments

3-4 A three-state non-homogeneous Markov process begins in State 0 at time 0. The process is defined by the transition probability matrices

$$\mathbf{P}^{(0)} = \mathbf{P}^{(1)} = \begin{bmatrix} .60 & .30 & .10 \\ 0 & 0 & 1 \\ 0 & 0 & 1 \end{bmatrix}$$

and

$$\mathbf{P}^{(k)} = \begin{bmatrix} 0 & .30 & .70 \\ 0 & 0 & 1 \\ 0 & 0 & 1 \end{bmatrix},$$

for $k=2,3,4,\cdots$.

(a) A payment of 1 is made at discrete times $t=0,1,2,\cdots$, provided the process is in either State 0 or State 1 at time t. Find the expected value of these payments.

(b) A payment of 4 is made at discrete times $t=1,2,3,\cdots$, provided the process is in State 1 at time t. Find the expected value of these payments.

Chapter Four

Characteristics of Insurance and Pensions

Throughout this text, we provide the mathematical tools and theory necessary for the analysis of contracts for contingent payments, with primary application to life insurance, annuities, and pensions. In order to give readers a context for their study of the text, we offer first some background on, and characteristics of, this aspect of modern financial markets.

4.1 Background and Principles

Insurance was developed and improved throughout history in order to limit individuals' and businesses' exposure to risk. The insuring party or organization would seek to take on a large number of contracts, in order to diversify and minimize their risk while covering each individual's potential loss. According to Trenerry, et al. [23], this practice existed as far back as Babylonian times, close to 1750 BC, when sea merchants would insure their cargoes against loss through storm or robbery, by paying an extra fee on their loan. In Roman times, burial clubs emerged, through which soldiers would provide for one another's proper burials at the time of death. This continued to evolve in the seventeenth and eighteenth centuries, as "amicable societies" and "ministers' widows' funds" were established as basic versions of the modern insurance company. The common theme running throughout this history is the *diversification of risk* among a large number of insured individuals, and the transfer of risk from an individual to an insurer or fund. This is the fundamental principle and motivation behind the development of insurance.

Edmund Halley, of Halley's Comet fame, is credited with developing the first age-specific life mortality table, which supported the development of age-specific life insurance premiums. Two Scottish ministers, Robert Wallace and Alexander Webster, helped found the "Scottish Ministers' Widows' Fund," which was the first fund of its type to be managed on a mathematical basis.[1] Through analysis of Halley's mortality data and the mortality statistics of Scottish ministers, Wallace and Webster found that Scottish ministers lived longer than the general population, and, consequently, they needed less funds to cover benefits.

In the late eighteenth century, life insurance companies developed the concept of *level premium payment* for long-term contracts, in order to encourage policyholders to keep their insurance in force for more time. This resulted in the need to recognize increasing mortality over time and the time-value of money in an environment of varying interest rates and investment returns. One way that this risk was addressed in *mutual insurance companies* (which are companies owned by their policyholders), was to charge conservatively high premiums, and to then return a portion of the profits to the policyholders. This arrangement

---

[1] See Hare and Scott [11].

led to the need for more sophisticated mathematical modeling and calculations, and helped lead to the development of the actuarial profession.

In modern times, insurance often combines risk transfer and investment. From the 1940s through the 1960s, when long-term interest rates were significantly higher than short-term interest rates, long-term insurance contracts with investment components gave policyholders access to improved investment returns and were thus more attractive.

4.2 LIFE INSURANCE AND ANNUITIES

A basic life insurance contract involves the payment of a premium, either annually or m^{thly} (such as monthly, quarterly, or semiannually), in return for a lump sum payment upon the death of the policyholder, or upon survival for a predetermined time period.

A basic annuity contract involves a single-sum premium payment, or a series of premium payments, in return for a regular series of future payments, conditional on the survival of the contract holder.

4.2.1 TYPES OF LIFE INSURANCE CONTRACTS

There are various types of life insurance contracts, which we review briefly here. They are purchased to mitigate the financial consequences of early death, and may include an investment component as well.[2]

Term Insurance: *Term insurance* pays a lump-sum cash amount upon the death of the policyholder, provided it occurs during the defined policy term. Premiums may be level for a certain length of time, or may increase each year. These policies are usually guaranteed to be renewed for a fixed period of time. *Convertible term insurance* offers the possibility of converting the term insurance contract to a whole life or endowment insurance (see below), during a certain period of time.

Whole Life Insurance: *Whole life insurance* pays a lump-sum cash amount upon the death of the policyholder, whenever that may occur. The premium is generally the same amount each year, and is payable for the whole of life or only up to a certain maximum age. This insurance will also pay the policyholder a cash amount, known as the *cash surrender value*, in the event that the policy is surrendered prior to death. This feature gives the product an investment and tax-benefit component, along with the life insurance protection.

Endowment Insurance: *Endowment insurance* pays a lump-sum cash benefit upon the earlier of the death of the policyholder, or the end of a specific time period. This combines term insurance and an investment component. These policies are not currently being sold in most countries; they are, however, becoming more popular in "micro-insurance", which are insurance policies with very small face amounts.

[2] Extensive details of basic insurance contracts are presented in Chapters 7 through 11.

Participating Insurance: In this variation of insurance, policyholders participate in the profits earned by the insurance company. This type of policy is generally only offered by mutual insurance companies (see Section 4.4), and was one historical method to charge conservative rates that were still acceptable to consumers. Policyholders are usually given the option of receiving their dividends in cash, or using them to reduce future premiums, or to purchase more insurance.[3]

Universal Life Insurance: The advent of modern computing facilitated the design of more complex and flexible insurance products. *Universal life insurance* was one of these, a hybrid between investment and life insurance protection. Policyholders choose a premium and a face amount for their life insurance coverage. Excess amounts paid above the cost of their life insurance coverage are placed in an interest-bearing account. Policyholders can then vary their premium payments as long as the balance in their account is sufficient to fund the cost of their insurance coverage.[4]

Equity-Linked Insurance: Equity-linked insurance is similar to universal life insurance. Instead of the policyholder's balance being placed in an interest-bearing account, its value is linked to the performance of a specific investment fund or stock index. In some cases, there may be a minimum guaranteed rate of return.[5]

4.2.2 TYPES OF LIFE ANNUITY CONTRACTS

Life annuities offer a periodic payment, contingent upon the continued survival of the policyholder. There are two types of premium-paying arrangements, namely single premium, which is a one-time payment, or regular premium, which is a payment made on an annual or m^{thly} basis for a designated length of time. (The latter case would be used for a deferred annuity only.) Annuity contracts are purchased to mitigate *longevity risk* (the risk of outliving one's savings), and to guarantee an income for a certain amount of time. Deferred annuities contain an investment component.[6]

Whole Life Immediate Annuity: Under this arrangement, the contract holder pays a single premium in return for regular annuity payments to begin immediately. Future payments are contingent on the annuitant's survival. This product is often used for the conversion of lump-sum pension or insurance benefits into a stream of monthly income.

Temporary Immediate Annuity: In this variation of the whole life immediate annuity, the contract holder again pays a single premium in return for regular annuity payments to begin immediately. In this case, the payments continue until the earlier of the annuitant's death or a certain pre-specified length of time.

Whole Life Deferred Annuity: With this product, the contract holder pays a single premium, or a sequence of periodic premiums, in exchange for a life annuity to begin at a specific date in the future. There is generally a certain guaranteed payment or death benefit in place should the policyholder die before the first annuity payment is scheduled to be made.

---

[3] Details of participating insurance, and the determination of dividends, are presented in Sections 17.4 and 17.5.
[4] Universal life insurance is presented in Chapter 16.
[5] This variation on universal life insurance is briefly described in Section 16.2.3.
[6] Details of life annuities issued to a single person are presented in Chapter 8.

Joint Life Annuity: This type of annuity is typically issued to a married couple, and is similar to a whole life annuity. The difference is that the payments cease upon the *first death* of the couple.

Last Survivor Annuity: This is similar to a joint life annuity, except that in this case the payments cease upon the *second death* of the couple. It is common for the annuity payments to reduce to 50% or 75% of the original amount upon the first death, in recognition of reduced living expenses.

Reversionary Annuity: This is also issued to a couple, where one person is viewed as the insured and the other as the annuitant. On the death of the insured life, if the annuitant is still alive, the annuitant receives a life annuity. If the annuitant dies first, there is no payment. This is often a lower cost protection option if one person depends on the pension or income of his or her spouse, or if a disabled child depends on the income of a parent.[7]

4.2.3 DISTRIBUTION

Insurance is a unique, and often complex, product that generally requires individual human interaction to meaningfully complete its sale. It is generally sold through *agents* or *brokers* on a commission basis, where the commission is a percentage of the premium. There is generally a much higher commission rate on the first-year premium, followed by lower commission rates in later years.

Due primarily to the high commission paid on the first-year premium, the insurer would show a net loss on a new policy for the first several years. If a company is writing a considerable amount of new business, it may experience *surplus strain* due to the drain on capital, and should evaluate whether it needs to stop or limit the writing of new business.

A lower-cost alternative, being implemented by some insurers, is the use of *direct marketing* through telemarketing, direct mail, or the internet. The type of insurance sold in this manner generally has a lower average face amount and is not underwritten as rigorously as are other products.

4.2.4 UNDERWRITING

The life insurance industry deals with uncertainty and risk. Just as individual insureds seek to minimize their risks, insurance companies also seek to minimize the company's risk while maximizing their potential benefit. One difficulty for the insurer is that applicants seeking insurance coverage will always know more about their own health situation than the insurer will, and this can put the company at a disadvantage when evaluating the relative risk of an applicant.

To mitigate this difficulty, insurers conduct *underwriting*, the process of gathering information and evaluating the risk of potential insureds. Applicants are asked to fill out an *application form*, giving information on certain characteristics such as age, gender, smoking habits, personal and family medical history, and occupation. For larger amounts of insurance,

[7] All three of these two-life annuity contracts (joint life, last-survivor, and reversionary) are described in Chapter 12.

applicants must undergo a blood test and physical examination. This process helps to classify applicants into risk groups that will pay varying levels of premium. Depending on the legislation in various jurisdictions, there are certain factors that cannot be legally taken into account when determining price, such as race (everywhere and for all insurance) or gender (depending on jurisdiction and type of insurance).

As the face amount of insurance increases, the underwriting process becomes more rigorous. A balance must be struck when determining the extent of underwriting. Underwriting that is too strict leads to a loss of potential clients and high expense levels, whereas underwriting that is too lax can lead to *anti-selection*, meaning that relatively more people with poor health will buy insurance from the company. Some companies also include pre-existing condition exclusion clauses that limit payment from the policy for death resulting from circumstances that were already present at the time of purchase.

Due to the fact that policies are underwritten, the mortality experience on insured lives is lower than that of the general population, and is referred to as *select mortality*. After a certain length of time, however, the effects of underwriting taper off, and the mortality of the selected insured is similar to that of the general insured population; this is referred to as *ultimate mortality*.[8]

It is interesting to note that most insurance companies do not underwrite for annuities, due to the fact that they are more concerned with good health than poor health for this type of contract. Nevertheless, it is possible to buy *underwritten annuities*, whereby applicants with certain health conditions can obtain higher monthly payments under their annuities than can applicants in excellent health.

4.2.5 OTHER TYPES OF INSURANCE

There are other types of insurance policies that can be used by their policyholders to mitigate other types of financial risk.

Disability Insurance: *Disability insurance* is used to cover the financial risk of being unable to generate income due to disability. These contracts require an annual or m^{thly} premium to be paid in return for a monthly benefit payable in the event of disability, the definition of which can vary. The benefits are often integrated with benefits from other sources, such as government plans.

Long-Term Care Insurance: *Long term care insurance* is purchased to mitigate the financial risk of paying for home health or nursing home care if the insured comes to be in need of professional assistance. Again premiums are paid while healthy, in return for a daily or monthly benefit that often varies depending upon the type of assistance required.

Hospital, Critical Illness, or Cancer Insurance: These specialized policies cover the financial risk of expenses and/or lost income due to hospital stays, a specified critical illness, or cancer. Again premiums are paid while healthy in return for a fixed benefit upon the occurrence of one of the covered events.

---

[8] The mathematics of select and ultimate mortality is presented in Sections 5.4 and 6.7.

Warranty Insurance: This insurance covers the financial risk related to the failure of a specific physical asset, such as a car or an appliance. The coverage is generally purchased for a single premium, paid in return for repair or replacement of the asset for a certain number of years beyond the manufacturer's basic warranty period.

4.3 PENSION BENEFITS[9]

Pension benefits have a great deal of similarity with life insurance and annuities, in that they are life-contingent benefits. Most pension plans are sponsored by employers, who pay most of the cost to fund the plans. Under these plans, employees receive a lump-sum or, more commonly, an annuity benefit upon retirement. Actuarial knowledge plays a critical role in the design and funding of pension plans.

4.3.1 DEFINED BENEFIT PLANS

Defined benefit plans offer retirement income based on an employee's years of service and salary, using a specified formula. For example, the New York City Teachers Fund offers retiring teachers a pension that pays an annual retirement benefit of

$$1\tfrac{2}{3}\% \times (\text{Final Average Salary}) \times (\text{Years of Credited Service}),$$

where the final average salary refers to the average of the retiring employee's last five years of salary and years of credited service refers to the years of employment.

U.S. Social Security is another example of a defined benefit plan, which is funded by employer and employee contributions through the FICA tax and administered by the Social Security Administration, an independent agency established by the U.S. federal government.

In defined benefit plans, the employer or government bears all the risk associated with variation in investment returns and life expectancy. There are a number of government regulations, such as ERISA[10], to ensure the ability of private pension funds to pay the amount of the pledged benefits.

4.3.2 DEFINED CONTRIBUTION PLANS

Defined contribution plans work like investment accounts. The employee and employer make contributions to (either a predetermined contribution or one based on cost sharing) into a fund that is invested and earns a rate of return. When the employee retires, this fund is available to provide income for retirement. It can be converted into an annuity or drawn down as desired by the employee.

In this case, life contingencies are not involved in the plan prior to retirement. Because the amount accumulated in the plan does not generate a predetermined amount of income at

---

[9] Pension plans are discussed more fully in Section 14.5.

[10] The Employee Retirement Income Security Act of 1974 (ERISA) is a federal law that sets minimum standards for pension plans in private industry.

retirement, the employee bears the risk associated with investment variations and longevity. As more plans are being converted to defined contribution plans in recent years, there are societal concerns regarding the adequacy of retirement savings. An attractive characteristic of defined contribution plans is that they are portable, and stay with the employee through changes in employment.

4.4 RECENT DEVELOPMENTS IN INSURANCE

A *mutual insurance company* is owned by its policyholders, and its profits are either held in surplus or distributed to its policyholders entitled to share in them. (These are referred to as "with-profit" policyholders.) Mutual insurance companies are more easily able to price conservatively and then return some or all of its profit to the policyholder.

A *stock insurance company* is owned by its shareholders; generally a much lower percentage of its profits are distributed to its policyholders, if any at all.

Beginning in the 1990s, there has been a significant transformation of mutual insurance companies into stock insurance companies, through the issuance of shares to their with-profit policyholders. Despite the sometimes negative perception of these *demutualizations* by the insurance-buying public, companies making this change argue that it is easier to raise capital and that they have more organizational flexibility to acquire or be acquired by other companies. In addition, stockholders often subject management to more scrutiny and hold them more accountable than do policyholders.

4.5 THE ROLE OF ACTUARIES

Actuaries have been described as the "high priests" of the insurance industry. A 1907 article in *The Spectator,* a weekly American Insurance Journal, said, with some hyperbolic professional pride, "While the demi-gods of finance were toppling from their pedestals and falling amid the ruins of their wrecked reputations, the actuaries stood unmoved, like High Priests with unpolluted garments beside the altars of life insurance." Although said in a tongue-in-cheek manner, the actuary's role is certainly important to the proper functioning and success of an insurance company. Throughout this text, we provide a description of the mathematics that actuaries apply to day-to-day business problems, and the areas in which it is applied. We preview here a few key areas in which actuaries apply their knowledge.

Premium Calculations: Actuaries apply their knowledge of contingencies, interest rates, investment returns, expense levels, and projected duration of insurance contracts to set appropriate premium rates that will maintain the desired level of profitability and adequately safeguard against adverse conditions.

Reserve Determination: Due to the existence of contingent liabilities and level premium contracts, insurance companies must establish financial liabilities (called *reserves*), to cover future benefit payments. Actuaries calculate appropriate reserve values consistent with generally accepted actuarial practice and statutory regulations.

Product Development: Given their unique knowledge of the numerical and financial effects of changes in distribution strategies, benefit design, underwriting techniques, and other aspects of an insurance product, actuaries are often called upon to marry technical expertise with marketing savvy and work on a team to develop and analyze new insurance products.

Pension Liabilities: Employers make regular contributions to provide for future pension benefits. Actuaries calculate appropriate contribution amounts, based on current pension law and assumptions regarding mortality, disability, salary data, and investment returns. Actuaries design new pension plans that will have the appropriate benefit and cost structure to meet the employer's goals. Actuaries also analyze the effects and costs of pension plan changes and variations in assumptions.

These are some key areas of actuarial practice which will be addressed throughout the text. They are just the highlights of the many areas in which actuaries work.

4.6 EXERCISES

4-1 Why do you think the design and complexity of insurance policies changed with the advent of modern technology?

4-2 You are a young actuary who understands risk and the value of insurance. Write a paragraph explaining the benefits and costs of investing in a term life versus a whole life policy. Write a paragraph for or against buying disability and/or long-term care insurance.

4-3 Why do insurers underwrite certain policies? Is it fair for different people to pay different premiums?

4-4 You decide to start a new insurance company, to be called Risk Mitigation, Inc. You persuade twenty of your friends to contribute $100 each, so the company starts with paid-in capital of $2,000. You sell a one-year renewable term insurance product with a $1,000 benefit. You charge $50 annual premium for this policy. How do you decide how many (if any) of these polices you should sell? How much capital would you want to hold to be reasonably certain that you will be able to meet claims? How will the accounting work, assuming that things go well and there are no claims in the first year? (Note: There is no "right" answer.)

4-5 What are the benefits and difficulties associated with charging unisex[11] rates for life insurance?

[11] Unisex rates are the same for males and females.

4-6 A biotech company, with a large population of young employees and a high turnover rate, is considering the impact of offering a defined benefit or a defined contribution pension plan. One of the company's main goals is to lower its turnover rate and build a base of stable employees. Describe the risks and rewards of each pension plan option.

4-7 What concerns would an insurer have if it decided to underwrite someone applying for an annuity?

4-8 After the failure of Risk Mitigation, Inc., due to lack of capital, you start another insurance company, called New Beginnings, Inc. You have a capitalization of $3,000 this time and sell a one-year renewable term insurance product with a $1,000 benefit. You have no business currently, but you find a company that wants to purchase a policy for each one of its 1,000 employees. One of your partners objects to this. What risks are involved with this transaction? What could you do to lessen this risk?

PART TWO

MODELS FOR SURVIVAL-CONTINGENT RISKS

The second section of the text addresses traditional contingent payment models where payments are dependent on the continued survival (or failure to survive) of a defined entity. This entire subject has traditionally been known as *life contingencies*, since the payment(s) were contingent on the continued life (or death) of a designated person. In this textbook the subject is treated in a more general fashion, where "survival" can just as easily mean the continuation of a labor strike, the functioning of a mechanical device (often called *reliability theory*), or the regular payment of scheduled coupons under a corporate bond.

Discrete functions numerically evaluated from a discrete survival model (i.e., a life table) are emphasized, since they represent most of the practical problems encountered by actuaries. The more abstract continuous functions are also considered, frequently for their interesting mathematical behavior. A random variable approach is employed along with a deterministic approach when that view is useful to broaden the reader's understanding.

In addition, the traditional actuarial models considered in this section can be presented as multi-state models, which are based on discrete-time or continuous-time Markov Chains. The background theory of Markov Chains was presented in Chapter 3.

The survival model is presented in Chapters 5 and 6, in both its parametric and tabular contexts.

The standard set of single-life, single-decrement actuarial topics is covered in Chapters 7-11: contingent payment models (with emphasis on their standard insurance applications), contingent annuities (life annuities), annual funding schemes (annual premiums), including their m^{thly} and continuous variations, and contingent contract reserves, now presented in two chapters. Extensions to the multi-status cases of joint and last-survivor are presented in Chapter 12 and multiple decrement models are covered in Chapters 13 and 14.

A discussion of using Microsoft Excel to calculate actuarial values from a life table is presented in Appendix A.

Standard actuarial notation is employed throughout this section.

CHAPTER FIVE

SURVIVAL MODELS (CONTINUOUS PARAMETRIC CONTEXT)

A *survival model* is simply a probability distribution for a particular type of random variable. Thus the general theory of probability, as reviewed in Chapter 2, is fully applicable here. However the particular history of the survival model random variable is such that specific terminology and notation has developed, particularly in an actuarial context. In this chapter (and the next) the reader will see this specialized terminology and notation, and recognize that it is *only* the terminology and notation that is new; the underlying probability theory is the same as that applying to any other continuous or discrete random variable and its distribution.

In actuarial science, the survival distribution is frequently summarized in tabular form, which is called a *life table*.[1] Because the life table form is so prevalent in actuarial work, we will devote a full chapter to it in this textbook (see Chapter 6).

5.1 THE AGE-AT-FAILURE RANDOM VARIABLE

We begin our study of survival distributions by defining the generic concept of *failure*. In any situation involving a survival model, there will be a defined entity and an associated concept of *survival*, and hence of failure, of that entity.[2] Here are some examples of entities and their associated random variables.

(1) The operating lifetime of a light bulb. The bulb is said to survive as long as it keeps burning, and fails at the instant it burns out.

(2) The duration of labor/management harmony. The state of harmony continues to survive as long as regular work schedules are met, and fails at the time a strike is called. (Conversely, we could model the duration of a strike, where the strike survives until it is settled and workers return to the job. The settlement event constitutes the failure of the strike status.)

(3) The lifetime of a new-born person. The person survives until death occurs, which constitutes the failure of the human entity. This will be the most common example considered in this text.

Let T_0 denote the continuous random variable for the age of the entity at the instant it fails.

[1] Alternatively, the tabular model is also called a *mortality table*.

[2] Another term for failure is *decrement*. If an entity has a particular status, such as survival, then failure to retain that status is often described as being *decremented* from that status. This terminology is particularly useful in the context of multiple decrements, which we encounter in Chapters 13 and 14.

We assume that the entity exists at age 0, so the domain of the random variable T_0 is $T_0 > 0$. We refer to T_0 as the *age-at-failure* random variable. We will consider the terms "failure" and "death" to be synonymous, so we will also refer to T_0 as the *age-at-death* random variable.[3]

It is easy to see that the numerical value of the age at failure is the same as the *length of time* that survival lasts until failure occurs, since the variable begins at age 0, so we can also refer to T_0 as the *time-to-failure* random variable. (If failure occurs at exact *age t*, then *t* is also the time until failure occurs.)

Later (see Section 5.3) we will consider the case where the entity of interest is known to have survived to some age $x > 0$. Then the time-to-failure random variable, to be denoted by T_x, will not be identical to the age-at-failure random variable T_0, although they will be related to each other by $T_0 = x + T_x$. When dealing with this more general case we will do our thinking in terms of the time-to-failure random variable.

5.1.1 THE CUMULATIVE DISTRIBUTION FUNCTION OF T_0

For the age-at-failure random variable T_0, we denote its CDF by

$$F_0(t) = Pr(T_0 \leq t), \tag{5.1}$$

for $t \geq 0$.[4] We have already noted, however, that $T_0 = 0$ is not possible, so we will always consider that $F_0(0) = 0$. We observe that $F_0(t)$ gives the probability that failure will occur prior to (or at) precise age *t* for our entity known to exist at age 0. In standard actuarial notation,[5] this probability is denoted by ${}_tq_0$, so we have

$${}_tq_0 = F_0(t) = Pr(T_0 \leq t). \tag{5.2}$$

5.1.2 THE SURVIVAL DISTRIBUTION FUNCTION OF T_0

The *survival distribution function* (SDF) for the survival random variable T_0 is denoted by $S_0(t)$, and is defined by

$$S_0(t) = 1 - F_0(t) = Pr(T_0 > t), \tag{5.3}$$

for $t \geq 0$. Since we take $F_0(0) = 0$, it follows that we will always take $S_0(0) = 1$. The SDF gives the probability that the age at failure exceeds *t*, which is the same as the probability that the entity known to exist at age 0 will survive to age *t*. Since the notion of infinite survival is unrealistic, we consider that

---

[3] In practice, age-at-failure is often used for inanimate objects, such as light bulbs or labor strikes, and age-at-death is used for animate entities, such as laboratory animals or human persons under an insurance arrangement.

[4] In probability theory, it is customary to subscript the CDF symbol with the name of the random variable, which suggests the notation $F_{T_0}(t)$ in this case. With the name of the random variable understood to be T_0 in this section, we prefer the notation $F_0(t)$ to avoid the awkwardness of subscripting a subscript.

[5] As stated in the Preface, this text uses Standard International Actuarial Notation whenever possible.

$$\lim_{t\to\infty} S_0(t) = 0 \tag{5.4a}$$

and

$$\lim_{t\to\infty} F_0(t) = 1. \tag{5.4b}$$

In actuarial notation, the probability represented by $S_0(t)$ is denoted ${}_tp_0$, so we have

$${}_tp_0 = S_0(t) = Pr(T_0 > t). \tag{5.5}$$

In probability textbooks in general, the CDF is given greater emphasis than is the SDF. (Some textbooks do not even define the SDF at all.) But when we are dealing with an age-at-failure random variable, and its associated distribution, the SDF will receive greater attention.

EXAMPLE 5.1

Use both the CDF and the SDF to express the probability that an entity known to exist at age 0 will fail between the ages of 10 and 20.

SOLUTION

We seek the probability that T_0 will take on a value between 10 and 20. In terms of the CDF we have

$$Pr(10 < T_0 \leq 20) = F_0(20) - F_0(10).$$

Since $S_0(t) = 1 - F_0(t)$, then we also have

$$Pr(10 < T_0 \leq 20) = S_0(10) - S_0(20).$$ ❐

5.1.3 THE PROBABILITY DENSITY FUNCTION OF T_0

For a continuous random variable in general, the *probability density function* (PDF) is defined as the derivative of the CDF. Thus we have here

$$f_0(t) = \frac{d}{dt} F_0(t) = -\frac{d}{dt} S_0(t), \tag{5.6}$$

for $t > 0$. Consequently,

$$F_0(t) = \int_0^t f_0(y)\, dy \tag{5.7}$$

and

$$S_0(t) = \int_t^\infty f_0(y)\, dy. \tag{5.8}$$

Of course it must be true that

$$\int_0^{\infty} f_0(y)\,dy = 1. \tag{5.9}$$

Although we have given mathematical definitions of $f_0(t)$, it will be useful to describe $f_0(t)$ more fully in the context of the age-at-failure random variable. Whereas $F_0(t)$ and $S_0(t)$ are probabilities that relate to certain *time intervals*, $f_0(t)$ relates to a *point of time*, and is not a probability. It is the density of failure *at* age t, and is therefore an *instantaneous* measure, as opposed to an interval measure.

It is important to recognize that $f_0(t)$ is the *unconditional* density of failure at age t. By this we mean that it is the density of failure at age t given *only* that the entity existed at $t = 0$. The concept of *conditional* density is presented in the next subsection.

5.1.4 THE HAZARD RATE FUNCTION OF T_0

Recall that the PDF of T_0, $f_0(t)$, is the *unconditional* density of failure at age t. We now define a *conditional* density of failure at age t, with such density conditional on survival to age t. This conditional instantaneous measure of failure at age t, given survival to age t, is called the *hazard rate* at age t, or the *hazard rate function* (HRF) when viewed as a function of t. (In some textbooks the hazard rate is called the *failure rate*.) It will be denoted by $\lambda_0(t)$.

In general, if a conditional measure is multiplied by the probability of obtaining the conditioning event, then the corresponding unconditional measure will result. Specifically,

(Conditional density of failure at age t, given survival to age t)
× (Probability of survival to age t)
= (Unconditional density of failure at age t).

Symbolically this states that

$$\lambda_0(t) \cdot S_0(t) = f_0(t), \tag{5.10}$$

or

$$\lambda_0(t) = \frac{f_0(t)}{S_0(t)}. \tag{5.11}$$

Equations (5.11) and (5.6) give formal definitions of the HRF and the PDF, respectively, of the age-at-failure random variable. Along with the definitions it is also important to have a clear understanding of the *conceptual meanings* of $\lambda_0(t)$ and $f_0(t)$. They are both instantaneous measures of the density of failure at age t; they differ from each other in that $\lambda_0(t)$ is conditional on survival to age t, whereas $f_0(t)$ is unconditional (i.e., given only existence at age 0).

In the actuarial context of survival models for animate objects, including human persons, failure means death, or mortality, and the hazard rate is normally called the *force of mortality*. We will discuss the actuarial context further in Section 5.1.6 and in Chapter 6.

Some important mathematical consequences follow directly from Equation (5.11). Since $f_0(t) = -\frac{d}{dt}S_0(t)$, it follows that

$$\lambda_0(t) = \frac{-\frac{d}{dt}S_0(t)}{S_0(t)} = -\frac{d}{dt}\ln S_0(t). \tag{5.12}$$

Integrating, we have

$$\int_0^t \lambda_0(y)\,dy = -\ln S_0(t), \tag{5.13}$$

or

$$S_0(t) = \exp\left[-\int_0^t \lambda_0(y)\,dy\right]. \tag{5.14}$$

The *cumulative hazard function* (CHF) is defined to be

$$\Lambda_0(t) = \int_0^t \lambda_0(y)\,dy = -\ln S_0(t), \tag{5.15}$$

so that

$$S_0(t) = e^{-\Lambda_0(t)}. \tag{5.16}$$

EXAMPLE 5.2

An age-at-failure random variable has a distribution defined by

$$F_0(t) = 1-.10(100-t)^{1/2},$$

for $0 \le t \le 100$. Find (a) the PDF and (b) the HRF for this random variable.

SOLUTION

(a) The PDF is given by

$$f_0(t) = \frac{d}{dt}F_0(t) = -(.10)(.50)(100-t)^{-1/2}\cdot(-1) = .05(100-t)^{-1/2}.$$

(b) The HRF is given by

$$\lambda_0(t) = \frac{f_0(t)}{S_0(t)} = \frac{.05(100-t)^{-1/2}}{.10(100-t)^{1/2}} = .50(100-t)^{-1}.$$ ❒

5.1.5 THE MOMENTS OF THE AGE-AT-FAILURE RANDOM VARIABLE T_0

The first moment, or expected value, of a continuous random variable defined on $[0,\infty)$ is given by

$$E[T_0] = \int_0^\infty t \cdot f_0(t)\, dt, \tag{5.17}$$

if the integral exists, and otherwise the first moment is undefined. Integration by parts yields the alternative formula

$$E[T_0] = \int_0^\infty S_0(t)\, dt, \tag{5.18}$$

provided $\lim_{t\to\infty} t \cdot S_0(t) = 0$. Equation (5.18) is frequently used to find the first moment of an age-at-failure random variable.

The second moment of T_0 is given by

$$E\left[T_0^2\right] = \int_0^\infty t^2 \cdot f_0(t)\ dt, \tag{5.19}$$

if the integral exists, so the variance of T_0 can be found from

$$Var(T_0) = E\left[T_0^2\right] - \left\{E[T_0]\right\}^2. \tag{5.20}$$

Specific expressions can be developed for the moments of T_0 for specific forms of $f_0(t)$. This will be pursued in the following section.

Another property of the age-at-failure random variable that is of interest is its *median* value. We recall that the median of a continuous random variable is the value for which there is a 50% chance that the random variable will exceed (and thus also not exceed) that value. Mathematically, y is the median of T_0 if

$$Pr(T_0 > y) = Pr(T_0 \le y) = \frac{1}{2}, \tag{5.21}$$

so that $S_0(y) = F_0(y) = \frac{1}{2}$.

5.1.6 ACTUARIAL SURVIVAL MODELS

When the age-at-failure random variable is considered in an actuarial context, special symbols are used for some of the concepts defined in this section. The hazard rate, now called the force of mortality, is denoted by μ_t, rather than $\lambda_0(t)$. Thus we have

$$\mu_t = \frac{-\frac{d}{dt}S_0(t)}{S_0(t)} = -\frac{d}{dt}\ln S_0(t). \tag{5.22}$$

It is customary to denote the first moment of T_0 by $\overset{\circ}{e}_0$. Thus we have

$$\overset{\circ}{e}_0 = E[T_0] = \int_0^\infty t \cdot f_0(t)\,dt. \tag{5.23}$$

Since $\overset{\circ}{e}_0$ is the unconditional expected value of T_0, given only alive at $t=0$, it is called the *complete expectation of life at birth.*[6]

We recognize that the moments of T_0 given above are all unconditional. Conditional moments, and other conditional measures, are defined in Section 5.3, and the standard actuarial notation for them is reviewed in Chapter 6.

EXAMPLE 5.3

For the distribution of Example 5.2, find (a) $E[T_0]$ and (b) the median of the distribution.

SOLUTION

(a) The expected value is given by Equation (5.18) as

$$\begin{aligned} E[T_0] &= \int_0^{100} .10(100-t)^{1/2}\,dt \\ &= -\left(\frac{2}{3}\right)(.10)(100-t)^{3/2}\Big|_0^{100} = \left(\frac{2}{3}\right)(.10)(100)^{3/2} = \frac{200}{3}. \end{aligned}$$

(b) The median is the value of y satisfying $S_0(y) = .10(100-y)^{1/2} = .50$, which solves for $y = 75$. ❒

5.2 EXAMPLES OF PARAMETRIC SURVIVAL MODELS

In this section we explore several non-negative continuous probability distributions that are candidates for serving as survival models. In practice, some distributions fit better than others to the empirical evidence of the shape of a survival distribution, so we will comment on each distribution we present regarding its suitability as a survival model.

5.2.1 THE UNIFORM DISTRIBUTION

The continuous uniform distribution, defined in Section 2.3.1, is a simple two-parameter distribution with a constant PDF. The parameters of the distribution are the limits of the interval

[6] The significance of the adjective "complete" will become clearer when we consider an alternative measure of the expectation of life in Sections 5.3.6 and 6.3.4.

on the real number axis over which it is defined, and its PDF is the reciprocal of that interval length. Thus if a generic random variable X is defined over the interval $[a,b]$, then $f_X(x) = \frac{1}{b-a}$, for $a \le x \le b$, and $f_X(x) = 0$ elsewhere.

For the special case of the age-at-failure random variable, $a = 0$ so b is the length of the interval, as well as the greatest value of t for which $f_0(t) > 0$. When the uniform distribution is used as a survival model, the Greek ω is frequently used for this parameter (which then represents the maximum survival age), so the distribution is defined by

$$f_0(t) = \frac{1}{\omega}, \tag{5.24}$$

for $0 < t \le \omega$. The following properties of the uniform distribution easily follow, and should be verified by the reader:

$$F_0(t) = \int_0^t f_0(y)\,dy = \frac{t}{\omega} \tag{5.25}$$

$$S_0(t) = 1 - F_0(t) = \int_t^\omega f_0(y)\,dy = \frac{\omega - t}{\omega} \tag{5.26}$$

$$\lambda_0(t) = \frac{f_0(t)}{S_0(t)} = \frac{1}{\omega - t} \tag{5.27}$$

$$E[T_0] = \int_0^\omega t \cdot f_0(t)\,dt = \frac{\omega}{2} \tag{5.28}$$

$$Var(T_0) = E\left[T_0^2\right] - \left\{E[T_0]\right\}^2 = \frac{\omega^2}{12} \tag{5.29}$$

The uniform distribution, as a survival model, is not appropriate over a broad range of age, at least as a model for *human* survival. It is of historical interest, however, to note that it was the first continuous probability distribution to be suggested for that purpose, in 1724, by Abraham de Moivre. As a result, actuarial literature and exams often refer to the uniform distribution as "de Moivre's law."

The major use of this distribution is over short ranges of time (or age). We will explore this use of the uniform distribution quite thoroughly in Section 6.5.1.

5.2.2 THE EXPONENTIAL DISTRIBUTION

This very popular one-parameter distribution (see Section 2.3.3) is defined by its SDF to be

$$S_0(t) = e^{-\lambda t}, \tag{5.30}$$

for $t > 0$ and $\lambda > 0$. It then follows that the PDF is

$$f_0(t) = -\frac{d}{dt}S_0(t) = \lambda \cdot e^{-\lambda t}, \tag{5.31}$$

so that the HRF is

$$\lambda_0(t) = \frac{f_0(t)}{S_0(t)} = \lambda, \tag{5.32}$$

a constant. In the actuarial context, where the hazard rate is generally called the force of mortality, the exponential distribution is referred to as the *constant force distribution*.

The exponential distribution, with its property of a constant hazard rate, is frequently used in reliability engineering as a survival model for inanimate objects such as machine parts. Like the uniform distribution, however, it is not appropriate as a model for human survival over a broad range, but might be used over short intervals, such as one year, due to its mathematical simplicity. This will be explored in Section 6.5.2.

5.2.3 THE GOMPERTZ DISTRIBUTION

This distribution was suggested as a model for human survival by Gompertz [9] in 1825. The distribution is usually defined by its force of mortality as

$$\mu_t = Bc^t, \tag{5.33}$$

for $t > 0, B > 0,$ and $c > 1$. Then the SDF is given by

$$S_0(t) = \exp\left[-\int_0^t Bc^y\,dy\right] = \exp\left[\frac{B}{\ln c}(1-c^t)\right]. \tag{5.34}$$

The PDF is given by $\mu_t \cdot S_0(t)$, and is clearly not a very convenient mathematical form. A closed-form expression for the mean of the distribution, $E[T_0]$, does not exist, but the mean can be approximated by numerical integration with a large finite upper limit replacing the actual upper limit of infinity.

5.2.4 THE MAKEHAM DISTRIBUTION

In 1860 Makeham [19] modified the Gompertz distribution by taking the force of mortality to be

$$\mu_t = A + Bc^t, \tag{5.35}$$

for $t > 0, B > 0, c > 1,$ and $A > -B$. Makeham was suggesting that part of the hazard at any age is independent of the age itself, due, for example, to the risk of accident, so a constant was added to the Gompertz force of mortality.

The SDF for this distribution is given by

$$S_0(t) = \exp\left[-\int_0^t (A+Bc^y)\,dy\right] = \exp\left[\frac{B}{\ln c}(1-c^t) - At\right]. \tag{5.36}$$

Again it is clear that the PDF for this distribution is not mathematically tractable. As with the Gompertz distribution, there is no closed-form expression for $E[T_0]$, although it can also be approximated by numerical integration.[7]

5.2.5 SUMMARY OF PARAMETRIC SURVIVAL MODELS

We have briefly explored four distributions here: two (uniform and exponential) which are mathematically simple, and two (Gompertz and Makeham) which are not. For many illustrations, where we wish to avoid mathematical complexity, we will use the uniform or the exponential for illustrative purposes only, not necessarily suggesting that they are applicable in practice. The exponential distribution has been applied in many situations not involving healthy human lives, and has been widely used in those situations.

5.3 THE TIME-TO-FAILURE RANDOM VARIABLE

In Section 5.1 we defined a continuous random variable, denoted T_0, which measured the length of time from age 0 until failure occurs. Now we turn to the case where our entity of interest is known to have survived to age x, where $x > 0$, and we wish to consider the random variable for the *additional* time that the entity might survive beyond age x. We denote this random variable by T_x, and note that its domain is $T_x > 0$. We define the random variable T_x to be the *time-to-failure* random variable for an entity known to be alive (i.e., known to have not yet failed) at age x. We will use the notation (x) to denote the entity known to be alive at age x.[8]

If T_x is the random time-to-failure for an entity alive at age x, it follows that the age-at-failure will be T_x more than age x, so we have the relationship $T_0 = x + T_x$ between our two basic random variables. This is illustrated in the following figure.

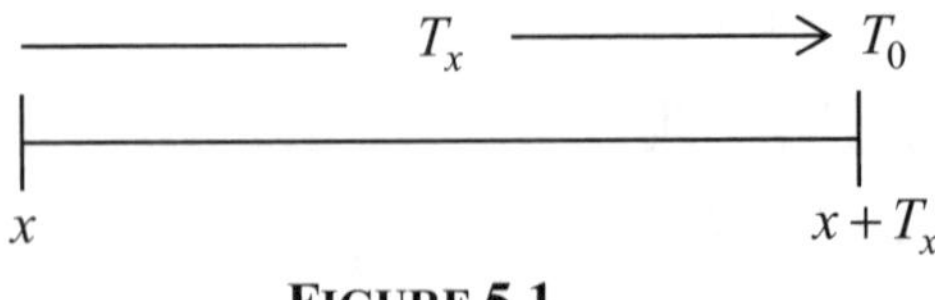

FIGURE 5.1

Rather than develop separate distributions for T_x for each different value of x, we will simply calculate probability values for T_x from the distribution of T_0. (An exception to this will be explored in Section 5.4.)

---

[7] A generalization of the Makeham distribution is presented in Exercise 5-10.

[8] The time until failure of (x) can also be called the future lifetime of (x), so T_x is therefore often called the *future lifetime* random variable for the entity (x).

5.3.1 THE SURVIVAL DISTRIBUTION FUNCTION OF T_x

For an entity known to be alive at age x, which we denote by (x), the probability of surviving an additional t time units[9] is denoted by ${}_tp_x$ in actuarial notation. In probability terminology, we note that this is simply the *conditional* probability of surviving to age $x+t$, given survival to age x (hence failure beyond age x). Thus we have

$$\begin{aligned} {}_tp_x &= Pr(T_x > t) \\ &= Pr(T_0 > x+t \mid T_0 > x). \end{aligned} \tag{5.37}$$

Recall from basic probability theory that the conditional probability $Pr(E \mid F)$ is defined to be

$$Pr(E \mid F) = \frac{Pr(E \cap F)}{Pr(F)}, \tag{5.38}$$

where $Pr(E \cap F)$ denotes the probability that both events E and F occur. In our example, E is the event $T_0 > x+t$ and F is the event $T_0 > x$. But if $T_0 > x+t$, then $T_0 > x$ necessarily, so the intersection of these two events is simply the event $T_0 > x+t$. Thus we have

$$\begin{aligned} {}_tp_x &= S_x(t)\,^{10} \\ &= Pr(T_x > t) \\ &= Pr(T_0 > x+t \mid T_0 > x) \\ &= \frac{Pr(T_0 > x+t)}{Pr(T_0 > x)} \\ &= \frac{S_0(x+t)}{S_0(x)}. \end{aligned} \tag{5.39}$$

5.3.2 THE CUMULATIVE DISTRIBUTION FUNCTION OF T_x

We denote the CDF of the random variable T_x by $F_x(t)$ in probability notation and by ${}_tq_x$ in actuarial notation. It gives the conditional probability that failure occurs not later than age $x+t$, given survival to age x. Thus we have

---

9 In the case of human persons under life insurance arrangements, time will normally be measured in years. For inanimate objects, such as light bulbs or mechanical devices operating under test conditions, time might be measured in hours.

10 As with the random variable T_0 defined earlier, the notational convention in probability theory would be to write the SDF symbol as $S_{T_x}(t)$. To avoid subscripting a subscript, we use the simpler $S_x(t)$. This notational principle will hold for the CDF, PDF, and HRF as well.

$$
\begin{aligned}
{}_tq_x = F_x(t) &= Pr(T_x \leq t) \\
&= Pr(T_0 \leq x+t \mid T_0 > x) \\
&= 1 - Pr(T_0 > x+t \mid T_0 > x) \\
&= 1 - \frac{S_0(x+t)}{S_0(x)},
\end{aligned}
\tag{5.40}
$$

where we use Equation (5.39) to express $Pr(T_0 > x+t \mid T_0 > x)$ in terms of $S_0(x)$, the SDF of the age-at-failure random variable T_0. We can easily write Equation (5.40) in terms of $F_0(x)$. We have

$$
{}_tq_x = 1 - \frac{1-F_0(x+t)}{1-F_0(x)} = \frac{F_0(x+t)-F_0(x)}{1-F_0(x)}. \tag{5.41}
$$

Since the CDF and SDF are complements of each other, then it follows that ${}_tp_x = 1 - {}_tq_x$ and vice versa.

In the special case of $t=1$, the notational convention is to suppress the t part of the symbol. Thus the probability of (x) surviving one additional year beyond age x is given by

$$
p_x = Pr(T_0 > x+1 \mid T_0 > x) = \frac{S_0(x+1)}{S_0(x)}, \tag{5.42}
$$

and the complementary probability that (x) will fail within the year following age x is given by

$$
q_x = 1 - p_x = Pr(T_0 \leq x+1 \mid T_0 > x) = \frac{F_0(x+1)-F_0(x)}{1-F_0(x)}. \tag{5.43}
$$

5.3.3 THE PROBABILITY DENSITY FUNCTION OF T_x

The PDF of the time-to-failure (or future lifetime) random variable T_x, denoted $f_x(t)$, gives the conditional density for failure at time t for an entity known to be alive at age x. Thus we can say that it gives the conditional density for failure at age $x+t$, given survival to age x. It is given by

$$
\begin{aligned}
f_x(t) = \frac{d}{dt}F_x(t) &= -\frac{d}{dt}S_x(t) \\
&= -\frac{d}{dt}\frac{S_0(x+t)}{S_0(x)} \\
&= \frac{f_0(x+t)}{S_0(x)},
\end{aligned}
\tag{5.44}
$$

since $f_0(x+t) = -\frac{d}{dt}S_0(x+t)$.

5.3.4 THE HAZARD RATE FUNCTION OF T_x

Recall that the HRF of T_0, denoted $\lambda_0(t)$, is itself a conditional measure, conditional on survival to age t. Therefore the hazard rate at age $x+t$ for (x), which we might denote by $\lambda_x(t\,|\,T_0>x)$, is the same concept as $\lambda_0(x+t)$ itself. The condition of survival to age $x+t$ supersedes the condition of survival to age x.

Considering together Equation (5.44) and Equation (5.10), with x replaced by $x+t$, we can express the PDF of T_x in terms of the distribution of T_0 as

$$f_x(t) \;=\; \frac{f_0(x+t)}{S_0(x)} \;=\; \frac{S_0(x+t)\cdot\lambda_0(x+t)}{S_0(x)}. \tag{5.45}$$

In the actuarial context and notation, where the hazard rate is called the force of mortality and denoted by μ_t, we have

$$f_x(t) \;=\; {}_tp_x\cdot\mu_{x+t}, \tag{5.46}$$

by using Equation (5.39) to substitute ${}_tp_x$ for $\frac{S_0(x+t)}{S_0(x)}$.

5.3.5 MOMENTS OF THE FUTURE LIFETIME RANDOM VARIABLE T_x

The expected value of T_x, given alive at age x, is called the *complete expectation of life at age x*, or the *expected future lifetime at age x*, and is denoted by $\mathring{e}_x$. Recall that the age-at-failure random variable T_0 and the time-to-failure (or future lifetime) random variable T_x are related by $T_0=T_x+x$, so $T_x=T_0-x$. Thus we have

$$\mathring{e}_x \;=\; E[T_x\,|\,T_0>x] \;=\; E[T_0-x\,|\,T_0>x] \;=\; E[T_0\,|\,T_0>x]-x. \tag{5.47}$$

Equation (5.47) makes the point that the expected future lifetime of (x) is the excess of the conditional expected age at failure, $E[T_0\,|\,T_0>x]$, over the value of x itself. It can be calculated from the conditional PDF of T_0 as

$$\mathring{e}_x \;=\; \int_0^\infty t\cdot f_0(x+t\,|\,T_0>x)\,dt. \tag{5.48a}$$

Using Equation (5.44) this can be written as

$$\mathring{e}_x \;=\; \int_0^\infty t\cdot\frac{f_0(x+t)}{S_0(x)}dt \;=\; \frac{1}{S_0(x)}\int_0^\infty t\cdot f_0(x+t)dt. \tag{5.48b}$$

Next, recall from Equation (5.18) that integration by parts on Equation (5.48b) leads to

$$\overset{\circ}{e}_x = \frac{1}{S_0(x)} \int_0^\infty S_0(x+t)dt, \tag{5.48c}$$

and finally to

$$\overset{\circ}{e}_x = \int_0^\infty \frac{S_0(x+t)}{S_0(x)} dt = \int_0^\infty {}_tp_x dt, \tag{5.48d}$$

by use of Equation (5.39). As we will see in Chapter 6, Equation (5.48d) is a common way to define, and eventually calculate, $\overset{\circ}{e}_x$.

Finally, since the age at failure, given alive at age x, is the future lifetime, given alive at age x, plus x itself, then it follows that

$$Var(T_0 \mid T_0 > x) = Var(T_x \mid T_0 > x), \tag{5.49}$$

since x is a constant. To calculate $Var(T_0 \mid T_0 > x)$ we first calculate

$$E[T_0 \mid T_0 > x] = \int_x^\infty y \cdot f_0(y \mid T_0 > x)\, dy \tag{5.50}$$

and

$$E\left[T_0^2 \mid T_0 > x\right] = \int_x^\infty y^2 \cdot f_0(y \mid T_0 > x)\, dy, \tag{5.51}$$

provided the two expectations exist. Then the variance of the age at failure and also of the time to failure is given by

$$Var(T_0 \mid T_0 > x) = Var(T_x \mid T_0 > x) = E\left[T_0^2 \mid T_0 > x\right] - \left\{E[T_0 \mid T_0 > x]\right\}^2. \tag{5.52}$$

EXAMPLE 5.4

For the distribution of Example 5.2, find each of (a) ${}_{20}p_{36}$, (b) $f_{36}(t)$, and (c) $\overset{\circ}{e}_{36}$.

SOLUTION

(a) From Equation (5.39) we have

$${}_{20}p_{36} = \frac{S_0(56)}{S_0(36)} = \frac{(100-56)^{1/2}}{(100-36)^{1/2}} = .82916.$$

(b) From Equation (5.44) we have

$$f_{36}(t) = \frac{f_0(36+t)}{S_0(36)} = \frac{.05(100-36-t)^{-1/2}}{.10(100-36)^{1/2}} = \frac{.0625}{(64-t)^{1/2}},$$

where we use the result of part (a) of Example 5.2 to find $f_0(36+t)$.

(c) In general we have

$${}_tp_{36} = \frac{S_0(36+t)}{S_0(36)} = .125(64-t)^{1/2}.$$

Then from Equation (5.48d) we find

$$\mathring{e}_{36} = .125\int_0^{64}(64-t)^{1/2}\,dt = \frac{128}{3}.$$

❐

5.3.6 DISCRETE TIME-TO-FAILURE RANDOM VARIABLE

In this section we present an important discrete random variable, which we denote by K_x. It is called the *curtate duration at failure* random variable, and is defined to be the integer part of T_x, the future lifetime of (x). This random variable is illustrated in Figure 5.2.

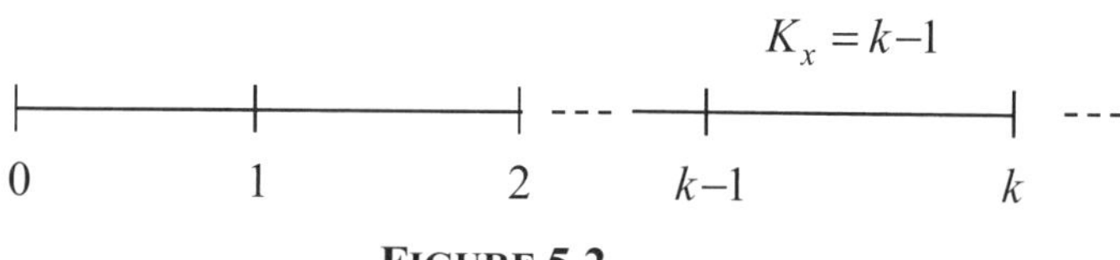

FIGURE 5.2

Consider the kth time interval, which we denote by $(k-1, k]$ to suggest that the precise time point k is included in the kth interval and the precise time point $k-1$ is included in the $(k-1)^{st}$ interval. If failure occurs in the kth interval, then $K_x = k-1$, the greatest integer in T_x. In particular, if failure occurs in the first time interval following age x, then we have $K_x = 0$.

The probability function of K_x is

$$Pr(K_x = k) = Pr(k < T_x \le k+1) \tag{5.53a}$$
$$= Pr(x+k < T_0 \le x+k+1 \mid T_0 > x), \tag{5.53b}$$

for $k = 0, 1, 2, \cdots$, and is denoted by ${}_{k|}q_x$ in actuarial notation.

The moments of K_x are all conditional on survival to age x, denoted by $T_0 > x$. The expected value of K_x is given by

$$E[K_x \mid T_0 > x] = \sum_{k=0}^{\infty} k \cdot {}_{k|}q_x. \tag{5.54}$$

It is denoted by e_x in actuarial notation, and is called the *curtate expectation of life at age x*.[11]

The variance of K_x would be found by first finding

$$E[K_x^{\,2} \mid T_0 > x] = \sum_{k=0}^{\infty} k^2 \cdot {}_{k|}q_x. \tag{5.55}$$

Next we define the continuous random variable R_x to represent the fractional part of the time interval lived through in the interval of failure for an entity alive at age x. This is illustrated in Figure 5.3.

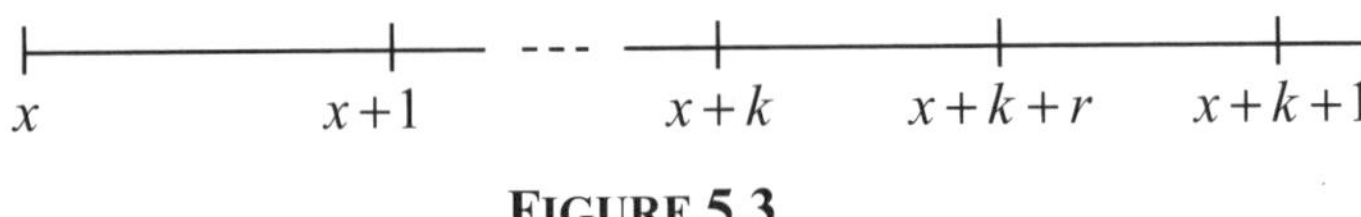

FIGURE 5.3

If failure occurs at time r, where $0 < r \leq 1$, within year $k+1$, then we have $K_x = k$, $R_x = r$, and $T_x = k+r$. In general we have

$$T_x = K_x + R_x.^{12} \tag{5.56}$$

5.4 SELECT SURVIVAL MODELS

Recall that ${}_tp_x$, defined in terms of the survival model $S_0(t)$ by Equation (5.39), is a conditional probability, where the given condition is simply that survival to age x has occurred. No other information beyond the basic fact of survival to age x is presumed.

In the life insurance context, a person being issued life insurance coverage at age x is certainly known to be alive at age x. But additional information is also available about this person as a result of the underwriting and selection process (see Chapter 4) that people seeking insurance would undergo. Therefore the probability of surviving on from age x to age $x+t$ for such a person would logically be different (likely greater) than the comparable probability for a person known only to have survived to age x. The probability of surviving from age x to age $x+t$ for a person *underwritten and selected for insurance at age x* is denoted by ${}_tp_{[x]}$, to distinguish it from ${}_tp_x$.

The survival probability ${}_tp_{[x]}$ can be represented in survival distribution form. We consider that the selection event defines time $t=0$, and the age at selection, denoted $[x]$, is merely an

[11]Note the similarity of $e_x = E[K_x \mid T_0 > x]$ to $\mathring{e}_x = E[T_x \mid T_0 > x]$, defined by Equation (5.47). Recall that the latter is called the *complete* expectation of life at age x whereas the former is called the *curtate* expectation.

[12] We will further discuss the relationship of the random variables T_x, K_x, and R_x in Section 6.6.1.

identifying characteristic of the person whose survival distribution we are considering. We denote such a survival distribution by $S_{[x]}(t;x)$, and denote the random variable for length of survival by $T_{[x]}$ in this case. The identifying characteristic $[x]$, the age of the person at selection, is called a *concomitant variable*. Note that since age x corresponds to time $t=0$, then ${}_tp_{[x]}$ is an unconditional probability whereas ${}_tp_x$ is a conditional probability.

The *select survival model* $S_{[x]}(t;x)$, in parametric form, would be a function of the two variables t and x. In actuarial practice, select models are generally presented in tabular form as a *select life table*. This is explored further in Section 6.7.

EXAMPLE 5.5

Find, in terms of $S_{[x]}(t;x)$, the probability that an entity selected at age x, and known to be alive at age $x+10$, will fail before age $x+20$.

SOLUTION

We seek the probability of failure prior to age $x+20$, given survival to age $x+10$, which is denoted by ${}_{10}q_{[x]+10}$ in standard actuarial notation. It is equal to

$$1-Pr(\textit{survival to } x{+}20 \mid \textit{survival to } x{+}10) \quad = \quad 1-{}_{10}p_{[x]+10}.$$

When the conditional probability ${}_{10}p_{[x]+10}$ is multiplied by the probability of the conditioning event, which is $S_{[x]}(10;x)$, the result is the unconditional probability of survival to $x+20$, which is $S_{[x]}(20;x)$. Thus we have

$$\begin{aligned} {}_{10}q_{[x]+10} &= 1-{}_{10}p_{[x]+10} \\ &= 1-\frac{S_{[x]}(20;x)}{S_{[x]}(10;x)}. \end{aligned}$$

❒

5.5 MULTI-STATE MODEL INTERPRETATION

The survival model presented in this chapter can be represented as a simple, two-state, continuous-time Markov model, where State 0 is continued survival and State 1 is failure (or death).[13] It is clear that the process must begin in State 0 and equally clear that State 1 is an absorbing state. Therefore there can be only one transition, from State 0 to State 1, over the entire process. The model is represented by the following diagram.

[13] In Chapter 6 we will represent the survival model as a discrete-time Markov model.

FIGURE 5.4

The arrow in Figure 5.4 reminds us that transition from State 1 back to State 0 is not possible.

Because the process cannot reenter State 0 once it has left it, it follows that the event of being in State 0 at time t, given in State 0 at time 0 at age x, can occur *only* if the process never leaves State 0 over that time interval. Then it follows that ${}_tp_x^{\overline{00}} = {}_tp_x^{00}$, as defined in Sections 3.1.6 and 3.2.

To show the correspondence of the multi-state model notation, defined in Chapter 3, with the actuarial notation, defined in this chapter, suppose we have a person alive at age x at time 0. The person constitutes the model; since the person is known to be alive, the model is known to be in State 0. Then the probability of still being in State 0 at time t is given by

$$ {}_tp_x = {}_tp_x^{\overline{00}} = {}_tp_x^{00}. \tag{5.57}$$

The probability of failure before time t, given alive at age x at time 0, is given by

$$ {}_tq_x = {}_tp_x^{01}. \tag{5.58}$$

The force of transition from State 0 to State 1 at time s, denoted by μ_{x+s}^{01} in Section 3.2.1, is also μ_{x+s}^{0}, the total force of transition out of State 0 since State 1 is the only state to which the process can move. Note that $\mu_{x+s}^{10} = 0$ for all s. In actuarial notation, the force of transition μ_{x+s}^{01} is called the force of failure, or the force of mortality, and is denoted simply by μ_{x+s}.

The Kolmogorov Forward Equation, given by Equation (3.14b), simplifies considerably when applied to this two-state survival model.

EXAMPLE 5.6

Solve the Kolmogorov differential equation for ${}_np_x^{00}$, and translate the result into standard actuarial notation.

SOLUTION

In this case, where $j = i = 0$, the index k in Equation (3.14b) takes on only the value $k = 1$, since $k \neq j = 0$. We have

$$\frac{d}{dt}\,{}_tp_x^{00} = {}_tp_x^{01} \cdot \mu_{x+t}^{10} - {}_tp_x^{00} \cdot \mu_{x+t}^{0}.$$

But $\mu_{x+t}^{10}=0,$ so this equation reduces to

$$\frac{d}{dt}\,{}_tp_x^{00} = -\,{}_tp_x^{00}\cdot\mu_{x+t}^{0}.$$

Dividing both sides by ${}_tp_x^{00}$ we have

$$\frac{\frac{d}{dt}\,{}_tp_x^{00}}{{}_tp_x^{00}} = \frac{d}{dt}\ln{}_tp_x^{00} = -\mu_{x+t}^{0},$$

or

$$d\ln{}_tp_x^{00} = -\mu_{x+t}^{0}\,dt.$$

Integrating both sides from $t=0$ to $t=n,$ we have

$$\int_0^n d\ln{}_tp_x^{00} = \int_0^n -\mu_{x+t}^{0}\,dt$$

or

$$\ln{}_tp_x^{00}\Big|_0^n = \int_0^n -\mu_{x+t}^{0}\,dt$$

or

$$\ln\left(\frac{{}_np_x^{00}}{{}_0p_x^{00}}\right) = -\int_0^n \mu_{x+t}^{0}\,dt$$

or

$${}_np_x^{00} = e^{-\int_0^n \mu_{x+t}^{0}\,dt}, \tag{5.59a}$$

since ${}_0p_x^{00}=1.$ State 0 is the surviving state, so ${}_np_x^{00}$ represents the probability that a process (or person) alive at age x at time 0 will be still alive at time $n,$ which we call ${}_np_x$ in actuarial notation. Also, in actuarial notation, our process (or person) is age $x+t$ at time $t,$ so we would use the actuarial notation μ_{x+t} in place of the multi-state model symbol $\mu_{x+t}^{0}.$ Then Equation (5.59a) would be written as

$${}_np_x = e^{-\int_0^n \mu_{x+t}\,dt}, \tag{5.59b}$$

an expression we will encounter frequently later in the text. ❒

We can similarly solve Kolmogorov's differential equation for ${}_np_x^{01},$ the probability of being failed (i.e., of being in State 1) at time $t,$ given alive (i.e., being in State 0) at age x at time 0. (The actuarial symbol for this probability is ${}_nq_x$.) The details of this are left to the reader as Exercise 5-22.

Finally, we observe that if the underlying survival model is exponential, so that the force of transition function μ_{x+t}^{01} is a constant, say μ, then we have a homogeneous Markov model, and the Kolmogorov differential equation is even more easily solved for ${}_np_x^{00}$ or ${}_np_x^{01}$. The details of this are left to the reader as Exercises 5-24 and 5-25.

5.6 WRITTEN-ANSWER QUESTION EXAMPLES

The examples in this, and later sections of the same name, are designed to provide the reader with some preparation for the written-answer type of questions appearing on Exam MLC, as of the Spring 2014 exam administration.

EXAMPLE 5.7

(a) Summarize the conditions that a function must satisfy in order to be a valid survival distribution function.

(b) Explain why each of the following functions is, or is not, a valid survival distribution function.

(i) $S_0(t) = e^{[t-.70(2^t-1)]}$

(ii) $S_0(t) = (1+t)^{-2}$

(iii) $S_0(t) = e^{-t^2}$

SOLUTION

(a) In order for $S_0(t)$ to be a valid survival function, it must satisfy the following conditions:

(i) $S_0(0) = 1$

(ii) $\lim_{t\to\infty} S_0(t) = 0$

(iii) It must be a non-increasing function.

(b) (i) This $S_0(t)$ does not qualify; although $S_0(0) = 1$ and $\lim_{t\to\infty} S_0(t) = 0$, as required, we find

$$S_0'(t) = e^{[t-.70(2^t-1)]} \cdot \left(1-.70(2^t)(\ln 2)\right)$$

and

$$S_0'(0) = 1-.70(\ln 2) = .5148,$$

so $S_0(t)$ is an increasing function near $t = 0$.

(ii) This $S_0(t)$ does qualify, since

$$S_0(0) = 1^{-2} = 1,$$

$$\lim_{t\to\infty} S_0(t) = \lim_{t\to\infty}(1+t)^{-2} = 0,$$

and

$$S_0'(t) = -2(1+t)^{-3} < 0,$$

so $S_0(t)$ is a decreasing function.

(iii) This $S_0(t)$ also qualifies, since

$$S_0(0) = e^0 = 1,$$

$$\lim_{t\to\infty} S_0(t) = \lim_{t\to\infty} e^{-t^2} = 0,$$

and

$$S_0'(t) = -2t \cdot e^{-t^2} < 0,$$

so $S_0(t)$ is a decreasing function. ❐

EXAMPLE 5.8

Consider the survival function

$$S_0(t) = \frac{9000-10t-t^2}{9000},$$

for $0 \le t \le \omega$.

(a) Find the value of ω.

(b) Find the unconditional density of failure at age 30.

(c) Find the conditional density of failure at age 30, given that $T_0 > 20$.

(d) Find $\lambda_0(30) = \mu_{30}$, the hazard rate, or force of mortality, at age 30.

(e) Find the conditional hazard rate at duration 10, for a person known to be surviving at age 20.

(f) Why are the answers to parts (d) and (e) the same?

SOLUTION

(a) The value of ω is found from

$$S_0(\omega) = \frac{9000-10\omega-\omega^2}{9000} = 0,$$

leading to the quadratic

$$\omega^2+10\omega-9000 = 0,$$

which solves for

$$\omega = \frac{-10 \pm \sqrt{100+36{,}000}}{2} = 90.$$

(b) The unconditional density of failure at age 30 is

$$f_0(30) = -\frac{d}{dt}S_0(t)\bigg|_{t=30} = \frac{7}{900}.$$

(c) The conditional density of failure at age 30, given survival to age 20, is

$$f_{20}(10) = \frac{f_0(30)}{S_0(20)} = \frac{70/9000}{8400/9000} = \frac{7}{840}.$$

(d) The hazard rate at age 30 is

$$\lambda_0(30) = \mu_{30} = \frac{f_0(30)}{S_0(30)} = \frac{70/9000}{7800/9000} = \frac{7}{780}.$$

(e) First we find the conditional survival function

$$S_{20}(t) = \frac{S_0(20+t)}{S_0(20)} = \frac{9000-10(20+t)-(20+t)^2}{8400}.$$

Then

$$\lambda_{20}(10|T_0>20) = \frac{-\frac{d}{dt}S_{20}(t)}{S_{20}(t)}\bigg|_{t=10} = \frac{10+2(20+t)}{9000-10(20+t)-(20+t)^2}\bigg|_{t=10} = \frac{7}{780}.$$

(f) The hazard rate, or force of mortality, has its meaning conditional on survival to the age where it is being measured, which is age 30 in this case. The condition $T_0 \geq 30$ supersedes the condition $T_0 > 20$, so the hazard rate is the same in both parts (d) and (e). ❐

5.7 EXERCISES

5.1 The Age-at-Failure Random Variable

5-1 The hazard rate of a survival distribution is a linear function, $\lambda_0(t) = a+bt$, where $a>0$ and $b>0$. Find each of the following:

(a) $S_0(t)$ (b) $f_0(t)$ (c) The mode of the distribution

5-2 Let a survival distribution be defined by $S_0(t) = at^2+b$, for $0<t\leq k$. If the expected value of T_0 is 60, find the median of T_0.

5-3 Explain why the hazard rate $\lambda_0(t) = e^{-rt}$, where $r>0$, is not appropriate for a survival distribution.

5.2 Examples of Parametric Survival Models

5-4 The survival function given by

$$S_0(t) = \left(1-\frac{t}{\omega}\right)^{\gamma},$$

for $\gamma>0$ and $0\leq t\leq\omega$, is called a *modified de Moivre distribution*. If $\gamma=4$, find an expression for $\overset{\circ}{e}_0$ as a function of ω.

5-5 If T_0 is uniformly distributed over (0, 2), find $Var(T_0)$.

5-6 Let X_1 and X_2 be independent generic random variables (i.e., not necessarily age-at-failure random variables). Define the new random variables $Y = \min(X_1, X_2)$ and $Z = \max(X_1, X_2)$.

(a) Show that $S_Y(y)$ is the product of the SDF's of X_1 and X_2.
(b) Show that $F_Z(z)$ is the product of the CDF's of X_1 and X_2.
(c) Show that if X_1 and X_2 both have exponential distributions, then Y also has an exponential distribution, but Z does not.

5-7 Let the independent generic random variables X_1 and X_2 both have exponential distributions, with parameters λ_1 and λ_2, respectively, where $\lambda_1 > \lambda_2$. Let Y and Z be as defined in Exercise 5-6. Given that $S_Y(2) = .24$ and $S_Z(2) = .86$, find the value of λ_1.

5-8 $_{m|}q_0 = S_0(m) - S_0(m+1)$ is the probability that an entity existing at age 0 will fail between $t = m$ and $t = m+1$. Determine whether $_{m|}q_0$ is an increasing, decreasing, or constant function of m for each of the following distributions:

(a) Uniform

(b) Exponential

(c) $f_0(t) = .00125t$, for $0 \le t \le 40$

5-9 Given that $\lambda_0(t) = k \cdot t^n$ and $\lambda_0(22) = 1.26$, where 22 is the median age of the distribution, find the value of n. (A model with this hazard rate is called a *Weibull distribution*.)

5-10 The *generalized Makeham distribution* is defined by its force of mortality as

$$\mu_t = p_1(t) + e^{p_2(t)},$$

where $p_1(t)$ and $p_2(t)$ are polynomials in t. Show that the Gomperz distribution, given by Equation (5.33), and the Makeham distribution, given by Equation (5.35), are special cases of the generalized distribution.[14]

5.3 The Time-to-Failure Random Variable

5-11 Given that T_0 has a uniform distribution and that $\overset{\circ}{e}_{16} = 42$, find $Var(T_{16})$.

5-12 Given that $S_0(t) = \frac{9000 - 10t - t^2}{9000}$, for $0 < t \le 90$, find the value of $q_{50} - \mu_{50}$.

5-13 Given that $\mu_t = kt$, for all $t > 0$, and $_{10}p_{35} = .81$, find the value of $_{20}p_{40}$.

5-14 Given that $S_0(t) = (1 - \frac{t}{\omega})^r$, for $0 < t < \omega$ and $r > 0$, and that $\mu_y = .10$ and $\overset{\circ}{e}_y = 8.75$ for some $0 < y < \omega$, find the value of r.

5-15 Given $\lambda_0(t) = (80 - t)^{-1/2}$, for $0 < t < 80$, find the median of the distribution of T_{20}.

5-16 Given $S_0(t) = \frac{\sqrt{k^2 - t}}{k}$, for $0 < t \le k^2$ and $k > 0$, and $\overset{\circ}{e}_{40} = 2 \cdot \overset{\circ}{e}_{80}$, calculate $\overset{\circ}{e}_{60}$.

5-17 Given that $S_0(t) = 1 - (.01t)^2$, for $0 < t \le 100$, find the expected future lifetime at the median age of the distribution.

---

[14] Other texts refer to this as the Gompertz-Makeham distribution.

5.4 Select Survival Models

5-18 A select survival distribution is defined by $S_{[x]}(t;x) = \left(1-\frac{t}{40-x}\right)$, for $0 \leq x < 40$ and $0 < t < 40-x$. Find each of the following:

(a) ${}_4p_{[30]}$ (b) $\overset{\circ}{e}_{[30]}$ (c) $\mu_{[20]+t}$

5-19 A select survival model is defined by $\lambda_{[x]}(t;x) = B \cdot r^t \cdot c^{x+t}$. Show that the select survival function is of the form

$$S_{[x]}(t;x) = \exp\left[\frac{B}{\ln r + \ln c}\left(c^x - r^t c^{x+t}\right)\right].$$

5.5 Multi-State Model Interpretation

5-20 Consider an entity age 0 at time 0, with age-at-failure random variable T_0 as defined in Section 5.1. Consider also the continuous-time Markov process $X(t)$ as defined in Section 3.2, with $X(0)=0$. Define the random variable T_0 in terms of the Markov process $X(t)$.

5-21 Consider an entity age x at time 0, with time-to-failure random variable T_x as defined in Section 5.3. Consider also the continuous-time Markov process $X(t)$, with $X(0)=0$. Define the random variable T_x in terms of the Markov process $X(t)$.

5-22 (a) Solve Kolmogorov's differential equation for ${}_np_x^{01}$.
(b) Translate the result into standard actuarial notation.

5-23 Give a formula in multi-state model notation for the expected time spent in State 0, given a continuous-time Markov survival process for an entity known to be in State 0 at age x at time 0.

5-24 Solve Kolmogorov's differential equation for ${}_np_x^{00}$ for a homogeneous Markov survival model, with constant force of transition function $\mu_{x+t}^{01} = \mu_{x+t}^{0} = \mu$.

5-25 Repeat Exercise 5-24 to solve for ${}_np_x^{01}$.

CHAPTER SIX

THE LIFE TABLE (DISCRETE TABULAR CONTEXT)

In this chapter we describe the nature of the traditional life table, showing that it can have all the properties of the survival models described in Chapter 5. When a survival model is presented in the life table format, it is customary to use notation and terminology which differ somewhat from that presented in Chapter 5. A major objective of this chapter will be to show clearly the correspondence between notation used in the probability model and that used in the life table model.

The reader should realize that life tables were developed by actuaries independently from (and a century earlier than) the development of the statistical theory of survival models as probability distributions[1]. For this reason, traditional life table notation and terminology will not tend to reveal the stochastic nature of the model as clearly as is done by the probability model in Chapter 5. By showing the correspondence of the life table symbols to those of the probability model, we intend to correct this.

6.1 DEFINITION OF THE LIFE TABLE

The life table can be defined as a table of numerical values of $S_0(x)$ for certain values of x (which we now prefer to use instead of t). Table 6.1 illustrates such a table.

TABLE 6.1

x	0	1	2	3	4	···	109	110
$S_0(x)$	1.00000	.97408	.97259	.97160	.97082	···	.00001	.00000

Typically a complete life table shows values of $S_0(x)$ for all integral values of $x, x=0,1,\ldots.$ Since $S_0(x)$ is represented by these values, it is clear that a practical upper limit on x must be adopted beyond which values of $S_0(x)$ are taken to be zero. Traditionally, ω is used for the smallest value of x for which $S_0(x)=0$. Then $S_0(\omega-1)>0$, but $S_0(\omega)=0$. In Table 6.1, $\omega=110$.

From Table 6.1, we can calculate the conditional probabilities represented by ${}_np_x$ and ${}_nq_x$ for integral x and n. However, these are the *only* functions that can be determined from the tabular model. Functions such as $f_0(x)$, $\lambda_0(x)$, and $\mathring{e}_x$ cannot be determined from the tabular model unless we expand the model by adopting assumed values for $S_0(x)$ between adjacent integers. We will pursue this in Section 6.6.

[1] The first modern life table, called the Breslau Table, dates from 1693 and is attributed to Edmund Halley [10] of Halley's Comet fame.

EXAMPLE 6.1

From Table 6.1, calculate (a) the probability that a life age 0 will fail before age 3; (b) the probability that a life age 1 will survive to age 4.

SOLUTION

(a) This is given directly by $F_0(3) = 1 - S_0(3) = .02840$.

(b) This conditional probability is given by ${}_3p_1 = \frac{S_0(4)}{S_0(1)} = .99665$. ❐

6.2 THE TRADITIONAL FORM OF THE LIFE TABLE

The tabular survival model was developed by the early actuaries many years ago. The history of this model is reported throughout actuarial literature, and a brief summary of this history is presented by Dobson [9].

Traditionally, the tabular survival model differs from Table 6.1 in two respects. Rather than presenting decimal values of $S_0(x)$, it is usual to multiply these values by, say, 100,000, and thereby present the $S_0(x)$ values as integers. Secondly, since these integers are not probabilities (which $S_0(x)$ values are), the column heading is changed from $S_0(x)$ to l_x, where l stands for *number living*, or *number of lives*. In this way the tabular survival model became known as the *life table.*

Since $S_0(0) = 1$, then l_0 is the same as the constant multiple which transforms all $S_0(x)$ into l_x. This constant is called the *radix* of the table. Formally,

$$l_x = l_0 \cdot S_0(x). \tag{6.1}$$

Using a radix of 100,000, we transform Table 6.1 into Table 6.1a.

TABLE 6.1a

x	0	1	2	3	4	⋯	109	110
l_x	100,000	97,408	97,259	97,160	97,082	⋯	1	0

The basic advantage of the traditional form of the life table is its susceptibility to interpretation. If we view $l_0 = 100,000$ as a hypothetical cohort group of newborn lives, or other new entities such as lightbulbs, electronic devices, or laboratory animals, then each value of l_x represents the survivors of that group to age x, according to the model. This is a convenient, deterministic, interpretation of the model. Of course, since $l_x = l_0 \cdot S_0(x)$, and $S_0(x)$ is a probability, then l_x is really the *expected number* of survivors to age x out of an original group of l_0 new entities. This connection between $S_0(x)$ and l_x is also given in Chapter 1 of Jordan [14].

Although the basic representation of the tabular survival model is in terms of the values of l_x, it is customary for the table to also show the value of several other functions derived from l_x. We define

$$d_x = l_x - l_{x+1}, \tag{6.2}$$

or, more generally,

$${}_nd_x = l_x - l_{x+n}. \tag{6.3}$$

Since l_x represents the size of the cohort at age x, and l_{x+n} is the number of them still surviving at age $x+n$, then clearly ${}_nd_x$ gives the number who fail (or die) between ages x and $x+n$. (This portrayal of number dying explains the frequent historical reference to these models as *mortality tables*.) Furthermore,

$$q_x = \frac{d_x}{l_x}, \tag{6.4}$$

or, more generally,

$${}_nq_x = \frac{{}_nd_x}{l_x} \tag{6.5}$$

gives the conditional probability of failure, given alive at age x. Finally, we have

$${}_np_x = 1 - {}_nq_x = \frac{l_x - {}_nd_x}{l_x} = \frac{l_{x+n}}{l_x} \tag{6.6}$$

as the conditional probability of surviving to age $x+n$, given alive at age x. With $n=1$, we have the special case

$$p_x = \frac{l_{x+1}}{l_x}. \tag{6.7}$$

Recall that the conditional probabilities ${}_np_x$ and ${}_nq_x$ were defined in Section 5.3 in terms of $S_0(x)$. The consistency of those definitions with the ones presented in this section is easily seen since l_x is simply $l_0 \cdot S_0(x)$. We redefined ${}_np_x$ and ${}_nq_x$ in terms of l_x here simply to complete our description of the life table form of the survival model.

EXAMPLE 6.2

From Table 6.1a, find (a) the number who fail between ages 2 and 4; (b) the probability that a life age 1 will survive to age 4.

SOLUTION

(a) This is given by ${}_2d_2 = l_2 - l_4 = 177.$

(b) This is given by ${}_3p_1 = \frac{l_4}{l_1} = .99665.$ (Compare with part (b) of Example 6.1.) ❐

6.3 OTHER FUNCTIONS DERIVED FROM l_x

Although a life table only presents values of l_x for certain (say, integral) values of x, we wish to adopt the view that the l_x function which produces these values is a continuous and differentiable function. In other words, we assume that a continuous and differentiable l_x function *exists*, but only certain values of it are presented in the survival model. The reason we make this assumption is that there are several other important functions that can be derived from l_x if l_x is continuous and differentiable.

If values of l_x are known only at integral x, the question of how to *evaluate* these additional functions then arises, and the usual way to accomplish this evaluation is to make an assumption about the form of l_x between adjacent integral values of x.

In this section we will derive these several new functions from l_x symbolically, assuming l_x to be continuous and differentiable. In Section 6.6 we will discuss three common distribution assumptions, and show how they allow us to evaluate the functions of this section from a table of l_x values at integral x only. We will also interpret these distribution assumptions in terms of both l_x and $S_0(x)$.

6.3.1 THE FORCE OF FAILURE

The derivative of l_x can be interpreted as the absolute instantaneous annual rate of change of l_x. Since l_x represents the number of survivors at age x, then the derivative, which is the annual rate at which l_x is changing, gives the annual rate at which failures are occurring at age x. This derivative is negative since l_x is a decreasing function. To obtain the absolute magnitude of this instantaneous rate of failure, we will use the negative of the derivative. Finally, since the magnitude of the derivative depends on the size of l_x itself, we obtain the *relative instantaneous rate of failure* by dividing the negative derivative of l_x by l_x itself. Thus we have

$$\mu_x = \frac{-\frac{d}{dx}l_x}{l_x}, \tag{6.8}$$

which we call the *force of failure* (or *force of mortality*) at age x. Since $l_x = l_0 \cdot S_0(x)$, we see that Equation (6.8) is the same as

$$\lambda(x) = \frac{-\frac{d}{dx}S_0(x)}{S_0(x)} = \frac{f_0(x)}{S_0(x)}. \tag{6.9}$$

Thus the hazard rate and the force of failure are identical.

If we multiply both sides of Equation (5.14) by l_0 and substitute μ_y for $\lambda_0(y)$, we obtain

$$l_x = l_0 \cdot S_0(x) = l_0 \cdot \exp\left[-\int_0^x \mu_y \, dy\right]. \tag{6.10}$$

In the life table context, $S_0(x) = {}_xp_0 = \exp[-\int_0^x \mu_y \, dy]$ can be interpreted as a decremental factor that reduces the initial cohort of size l_0 to size l_x at age x.

By a simple variable change we can write Equation (6.8) as

$$\mu_{x+t} = \frac{-\frac{d}{dt}l_{x+t}}{l_{x+t}}, \tag{6.8a}$$

a form in which the force of failure will frequently be expressed.

EXAMPLE 6.3

Show that the force of failure, μ_x, is the limiting value of the probability of failure over an interval divided by the interval length (in years), as the interval length approaches zero.

SOLUTION

Consider first a one-year interval, with $q_x = \frac{d_x}{l_x}$. Then consider a half-year interval with $\frac{{}_{1/2}q_x}{1/2} = \frac{l_x - l_{x+1/2}}{1/2 \cdot l_x}$. Now, in general, consider $\frac{{}_{\Delta x}q_x}{\Delta x} = \frac{l_x - l_{x+\Delta x}}{\Delta x \cdot l_x}$, and show that $\lim_{\Delta x \to 0} \frac{{}_{\Delta x}q_x}{\Delta x} = \mu_x$. We have

$$\lim_{\Delta x \to 0}\left[\frac{l_x - l_{x+\Delta x}}{\Delta x \cdot l_x}\right] = \frac{1}{l_x} \cdot \lim_{\Delta x \to 0}\left[\frac{l_x - l_{x+\Delta x}}{\Delta x}\right] = \frac{1}{l_x}\left[-\frac{d}{dx}l_x\right] = \mu_x,$$

by Equation (6.8). ❐

6.3.2 THE PROBABILITY DENSITY FUNCTION OF T_0

With the force of failure, which is the same as the hazard rate, now defined, the next function to develop from l_x is the PDF of the age-at-failure random variable T_0 (Remember that we wish to show that the life table is a representation of the distribution of this random variable.)

From Equation (5.10) we have $f_0(x) = \lambda_0(x) \cdot S_0(x)$. In the life table context, $\lambda_0(x) = \mu_x$ and $S_0(x) = \frac{l_x}{l_0}$. Thus we have, for $x \geq 0$,

$$f_0(x) = \mu_x \left(\frac{l_x}{l_0} \right) = {}_xp_0\mu_x. \tag{6.11}$$

Also, from Equation (6.8), $\frac{d}{dx} l_x = -l_x\mu_x$. Dividing both sides by l_0 gives

$$\frac{d}{dx}\,{}_xp_0 = -{}_xp_0\mu_x. \tag{6.12}$$

EXAMPLE 6.4

Show that $\int_0^\infty f_0(x)\,dx = 1$.

SOLUTION

Since $f_0(x) = {}_xp_0\mu_x$, we have $\int_0^\infty {}_xp_0\mu_x\,dx = -{}_xp_0\,\big|_0^\infty$, from Equation (6.12). Thus we have ${}_0p_0 - {}_\infty p_0 = 1$, since ${}_0p_0 = 1$ and ${}_\infty p_0 = 0$. ❐

With the PDF in hand, we can now find $E[T_0]$, which we recall is denoted by $\overset{\circ}{e}_0$. (Throughout this and the following section, all expectations are assumed to exist.) We have

$$\overset{\circ}{e}_0 = E[T_0] = \int_0^\infty x \cdot f_0(x)\,dx = \int_0^\infty x \cdot {}_xp_0\mu_x\,dx. \tag{6.13}$$

Integration by parts produces the alternative formula

$$\overset{\circ}{e}_0 = E[T_0] = \int_0^\infty {}_xp_0\,dx = \frac{1}{l_0} \cdot \int_0^\infty l_x\,dx. \tag{6.14}$$

The second moment of T_0 is found from

$$E[T_0^{\,2}] = \int_0^\infty x^2 \cdot {}_xp_0\mu_x\,dx. \tag{6.15a}$$

Integration by parts produces

$$E[T_0^{\,2}] = 2\int_0^\infty x \cdot {}_xp_0\,dx = \frac{2}{l_0} \cdot \int_0^\infty x \cdot l_x\,dx. \tag{6.15b}$$

Then the variance of T_0 is given by

$$Var(T_0) = E[T_0^2]-\{E[T_0]\}^2 = \frac{2}{l_0}\cdot\int_0^\infty x\cdot l_x\ dx-\left(\frac{1}{l_0}\cdot\int_0^\infty l_x\ dx\right)^2. \qquad (6.16)$$

6.3.3 CONDITIONAL PROBABILITIES AND DENSITIES

We have already discussed the conditional probabilities ${}_np_x$ and ${}_nq_x$ in terms of both $S_0(x)$ and l_x.

Another conditional probability of some interest is denoted by ${}_{n|m}q_x$. It represents the probability that an entity known to be alive at age x will fail between ages $x+n$ and $x+n+m$. In terms of the probability notation of Chapter 5, ${}_{n|m}q_x = Pr[(x+n) < T_0 \le (x+n+m) \mid T_0 > x]$. This can also be expressed as the probability that an entity age x will survive n years, but then fail within the next m years. This way of stating the probability suggests that we can write

$${}_{n|m}q_x = {}_np_x \cdot {}_mq_{x+n}. \qquad (6.17)$$

Here ${}_mq_{x+n}$ is the conditional probability of failing between ages $x+n$ and $x+n+m$, given alive at age $x+n$. In turn, ${}_np_x$ is the conditional probability of surviving to age $x+n$, given alive at age x. Their product gives the probability of failing between ages $x+n$ and $x+n+m$, given alive at age x. In terms of l_x, we have, from Equations (6.6) and (6.5),

$${}_{n|m}q_x = \frac{l_{x+n}}{l_x}\cdot\frac{{}_md_{x+n}}{l_{x+n}} = \frac{{}_md_{x+n}}{l_x}. \qquad (6.18a)$$

When $m=1$ we use the notation

$${}_{n|}q_x = \frac{d_{x+n}}{l_x}. \qquad (6.18b)$$

Recall that ${}_{n|}q_x$ was defined in Section 5.3.6 as $Pr(K_x = n)$ or $Pr(K_x^* = n+1)$, the probability that an entity alive at age x would fail in the $(n+1)^{st}$ year.

EXAMPLE 6.5

Show that ${}_{n|m}q_x = {}_np_x - {}_{n+m}p_x$, and give an interpretation of this result.

SOLUTION

Since, from Equation (6.3), ${}_md_{x+n} = l_{x+n} - l_{x+n+m}$, then Equation (6.18a) becomes ${}_{n|m}q_x = \frac{l_{x+n}-l_{x+n+m}}{l_x} = {}_np_x - {}_{n+m}p_x$. Since ${}_np_x$ is the probability of surviving to age $x+n$, we can think of it as containing the probability of surviving to any age beyond $x+n$. If we remove from ${}_n p_x$ the probability of surviving to $x+n+m$, which is ${}_{n+m} p_x$, we have the probability of surviving to $x+n$, but not to $x+n+m$, which is ${}_{n|m} q_x$. ❐

Next we wish to explore the conditional PDF for death at age y, given alive at age x, where $y > x$. From Equation (5.44) we know this conditional PDF is $f_0(y \mid T_0 > x) = \frac{f_0(y)}{S_0(x)}$. Now from Equation (6.11) we have $f_0(y) = \frac{1}{l_0} \cdot l_y \mu_y$, and from Equation (6.1) we have $S_0(x) = \frac{l_x}{l_0}$. Thus

$$f_0(y \mid T_0 > x) = \frac{l_y \mu_y}{l_x} = {}_{y-x} p_x \mu_y. \tag{6.19a}$$

Letting $t = y-x$, so $y = x+t$, we have

$$f_0(x+t \mid T_0 > x) = {}_t p_x \mu_{x+t}, \tag{6.19b}$$

the conditional PDF of the random variable for the length of future lifetime of an entity alive at age x. This conditional PDF is a very useful function for developing other results.

If both numerator and denominator on the right side of Equation (6.8a) are divided by l_x, we obtain

$$\mu_{x+t} = \frac{-\frac{d}{dt} {}_t p_x}{{}_t p_x}, \tag{6.20}$$

which is equivalent to

$$\frac{d}{dt} {}_t p_x = -{}_t p_x \mu_{x+t}. \tag{6.21}$$

The expected future lifetime of an entity alive at age x is given by

$$\overset{\circ}{e}_x = E[T_x] = \int_0^\infty t \cdot {}_t p_x \mu_{x+t}\, dt = \int_0^\infty {}_t p_x\, dt, \tag{6.22}$$

by evaluating the first integral using integration by parts. The second moment of T_x is

$$E[T_x^2] = \int_0^\infty t^2 \cdot {}_t p_x \mu_{x+t}\, dt = 2\int_0^\infty t \cdot {}_t p_x\, dt, \tag{6.23}$$

again by using integration by parts on the first integral, so its variance is

$$Var(T_x) = E[T_x^2] - \{E[T_x]\}^2 = 2\int_0^\infty t \cdot {}_t p_x\, dt - \left(\int_0^\infty {}_t p_x\, dt\right)^2. \tag{6.24}$$

The concept of complete expectation of future lifetime can be restricted to a temporary period. We let $\overset{\circ}{e}_{x:\overline{n}|}$ denote the expected future lifetime for an entity alive at age x *over the next n years only*. It is called the *temporary complete expectation of life*, and is given by

$$\overset{\circ}{e}_{x:\overline{n}|} = \int_0^n {}_tp_x \, dt = \frac{1}{l_x} \int_0^n l_{x+t} \, dt. \tag{6.25}$$

EXAMPLE 6.6

A survival model is defined by $l_x = \frac{10{,}000}{(x+1)^3}$, for $x \geq 0$. Determine $Var(T_0 \mid T_0 > x)$, where T_0 is the age-at-failure random variable.

SOLUTION

We recognize that the age-at-failure random variable T_0 and the future lifetime random variable T_x are related by $T_0 = x + T_x$, where x is a constant. Thus, $Var(T_0 \mid T_0 > x) = Var(T_x \mid T_0 > x)$. To use Equation (6.24), we first find

$${}_tp_x = \frac{l_{x+t}}{l_x} = \frac{(x+1)^3}{(x+t+1)^3}.$$

Then

$$E[T_x] = \int_0^\infty {}_tp_x \, dt = (x+1)^3 \cdot \int_0^\infty (x+t+1)^{-3} \, dt = \frac{x+1}{2}$$

and

$$E[T_x^{\,2}] = 2\int_0^\infty t \cdot {}_tp_x \, dt = 2(x+1)^3 \cdot \int_0^\infty t(x+t+1)^{-3} \, dt = (x+1)^2,$$

so

$$Var(T_x \mid T_0 > x) = (x+1)^2 - \left(\frac{x+1}{2}\right)^2 = \frac{3(x+1)^2}{4}.$$

❐

6.3.4 THE CURTATE EXPECTATION OF LIFE

Recall the concept of the *curtate expectation of life at age x*, defined in Section 5.3.6 as $e_x = E[K_x \mid T_0 > x]$. Now we return to the e_x concept and present it in the context of the life table model. If we define e_x as the expected (or average) number of *whole years of future lifetime* for an entity in the l_x group, then it is given by

$$e_x = \frac{1}{l_x} \sum_{y=x+1}^{\infty} l_y = \frac{1}{l_x} \sum_{k=1}^{\infty} l_{x+k} = \sum_{k=1}^{\infty} {}_kp_x. \tag{6.26}$$

If we make the reasonable assumption that an entity survives approximately one-half year in the year of failure, then we see that $\overset{\circ}{e}_x$ exceeds e_x by that half-year. Thus

$$\overset{\circ}{e}_x \approx e_x + \frac{1}{2}.^{2} \tag{6.27}$$

The *temporary curtate expectation of life* at age x, denoted $e_{x:\overline{n}|}$, can also be defined. We have

$$e_{x:\overline{n}|} = \frac{1}{l_x}\sum_{k=1}^{n} l_{x+k} = \sum_{k=1}^{n} {}_kp_x, \tag{6.28}$$

and note that this represents the expected (or average) number of whole years lived over the interval $(x, x+n]$ by an entity in the l_x group.

EXAMPLE 6.7

Show that the stochastic definition of e_x given in Section 5.3.6 and the life table definition given by Equation (6.26) are the same.

SOLUTION

In Section 5.3.6 we defined e_x as

$$\begin{aligned}
e_x &= E[K_x \,|\, T_0 > x] \\
&= \sum_{k=1}^{\infty} k \cdot Pr(K_x = k) \\
&= \sum_{k=1}^{\infty} k \cdot {}_{k|}q_x \\
&= \sum_{k=1}^{\infty} k({}_kp_x - {}_{k+1}p_x) \\
&= 1(p_x - {}_2p_x) + 2({}_2p_x - {}_3p_x) + \cdots \\
&= p_x + {}_2p_x + \cdots,
\end{aligned}$$

which is the right side of Equation (6.26). ❒

[2] See Section 6.6.1, where we show that this result is exact under a particular assumption.

6.4 SUMMARY OF CONCEPTS AND NOTATION

Thus far we have been striving for an understanding of the nature and properties of survival models, both in the notation of the probability model of Chapter 5 and the life table model of Chapter 6. At this point we summarize the concepts developed thus far, and give the standard formulas or symbols for them in the notation of both chapters. (See Table 6.2 on page 96.)

6.5 MULTI-STATE MODEL INTERPRETATION

Recall the formulation of the two-state survival model as a multi-state model in Section 5.5 and illustrated in Figure 5.4. In Section 5.5 we analyzed the parametric survival model as a continuous-time Markov model; in this section we view the tabular survival model as a discrete-time Markov model.

The basic properties of this two-state model remain as described in Section 5.5. These include the notion that State 0 cannot be reentered once left, and that State 1 is an absorbing state. Consequently we have ${}_r p_x^{\overline{00}} = {}_r p_x^{00}$.

Consider that we have an entity that is surviving (i.e., in State 0) at age x at time 0, so that $X_0 = 0$. Then the event of being in State 0 at time 1 is the same as the event of surviving from age x to age $x+1$, so their probabilities are the same. That is,

$$p_x^{00} = Pr[X_1 = 0 \mid X_0 = 0] = p_x. \tag{6.29a}$$

Similarly,

$$p_x^{01} = Pr[X_1 = 1 \mid X_0 = 0] = q_x, \tag{6.29b}$$

where the right side of each equation writes the probability in standard actuarial notation. Then the matrix of transition probabilities for the first interval is

$$\mathbf{P}^{(0)} = \begin{vmatrix} p_x^{00} & p_x^{01} \\ 0 & 1 \end{vmatrix} = \begin{vmatrix} p_x & q_x \\ 0 & 1 \end{vmatrix}. \tag{6.30}$$

For the discrete time interval from time 1 to time 2, we similarly have

$$p_{x+1}^{00} = Pr[X_2 = 0 \mid X_1 = 0] = p_{x+1}, \tag{6.31a}$$

$$p_{x+1}^{01} = Pr[X_2 = 1 \mid X_1 = 0] = q_{x+1}, \tag{6.31b}$$

and

$$\mathbf{P}^{(1)} = \begin{vmatrix} p_{x+1}^{00} & p_{x+1}^{01} \\ 0 & 1 \end{vmatrix} = \begin{vmatrix} p_{x+1} & q_{x+1} \\ 0 & 1 \end{vmatrix}. \tag{6.32}$$

TABLE 6.2

Concept	Chapter 5 Formulas	Chapter 6 Formulas
1. Unconditional probability of survival from age 0 to age x	$S_0(x)$	${}_xp_0 = \frac{l_x}{l_0}$
2. Unconditional probability of failure not later than age x	$F_0(x)$	${}_xq_0 = \frac{l_0-l_x}{l_0}$
3. Conditional probability of survival from age x to age $x+n$	$\frac{S_0(x+n)}{S_0(x)}$	${}_np_x = \frac{l_{x+n}}{l_x}$
4. Conditional probability of failure before age $x+n$, given alive at age x	$\frac{S_0(x)-S_0(x+n)}{S_0(x)}$	${}_nq_x = \frac{l_x-l_{x+n}}{l_x} = \frac{{}_nd_x}{l_x}$
5. Hazard rate (force of failure) at exact age x	$\lambda_0(x) = \frac{-\frac{d}{dx}S_0(x)}{S_0(x)} = -\frac{d}{dx}\ln S_0(x)$	$\mu_x = \frac{-\frac{d}{dx}l_x}{l_x} = -\frac{d}{dx}\ln l_x$
6. Unconditional density function for failure at exact age x	$f_0(x) = \frac{d}{dx}F_0(x) = -\frac{d}{dx}S_0(x)$	${}_xp_0\mu_x = -\frac{d}{dx}\,{}_xp_0$
7. Unconditional expectation of future lifetime at birth	$E[T_0] = \int_0^\infty x\cdot f_0(x)\,dx = \int_0^\infty S_0(x)\,dx$	$\overset{\circ}{e}_0 = \int_0^\infty x\cdot{}_xp_0\mu_x\,dx = \int_0^\infty {}_xp_0\,dx$
8. Unconditional variance of future lifetime at birth	$Var(T_0) = \int_0^\infty x^2\cdot f_0(x)\,dx - \{E[T_0]\}^2$	$\int_0^\infty x^2\cdot{}_xp_0\mu_x\,dx - (\overset{\circ}{e}_0)^2$ (no specific symbol)
9. Conditional density function for failure at age y, given alive at age x, where $y > x$	$f_0(y\,\|\,T_0 > x) = \frac{f_0(y)}{S_0(x)}$	${}_{y-x}p_x\mu_y = {}_tp_x\mu_{x+t}$, where $t = y-x$
10. Conditional expectation of future lifetime at age x	$E[T_0-x\,\|\,T_0>x] = E[T_x\,\|\,T_0>x] = \int_0^\infty t\cdot f_0(x+t\,\|\,T_0>x)\,dt = \int_0^\infty \frac{S_0(x+t)}{S_0(x)}\,dt$	$\overset{\circ}{e}_x = \int_0^\infty t\cdot{}_tp_x\mu_{x+t}\,dt = \int_0^\infty {}_tp_x\,dt$
11. Conditional variance of future lifetime at age x	$Var(T_x\,\|\,T_0>x) = Var(T_0\,\|\,T_0>x)^*$ $= \int_0^\infty t^2\cdot f_0(x+t\,\|\,T_0>x)\,dt - \{E[T_x\,\|\,T_0>x]\}^2$	$\int_0^\infty t^2\cdot{}_tp_x\mu_{x+t}\,dt - (\overset{\circ}{e}_x)^2$ (no specific symbol)

*Variance of future lifetime and variance of age at failure are equal, since $T_x = T_0 - x$, and x is a constant.

When the discrete-time Markov process is used to represent the tabular survival model, it should be clear that the model is non-homogeneous.

Since the process necessarily begins in State 0, it follows that the initial state vector is $\boldsymbol{\pi}_0 = (1, 0)$. At time n in general, the state vector $\boldsymbol{\pi}_n$ contains the two probability values

$${}_n p_x^{00} = {}_n p_x$$

and

$${}_n p_x^{01} = {}_n q_x,$$

and is given by

$$\boldsymbol{\pi}_n = (1, 0) \cdot \begin{vmatrix} p_x & q_x \\ 0 & 1 \end{vmatrix} \cdot \begin{vmatrix} p_{x+1} & q_{x+1} \\ 0 & 1 \end{vmatrix} \cdot \cdots \cdot \begin{vmatrix} p_{x+n-1} & q_{x+n-1} \\ 0 & 1 \end{vmatrix}. \tag{6.33}$$

EXAMPLE 6.8

Develop expressions for the elements in the state vector $\boldsymbol{\pi}_3$, using standard actuarial notation.

SOLUTION

The two elements in the state vector $\boldsymbol{\pi}_3$ are $\pi_{03} = {}_3 p_x$ and $\pi_{13} = {}_3 q_x$. (Recall from Section 3.1.2 that π_{in} is the probability of being in State i at time n.) We have

$$\begin{aligned}
\boldsymbol{\pi}_3 &= (1, 0) \cdot \begin{vmatrix} p_x & q_x \\ 0 & 1 \end{vmatrix} \cdot \begin{vmatrix} p_{x+1} & q_{x+1} \\ 0 & 1 \end{vmatrix} \cdot \begin{vmatrix} p_{x+2} & q_{x+2} \\ 0 & 1 \end{vmatrix} \\
&= (p_x, q_x) \cdot \begin{vmatrix} p_{x+1} & q_{x+1} \\ 0 & 1 \end{vmatrix} \cdot \begin{vmatrix} p_{x+2} & q_{x+2} \\ 0 & 1 \end{vmatrix} \\
&= (p_x \cdot p_{x+1}, q_x + p_x \cdot q_{x+1}) \cdot \begin{vmatrix} p_{x+2} & q_{x+2} \\ 0 & 1 \end{vmatrix} \\
&= (p_x \cdot p_{x+1} \cdot p_{x+2},\ q_x + p_x \cdot q_{x+1} + p_x \cdot p_{x+1} \cdot q_{x+2}).
\end{aligned}$$

Then we have

$$\pi_{03} = {}_3 p_x = p_x \cdot p_{x+1} \cdot p_{x+2}$$

and

$$\pi_{13} = {}_3 q_x = q_x + p_x \cdot q_{x+1} + p_x \cdot p_{x+1} \cdot q_{x+2},$$

as already developed earlier in this chapter. ❐

Further analysis of the tabular survival model as a discrete-time Markov process will be pursued in the exercises (see Exercises 6-19 through 6-21).

6.6 METHODS FOR NON-INTEGRAL AGES

A review of the functions that we have developed, and summarized in Table 6.2, shows that not many of them can be numerically determined from a life table that gives values of l_x only for integral x. Actually, only the probability function ${}_np_x$ (and its complement ${}_nq_x$) for integral x and n can be so determined. (Note that ${}_xp_0$ and ${}_xq_0$, for integral x, are special cases of ${}_np_x$ and ${}_nq_x$.)

The determination of all other functions requires that values of l_{x+t} be available for all t, $0<t<1$. This is obtained in the life table model by assuming that l_{x+t} has a certain mathematical form between x and x+1. This assumed form for l_{x+t} will be differentiable on the open interval $0<t<1$, but not at $t=0$ or $t=1$.

The ability to determine l_{x+t} numerically for any t, $0<t<1$, will allow us to calculate probabilities of the form ${}_tp_x$ and its complement ${}_tq_x$ for all t. The differentiability of l_{x+t} will allow us to evaluate μ_{x+t}, and hence the conditional density function $f_x(t\,|\,T_0>x) \;=\; {}_tp_x\mu_{x+t}$, for all t on the open interval $0<t<1$. The integrability of l_{x+t} will allow us to calculate $\overset{\circ}{e}_x$ and the conditional variance of future lifetime (or age at failure), $Var(T_0\,|\,T_0>x)$.

We should not lose sight of the fact that we are assuming a mathematical form for l_{x+t} *only* between x and x+1, not for the entire domain of x; the latter case would return us to the continuous parametric models described in Chapter 5. We will also see that each particular mathematical function that we assume for l_{x+t} will correspond to a certain interpolation method.

To recapitulate, we assume that we have a life table with numerical values of l_x given for all integral x. We then assume a mathematical form for $l_{x+t}, 0\le t\le 1$, and show how to calculate, from the given life table, values of ${}_tp_x$ and $\overset{\circ}{e}_x$. (The function $Var(T_0\,|\,T_0>x)$ can also be evaluated, but with greater difficulty.) We will now pursue three different assumptions of a mathematical form for l_{x+t}.

6.6.1 LINEAR FORM FOR l_{x+t}

If l_{x+t} is a linear function between x and x+1, then it is of the form $a+bt$. To provide continuity for l_{x+t}, we require, at $t=0$, that $l_x=a$, and at $t=1$, that $l_{x+1}=a+b$, so that $b=l_{x+1}-a$, or $b=l_{x+1}-l_x=-d_x$. Thus we have

$$l_{x+t} \;=\; l_x - t\cdot d_x. \tag{6.34}$$

An alternate form is to use $l_x - l_{x+1}$ in place of d_x, obtaining

$$l_{x+t} \;=\; l_x - t(l_x - l_{x+1}) \;=\; t\cdot l_{x+1} + (1-t)\cdot l_x. \tag{6.35}$$

Both Equations (6.34) and (6.35) reveal that the linear assumption for l_{x+t} means we are determining values of l_{x+t} from l_x and l_{x+1} by *linear interpolation*.

The determination of other functions follows from Equation (6.34). We have

$$ {}_t p_x = \frac{l_{x+t}}{l_x} = 1 - t \cdot \frac{d_x}{l_x} = 1 - t \cdot q_x, \tag{6.36}$$

and

$$ {}_t q_x = 1 - {}_t p_x = t \cdot q_x. \tag{6.37}$$

We also have

$$ \mu_{x+t} = \frac{-\frac{d}{dt} l_{x+t}}{l_{x+t}} = \frac{d_x}{l_x - t \cdot d_x} = \frac{q_x}{1 - t \cdot q_x}, \tag{6.38}$$

which, when multiplied by Equation (6.36), leads to the convenient result

$$ f_x(t \mid T_0 > x) = {}_t p_x \mu_{x+t} = q_x, \tag{6.39}$$

for $0 < t < 1$. Note that μ_{x+t}, and hence $f_x(t \mid T_0 > x)$, are not defined at $t = 0$ and $t = 1$ since l_{x+t} is not differentiable there.

We can find $\overset{\circ}{e}_x = E[T_x]$ from Equation (6.22) as

$$\begin{aligned}
\overset{\circ}{e}_x &= \int_0^\infty {}_t p_x \; dt \\
&= \sum_{r=0}^\infty {}_r p_x \int_0^1 {}_s p_{x+r} \; ds \\
&= \sum_{r=0}^\infty {}_r p_x \int_0^1 (1 - s \cdot q_{x+r}) \; ds \\
&= \sum_{r=0}^\infty {}_r p_x \, (1 - \tfrac{1}{2} \cdot q_{x+r}) \\
&= \sum_{r=0}^\infty ({}_r p_x - \tfrac{1}{2} \cdot {}_{r|} q_x) \\
&= 1 + e_x - \frac{1}{2} = e_x + \frac{1}{2},
\end{aligned} \tag{6.40}$$

which we developed intuitively in Equation (6.27).

EXAMPLE 6.9

The function ${}_{r|h}q_x = {}_rp_x \cdot {}_hq_{x+r}$ denotes the probability that an entity alive at age x will fail between ages $x+r$ and $x+r+h$, where $r>0$, $h>0$, and $r+h<1$. Show that

$$ {}_{r|h}q_x = h \cdot q_x, \tag{6.41} $$

under the linear form for l_{x+t}.

SOLUTION

$$ \begin{aligned} {}_{r|h}q_x &= \frac{l_{x+r} - l_{x+r+h}}{l_x} \\ &= \frac{(l_x - r \cdot d_x) - (l_x - (r+h)d_x)}{l_x} = \frac{h \cdot d_x}{l_x} = h \cdot q_x. \end{aligned} $$ ❐

Turning to the question of the associated probability distribution over the interval $(x, x+1]$, we note that the PDF for time of failure within the interval is a constant, and the CDF, which is ${}_tq_x$, is a linear function. This shows that the random variable T_x has a uniform distribution over $(x, x+1]$. Furthermore, the linear nature of Equation (6.34) shows that l_{x+t} decreases uniformly (i.e., entities are failing uniformly) over the interval. For these reasons, this linear assumption for l_{x+t} has traditionally been called the *uniform distribution of failures* or *uniform distribution of deaths* assumption, which is commonly referred to as UDD.

Without question the UDD assumption is extremely useful for making calculations from the life table. No doubt the ability to analyze the assumption in terms of the uniform (or even) distribution pattern of the occurring failures, along with the mathematical simplicity afforded by the constant PDF, are the major reasons for this assumption's popularity.

6.6.2 EXPONENTIAL FORM FOR l_{x+t}

If l_{x+t} is an exponential function between x and $x+1$, then it is of the form $l_{x+t} = a \cdot b^t$. To assure continuity, at $t=0$ we have $l_x = a$ and at $t=1$ we have $l_{x+1} = ab$, so $b = \frac{l_{x+1}}{a} = \frac{l_{x+1}}{l_x}$. Thus we have

$$ l_{x+t} = l_x \left(\frac{l_{x+1}}{l_x} \right)^t = (l_{x+1})^t \cdot (l_x)^{1-t}, \tag{6.42} $$

which shows that the exponential assumption for l_{x+t} allows us to determine values of l_{x+t} from values of l_x and l_{x+1} by *exponential interpolation*. (Note the similarity of Equations (6.42) and (6.35).) An alternative form of Equation (6.42), which results from substituting $l_{x+1} = l_x \cdot p_x$, is

$$l_{x+t} = l_x \cdot (p_x)^t. \tag{6.43}$$

The determination of other functions follows from Equation (6.42) or (6.43). Thus

$$_tp_x = \frac{l_{x+t}}{l_x} = (p_x)^t, \tag{6.44}$$

and

$$_tq_x = 1 - {_tp_x} = 1-(p_x)^t = 1-(1-q_x)^t, \tag{6.45}$$

We also have

$$\mu_{x+t} = \frac{-\frac{d}{dt}l_{x+t}}{l_{x+t}} = \frac{-l_x(p_x)^t \cdot \ln p_x}{l_x(p_x)^t} = -\ln p_x, \tag{6.46}$$

a constant, for $0<t<1$. Thus we have the useful result that if l_{x+t} is exponential, then the force of failure, μ_{x+t}, is constant over $(x,x+1]$. We call this constant force μ_x^*. Then Equation (6.46), which says $\mu_x^* = -\ln p_x$, can be rearranged to read

$$p_x = e^{-\mu_x^*}, \tag{6.47}$$

from which Equation (6.44) becomes

$$_tp_x = e^{-t \cdot \mu_x^*}. \tag{6.48}$$

The conditional PDF is then found by multiplying Equations (6.48) and (6.46), obtaining

$$f_x(t \mid T_0 > x) = {_tp_x}\mu_{x+t} = \mu_x^* \cdot e^{-t \cdot \mu_x^*}. \tag{6.49}$$

The PDF of T_x, given by Equation (6.49), and its SDF, given by Equation (6.48), clearly show us that T_x has an exponential distribution over $(x,x+1]$. (Recall from Section 5.2.2 that this distribution has a constant hazard rate, which is the same as the force of failure.) This constant force of failure has led to this assumption being traditionally called the *constant force assumption.*

Of course this μ_x^* is the constant value of $\mu_{x+t}, 0<t\le 1$. For the interval $(x+1, x+2]$ we have a different constant force, namely $\mu_{x+1}^* = -\ln p_{x+1}$. Then it can be shown (see Exercise 6-32) that

$$\overset{\circ}{e}_x = \frac{1}{l_x} \cdot \sum_{y=x}^{\infty} \frac{d_y}{\mu_y^*}. \tag{6.50}$$

6.6.3 HYPERBOLIC FORM FOR l_{x+t}

Historically, textbooks on actuarial mathematics have included a third method for non-integral ages, namely the assumption that l_{x+t} is a hyperbolic function between x and $x+1$. A hyperbolic function is a reciprocal linear function of the form $l_{x+t} = (a+bt)^{-1}$, so we have $l_x = \frac{1}{a}$ and $l_{x+1} = \frac{1}{a+b}$. From this we find

$$\frac{1}{l_{x+t}} = t \cdot \frac{1}{l_{x+1}} + (1-t) \cdot \frac{1}{l_x}, \tag{6.51}$$

showing that we can find values of l_{x+t} by linear interpolation between the reciprocals of l_x and l_{x+1}. (Linear interpolation on the reciprocal of a function is called *harmonic interpolation* on the function itself.) From Equation (6.51) we can find

$$({}_t p_x)^{-1} = \frac{l_x}{l_{x+t}} = t \cdot \frac{l_x}{l_{x+1}} + (1-t) \cdot \frac{l_x}{l_x} = \frac{t}{p_x} + (1-t) = \frac{t + (1-t) \cdot p_x}{p_x},$$

so that

$${}_t p_x = \frac{p_x}{t + (1-t) \cdot p_x} = \frac{1-q_x}{1-(1-t) \cdot q_x} \tag{6.52}$$

and therefore

$${}_t q_x = 1 - {}_t p_x = \frac{t \cdot q_x}{1-(1-t) \cdot q_x}. \tag{6.53}$$

Using Equation (6.52) we can then find

$$\mu_{x+t} = \frac{-\frac{d}{dt}\, {}_t p_x}{{}_t p_x} = \frac{(1-q_x) \cdot q_x}{[1-(1-t) \cdot q_x]^2} \div \frac{1-q_x}{1-(1-t) \cdot q_x} = \frac{q_x}{1-(1-t) \cdot q_x}, \tag{6.54}$$

for $0 < t < 1$, which is a decreasing function of t. It can also be shown (see Exercise 6-33) that

$${}_{1-t} q_{x+t} = (1-t) \cdot q_x. \tag{6.55}$$

In the past, a common actuarial approach to survival model estimation utilized a method that frequently involved functions of the form ${}_{1-t} q_{x+t}$, which could be simplified to $(1-t) \cdot q_x$ under the hyperbolic assumption. This approach to estimation work is no longer commonly used, so this major use of the hyperbolic assumption no longer exists. Today we might view it as being primarily of historical interest.

The Italian actuary Gaetano Balducci made major use of the hyperbolic distribution in several of his writings, such as [1] and [2]. Although he did not originate the use of this assumption, it has come to be called the *Balducci assumption*, or Balducci distribution.

EXAMPLE 6.10

In a certain life table, $l_x = 1000$ and $l_{x+1} = 900$. Evaluate $\mu_{x+1/4}$ under each of the UDD, constant force, and hyperbolic assumptions.

SOLUTION

From the given values we find $q_x = .10$ and $p_x = .90$. Then under UDD we have

$$\mu_{x+1/4} = \frac{.10}{.975} = .10256.$$

Under constant force we have

$$\mu_{x+1/4} = \mu_x^* = -\ln p_x = .10536.$$

Under hyperbolic we have

$$\mu_{x+1/4} = \frac{.10}{.925} = .10811.$$

❒

6.6.4 SUMMARY

Table 6.3 summarizes most of the results developed in this section. Further analysis of these assumptions is given by Batten [3], and Mereu [20] gives a presentation of the use of these assumptions in actuarial calculations. (Note that we have used simply μ in place of μ_x^* as defined on page 101.)

TABLE 6.3

Function	Linear (UDD)	Exponential (Constant Force)	Hyperbolic (Balducci)
l_{x+t}	$t\cdot l_{x+1}+(1-t)\cdot l_x$	$(l_{x+1})^t\cdot(l_x)^{1-t}$	$\left(\frac{t}{l_{x+1}}+\frac{1-t}{l_x}\right)^{-1}$
${}_tp_x$	$1-t\cdot q_x$	$(p_x)^t=e^{-\mu t}$	$\frac{1-q_x}{1-(1-t)\cdot q_x}$
${}_tq_x$	$t\cdot q_x$	$1-(1-q_x)^t$	$\frac{t\cdot q_x}{1-(1-t)\cdot q_x}$
μ_{x+t}	$\frac{q_x}{1-t\cdot q_x}$	$\mu=-\ln p_x$	$\frac{q_x}{1-(1-t)\cdot q_x}$
${}_tp_x\mu_{x+t}$	q_x	$\mu\cdot e^{-\mu t}$	$\frac{q_x(1-q_x)}{[1-(1-t)\cdot q_x]^2}$

6.7 SELECT LIFE TABLES

In this section we consider life tables developed from the select survival distribution defined in Section 5.4 as $S_{[x]}(t;x)$, for $t \geq 0$.

It is easy to see that a life table based on this SDF is completely parallel to one based on $S_0(x)$. Thus we begin with a radix which represents a hypothetical cohort of lives selected at age x, which we call $l_{[x]}$. Then subsequent values are developed from

$$l_{[x]+t} = l_{[x]} \cdot S_{[x]}(t;x). \tag{6.56}$$

If values of $l_{[x]+t}$ are specified for all integral t, the resulting select life table (for age at selection x) can then be used to obtain other values, just as we did for the aggregate life table earlier in this chapter. It is important to specify the age at selection in the symbols for the functions derived from a select table. For example, if selection is at age x, the conditional probability of failure between ages $x+7$ and $x+10$, for an entity known to be alive at age $x+5$, is given by

$$_{2|3}q_{[x]+5} = \frac{l_{[x]+7} - l_{[x]+10}}{l_{[x]+5}}. \tag{6.57}$$

Select life tables do not normally extend to all values of t in a manner that is unique to the selection age. For example, consider two entities, one selected at age 20 and now age 30 $(t=10)$, and the other selected at age 21 and now age 30 $(t=9)$. Their conditional probabilities of survival for another n years are $_n p_{[20]+10} = \frac{l_{[20]+10+n}}{l_{[20]+10}}$ and $_n p_{[21]+9} = \frac{l_{[21]+9+n}}{l_{[21]+9}}$, respectively. If we believe that selection no longer has an effect on failure at these durations, then the two probabilities should have the same value, denoted by $\frac{l_{30+n}}{l_{30}}$. A life table with this characteristic is called a *select and ultimate table.*

The first step in developing a select and ultimate table is to determine the length of the *select period*, the time over which selection is assumed to have an effect on failure. Although there is evidence that effects of selection can persist for many years, published tables will seldom show a select period greater than 15 years. For illustration in this text, however, we will assume only a four-year select period. This means that for entities four and more years beyond selection, failure is a function of attained age only.

Suppose $[x]$ is the youngest age at selection in the table which we wish to construct. Then we select a radix, l_x, and generate

$$l_{[x]+t} = l_{[x]} \cdot S_{[x]}(t;x), \tag{6.58a}$$

for $t = 1,2,3$, and

$$l_{x+t} = l_{[x]} \cdot S_{[x]}(t;x), \tag{6.58b}$$

for $t \geq 4$. Instead of arranging these values of $l_{[x]+t}$ and l_{x+t} in a column, as in our earlier Table 6.1a, we arrange them in the row-and-column format shown in Table 6.4.

TABLE 6.4

$l_{[x]}$	$l_{[x]+1}$	$l_{[x]+2}$	$l_{[x]+3}$	l_{x+4}
				l_{x+5}
				l_{x+6}
				⋮
				⋮

Next, consider age at selection $[x+1]$. If a radix, $l_{[x+1]}$, were arbitrarily chosen, then we would generate

$$l_{[x+1]+t} = l_{[x+1]} \cdot S_{[x+1]}(t;x+1), \tag{6.59a}$$

for $t = 1,2,3,$ and

$$l_{x+1+t} = l_{[x+1]} \cdot S_{[x+1]}(t;x+1), \tag{6.59b}$$

for $t \geq 4$. But the basic idea of the select and ultimate table is that the same values of l_{x+t}, for $t \geq 5$, should be common to the cohorts $l_{[x]}$ and $l_{[x+1]}$. Thus $l_{[x+1]}$ must be chosen so that $l_{[x+1]} \cdot S_{[x+1]}(4;x+1)$, produces the same l_{x+5} as was produced by $l_{[x]} \cdot S_{[x]}(5;x)$. This is easily accomplished by taking

$$l_{[x+1]} = \frac{l_{x+5}}{S_{[x+1]}(4;x+1)}. \tag{6.60}$$

Then $l_{[x+1]+1}, l_{[x+1]+2}$, and $l_{[x+1]+3}$ can be found from this $l_{[x+1]}$ by using Equation (6.59a). Note that values of $S_{[x+1]}(t;x+1)$ for $t > 4$ are not utilized once it has been decided to use a four-year select period.

Similarly, $l_{[x+2]}$ would be found from the already established value of l_{x+6} by

$$l_{[x+2]} = \frac{l_{x+6}}{S_{[x+2]}(4;x+2)}, \tag{6.61}$$

and then values of $l_{[x+2]+t}$, for $t = 1,2,3,$ are found from

$$l_{[x+2]+t} = l_{[x+2]} \cdot S_{[x+2]}(t;x+2). \tag{6.62}$$

The complete select and ultimate table is in the format of Table 6.5, where we assume age 20 is the youngest age at selection.

TABLE 6.5

$[x]$	$l_{[x]}$	$l_{[x]+1}$	$l_{[x]+2}$	$l_{[x]+3}$	l_{x+4}	$x+4$
[20]	$l_{[20]}$	$l_{[20]+1}$	$l_{[20]+2}$	$l_{[20]+3}$	l_{24}	24
[21]	$l_{[21]}$	$l_{[21]+1}$	$l_{[21]+2}$	$l_{[21]+3}$	l_{25}	25
[22]	$l_{[22]}$	$l_{[22]+1}$	$l_{[22]+2}$	$l_{[22]+3}$	l_{26}	26
⋮	⋮	⋮	⋮	⋮	⋮	⋮

Other functions derived from the $l_{[x]}$ function of a select life table, as presented in Section 6.3 for the regular life table, would be similarly notated. For example, the select force of mortality at duration t, for a person selected at age $[x]$, would be given by

$$\mu_{[x]+t} = \frac{\frac{-d}{dt}\, l_{[x]+t}}{l_{[x]+t}}. \tag{6.63}$$

EXAMPLE 6.11

Express the conditional probabilities (a) ${}_{2|4}q_{[20]+1}$ and (b) ${}_{2|4}q_{[22]+3}$ in terms of l functions, assuming a 4-year select period.

SOLUTION

(a) This is the probability of failure between ages 23 and 27 for an entity age 21, selected at age 20. The number of such failures, from Table 6.5, is $l_{[20]+3} - l_{27}$, so the desired probability is $\frac{l_{[20]+3} - l_{27}}{l_{[20]+1}}$.

(b) Here we seek the probability of failure between ages 27 and 31 for an entity age 25, selected at age 22. For this entity, age 27 is already beyond the select period, so the probability is $\frac{l_{27} - l_{31}}{l_{[22]+3}}$. ❐

6.8 LIFE TABLE SUMMARY

This chapter has described, in great detail, the generic life table, which is the most fundamental model supporting the actuarial determination of financial values associated with life insurance and pension plans. Although all life tables are basically of the same form, they may vary considerably with respect to their numerical values, their applicability, and the experience data upon which they are based.

All life tables arise from statistical studies of experience data.[3] Logically, a life table developed for the purpose of pricing life insurance should be based on data derived from life insurance

[3] The statistical estimation procedures used to construct life tables are described in several textbooks, including Batten [3], London [18],and Kellison and London [16], and are covered on Society of Actuaries Exam C.

experience. Similarly, a life table used for annuity calculations should be based on data derived from the survival experience of annuitants, a pension life table should be based on the survival experience of pensioners, and so on.

Life insurance coverage is available through *individual* insurance policies, which is the focus of most of the discussion throughout this text, and also through *group* insurance coverage generally provided by an employer. Under group insurance coverage, the degree of screening of individual participants for healthiness is considerably less than under individual insurance coverage.[4] Consequently, the survival patterns of persons insured under individual policies versus those insured under group coverages would be expected to differ. It logically follows that life tables used for group insurance should be based on group insurance experience and those used for individual insurance should be based on individual insurance experience.

Within individual insurance, it is common to use different life tables to calculate premiums (see Chapter 9) from those used to calculate reserves (see Chapters 10 and 11). A major concern in determining premiums is that of *competitiveness* in the marketplace, whereas a major concern in determining reserves is that of *adequacy*. Consequently, tables used for calculating reserves (also called *valuation*) might be more conservative than those used for pricing.

By definition, tables based on experience data reflect recent historical patterns of survival and failure. If such tables are used to determine contract values that apply in the future, it is inherently being assumed that past and future survival patterns will be the same. If future improvements in medicine and other factors influencing survival occur, which is likely, then tables based on historical data will be overly conservative for life insurance, but may be significantly inappropriate for life annuities. To address this possibility, actuaries frequently apply survival-improvement projections to tables based on historical data for use with annuity calculations. This is discussed more fully in Section 8.7.

Experience data consistently shows that females live longer than males, so separate tables for the genders have traditionally been used. For political reasons, however, it has become common practice in recent years to use the same table, referred to as a *unisex table*, for both genders. Of course, a unisex table should be estimated from historical data derived from a group that includes both genders.

A very special life table, not related to insurance or pension applications, is the *population life table* which is naturally based on the survival experience of the population of a nation or a political subdivision thereof. This topic belongs to the general field of demography (see, for example, Brown [6]). In general, mortality rates derived from general population experience will exceed those derived from insurance or annuity experience.

In Section 6.7 we explored the concept of the select and ultimate life table. When such a model is derived from experience data, the select portion of the table would be estimated from the survival experience during the first k years of insurance coverage (where k is the length of the select period), and the ultimate portion would be estimated from survival experience beyond the first k years. A life table estimated from *all* years of experience, without regard to duration since selection, is called an *aggregate table*.

---

[4] The screening of proposed insured persons for healthiness, and other elements of insurability, is referred to as *underwriting*.

6.9 WRITTEN-ANSWERS QUESTION EXAMPLES

EXAMPLE 6.12

A life table is defined by the following values of p_x:

x	p_x
0	.90
1	.80
2	.60
3	.30
4	.00

(a) Find the corresponding values of $S_0(x)$, for $x=0,1,2,3,4,5$.

(b) Derive a life table showing the values of l_x and d_x, using a radix of 10,000.

(c) What is the value of ω in this table?

(d) Verify that $\sum_{x=0}^{\omega-1} d_x = l_0$.

SOLUTION

(a) Each $S_0(x)$ is calculated by $S_0(x)=S_0(x-1)\cdot p_{x-1}$, with $S_0(0)=1$. Then $S_0(1)=p_0=.90$, $S_0(2)=S_0(1)\cdot p_1=.72$, and so on.

(b) Each ℓ_x is found from $\ell_x=\ell_0\cdot S_0(x)$, where $\ell_0=10{,}000$. Then $\ell_1=(10{,}000)(.90)=9000$, $\ell_2=(10{,}000)(.72)=7200$, and so on. Each d_x is found from $d_x=\ell_x-\ell_{x+1}$. Then $d_0=\ell_0-\ell_1=1000$, $d_1=\ell_1-\ell_2=1800$, and so on.

(c) $S_0(x)=0$ is first reached age $x=5$, and that defines $\omega=5$.

(d) From the answers,

$$\sum_{x=0}^{4} d_x = (1000+1800+2880+3024+1296) = 10{,}000.$$

❑

EXAMPLE 6.13

Consider the survival function

$$S_0(t) = \frac{9000-10t-t^2}{9000},$$

for $0\le t\le 90$, which is used to construct a life table with radix of 100,000.

(a) Calculate the life table values of l_{60} and l_{61},

(b) Calculate the value of ${}_{.25}p_{60}$, under each of the UDD, constant force, and Balducci assumptions.

(c) Calculate the value of e_{60} under the UDD assumption.

(d) Calculate the exact value of $\mu_{60.75}$.

(e) Calculate the value of $\mu_{60.75}$ under each of the three assumptions.

(f) Which assumption gives the best, and worst, approximation to the exact value?

SOLUTION

(a) First we calculate

$$S_0(60) = \frac{9000-600-3600}{9000} = .53333$$

and

$$S_0(61) = \frac{9000-610-3721}{9000} = .51878.$$

Then we directly have $l_{60} = 53{,}333$ and $l_{61} = 51{,}878$.

(b) From part (a) we find $q_{60} = \frac{1{,}455}{53{,}333} = .02728$. Then under UDD we have

$${}_{.25}p_{60} = 1 - {}_{.25}q_{60} = 1-(.25)(.02728) = .99318,$$

under constant force we have

$${}_{.25}p_{60} = (p_{60})^{.25} = (1-.02728)^{.25} = .99311,$$

and under Balducci we have

$${}_{.25}p_{60} = \frac{1-q_{60}}{1-.75q_{60}} = \frac{.97272}{1-(.75)(.02728)} = .99304.$$

(c) First we find

$${}_tp_{60} = \frac{S_0(60+t)}{S_0(60)} = \frac{9000-10(60+t)-(60+t)^2}{9000-600-3600}.$$

Next we find

$$\begin{aligned}
\overset{\circ}{e}_{60} &= \frac{1}{4800}\int_0^{30}\left[9000-10(60+t)-(60+t)^2\right]dt \\
&= \frac{1}{4800}\left[9000t-5(60+t)^2-\tfrac{1}{3}(60+t)^3\right]_0^{30} \\
&= \frac{1}{4800}\left\{(9000)(30)-5\left[(90)^2-(60)^2\right]-\tfrac{1}{3}\left[(90)^3-(60)^3\right]\right\} = 15.9375.
\end{aligned}$$

Under UDD, $\overset{\circ}{e}_x = e_x + .50$, so we find

$$e_{60} = \overset{\circ}{e}_{60} - .50 = 15.4375.$$

(d) Exactly,

$$\mu_{60.75} = \left. \frac{-\frac{d}{dt}S_0(t)}{S_0(t)} \right|_{t=60.75}.$$

The derivative is $\frac{d}{dt}S_0(t) = \frac{-10-2t}{9000}$, so

$$\mu_{60.75} = \left. \frac{10+2t}{9000-10t-t^2} \right|_{t=60.75} = .02797.$$

(e) Under UDD we have

$$\mu_{60.75} = \frac{q_{60}}{1-.75q_{60}} = \frac{.02728}{1-(.75)(.02728)} = .02785,$$

under constant force we have

$$\mu_{60.75} = -\ln p_{60} = -\ln(.97272) = .02766,$$

and under Balducci we have

$$\mu_{60.75} = \frac{q_{60}}{1-.25q_{60}} = \frac{.02728}{1-(.25)(.02728)} = .02747.$$

(f) The best approximation is given by the UDD assumption, the worst by the Balducci assumption. ❑

EXAMPLE 6.14

Refer to Equation (5.56) and Figure 5.3, given in Section 5.3.6. Consider the event that a person known to be alive at age x dies between ages $x+k$ and $x+k+r$, as shown in Figure 5.3.

(a) Represent this event in terms of the random variable T_x.

(b) Represent this event in terms of the random variables K_x and R_x.

(c) State the probability of this event in standard actuarial notation.

(d) Now assume that R_x has a uniform distribution on the interval $(0,1]$. Show that this implies that the random variables K_x and R_x are independent.

SOLUTION

(a) The event can be stated as $\{k < T_x \le k+r\}$ showing that failure (death) occurs between ages $x+k$ and $x+k+r$, with the precise value of $x+k+r$ included in the interval.

(b) The curtate duration at failure is $K_x = k$, and the random variable R_x assumes a value in the interval $(0,r]$, so we can write the event as $\{K_x = k \cap 0 < R_x \le r\}$.

(c) In actuarial notation, the probability of this event is ${}_k p_x \cdot {}_r q_{x+k}$, since (x) survives to age $x+k$ and then fails before (or at) age $x+k+r$.

(d) If R_x is uniform over $(0,1]$, then ${}_r q_{x+k} = r \cdot q_{x+k}$, and the probability becomes

$$ {}_k p_x \cdot r \cdot q_{x+k} \; = \; {}_{k|}q_x \cdot r. $$

But

$$ Pr(K_x = k) \; = \; {}_{k|}q_x $$

and

$$ Pr(0 < R_x \le r) \; = \; r, $$

so we have

$$ Pr(K_x = k \cap 0 < R_x \le r) \; = \; {}_{k|}q_x \cdot r \quad = Pr(K_x = k) \cdot Pr(0 < R_x \le r), $$

which shows that K_x and R_x are independent random variables under the uniform distribution assumption for R_x. ❑

EXAMPLE 6.15

Values of μ_x can be determined exactly from a parametric survival model, but can only be approximated from a life table. Assuming a Makeham distribution (see Section 5.2.4), with $A = .002$, $B = 10^{-5}$, and $c = 1.10$, find, to seven decimal places, the value of μ_{40} by each of the following methods:

(a) Exactly.

(b) Under UDD, using $\lim_{t \to 0} \mu_{40+t}$.

(c) Under UDD, using $\lim_{t \to 1} \mu_{39+t}$.

(d) Explain why the answers to parts (b) and (c) are not the same.

(e) Define ${}_2 p_{39}$ in terms of μ_{40+t}, and use the mid-point rule to approximate the integral.

(f) Summarize the quality of the three approximations.

SOLUTION

(a) Exactly we have

$$\mu_{40} = A+Bc^{40} = .002+(10^{-5})(1.10)^{40} = .0024526.$$

(b) From Equation (6.39) we have $\mu_{40+t} = \frac{q_{40}}{1-t\cdot q_{40}}$, so

$$\mu_{40} = \lim_{t\to 0} \mu_{40+t} = q_{40}.$$

To find q_{40}, we first use Equation (5.36) to find

$$\begin{aligned} S_0(40) &= exp\left[\frac{10^{-5}}{\ln 1.10}(1-1.10^{40})-(.002)(40)\right] \\ &= exp[.000104921(1-45.25925557)-.08] = .918839585 \end{aligned}$$

and

$$S_0(41) = exp[.000104921(1-49.78518113)-.082] = .916568393,$$

so

$$p_{40} = \frac{S_0(41)}{S_0(40)} = \frac{.916568393}{.918839585} = .997528196.$$

Then

$$\mu_{40} = q_{40} = 1-p_{40} = .0024718.$$

(c) We now need

$$S_0(39) = exp[.000104921(1-41.14477779)-.078] = .921076642.$$

Then

$$p_{39} = \frac{S_0(40)}{S_0(39)} = \frac{.918839585}{.921076642} = .997571259.$$

Again using Equation (6.39) we find

$$\mu_{40} = \lim_{t\to 1} \mu_{39+t} = \frac{q_{39}}{1-q_{39}} = \frac{1-.997571259}{.997571259} = .0024347.$$

(d) Under UDD, the function l_x is piecewise-linear, so its derivative is not unique at integral values of x. Since $\mu_x = \frac{-\frac{d}{dx}l_x}{l_x}$, it follows that μ_x is also not unique at integral values of x.

(e) We know from Exercise 6-17 that

$$_2p_{39} = e^{-\int_0^2 \mu_{39+t}\,dt},$$

but this can also be written as

$$_2p_{39} = p_{39} \cdot p_{40} = e^{-\int_{-1}^{1} \mu_{40+t}\,dt} = e^{-2\cdot\mu_{40}},$$

when the integral is approximated by the mid-point rule. Then we find

$$\begin{aligned}\mu_{40} &= -\frac{1}{2}\left[\ln p_{39} + \ln p_{40}\right] \\ &= -\frac{1}{2}\left[\ln(.997571259) + \ln(.997528196)\right] = .0024533.\end{aligned}$$

(f) The results are summarized in the following table:

Method	Exact Value	Approximate Value	Error
(b)	.0024526	.0024718	+0.0000192
(c)	.0024526	.0024347	−0.0000179
(e)	.0024526	.0024533	+0.0000007

❑

6.10 EXERCISES

6.1 Definition of the Life Table
6.2 The Traditional Form of the Life Table

6-1 From the life table developed in Example 6.12, calculate each of the following:

(a) $_3d_0$ (b) $_2q_1$ (c) $_3p_1$ (d) $_3q_2$

6-2 The unconditional probability of failure between ages x and $x+1$, given only alive at age 0, is denoted by $_{x|}q_0$.

(a) Define $_{x|}q_0$ in terms of $S_0(x)$ and l_x.

(b) Show that $\sum_{x=0}^{\omega-1} {}_{x|}q_0 = 1$.

6-3 A life table shows the following values of q_x:

x	0	1	2	3	4
q_x	.10	.20	.30	.40	.50

Let $Y = \min(K_0, 4)$, where K_0 is the curtate duration at failure random variable defined in Section 5.3.6. Find the variance of Y.

6-4 A survival model is defined by $S_0(x) = \frac{c-x}{c+x}$, for $0 \le x \le c$. A life table is then developed from this SDF using a radix of 100,000. In the resulting life table, $l_{35} = 44,000$.

(a) Find the value of ω in the life table.

(b) Find the probability of surviving from birth to age 60.

(c) Find the probability that a life age 10 will fail between age 30 and age 45.

6.3 Other Functions Derived from l_x

6.4 Summary of Concepts and Notation

6-5 Given that

$$\mu_x = \frac{2}{x+1} + \frac{2}{100-x},$$

for $0 \le x < 100$, find the number of failures which occur between ages 1 and 4 in a life table with a radix of 10,000.

6-6 Find each of the following derivatives:

(a) $\frac{\partial}{\partial t}\, {}_tp_x$ (b) $\frac{\partial}{\partial x}\, {}_tp_x$

6-7 A simple approximation for the derivative of l_x is $\frac{l_{x+1} - l_{x-1}}{2}$. Use this approximation to determine a value for μ_2 from the life table shown in Table 6.1a.

6-8 Given that $\mu_x = k + e^{2x}$, for $x \ge 0$, and that ${}_{.40}p_0 = .50$, find the value of k.

6-9 Given that

$$l_x = 2500(64-.80x)^{1/3},$$

for $0 \leq x \leq 80$, find each of the following:

(a) $f_0(x)$

(b) $E[T_0]$

(c) $Var(T_0)$

6-10 Given that $\overset{\circ}{e}_0 = 25$ and $l_x = \omega - x$, for $0 \leq x \leq \omega$, find the value of $Var(T_{10})$.

6-11 Given that ${}_{1|}q_{x+1} = .095$, ${}_{2|}q_{x+1} = .171$, and $q_{x+3} = .200$, find the value of $q_{x+1} + q_{x+2}$.

6-12 For the l_x function given in Exercise 6-9, find $\overset{\circ}{e}_{70}$ and the variance of future lifetime for a person age 70.

6-13 A survival model follows a uniform distribution with limiting age $\omega = 100$. It is estimated that a certain medical breakthrough will increase the value of $\overset{\circ}{e}_{30}$ by 4 years. Assuming the survival model is still uniform after the medical breakthrough, find the new limiting age of the model.

6-14 Given $\mu_x = .04$ for $0 < x \leq 40$, and $\mu_x = .05$ for $x > 40$, find the value of $\overset{\circ}{e}_{25:\overline{25|}}$.

6-15 Show that $e_x = p_x(1+e_{x+1})$.

6-16 Let e_x be the curtate expectation of life at age x according to a certain life table, and let e'_x be the same concept according to a second life table. For all x it is known that $\frac{1+e_x}{1+e'_x} = 1+k$, where k is a constant. Show that $q'_x = q_x + \frac{k}{1+e_{x+1}}$.

6-17 Use Equation (6.20) to show that ${}_tp_x = e^{-\int_0^t \mu_{x+r}\,dr}$.

6-18 If $\mu'_{x+r} = \mu_{x+r} + c$ for all r, where c is a constant, show that ${}_tp'_x = {}_tp_x \cdot e^{-ct}$.

6.5 Multi-State Model Interpretation

6-19 Use Table 6.1 (or Table 6.1a) to calculate p_x and q_x, for $x = 0, 1, 2, 3$. Then define the state vector $\boldsymbol{\pi}_4$ in terms of $\boldsymbol{\pi}_0$ and $\mathbf{P}^{(k)}$, for $k = 0, 1, 2, 3$, and show that $\boldsymbol{\pi}_4 = (.97082, .02918)$.

6-20 Consider a tabular survival model for an inanimate object (such as a light bulb) for which the probability of continued survival over each successive discrete time interval, say, p, is the same regardless of the attained age of the object, so that the survival model can be represented by a homogeneous discrete-time Markov model with $X_0 = 0$. (Assume that the object, once failed, remains failed forever.) Define each of the following mulit-state model concepts.

(a) $Pr[X_7 = 1 \mid X_6 = 0]$
(b) The homogeneous transition matrix **P**.
(c) The state vector at time n, $\boldsymbol{\pi}_n$.

6-21 For the homogeneous model of Exercise 6-20, find the expected whole number of time intervals that the object will survive.

6.6 Methods for Non-Integral Ages

6-22 Which of the following relationships are correct under the linear assumption for ℓ_{x+t}, for $0 < t < 1$?

(a) ${}_{1/2}q_x < {}_{1/2}q_{x+1/2}$
(b) ${}_tq_x = {}_{1-t}p_x \cdot {}_tq_{x+1-t}$
(c) $\mu_{x+t} > {}_tq_x$

6-23 Given the UDD assumption and the value $\mu_{45.5} = .50$, find the value of $\mathring{e}_{45:\overline{1}|}$.

6-24 Given the UDD assumption and the values $q_{70} = .040$ and $q_{71} = .044$, find the value of $\mathring{e}_{70:\overline{1.5}|}$.

6-25 Given the UDD assumption and the values $\mu_{80.5} = .0202$, $\mu_{81.5} = .0408$, and $\mu_{82.5} = .0619$, find the value of ${}_2q_{80.5}$.

6-26 Show that linear interpolation on the log of a function is the same as exponential interpolation on the function itself.

6-27 Given that $l_x = 1000(100-x)^{1/2}$, for $0 \le x \le 100$, calculate the exact value of $\mu_{36.25}$, and compare it with the value obtained from each of the linear, exponential, and hyperbolic assumptions. (Round the value of l_{37} to the nearer integer.)

6-28 Let μ^*_{x+k} denote a constant force of mortality for the age interval $(x+k, x+k+1)$. Find the value of $\mathring{e}_{x:\overline{3}|}$, the expected number of years to be lived over the next three years by a life age x, given the following data:

k	$e^{-\mu^*_{x+k}}$	$\dfrac{1-e^{-\mu^*_{x+k}}}{\mu^*_{x+k}}$
0	.9512	.9754
1	.9493	.9744
2	.9465	.9730

6-29 Find the median of future lifetime for an entity age 50, under each of the (a) uniform and (b) exponential assumptions, given the following excerpt from a life table:

x	l_x
50	80,000
74	42,693
75	40,280
76	37,480

6-30 The following excerpt from a life table shows values of l_x at non-integral ages calculated under the linear assumption. If the values of l_x at integral ages are retained, but the values at non-integral ages are recalculated under the exponential assumption, find the recalculated value of $l_{97.5}$.

x	l_x
95.0	1,000
95.5	800
96.0	600
96.5	480
97.0	---
97.5	288
98.0	---

6-31 Each individual in a population is subject to a constant force of mortality, where that constant force is itself a random variable distributed uniformly over the interval (0, 2). Find the probability that an individual drawn at random from the population will fail within one year.

6-32 Show that

$$Var(T_x \mid T_0 > x) = Var(K_x \mid T_0 > x) + \frac{1}{12},$$

under the UDD assumption.

6-33 Derive Equation (6.50).

6-34 Derive Equation (6.55).

6.7 Select Life Tables

6-35 For a select and ultimate table with a four-year select period, show that

$$\mathring{e}_{[20]} = \mathring{e}_{[20]:\overline{4}|} + {}_4p_{[20]} \cdot \mathring{e}_{24}.$$

6-36 A select and ultimate table with a three-year select period begins at selection age 0. Given the following values, find the radix $l_{[0]}$.

$$l_6 = 90{,}000$$

$$q_{[0]} = \frac{1}{6}$$

$$_5p_{[1]} = \frac{4}{5}$$

$$d_x = 5{,}000 \text{ for all } x \geq 3$$

$$_3p_{[0]+1} = \frac{9}{10} \cdot {}_3p_{[1]}$$

6-37 Given the following excerpt from a select and ultimate table with a two-year select period, and assuming UDD between integral ages, find the value of $_{.90}q_{[60]+.60}$.

x	$l_{[x]}$	$l_{[x]+1}$	l_{x+2}	$x+2$
60	80,625	79,954	78,839	62
61	79,137	78,402	77,252	63
62	77,575	76,770	75,578	64

6-38 Given the following excerpt from a select and ultimate table with a three-year select period, find the probability that a person selected on 01/01/Z, and known to be alive at exact age 61 on 01/01/Z+1, will still be alive on 01/01/Z+6.

x	$q_{[x]}$	$q_{[x]+1}$	$q_{[x]+2}$	q_{x+3}	$x+3$
60	.09	.11	.13	.15	63
61	.10	.12	.14	.16	64
62	.11	.13	.15	.17	65
63	.12	.14	.16	.18	66
64	.13	.15	.17	.19	67

6.8 Life Table Summary

6-39 Why is there a difference between the survival patterns for insureds with individual life insurance versus group life insurance? How do these survival patterns differ from the general population?

6-40 What are some possible applications of a population life table?

6-41 What are some of the potential difficulties associated with creating a unisex life table?

6-42 If a company adopts a more rigorous underwriting process for their individual life insurance, how might this affect the select and ultimate portion of their life table?

CHAPTER SEVEN

CONTINGENT PAYMENT MODELS (INSURANCE MODELS)

In this chapter we address the concept of models for a single payment arising from the occurrence of a defined random event. This description, and the mathematics that follows, is intended to be very general.

A particular random event is defined. If, and when, that event occurs, a single payment of predetermined amount is paid as a consequence of the occurrence of the event. A wide variety of examples can be cited, including the following:

(1) I will pay you \$10.00 the next time your favorite football team wins a game.

(2) The outstanding balance of a loan becomes payable if the borrower defaults on the loan.

(3) The face amount of a life insurance policy becomes payable upon the death of the person insured under the policy.

Note what is common to all three examples: a payment is made due to the occurrence of a defined random event. The payments are *contingent* on the occurrence of the associated events. Models representing such payments are collectively referred to as *contingent payment models.* In those cases where a financial loss results from the occurrence of the event, and the loss is reimbursed (in whole or in part) by another party, then we say the loss is *insured.* The party reimbursing the loss is an *insurer*, and the model describing the reimbursement arrangement is an *insurance model.*

Note that the mathematics of a contingent payment model does not depend on whether or not the loss is insured. Thus we use *contingent payment model* as the more general concept, and *insurance model* as a special case. The meaning of this will become clearer as the mathematics unfolds throughout the chapter.

7.1 DISCRETE STOCHASTIC MODELS

A common feature of the contingent payment models presented in this text is that the associated random event occurs at some *point in time* (if indeed it occurs at all). Furthermore, in many actuarial applications, the random event of interest is the *failure* of some defined *status* to continue to exist. In the examples presented at the beginning of this chapter, (1) the event of winning a game represents the "failure" of the continuation of a losing streak, (2) the event of default represents the failure of the loan to continue to be in good standing, and (3) the event of death represents the failure of the continued survival of the person insured under the policy. In this section of the chapter we develop the mathematics of contingent payment models wherein the time of failure of the status of interest is observed to occur in some finite time interval.

7.1.1 THE DISCRETE RANDOM VARIABLE FOR TIME OF FAILURE

Recall the discrete random variable defined in Section 5.3.6, denoted K_x, for the curtate duration at failure. We think of x as an *identifying characteristic* of the status of interest as of time 0. A common example of this will be that x denotes the age of the status at that time. Thus, in the life insurance example, K_x will denote the curtate duration at failure for a person (the "status") who is age x at time 0, the time at which the insurance is issued. This is further pursued in Section 7.1.4.

7.1.2 THE PRESENT VALUE RANDOM VARIABLE

Suppose a unit of money is payable at the *end* of the time interval in which failure occurs. Then if failure occurs in the interval $(k-1, k]$, a unit is paid at time k. Assuming a constant rate of compound interest throughout the model, the present value at time 0 of this payment is denoted by v^k. But the time of payment is a random variable, so the present value of payment is likewise a random variable, which we denote by Z_x.

If failure occurs in $(k-1, k]$, with payment at time k, then $K_x = k-1$. Then the present value random variable Z_x is defined as

$$Z_x = v^{K_x+1}, \tag{7.1}$$

for $K_x = 0, 1, 2, \cdots$.

The expected value (first moment) of the random variable Z_x is denoted by A_x. We have

$$A_x = E[Z_x] = \sum_{k=1}^{\infty} v^k \cdot Pr(K_x = k-1) = \sum_{k=0}^{\infty} v^{k+1} \cdot Pr(K_x = k), \tag{7.2}$$

where $Pr(K_x = k) = {}_{k|}q_x$ in actuarial notation. (This is a case of finding the expected value of a function of the discrete random variable K_x; see Equation 2.3 in Section 2.1.1.) The second moment of Z_x is denoted by ${}^2A_x$, and is given by

$${}^2A_x = E[Z_x^{\,2}] = \sum_{k=0}^{\infty} (v^{k+1})^2 \cdot Pr(K_x = k). \tag{7.3}$$

Recall from the theory of compound interest (see Section 1.1) that the discount factor v is related to the force of interest δ by $v = e^{-\delta}$. If we let $v' = v^2$, then it follows that $v' = (e^{-\delta})^2 = e^{-2\delta}$. In Equation (7.3) we can substitute $(v^{k+1})^2 = v^{2(k+1)} = (v^2)^{k+1} = (v')^{k+1}$, so that Equation (7.3) becomes

$$^2A_x = E[Z_x^2] = \sum_{k=0}^{\infty} (v')^{k+1} \cdot Pr(K_x = k). \tag{7.4}$$

This shows that ^2A_x is the same kind of function as is A_x, except that it is calculated at a force of interest that is double the force of interest used to calculate A_x. Recall also from compound interest theory that if $\delta' = 2\delta$, then $1+i' = e^{\delta'} = e^{2\delta} = (e^{\delta})^2 = (1+i)^2$, so that $i' = (1+i)^2 - 1$. Thus if interest rate i is used to calculate A_x, then ^2A_x is calculated at rate $i' = (1+i)^2 - 1 = 2i + i^2$, but not $i' = 2i$. It is important to remember that ^2A_x is calculated at double the *force of interest*, not double the *effective rate of interest*.

The variance of the present value random variable Z_x is then given by

$$Var(Z_x) = {}^2A_x - A_x^2. \tag{7.5}$$

Because K_x is discrete, then $Z_x = v^{K_x+1}$ is also discrete, so the full distribution of Z_x can be tabulated from the distribution of K_x. Having the full distribution enables us to find the median (or any other percentile) of the random variable Z_x. This is illustrated in part (c) of the following example.

EXAMPLE 7.1

A payment of $10.00 will be made at the end of the week during which a family's supply of laundry detergent runs out. The family's usage of detergent is variable, so the curtate duration at exhaustion of the supply is a random variable *K*, with the following distribution:

k	$Pr(K=k)$ [1]
0	.20
1	.30
2	.20
3	.15
4	.15

Let $Z = 10v^{K+1}$ denote the present value of payment random variable. Find (a) the mean, (b) the variance, and (c) the median of *Z*, using an interest rate of $i = .01$, effective per week.

SOLUTION

(a) By Equation (7.2) the mean of *Z* is

$$\begin{aligned} E[Z] &= \sum_{k=0}^{4} 10v^{k+1} \cdot Pr(K=k) \\ &= 10\left[\frac{.20}{1.01} + \frac{.30}{(1.01)^2} + \frac{.20}{(1.01)^3} + \frac{.15}{(1.01)^4} + \frac{.15}{(1.01)^5}\right] = 9.73094. \end{aligned}$$

[1] It is not possible for the supply to last more than five weeks.

(b) First we find $i' = (1.01)^2 - 1 = .0201$. Then from Equation (7.3) we have

$$E[Z^2] = \sum_{k=0}^{4} \left(10v^{k+1}\right)^2 \cdot Pr(K=k)$$

$$= 100\sum_{k=0}^{4} (v')^{k+1} \cdot Pr(K=k)$$

$$= 100\left[\frac{.20}{1.0201} + \frac{.30}{(1.0201)^2} + \frac{.20}{(1.0201)^3} + \frac{.15}{(1.0201)^4} + \frac{.15}{(1.0201)^5}\right] = 94.70782.$$

Then $Var(Z) = 94.70782 - (9.73094)^2 = .01663$.

(c) The five possible values of $Z = 10v^{K+1}$ follow from the five possible values of K itself. The complete distribution of Z is as follows:

k	$z = 10v^{k+1}$	$Pr(Z=z)$
4	9.51466	.15
3	9.60980	.15
2	9.70591	.20
1	9.80296	.30
0	9.90099	.20

We take the median of Z to be the smallest value m for which

$$Pr(Z \le m) = .50. \tag{7.6}$$

In this case the median is $z = 9.70591$, since $Pr(Z \le 9.70591) = .50$. (Note that the median of a discrete random variable is not always so easy to define as it is in this case. See Footnote 3 on page 17.) ❐

7.1.3 MODIFICATIONS OF THE PRESENT VALUE RANDOM VARIABLE

Equations (7.1a) and (7.1b) define the present value random variable in the case where payment is made at the end of the time interval of failure, with no restriction as to when that might be. In this section we consider three alternatives to that model.

For our first alternative, consider the case where payment is made at the end of the interval of failure *only if* failure occurs *within* the first n time intervals, i.e., only if $K_x < n$. We denote the present value random variable in this case by $Z^1_{x:\overline{n}|}$. (The reasoning behind this choice will be explained in Section 7.1.4.) From the description of the case, it follows that

$$Z^1_{x:\overline{n}|} = \begin{cases} v^{K_x+1} & \text{for } K_x < n \\ 0 & \text{for } K_x \ge n \end{cases}, \tag{7.7}$$

since there is no payment if $K_x \ge n$.

Analogous to the case of the random variable Z_x presented in Section 7.1.2, we can define the first moment of $Z^1_{x:\overline{n}|}$ to be

$$A^1_{x:\overline{n}|} = E\left[Z^1_{x:\overline{n}|}\right] = \sum_{k=0}^{n-1} v^{k+1} \cdot Pr(K_x = k), \tag{7.8}$$

and the second moment to be

$${}^2A^1_{x:\overline{n}|} = E\left[Z^1_{x:\overline{n}|}{}^2\right] = \sum_{k=0}^{n-1} (v')^{k+1} \cdot Pr(K_x = k), \tag{7.9}$$

where, again, $v' = v^2$ which means $i' = (1+i)^2 - 1$ and $\delta' = 2\delta$. Then the variance of $Z^1_{x:\overline{n}|}$ is

$$Var\left(Z^1_{x:\overline{n}|}\right) = {}^2A^1_{x:\overline{n}|} - A^1_{x:\overline{n}|}{}^2. \tag{7.10}$$

EXAMPLE 7.2

For the model of Example 7.1, find the first and second moments of the present value of payment random variable if payment is made only for failure of the detergent supply *within the first three weeks*.

SOLUTION

The first moment is

$$E[Z] = \sum_{k=0}^{2} 10v^{k+1} \cdot Pr(K=k) = 10\left[\frac{.20}{1.01} + \frac{.30}{(1.01)^2} + \frac{.20}{(1.01)^3}\right] = 6.86227.$$

The second moment is

$$\begin{aligned} E[Z^2] &= \sum_{k=0}^{2} \left(10v^{k+1}\right)^2 \cdot Pr(K=k) \\ &= 100\left[\frac{.20}{1.0201} + \frac{.30}{(1.0201)^2} + \frac{.20}{(1.0201)^3}\right] \\ &= 67.27624. \end{aligned}$$

❐

Our second alternative is the flip side of the first. Here we consider the case where payment is made at the end of the interval of failure *only if* failure occurs *after* the first n time intervals, *i.e.*, only if $K_x \geq n$. The present value random variable in this case is denoted by ${}_{n|}Z_x$, a choice to be explained in Section 7.1.4. Then we have

$${}_{n|}Z_x = \begin{cases} 0 & \text{for } K_x < n \\ v^{K_x+1} & \text{for } K_x \geq n \end{cases}, \tag{7.11}$$

since there is no payment if $K_x < n$.

The first moment of ${}_{n|}Z_x$ is given by

$$ {}_{n|}A_x = E[{}_{n|}Z_x] = \sum_{k=n}^{\infty} v^{k+1} \cdot Pr(K_x = k), \tag{7.12}$$

the second moment is given by

$$ {}^2_{n|}A_x = E[{}_{n|}Z_x^2] = \sum_{k=n}^{\infty} (v')^{k+1} \cdot Pr(K_x = k), \tag{7.13}$$

and the variance is given by

$$ Var({}_{n|}Z_x) = {}^2_{n|}A_x - {}_{n|}A_x^2. \tag{7.14}$$

Taking Equations (7.7) and (7.11) together, it is clear that

$$ Z_x = Z^1_{x:\overline{n}|} + {}_{n|}Z_x, \tag{7.15}$$

so that

$$ A_x = E[Z_x] = E\left[Z^1_{x:\overline{n}|}\right] + E[{}_{n|}Z_x] = A^1_{x:\overline{n}|} + {}_{n|}A_x. \tag{7.16}$$

This is also clear by considering Equations (7.2), (7.8), and (7.12). Similarly, by considering Equations (7.4), (7.9), and (7.13), it is clear that

$$ {}^2A_x = {}^2A^1_{x:\overline{n}|} + {}^2_{n|}A_x. \tag{7.17}$$

This may appear surprising at first, because Equation (7.15) shows us that

$$ Z_x^2 = Z^{1\,2}_{x:\overline{n}|} + {}_{n|}Z_x^2 + 2 \cdot Z^1_{x:\overline{n}|} \cdot {}_{n|}Z_x. $$

However Equations (7.7) and (7.11) show us that for any value of K_x one of $Z^1_{x:\overline{n}|}$ or ${}_{n|}Z_x$ is zero, so it follows that

$$ Z^1_{x:\overline{n}|} \cdot {}_{n|}Z_x = 0 $$

for all K_x. Thus we have

$$ Z_x^2 = Z^{1\,2}_{x:\overline{n}|} + {}_{n|}Z_x^2 $$

for all K_x, and Equation (7.17) follows.

Clearly $Z^1_{x:\overline{n}|}$ and ${}_{n|}Z_x$ are not independent, so again from Equation (7.15) we have

$$ Var(Z_x) = Var\left(Z^1_{x:\overline{n}|}\right) + Var\left({}_{n|}Z_x\right) + 2 \cdot Cov\left(Z^1_{x:\overline{n}|}, {}_{n|}Z_x\right). \tag{7.18}$$

With the three variances given by Equations (7.5), (7.10), and (7.14), respectively, we can solve for

$$Cov\left(Z^{1}_{x:\overline{n}|},\ {}_{n|}Z_x\right) = \frac{1}{2}\left({A^{1}_{x:\overline{n}|}}^2 + {}_{n|}{A_x}^2 - {A_x}^2\right). \tag{7.19a}$$

This result can be obtained in another way. Recall that

$$Cov(U,V) = E[U\cdot V]-E[U]\cdot E[V],$$

where here $U=Z^{1}_{x:\overline{n}|}$ and $V={}_{n|}Z_x$. But we know that $U\cdot V=0$ so $E[U\cdot V]=0$. Thus we have

$$Cov\left(Z^{1}_{x:\overline{n}|},\ {}_{n|}Z_x\right) = -A^{1}_{x:\overline{n}|}\cdot {}_{n|}A_x. \tag{7.19b}$$

With the help of Equation (7.16) we can easily see that the right hand sides of Equations (7.19a) and (7.19b) are equal. (The details of this are left to the reader as Exercise 7-2.)

EXAMPLE 7.3

For the model of Example 7.1, find the first and second moments of the present value of payment random variable if payment is made only for failure of the detergent supply *after the first three weeks.*

SOLUTION

The first moment is

$$E[Z] = \sum_{k=3}^{4} 10v^{k+1}\cdot Pr(K{=}k) = 10\left[\frac{.15}{(1.01)^4}+\frac{.15}{(1.01)^5}\right] = 2.86867.$$

The second moment is

$$E[Z^2] = \sum_{k=3}^{4} \left(10v^{k+1}\right)^2\cdot Pr(K{=}k) = 100\left[\frac{.15}{(1.0201)^4}+\frac{.15}{(1.0201)^5}\right] = 27.43158. \quad \square$$

(Note that the results in Examples 7.2 and 7.3 sum to the corresponding results in Example 7.1, as expected from Equations (7.16) and (7.17).)

For our third alternative, consider the case where payment is made at precise time n *if and only if* failure occurs *after* the first n time intervals, i.e., only if $K_x \geq n$. The present value random variable in this case is denoted by $Z_{x:\overline{n}|}^{\ \ \ 1}$, and we have

$$Z_{x:\overline{n}|}^{\ \ \ 1} = \begin{cases} 0 & \text{for } K_x < n \\ v^n & \text{for } K_x \geq n \end{cases}. \tag{7.20}$$

It is important to note the similarity, and the important difference, between $Z_{x:\overline{n}|}^{\;1}$ and $_{n|}Z_x$, as defined by Equation (7.11). In both cases a payment is made only if $K_x \geq n$. The distinction is that for $Z_{x:\overline{n}|}^{\;1}$ the payment is made at time n, whereas for $_{n|}Z_x$ it is made at time K_x+1, the end of the interval during which failure occurs.

The first moment of $Z_{x:\overline{n}|}^{\;1}$ is given by

$$A_{x:\overline{n}|}^{\;1} = E\left[Z_{x:\overline{n}|}^{\;1}\right] = v^n \cdot Pr(K_x \geq n), \tag{7.21}$$

the second moment is given by

$$^2A_{x:\overline{n}|}^{\;1} = E\left[Z_{x:\overline{n}|}^{\;1\;2}\right] = (v')^n \cdot Pr(K_x \geq n), \tag{7.22}$$

where, once again, $v' = v^2$ follows from $\delta' = 2\delta$, and the variance is given by

$$Var\left(Z_{x:\overline{n}|}^{\;1}\right) = {}^2A_{x:\overline{n}|}^{\;1} - A_{x:\overline{n}|}^{\;1\;2}. \tag{7.23}$$

An interesting special case is created by combining the first and third alternatives, with features similar to what we found when we combined the first and second alternatives in Equation (7.15). The combination of the first and third alternatives has its meaning primarily within the context of life insurance, so we will defer this until the next section.

EXAMPLE 7.4

For the model of Example 7.1, calculate the values of $A_{x:\overline{3}|}^{\;1}$ and $^2A_{x:\overline{3}|}^{\;1}$.

SOLUTION

From Example 7.1 we find $Pr(K \geq 3) = .30$, so we have

$$A_{x:\overline{3}|}^{\;1} = v^3 \cdot Pr(K \geq 3) = \frac{.30}{(1.01)^3} = .29117$$

and

$$^2A_{x:\overline{3}|}^{\;1} = (v')^3 \cdot Pr(K \geq 3) = \frac{.30}{(1.0201)^3} = .28261.$$ ❐

7.1.4 APPLICATION TO LIFE INSURANCE

The models, mathematics, and notation developed thus far in Section 7.1 have their origins in actuarial science, with particular reference to life insurance. In this text we prefer to develop the theory in as general a setting as possible, and then show how the theory is adapted to various applications. With life insurance as a very important one of these applications, we have chosen to use standard life insurance notation as much as possible. In this section we describe the terminology used when the general models are applied to life insurance.

Let the identifying characteristic of the status whose failure occurs in the kth time interval, denoted by x, represent the attained age of a person being issued life insurance at time 0. It is customary to presume that x is an integer. Then the time line diagram of Figure 5.2 can be replaced by the age line diagram of Figure 7.1.

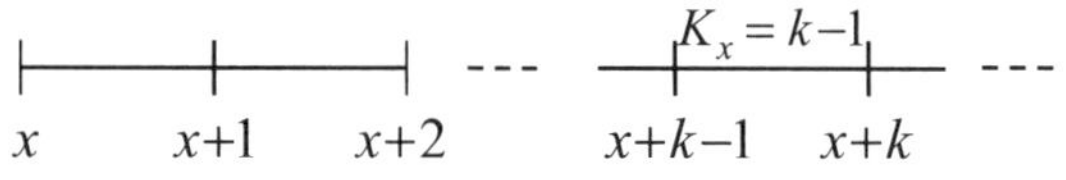

$$
\begin{array}{ccccccc}
 & & & & K_x = k-1 & & \\
x & x+1 & x+2 & \cdots & x+k-1 & x+k & \cdots
\end{array}
$$

FIGURE 7.1

The present value random variable Z_x, defined by Equation (7.1a) for $K_x = 0, 1, \cdots$, represents the present value of a unit payment made at the end of the time interval in which the insured person dies, regardless of when that may be. In the life insurance context, time will be measured in years. Thus we refer to Z_x as the present value random variable for a *whole life insurance, of unit payment, made at the end of the year of death.* Since payment will be made regardless of when death occurs, the insurance coverage is for the *whole of life*, which explains the name *whole life insurance.*[2]

The expected value of Z_x, denoted A_x, is called the *expected present value* (EPV), or the *actuarial present value* (APV), of a whole life insurance. A_x is also called the *net single premium* (NSP) for a unit whole life insurance, a term whose meaning will be more fully explained in Section 7.2.

The present value random variable $Z^1_{x:\overline{n}|}$ is the random variable for an *n-year temporary insurance*, also called an *n-year term insurance*, since the insurance coverage is limited to the first n years (from age x to age $x+n$) only. Its expected value, denoted $A^1_{x:\overline{n}|}$, is called the EPV, or APV, or NSP for a unit n-year term insurance.

The present value random variable ${}_{n|}Z_x$ is the random variable for an *n-year deferred insurance*, since the insurance coverage is deferred for n years after age x and is effective only from age $x+n$ onward. Its expected value, denoted ${}_{n|}A_x$, is called the EPV, or APV, or NSP for a unit n-year deferred insurance.

The present value random variable $Z_{x:\overline{n}|}^{\;\;1}$ is the random variable for an *n-year pure endowment*, since the benefit is paid (or *endowed*) to the insured if survival to age $x+n$ occurs. (Note that the condition $K_x \geq n$ implies failure (death) after time n, or age $x+n$, so that survival to age $x+n$ has occurred.) Its expected value, $A_{x:\overline{n}|}^{\;\;1}$, is called the EPV, or APV, or NSP for a unit n-year pure endowment. An alternative symbol for $A_{x:\overline{n}|}^{\;\;1}$ is ${}_nE_x$, which we will often use in this text.

---

[2] The benefit payment under an insurance policy is called the *face amount* of the contract. We develop much of the theory under the convenient assumption that the face amount is one unit of money.

We now consider the special case, mentioned at the end of Section 7.1.3, that results from combining the n-year term insurance model, defined by Equation (7.7), with the n-year pure endowment model, defined by Equation (7.20). Letting $Z_{x:\overline{n}|}$ denote the present value random variable for the combined model, we have

$$Z_{x:\overline{n}|} = \begin{cases} v^{K_x+1} & \text{for } K_x < n \\ v^n & \text{for } K_x \geq n \end{cases}. \tag{7.24}$$

It is clear that

$$Z_{x:\overline{n}|} = Z^1_{x:\overline{n}|} + Z_{x:\overset{1}{\overline{n}|}}, \tag{7.25}$$

with expected value given by

$$A_{x:\overline{n}|} = A^1_{x:\overline{n}|} + A_{x:\overset{1}{\overline{n}|}}, \tag{7.26}$$

and, since $Z^1_{x:\overline{n}|} \cdot Z_{x:\overset{1}{\overline{n}|}} = 0$ for all K_x, then

$$Z_{x:\overline{n}|}^2 = Z^{1\ 2}_{x:\overline{n}|} + Z_{x:\overset{1}{\overline{n}|}}^{\ 2} \tag{7.27}$$

as well, so that

$${}^2A_{x:\overline{n}|} = {}^2A^1_{x:\overline{n}|} + {}^2A_{x:\overset{1}{\overline{n}|}} \tag{7.28}$$

gives the second moment of $Z_{x:\overline{n}|}$.

In the context of life insurance this combination is called an *n-year endowment insurance*, and its expected value $A_{x:\overline{n}|}$ is the EPV, or APV, or NSP for a n-year endowment insurance. The insurance pays its unit benefit at the end of the year of death, if death occurs within the first n years, or at the end of n years if death has not occurred.

It is clear that $Z^1_{x:\overline{n}|}$ and $Z_{x:\overset{1}{\overline{n}|}}$ are not independent random variables, so we have

$$Var\left(Z_{x:\overline{n}|}\right) = Var\left(Z^1_{x:\overline{n}|}\right) + Var\left(Z_{x:\overset{1}{\overline{n}|}}\right) + 2 \cdot Cov\left(Z^1_{x:\overline{n}|}, Z_{x:\overset{1}{\overline{n}|}}\right).$$

Since $Z^1_{x:\overline{n}|} \cdot Z_{x:\overset{1}{\overline{n}|}} = 0$ for all K_x, then $E\left[Z^1_{x:\overline{n}|} \cdot Z_{x:\overset{1}{\overline{n}|}}\right] = 0$ as well, so the covariance is given by

$$Cov\left(Z^1_{x:\overline{n}|}, Z_{x:\overset{1}{\overline{n}|}}\right) = -E\left[Z^1_{x:\overline{n}|}\right] \cdot E\left[Z_{x:\overset{1}{\overline{n}|}}\right] = -A^1_{x:\overline{n}|} \cdot A_{x:\overset{1}{\overline{n}|}}. \tag{7.29}$$

Finally, we can explain the notational devices used in this section. In the symbol $Z^1_{x:\overline{n}|}$, the first subscript (x) denotes the age of the person insured as of time 0 and the second subscript ($\overline{n}|$) denotes the length of the term during which failure (death) must occur in order that payment be made. The "upper one" over the x indicates that the life (x) must fail *before* the n-year term fails. Conversely, the symbol $Z_{x:\overline{n}|}^{\ \ 1}$ is used to show that the n-year term must fail *before* the life (x) fails in order for the benefit to be paid.

The combination of $Z^{1}_{x:\overline{n}|}$ and $Z_{x:\overline{n}|}^{\ \ 1}$ into $Z_{x:\overline{n}|}$, the n-year endowment insurance, represents a situation where the benefit is paid upon the *first* failure between the life (x) and the n-year term, whichever it may be. Hence there is no required order of failure, so there is no "upper one." Such situations are called *joint status* situations, and will be further explored in Chapter 12.

EXAMPLE 7.5

For the model of Example 7.1, calculate (a) $A_{x:\overline{3}|}$, (b) ${}^2A_{x:\overline{3}|}$, and (c) $Cov\left(Z^{1}_{x:\overline{3}|}, Z_{x:\overline{3}|}^{\ \ 1}\right)$.

SOLUTION

(a) From Equation (7.26) we have

$$A_{x:\overline{3}|} = A^{1}_{x:\overline{3}|} + A_{x:\overline{3}|}^{\ \ 1} = .68623 + .29117 = .97740.$$

(b) From Equation (7.27) we have

$${}^2A_{x:\overline{3}|} = {}^2A^{1}_{x:\overline{3}|} + {}^2A_{x:\overline{3}|}^{\ \ 1} = .67276 + .28261 = .95537.$$

(c) From Equation (7.29) we have

$$Cov\left(Z^{1}_{x:\overline{3}|}, Z_{x:\overline{3}|}^{\ \ 1}\right) = -A^{1}_{x:\overline{3}|} \cdot A_{x:\overline{3}|}^{\ \ 1} = -(.68623)(.29117) = -.19980.$$ ❐

All uses of actuarial notation to this point have assumed calculation from an aggregate life table, as defined in Section 6.8. More commonly, the APVs for the discrete insurance models described in this section would be calculated from a select and ultimate life table. When this is the case, the subscript x in any of the random variable or APV symbols would appear in brackets, such as $Z_{[x]}$, $A_{[x]}$, ${}_{n|}A_{[x]}$, and so on. Note, however, that the process of determining $A_{[x]}$, for example, is the same as the process of determining A_x.

7.2 GROUP DETERMINISTIC APPROACH

In this section we will develop the same models as we did in Section 7.1, but from a different perspective that will add to our understanding of the models.

Consider the life table model described in Chapter 6. Recall that l_x denotes the number of entities (in this case, persons) in the survivorship group when all are age x. Suppose all l_x persons purchase a whole life insurance of unit benefit, with each person paying amount X to purchase the insurance. Then we have an initial fund of $X \cdot l_x$ dollars at time 0.

According to the life table model, d_x persons fail (die) in the age interval $(x, x+1]$, d_{x+1} fail in the age interval $(x+1, x+2]$, and so on, until all have failed. Since each insurance pays a unit benefit, then the sequence $d_x, d_{x+1}, d_{x+2}, \ldots$ represents the sequence of payments made under the insurances in total. This is represented in Figure 7.2.

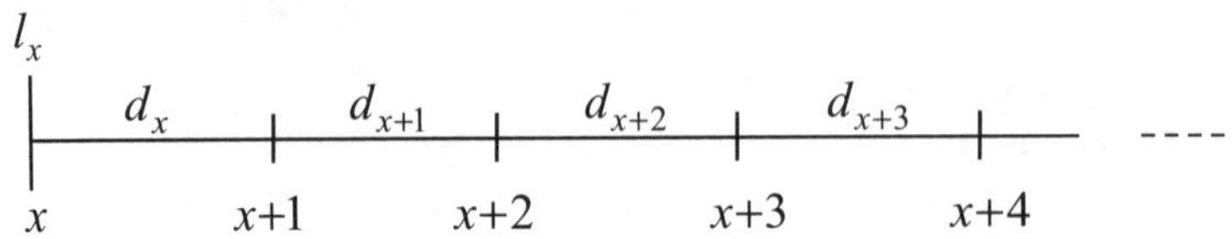

FIGURE 7.2

All payments are made at the end of the year of failure. The total present value at time 0 (age x) of all the payments is

$$v \cdot d_x + v^2 \cdot d_{x+1} + v^3 \cdot d_{x+2} + \cdots,$$

which is set equal to the initial fund. That is,

$$X \cdot l_x = v \cdot d_x + v^2 \cdot d_{x+1} + v^3 \cdot d_{x+2} + \cdots. \tag{7.30}$$

If we divide both sides of Equation (7.30) by l_x we obtain

$$X = v \cdot \frac{d_x}{l_x} + v^2 \cdot \frac{d_{x+1}}{l_x} + v^3 \cdot \frac{d_{x+2}}{l_x} + \cdots, \tag{7.31a}$$

where X represents each person's share of the total present value of all the benefit payments. Thus X can be interpreted as the price, or *premium*, each of the l_x persons should pay for the insurance coverage, and is called the *net single premium* (NSP) for the whole life insurance.

Finally we observe that the general term in Equation (7.31a), namely $\frac{d_{x+t}}{l_x}$, can be regarded as the probability that the life (x) fails in the age interval $(x+t, x+t+1]$, which, from Equation (6.18b), is denoted ${}_{t|}q_x$. Thus we have

$$X = \sum_{t=0}^{\infty} v^{t+1} \cdot {}_{t|}q_x. \tag{7.31b}$$

But ${}_{t|}q_x$, the probability that failure occurs between ages $x+t$ and $x+t+1$ is the same as the probability that failure occurs in the $(t+1)^{st}$ year, which was denoted earlier by $Pr(K_x = t)$. Thus the right hand sides of Equations (7.2) and (7.31b) are the same, so $X = A_x$.

This is a very important result. The net single premium per life in the group deterministic approach of this section is the same as the expected present value of the benefit in the stochastic approach of Section 7.1. Although either approach can be used to find A_x, the stochastic approach is the more useful one for us to consider since it also allows us to explore the second moment, variance, and percentiles of the random variable Z_x.

The group deterministic approach applies to the other models presented in Section 7.1 as well. The simplest is the pure endowment model. If l_x persons each pay X to purchase an n-year pure endowment, the initial fund at time 0 (age x) is of size $X \cdot l_x$. But this must represent the present value of the l_{x+n} dollars paid out at time n, one dollar to each of the l_{x+n} survivors. Thus we have

$$X \cdot l_x = v^n \cdot l_{x+n},$$

which becomes, upon division by l_x,

$$X = v^n \cdot \frac{l_{x+n}}{l_x} = v^n \cdot {}_n p_x, \tag{7.32}$$

where ${}_n p_x = \frac{l_{x+n}}{l_x}$ is defined by Equation (6.6). But ${}_n p_x$ is the probability of survival to age $x+n$, so ${}_n p_x = Pr(K_x \geq n)$. Therefore the right hand sides of Equations (7.21) and (7.32) are the same, so $X = A_{x:\overline{n|}}^{\;\;1} = {}_nE_x$.

The group interpretation can also be used to derive $A^1_{x:\overline{n|}}$, ${}_n|A_x$, and $A_{x:\overline{n|}}$. These derivations are completely parallel to the two cases presented here and are therefore left as exercises. Note that if the several insurance APVs are calculated from a select table, the subscript x in the APV symbol would be replaced by $[x]$.

EXAMPLE 7.6

Convert the probability distribution of Example 7.1 into a life table model, using a radix of $l_0 = 100$. Then repeat the calculation of part (a) of Example 7.1.

SOLUTION

Using standard life table notation from Chapter 6 we obtain the following result:

x	${}_{x\|}q_0$	d_x	l_x	p_x	q_x
0	.20	20	100	.800	.200
1	.30	30	80	.625	.375
2	.20	20	50	.600	.400
3	.15	15	30	.500	.500
4	.15	15	15	.000	1.000

Note that ${}_{x|}q_0 = Pr(K = x)$, the probability that the entity of interest fails in the $(x+1)^{st}$ interval. Note also that $l_5 = 0$, so $p_4 = 0$ and $q_4 = 1$.

The point of this example is to show that the net single premium found by the group deterministic approach is the same as the actuarial present value found by the stochastic (i.e., random variable) approach. Here we have

$$NSP = \frac{10}{l_0}\left[v \cdot d_0 + v^2 \cdot d_1 + \cdots + v^5 \cdot d_4\right] = \frac{10}{l_0}\left[\frac{20}{1.01} + \frac{30}{(1.01)^2} + \cdots + \frac{15}{(1.01)^5}\right] = 9.73094,$$

which agrees with the result of part (a) of Example 7.1. ❐

7.3 CONTINUOUS STOCHASTIC MODELS

Four of the five models discussed in Sections 7.1 and 7.2 have continuous counterparts, which we will develop in this section.

7.3.1 THE CONTINUOUS RANDOM VARIABLE FOR TIME TO FAILURE

Let the continuous random variable T denote the *point of time of failure* for the status of interest, so that $T = t$, for $t > 0$, denotes the event of failure at precise time t, as shown in Figure 7.3.

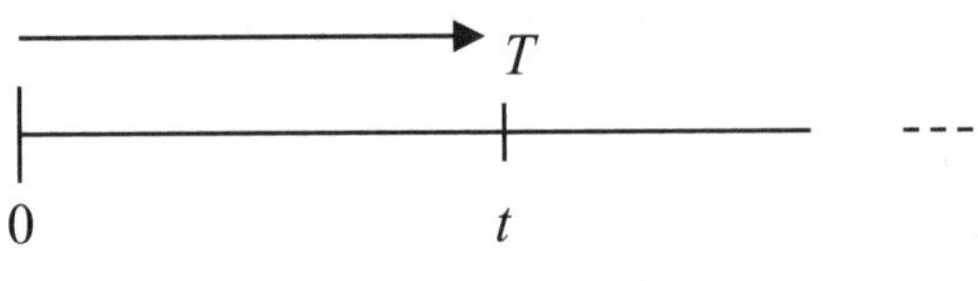

FIGURE 7.3

Let $f(t)$ denote the probability density function (PDF) of the random variable T. Since failure must eventually occur at some time, then

$$\int_0^\infty f(t)\, dt = 1. \tag{7.33}$$

We again use the subscript x to denote an identifying characteristic of the status of interest, such as the age of the status (possibly, person) at time 0. Then T_x is called the *future lifetime random variable* for the person age x at time 0, as already defined in Section 5.3.[3]

7.3.2 THE PRESENT VALUE RANDOM VARIABLE

If a unit of money is payable at time t as a result of failure at time t, then the present value random variable (in the continuous case), which we denote by $\overline{Z}_x$, is

$$\overline{Z}_x = v^{T_x}, \tag{7.34}$$

for $T_x > 0$. The expected value of $\overline{Z}_x$, denoted $\overline{A}_x$, is given by

[3] Some texts (see, for example, Bowers et al. [4]) use the notation $T(x)$ instead of T_x for this random variable.

$$\bar{A}_x = E[\bar{Z}_x] = \int_0^\infty v^t \cdot f(t)\,dt = \int_0^\infty v^t \cdot {}_tp_x\mu_{x+t}\,dt, \tag{7.35}$$

where ${}_tp_x\mu_{x+t}$ is the PDF of T_x (see Equation (6.19b)).

In a manner completely parallel to the discrete case of Section 7.1, the second moment of $\bar{Z}_x$, denoted ${}^2\bar{A}_x$, is given by

$${}^2\bar{A}_x = E[\bar{Z}_x^{\,2}] = \int_0^\infty (v')^t \cdot {}_tp_x\mu_{x+t}\,dt, \tag{7.36}$$

where, once again, $v' = v^2$ which follows from $\delta' = 2\delta$. The variance of $\bar{Z}_x$ is then

$$Var(\bar{Z}_x) = {}^2\bar{A}_x - \bar{A}_x^{\,2}. \tag{7.37}$$

EXAMPLE 7.7

A continuously-operating air conditioning unit has an exponential lifetime distribution with mean 4 years. When the unit fails it must be replaced at a cost of \$1000.00, which we consider to be one unit of money. Let $\bar{Z}$ denote the present value random variable for the unit payment made at the time point of failure. Using an effective annual interest rate of 5%, calculate each of (a) $E[\bar{Z}]$, (b) $Var(\bar{Z})$, and (c) the 90th percentile of the distribution of $\bar{Z}$.

SOLUTION

(a) The PDF of T is $f(t) = .25e^{-.25t}$. The force of interest associated with $i = .05$ is $\delta = \ln(1.05) = .04879$, so we have $v^t = (1+i)^{-t} = e^{-\delta t}$ and $(v')^t = (1+i')^{-t} = e^{-\delta' t} = e^{-2\delta t}$. Then

$$E[\bar{Z}] = \int_0^\infty e^{-\delta t} \cdot f(t)\,dt = .25\int_0^\infty e^{-(.04879+.25)t}\,dt = \frac{.25}{.04879+.25} = .83670.$$

(b) $$E[\bar{Z}^2] = \int_0^\infty e^{-2\delta t} \cdot f(t)\,dt = .25\int_0^\infty e^{-(.09758+.25)t}\,dt = \frac{.25}{.09758+.25} = .71925.$$

Then we have $Var(\bar{Z}) = .71925 - (.83670)^2 = .01918$.

(c) Let p denote the 90th percentile of $\bar{Z}$. Then we have

$$Pr(\bar{Z} \le p) = Pr\left(T \ge \frac{-\ln p}{\delta}\right) = .90.$$

Since T has an exponential distribution, then

$$Pr\left(T \ge \frac{-\ln p}{\delta}\right) = e^{-.25(-\ln p/\delta)},$$

so we have $e^{-.25(-\ln p/.04879)} = e^{5.124(\ln p)} = p^{5.124} = .90$, which solves for $p = .97965$.[4] ❐

[4] The 90th percentile of $\bar{Z} = e^{-\delta T}$ corresponds to the 10th percentile of T, denoted by t. We easily solve $1-e^{-.25t} = .10$ for $t = .42144$. Then $p = e^{-\delta t} = e^{-(.04879)(.42144)} = .97965$.

7.3.3 MODIFICATIONS OF THE PRESENT VALUE RANDOM VARIABLE

The random variables $\bar{Z}^1_{x:\overline{n}|}$ and $_{n|}\bar{Z}_x$ are defined as the continuous counterparts to $Z^1_{x:\overline{n}|}$ and $_{n|}Z_x$. Their first moments, second moments, and variances are found in a similar manner, and these are all left as exercises for the reader.

Note, however, that the pure endowment random variable $Z_{x:\overline{n}|}^{\;\;1}$ does not have a continuous counterpart, since the payment is made at time n for failure after time n, whether denoted by $K_x \geq n$ or $T_x > n$. Then the continuous version of the n-year endowment insurance model is

$$\bar{Z}_{x:\overline{n}|} = \bar{Z}^1_{x:\overline{n}|} + Z_{x:\overline{n}|}^{\;\;1}, \tag{7.38a}$$

with expected value given by

$$\bar{A}_{x:\overline{n}|} = \bar{A}^1_{x:\overline{n}|} + A_{x:\overline{n}|}^{\;\;1}. \tag{7.38b}$$

7.3.4 APPLICATIONS TO LIFE INSURANCE

Under the continuous model the benefit is paid at the precise time point of failure. In the insurance context, this is referred to as *benefit payable at the moment of death* or sometimes called *immediate payment of claims*.

Clearly the payment of insurance benefits at the precise moment of death cannot be done in practice, but neither is it true that insurance benefits are delayed until the end of the year of death. Thus neither the Z_x nor $\bar{Z}_x$ models are completely correct in practice, but both are used to approximately evaluate insurance arrangements.

A compromise between the end-of-year-of-death and moment-of-death models would be one in which the benefit is paid at the end of the mth of the year of death, such as paid at the end of the quarter of death $(m=4)$. We let $K_x^{(m)}$ denote the random variable for the curtate m^{thly} duration where failure (death) occurs, where $K_x^{(m)} = 0, 1, \cdots$. Then the event $K_x^{(m)} = k$ denotes failure in the $(k+1)^{st}$ m^{thly} time interval, and the present value of a unit paid at the end of this interval is v^{k+1}, where the interest rate upon which v^{k+1}, is based is effective over $1/m$ of a year. The random variable for the present value of payment, which we denote by $Z_x^{(m)}$, is

$$Z_x^{(m)} = v^{K_x^{(m)}+1}, \tag{7.39}$$

for $K_x^{(m)} = 0,1,\ldots,$ with expected value given by

$$A_x^{(m)} = E[Z_x^{(m)}] = \sum_{k=0}^{\infty} v^{k+1} \cdot Pr(K_x^{(m)} = k), \tag{7.40a}$$

and variance given by

$$Var(Z_x^{(m)}) = {}^2A_x^{(m)} - A_x^{(m)\,2}. \tag{7.40b}$$

The m^{thly} counterpart to the annual recursion formula given in Exercise 7-6 would be

$$A_x^{(m)} = v^{1/m} \cdot {}_{1/m}q_x + v^{1/m} \cdot {}_{1/m}p_x \cdot A_{x+1/m}^{(m)}. \tag{7.40c}$$

In order to evaluate $A_x^{(m)}$ exactly, we would need a life table with values of l_x at all m^{thly} values of x. For example, if $m=4$ then we would need values of $l_x, l_{x+.25}, l_{x+.50},$ and $l_{x+.75}$ for all integral values of x. On the other hand, if $A_x^{(m)}$ is evaluated from a life table showing values of l_x only for integral (annual) values of x, then we will have to use methods of approximation. We will pursue this in Section 7.5. The random variable $Z_x^{(m)}$ and its expected value $A_x^{(m)}$ will arise again in Chapter 8 when we discuss contingent annuities payable at m^{thly} intervals.

7.3.5 CONTINUOUS FUNCTIONS EVALUATED FROM PARAMETRIC SURVIVAL MODELS

In this section we consider the evaluation of continuous functions directly from a parametric survival model. Only the exponential and continuous uniform distributions are considered here, since they are sufficiently simple mathematically to allow for easy determination of results. We repeat the observations made in Sections 5.2.1 and 5.2.2 that these distributions are not at all appropriate as models for human survival over the full life span. In this section the contingent payment models depending on the concept of survival should be viewed as applying to entities for which the presumed survival distributions are realistic. An example of this was presented in Example 7.7.

The properties of the exponential distribution are described in Section 2.3.3 in general, and again in Section 5.2.2 in the context of its use as a survival model. Starting with Equation (5.30) which defines the exponential survival function as $S_0(x)=e^{-\lambda x}$, we then easily find

$${}_tp_x = \frac{S_0(x+t)}{S_0(x)} = e^{-\lambda t}, \tag{7.41}$$

$$\mu_{x+t} = \lambda_0(x+t) = \lambda, \tag{7.42}$$

which is a constant, and

$${}_tp_x\mu_{x+t} = \lambda \cdot e^{-\lambda t}. \tag{7.43}$$

With these building blocks we can easily find expressions for the basic continuous contingent functions defined earlier in this chapter. The continuous function $\bar{A}_x$ (see Section 7.3.2) is

$$\bar{A}_x = \int_0^\infty v^t \cdot {}_tp_x\mu_{x+t}\, dt = \lambda \int_0^\infty e^{-\delta t} \cdot e^{-\lambda t}\, dt = \frac{\lambda}{\delta+\lambda}. \tag{7.44}$$

The pure endowment function ${}_nE_x$ evaluated under an exponential distribution is

$${}_nE_x = v^n \cdot {}_np_x = e^{-n\delta} \cdot e^{-\lambda n} = e^{-(\delta+\lambda)n}. \tag{7.45}$$

Then expressions for other continuous insurance models can be obtained from the whole life function given by Equation (7.44) by using the various identities developed earlier in the chapter.

EXAMPLE 7.8

Evaluate $\bar{A}_{x:\overline{n|}}$ under the exponential distribution.

SOLUTION

Recall that

$$\begin{aligned}
\bar{A}_{x:\overline{n|}} &= \bar{A}^{\,1}_{x:\overline{n|}} + {}_nE_x \\
&= \bar{A}_x - {}_{n|}\bar{A}_x + {}_nE_x \\
&= \bar{A}_x - {}_nE_x \cdot \bar{A}_{x+n} + {}_nE_x \\
&= \bar{A}_x + {}_nE_x\left(1 - \bar{A}_{x+n}\right) \\
&= \frac{\lambda}{\delta+\lambda} + e^{-(\delta+\lambda)n}\left(1 - \frac{\lambda}{\delta+\lambda}\right) = \frac{\lambda + \delta \cdot e^{-(\delta+\lambda)n}}{\delta+\lambda},
\end{aligned}$$

under the exponential distribution. ❐

The basic properties of the continuous uniform distribution are presented in Section 2.3.1 and again in Section 5.2.1 in the context of a survival model. Starting with Equation (5.26) for the SDF as $S_0(x) = \frac{\omega - x}{\omega}$, we then find

$$ {}_tp_x = \frac{S_0(x+t)}{S_0(x)} = \frac{\omega - x - t}{\omega - x}, \tag{7.46}$$

$$ \mu_{x+t} = \lambda_0(x+t) = \frac{1}{\omega - x - t}, \tag{7.47}$$

and

$$ {}_tp_x\mu_{x+t} = \frac{1}{\omega - x}, \tag{7.48}$$

which is a constant. The basic continuous contingent payment functions then follow from these building blocks. For example, the continuous whole life insurance APV would be

$$\begin{aligned}
\bar{A}_x &= \int_0^{\omega-x} v^t \cdot {}_tp_x\mu_{x+t}\, dt \\
&= \frac{1}{\omega - x}\int_0^{\omega-x} v^t\, dt \\
&= \frac{\bar{a}_{\overline{\omega-x|}}}{\omega - x} && (7.49a) \\
&= \frac{1 - v^{\omega-x}}{\delta(\omega - x)}. && (7.49b)
\end{aligned}$$

7.4 CONTINGENT PAYMENT MODELS WITH VARYING PAYMENTS

The expected present value of payment formula, given by Equation (7.2), can be generalized to incorporate the case of non-level, or varying, contingent payment. Let the contingent benefit payment be denoted by b_k for failure in the kth time interval, with payment made at time k, where $k = 1, 2, \ldots,$ and let B_x denote, in general, a present value of payment random variable with varying payment for an entity of interest with identifying characteristic x. Then the actuarial present value is given by

$$E[B_x] = \sum_{k=0}^{\infty} b_{k+1} \cdot v^{k+1} \cdot Pr(K_x = k) \tag{7.50}$$

in the whole life case. (Note that $B_x = Z_x$ in the special case where $b_k = 1$ for all k.)

Another special case arises if $b_k = k$ for all k. In this case the APV, which we denote by $(IA)_x$, is given by

$$(IA)_x = E[B_x] = \sum_{k=0}^{\infty} (k+1) \cdot v^{k+1} \cdot Pr(K_x = k). \tag{7.51}$$

In the life insurance context, we define the APV for an n-year unit *increasing term insurance* to be

$$(IA)^1_{x:\overline{n}|} = \sum_{k=0}^{n-1} (k+1) \cdot v^{k+1} \cdot Pr(K_x = k) \tag{7.52}$$

and the APV for an n-year unit *decreasing term insurance* to be

$$(DA)^1_{x:\overline{n}|} = \sum_{k=0}^{n-1} (n-k) \cdot v^{k+1} \cdot Pr(K_x = k). \tag{7.53}$$

EXAMPLE 7.9

Calculate $(IA)_x$ and $(DA)^1_{x:\overline{3}|}$ for the probability model of Example 7.1.

SOLUTION

From Equation (7.51) we have

$$\begin{aligned}(IA)_x &= 1 \cdot v \cdot Pr(K_x = 0) + 2 \cdot v^2 \cdot Pr(K_x = 1) + \cdots + 5 \cdot v^5 \cdot Pr(K_x = 4) \\ &= \frac{(1)(.20)}{1.01} + \frac{(2)(.30)}{(1.01)^2} + \frac{(3)(.20)}{(1.01)^3} + \frac{(4)(.15)}{(1.01)^4} + \frac{(5)(.15)}{(1.01)^5} = 2.65874.\end{aligned}$$

From Equation (7.53) we have

$$\begin{aligned}(DA)^1_{x:\overline{3}|} &= 3\cdot v\cdot Pr(K_x=0)+2\cdot v^2\cdot Pr(K_x=1)+1\cdot v^3\cdot Pr(K_x=2)\\ &= \frac{(3)(.20)}{1.01}+\frac{(2)(.30)}{(1.01)^2}+\frac{(1)(.20)}{(1.01)^3} = 1.37636.\end{aligned}$$ ❒

We can also consider the continuous case (that is, the immediate payment of claims) with non-level benefit. Let the contingent benefit payment be b_t for failure at time t, and payable at precise time t, and let $\bar{B}_x$ denote the present value of payment random variable. Then the APV is given by

$$E[\bar{B}_x] = \int_0^\infty b_t\cdot v^t\cdot f(t)\,dt. \tag{7.54}$$

In particular, let $b_t = t$ for all t. Then the APV, which we denote by $(\bar{I}\bar{A})_x$ is given by

$$\begin{aligned}(\bar{I}\bar{A})_x &= \int_0^\infty t\cdot v^t\cdot f(t)\,dt\\ &= \int_0^\infty t\cdot v^t\cdot {}_tp_x\mu_{x+t}\,dt.\end{aligned} \tag{7.55}$$

Another model of interest is the piece-wise continuous model with benefit paid at the instant of failure, but with benefit amount changing only at the end of the interval. In this case we have $b_t = \lfloor t+1 \rfloor$, the greatest integer less than $t+1$. Thus the benefit is 1 for failure at time t for $0 < t \leq 1$, 2 for failure at time t for $1 < t \leq 2$, and so on. The APV in this case is given by

$$(I\bar{A})_x = \int_0^\infty \lfloor t+1 \rfloor\cdot v^t\cdot {}_tp_x\mu_{x+t}\,dt. \tag{7.56}$$

For n-year increasing term insurance we have

$$(\bar{I}\bar{A})^1_{x:\overline{n}|} = \int_0^n t\cdot v^t\cdot {}_tp_x\mu_{x+t}\,dt \tag{7.57}$$

in the fully continuous model and

$$(I\bar{A})^1_{x:\overline{n}|} = \int_0^n \lfloor t+1 \rfloor\cdot v^t\cdot {}_tp_x\mu_{x+t}\,dt \tag{7.58}$$

in the piece-wise continuous model. For n-year decreasing term insurance the formulas are

$$(\bar{D}\bar{A})^1_{x:\overline{n}|} = \int_0^n (n-t)\cdot v^t\cdot {}_tp_x\mu_{x+t}\,dt \tag{7.59}$$

in the fully continuous case and

$$(D\bar{A})^1_{x:\overline{n}|} = \int_0^n \lfloor n+1-t \rfloor\cdot v^t\cdot {}_tp_x\mu_{x+t}\,dt \tag{7.60}$$

in the piece-wise continuous case.

EXAMPLE 7.10

It is instructive to determine the change to a particular actuarial function if the value of one parameter underlying that function is changed. For example, consider the increasing whole life insurance with net single premium given by Equation (7.51). Suppose the NSP for such an insurance issued to (80) is $(IA)_{80} = 4$, based on $q_{80} = .10$ and $v = .925$. Find the value of $(IA)_{80}$ if q_{80} is changed to .20, with all other q_x values unchanged.

SOLUTION

We can write

$$(IA)_{80} = v \cdot q_{80} + v \cdot p_{80} \cdot APV_{81},$$

where APV_{81} is the actuarial present value at age 81 of all future benefits. We are given that

$$4 = (.925)(.10) + (.925)(.90) APV_{81},$$

from which we find

$$APV_{81} = \frac{4-(.925)(.10)}{(.925)(.90)} = 4.69369.$$

Since only q_{80} is changed, the value of APV_{81} is not affected. Then the revised value of $(IA)_{80}$ is

$$(IA)_{80} = (.925)(.20) + (.925)(.80)(4.69369) = 3.65833.$$ ❐

EXAMPLE 7.11

Consider a contingent payment contract whose benefit amount includes the return of the net single premium itself, with or without interest, along with a fixed benefit amount. For example, suppose a whole life insurance pays a fixed benefit of 1 plus the NSP with interest at $\delta = .08$, payable at the exact time of failure. Calculate the NSP assuming an exponential distribution for T_x with $\lambda = .04$ and interest at $\delta = .16$. (Note that the interest rate used to find the present value of benefit is not the same as the rate used to accumulate the NSP as a failure benefit.)

SOLUTION

The benefit amount is non-level, so this is a special case of the model represented by Equation (7.54). In this case we have

$$\begin{aligned} E[\bar{B}_x] = NSP &= \int_0^\infty b_t \cdot v^t \cdot {}_tp_x \mu_{x+t}\, dt \\ &= \int_0^\infty (1 + NSP \cdot e^{.08t}) \cdot e^{-.16t} \cdot e^{-.04t}(.04) dt \\ &= .04 \int_0^\infty e^{-.20t}\, dt + .04 NSP \int_0^\infty e^{-.12t}\, dt \\ &= (.04)\left(\frac{1}{.20}\right) + (.04 NSP)\left(\frac{1}{.12}\right). \end{aligned}$$

Solving for *NSP* we have $NSP\left(1-\frac{.04}{.12}\right)=\frac{.04}{.20}$, which gives us $NSP=.30$. Note that, without the return-of-premium feature, the *NSP* would be $\frac{.04}{.20}=.20$, so the return feature increases the *NSP* by 50%. ❒

7.5 CONTINUOUS AND m^{thly} FUNCTIONS APPROXIMATED FROM THE LIFE TABLE

For many contingent models, including insurance models dependent on human survival, a mathematically convenient parametric survival model that sufficiently closely represents the human survival distribution might not be known to us. Consequently, we will adopt an approach of evaluating continuous contingent model functions from the discrete life table by imposing an additional assumption on the discrete model.

Recall the discussion of the *uniform distribution of deaths* (UDD) assumption defined and illustrated in Section 6.6.1. In this section we will now show how to evaluate continuous and m^{thly} functions from the discrete life table by imposing the UDD assumption on each separate annual age interval $(x,x+1)$.

7.5.1 CONTINUOUS CONTINGENT PAYMENT MODELS

Consider first the n-year term insurance model with immediate payment of claims, with expected value given by Exercise 7-16(b), and consider the special case with $n=1$. The expected value of the present value random variable $\bar{Z}^{1}_{x:\overline{1}|}$ is denoted by $\bar{A}^{1}_{x:\overline{1}|}$, and is given by

$$\bar{A}^{1}_{x:\overline{1}|} = \int_0^1 v^t \cdot {}_tp_x\mu_{x+t}\, dt. \tag{7.61}$$

From Equation (6.38) we know that ${}_tp_x\mu_{x+t}=q_x$ under the UDD assumption over the interval $(x,x+1)$. Substituting into Equation (7.61) we have

$$\bar{A}^{1}_{x:\overline{1}|} = q_x\int_0^1 v^t\, dt, \tag{7.62}$$

since q_x is constant with respect to t. The integral evaluates to

$$-\frac{v^t}{\delta}\bigg|_0^1 = \frac{1-v}{\delta} = \frac{d}{\delta} = \frac{iv}{\delta},$$

so Equation (7.62) becomes

$$\bar{A}^{1}_{x:\overline{1}|} = \frac{i}{\delta}\cdot v\cdot q_x = \frac{i}{\delta}\cdot A^{1}_{x:\overline{1}|}, \tag{7.63}$$

since

$$v\cdot q_x = v\cdot Pr(K_x=0) = E\left[Z^{1}_{x:\overline{1}|}\right] = A^{1}_{x:\overline{1}|}$$

by Equation (7.8).

The result given by Equation (7.63) is very important, and extends to other contingent payment models. For n-year term insurance in general we have, from Exercise 7-16(b),

$$\begin{aligned}
\bar{A}^{1}_{x:\overline{n}|} &= \int_0^n v^t \cdot {}_tp_x\mu_{x+t}\,dt \\
&= \sum_{k=0}^{n-1}\int_k^{k+1} v^t \cdot {}_tp_x\mu_{x+t}\,dt \\
&= \sum_{k=0}^{n-1}\int_0^{1} v^{s+k} \cdot {}_{s+k}p_x\mu_{x+s+k}\,ds \\
&= \sum_{k=0}^{n-1} v^k \cdot {}_kp_x \int_0^{1} v^{s} \cdot {}_{s}p_{x+k}\mu_{x+k+s}\,ds \\
&= \sum_{k=0}^{n-1} v^k \cdot {}_kp_x \cdot \bar{A}^{\;1}_{x+k:\overline{1}|}.
\end{aligned} \tag{7.64a}$$

By imposing the UDD assumption on each interval $(x+k,\, x+k+1)$ separately, we have

$$\bar{A}^{\;1}_{x+k:\overline{1}|} = \frac{i}{\delta}\cdot A^{\;1}_{x+k:\overline{1}|}$$

as given by Equation (7.63). Then Equation (7.64a) becomes

$$\begin{aligned}
\bar{A}^{1}_{x:\overline{n}|} &= \frac{i}{\delta}\sum_{k=0}^{n-1} v^k \cdot {}_kp_x \cdot A^{\;1}_{x+k:\overline{1}|} \\
&= \frac{i}{\delta}\sum_{k=0}^{n-1} v^k \cdot {}_kp_x \cdot v \cdot q_{x+k} \\
&= \frac{i}{\delta}\sum_{k=0}^{n-1} v^{k+1} \cdot {}_{k|}q_x \\
&= \frac{i}{\delta}\sum_{k=0}^{n-1} v^{k+1} \cdot Pr(K_x = k) = \frac{i}{\delta}\cdot A^{1}_{x:\overline{n}|},
\end{aligned} \tag{7.64b}$$

from Equation (7.8).

Letting $n \to \infty$ in Equation (7.64b) leads immediately to a similar relationship for the continuous whole life model evaluated under UDD, namely

$$\bar{A}_x = \frac{i}{\delta}\cdot A_x. \tag{7.65}$$

Furthermore, since

$$ {}_{n|}\bar{A}_x = \bar{A}_x - \bar{A}^{1}_{x:\overline{n}|}$$

(see Exercise 7-17(c)), then we have

$$\begin{aligned} {}_{n|}\bar{A}_x &= \bar{A}_x - \bar{A}^{1}_{x:\overline{n}|} \\ &= \frac{i}{\delta}\left(A_x - A^{1}_{x:\overline{n}|}\right) \\ &= \frac{i}{\delta} \cdot {}_{n|}A_x, \end{aligned} \tag{7.66}$$

from Equation (7.16).

Finally, from Equation (7.38b) we have

$$\bar{A}_{x:\overline{n}|} = \bar{A}^{1}_{x:\overline{n}|} + A_{x:\overline{n}|}^{\;\;1} = \frac{i}{\delta} \cdot A^{1}_{x:\overline{n}|} + A_{x:\overline{n}|}^{\;\;1}. \tag{7.67}$$

(It is important to note that since there is no continuous counterpart to the discrete $A_{x:\overline{n}|}^{\;\;1}$, then it is *not* true that $\bar{A}_{x:\overline{n}|} = \frac{i}{\delta} \cdot A_{x:\overline{n}|}$.)

Finally, any of the continuous functions based on the doubled force of interest, such as ${}^2\bar{A}_x$, can be evaluated from the corresponding discrete function under the UDD assumption as

$${}^2\bar{A}_x = \frac{i'}{\delta'} \cdot {}^2A_x = \frac{(1+i)^2 - 1}{2\delta} \cdot {}^2A_x. \tag{7.68}$$

An alternative to using UDD is to simply assume that failure benefits are paid in the middle of the discrete interval used in the life table. In the annual case this suggests that we take

$$\bar{A}_x = (1+i)^{1/2} \cdot A_x, \tag{7.69}$$

since A_x assumes payment at the end of the year. This approach is referred to as *claims acceleration*. (Another approximation for $\bar{A}_x$ is given in Exercise 8-46(b).)

7.5.2 m^{thly} CONTINGENT PAYMENT MODELS

Our discussion of m^{thly} contingent functions will parallel the discussion of continuous functions in Section 7.5.1. Indeed m^{thly} functions represent a generalization of continuous functions, or, conversely, continuous functions represent a special case of m^{thly} functions, namely the limiting case as $m \to \infty$.

As we did with the continuous models of Section 7.5.1, we begin with the function $A^{1\,(m)}_{x:\overline{1}|}$ the APV for one-year term insurance with contingent benefit paid at the end of the mth of failure. We have

$$A^{1\,(m)}_{x:\overline{1}|} = \sum_{r=0}^{m-1} v^{(r+1)/m} \cdot {}_{r/m}p_x \cdot {}_{1/m}q_{x+r/m}. \tag{7.70}$$

To evaluate this function under the UDD assumption, we recall from Example 6.9 that

$$_{r/m}p_x \cdot {}_{1/m}q_{x+r/m} = \frac{1}{m} \cdot q_x.$$

Then Equation (7.70) simplifies to

$$\begin{aligned} A_{x:\overline{1}|}^{1\,(m)} &= \frac{1}{m} \cdot q_x \sum_{r=0}^{m-1} v^{(r+1)/m} \\ &= q_x \cdot a_{\overline{1}|}^{(m)} \\ &= \frac{d}{i^{(m)}} \cdot q_x \\ &= \frac{i}{i^{(m)}} \cdot v \cdot q_x = \frac{i}{i^{(m)}} \cdot A_{x:\overline{1}|}^{1}. \end{aligned} \tag{7.71}$$

Note the consistency of Equations (7.63) and (7.71), since

$$\bar{A}_{x:\overline{1}|}^{1} = \lim_{m\to\infty} A_{x:\overline{1}|}^{1\,(m)} = \lim_{m\to\infty} \frac{i}{i^{(m)}} \cdot A_{x:\overline{1}|}^{1} = \frac{i}{\delta} \cdot A_{x:\overline{1}|}^{1}.$$

Then in a manner totally parallel with the continuous cases of Section 7.5.1 we have

$$A_{x:\overline{n}|}^{1\,(m)} = \frac{i}{i^{(m)}} \cdot A_{x:\overline{n}|}^{1} \tag{7.72}$$

for n-year term insurance,

$$A_x^{(m)} = \frac{i}{i^{(m)}} \cdot A_x \tag{7.73}$$

for whole life insurance,

$$_{n|}A_x^{(m)} = \frac{i}{i^{(m)}} \cdot {}_{n|}A_x \tag{7.74}$$

for deferred insurance, and

$$A_{x:\overline{n}|}^{(m)} = \frac{i}{i^{(m)}} \cdot A_{x:\overline{n}|}^{1} + A_{x:\overline{n}|}^{\;\;1} \tag{7.75}$$

for endowment insurance, since only the term insurance component has the m^{thly} nature.

The m^{thly} claims acceleration counterpart to Equation (7.69) would be

$$A_x^{(m)} = (1+i)^{(m-1)/2m} \cdot A_x, \tag{7.76a}$$

to reflect the payment being made $\frac{m-1}{2m}$ of a year earlier than the end of the year, on average. For example, if payment is made at the end of the quarter-year of failure, then we would have

$$A_x^{(4)} = (1+i)^{3/8} \cdot A_x. \tag{7.76b}$$

7.6 MULTI-STATE MODEL REPRESENTATION

In Section 5.5 we represented the parametric survival model as a continuous-time Markov Chain, and in Section 6.5 we represented the tabular survival model as a discrete-time Markov Chain. We now return to those representations and express the discrete and continuous contingent payment models of this chapter in the multi-state model context. It is important to note that no new results are introduced here; we will only be expressing various actuarial present values in multi-state model, rather than standard actuarial, notation.

7.6.1 DISCRETE MODELS

The whole life contingent payment model makes a payment at time k if failure occurs in the kth time interval, with probability ${}_{k-1}p_x \cdot q_{x+k-1}$, for an entity alive at age x at time 0. In the context of our two-state discrete-time Markov model, we say that payment is made at time k if transition from State 0 (survival) to State 1 (failure) occurs in the kth time interval, for a person known to be in State 0 at age x at time 0. In the notation of Section 6.5, the probability of this is ${}_{k-1}p_x^{00} \cdot p_{x+k-1}^{01}$.

There is no existing standardized multi-state model notation for the APV symbol itself, in the case of a payment made upon transition from State i to State j. However, for the two-state model considered in this chapter, with benefit paid upon failure, we observe that the benefit is paid upon transition from State 0 to State 1. Borrowing from standard actuarial notation, we define

$$A_x^{01} = \sum_{k=1}^{\infty} v^k \cdot {}_{k-1}p_x^{00} \cdot p_{x+k-1}^{01}, \tag{7.77}$$

where the probability values in Equation (7.77) are understood to be appropriate for an entity age x at time 0.

The APVs for other discrete contingent payment models developed in Section 7.1, now expressed in multi-state model notation, are considered in Exercise 7-32, and those involving more than two states are considered in Chapters 12 and 14.

7.6.2 CONTINUOUS MODELS

In the continuous whole life contingent payment model, a payment is made at the precise time of failure. In the multi-state context, we would say that payment is made at the precise time of transition from State 0 to State 1, for an entity known to be in State 0 at age x at time 0.

In Section 5.5 we denoted the probability of surviving in State 0 from time 0 to time t, for a person age x at time 0, by ${}_tp_x^{00} = {}_tp_x^{\overline{00}}$, and the force of transition from State 0 to State 1 at time t by μ_{x+t}^{01}. Then the APV for a continuous whole life contingent payment model is given by

$$\bar{A}_x^{01} = \int_0^{\infty} v^t \cdot {}_tp_x^{00} \cdot \mu_{x+t}^{01}\,dt, \tag{7.78}$$

where, as before, the probability and force functions in Equation (7.78) are understood to be appropriate for an entity age x at time 0.

APVs for other continuous contingent payment models developed in Section 7.3 are pursued in Exercise 7-33, and those involving more than two states are considered in Chapters 12 and 14.

7.6.3 EXTENSION TO MODELS WITH VARYING PAYMENTS

The discrete and continuous models considered above can be generalized to those with a payment amount that depends on the interval of failure (in the discrete case) or the precise time of failure (in the continuous case). No new concepts are involved beyond those introduced in Section 7.4. Writing APVs with varying payments in terms of multi-state model notation is pursued in Exercise 7-34.

7.7 WRITTEN-ANSWER QUESTION EXAMPLES

EXAMPLE 7.12

An important application of the results developed for individual contingent payment contracts is to investigate the aggregate outcome for a group of such contracts. Here it is customary to assume independence among the individual risks and employ the normal approximation for the sum of random variables. As an example of this, consider a group of $n=100$ persons, all age x, each of whom contribute an amount k to a fund. A failure benefit of 1000 is paid to each person at the end of the year of failure. What does the amount k need to be in order that the fund will be able to make all the promised benefit payments with 95% probability, given the values $A_x=.06$ and ${}^2A_x=.01$?

SOLUTION

The initial fund is $100k$. We want the random variable for present value of all benefits to be less than $100k$ with probability .95. We let

$$Z_{Agg} = Z_1+Z_2+\cdots+Z_{100}$$

denote the aggregate present value random variable, where Z_i denotes the present value random variable for the ith individual risk, and each Z_i is Z_x. Assuming independence, we have

$$E[Z_{Agg}] = 100\cdot E[Z_x] = (100)(1000)(.06) = 6000$$

and

$$Var(Z_{Agg}) = 100 \cdot Var(Z_x) = (100)\left[(1000)^2(.01)-((1000)(.06))^2\right] = 640{,}000$$

so $SD(Z_{Agg}) = 800$. Then, assuming that Z_{Agg} is approximately normal, we have

$$Pr(Z_{Agg} < 100k) = Pr\left(Z < \frac{100k-6000}{800}\right) = .95,$$

so

$$\frac{100k-6000}{800} = 1.645,$$

which solves for $k = 73.16$. ❐

EXAMPLE 7.13

There are three parameters in the Example 7.12 model, namely the value of n, the value of k, and the value, p, of the probability of making all the promised benefit payments. These examples illustrate the important concept of *diversification of risk*. The following outcomes are intuitive; show that they are correct.

(a) For a given value of k, the value of p increases as n increases.

(b) For a given value of n, the value of p increases as k increases.

(c) For a given value of p, the value of k decreases as n increases.

SOLUTION

(a) Arbitrarily, hold $k = 73.16$ and let $n = 200$ instead of 100. Then we have

$$E\left[Z_{Agg}\right] = 200 \cdot E\left[Z_x\right] = (200)(1000)(.06) = 12{,}000$$

and

$$Var\left(Z_{Agg}\right) = 200 \cdot Var\left(Z_x\right) = (200)\left[(1000)^2(.01)-((1000)(.06))^2\right] = 1{,}280{,}000$$

so $SD\left(Z_{Agg}\right) = 1131.37085$. Then

$$Pr\left(Z_{Agg} < (200)(73.16)\right) = Pr\left(Z < \frac{14{,}632-12{,}000}{1131.37085}\right) = Pr(Z < 2.326) \approx .9900,$$

which exceeds $p = .95$, as expected.

(b) Arbitrarily, hold $n = 100$ and let $k = 80.00$. Then we have the same values of $E\left[Z_{Agg}\right]$ and $SD\left(Z_{Agg}\right)$ as in Example 7.12, and we find

$$Pr\left(Z_{Agg} < (100)(80.00)\right) = Pr\left(Z < \frac{8,000-6,000}{800}\right) = Pr(Z < 2.50) \approx .9938,$$

which exceeds $p = .95$, as expected.

(c) This time we hold $p = .95$ and let $n = 200$. Then we have

$$Pr\left(Z_{Agg} < 200k\right) = Pr\left(Z < \frac{200k-12,000}{1131.37085}\right) = .95,$$

so

$$\frac{200k-12,000}{1131.37085} = 1.645,$$

which solves for

$$k = \frac{(1.645)(1131.37085)+12,000}{200} = 69.31,$$

which is less than 73.16, as expected. ❒

EXAMPLE 7.14

In the model of Examples 7.12 and 7.13, suppose the amount collected from each person is $k = 60.00$, which is the net single premium (or expected present value) for each individual contract. Again assuming $n = 100$ persons in the group, find the probability of making all the promised benefit payments. How does this probability value change if n is increased without changing the value of k? How can we explain this result?

SOLUTION

In this case we again have $E\left[Z_{Agg}\right] = 6000$ and $SD\left(Z_{Agg}\right) = 800$. Then

$$Pr\left(Z_{Agg} < (100)(60.00)\right) = Pr\left(Z < \frac{6000-6000}{800}\right) = Pr(Z < 0) = .5000.$$

For a group of size n, we have

$$E\left[Z_{Agg}\right] = n \cdot E\left[Z_x\right] = n(1000)(.06) = 60n$$

and

$$Var(Z_{Agg}) = n \cdot Var(Z_x) = n\left[(1000)^2(.01)-((1000)(.06))^2\right] = 6{,}400n$$

so $SD(Z_{Agg}) = 80\sqrt{n}$. Then

$$Pr(Z_{Agg} < 60n) = Pr\left(Z < \frac{60n-60n}{80\sqrt{n}}\right) = Pr(Z<0) = .5000.$$

If the individual payment is set at the expected present value, then the probability of making all the promised benefit payments is fixed at 50%, regardless of the size of the group. Although this result appears counterintuitive, it reflects the characteristics of the normal approximation for the sum of random variables. In general, as n increases, the numerator of z increases linearly and the denominator increases as $\sqrt{n}$. This increases the value of z and thus increases the probability of making all the payments. However, with $k = 60.00$ we are at the midpoint of the normal distribution, so $z = 0$ regardless of the value of n. (Note further that if $k < 60.00$, then $z < 0$ and increasing n would decrease the probability of making all the payments.) ❐

7.8 EXERCISES

7.1 Discrete Stochastic Models

7-1 Derive Equation (7.19a).

7-2 Show that the right hand sides of Equations (7.19a) and (7.19b) are equal.

7-3 For the model of Example 7.1, calculate $Cov(Z^1_{x:\overline{3|}}, {}_{3|}Z_x)$.

7-4 A 2-year discrete term insurance is issued to (x) at interest rate $i = 0$. Given $q_x = .50$ and $Var(Z^1_{x:\overline{2|}}) = .1771$, calculate q_{x+1}.

7-5 A one-year endowment insurance issued to (x) pays b at the end of the year if (x) fails in $(x, x+1]$ and pays e at the end of the year if (x) survives to $x+1$. Let $Z^*_{x:\overline{1|}}$ denote the present value of benefit for this insurance. Show that $Var(Z^*_{x:\overline{1|}}) = v^2(b-e)^2 \cdot p_x \cdot q_x$.

7-6 Show that $A_x = v \cdot q_x + v \cdot p_x \cdot A_{x+1}$.

7-7 Calculate the value of $Var(Z_{51})$, given the following values:

$$A_{51} - A_{50} = .004 \qquad i = .02$$
$$^2A_{51} - {}^2A_{50} = .005 \qquad p_{50} = .98$$

7-8 Let Z_1 denote the present value random variable for a 25-year term insurance of amount 7, and let Z_2 denote the present value random variable for a 10-year term insurance of amount 4 that is deferred for 25 years. Calculate the value of $Var(Z_1+Z_2)$, given the following values:

$$E[Z_1]=2.80 \qquad Var(Z_1)=5.76$$
$$E[Z_2]=0.12 \qquad Var(Z_2)=0.10$$

7-9 Let $Z=1000Z_{x:\overline{n}|}$ denote the present value random variable for an n-year endowment insurance of amount 1000. Calculate the value of $Var(Z)$, given the following values:

$$^2A_x=.2196 \qquad A_{x:\overline{n}|}=.7896$$
$$^2A_{x+n}=.2836 \qquad {}^2A_{x:\overline{n}|}^{\;\;1}=.5649$$

7-10 A special ten-year endowment insurance pays 1000 for survival to time 10, or a benefit at the end of the year of failure, whichever occurs first. Let Z_1 denote the present value random variable for this insurance if the failure benefit is $1000\cdot{}_{10}E_x$, let Z_2 denote the present value random variable if the failure benefit is $750\cdot{}_{10}E_x$, and let Z_3 denote the present value random variable if the failure benefit is $500\cdot{}_{10}E_x$. Given also that $A_{x:\overline{10}|}=.57$ and $\frac{E[Z_1]}{E[Z_2]}=1.005$, calculate the value of $E[Z_3]$.

7.2 Group Deterministic Approach

7-11 Show that ${}_{n|}A_x = {}_nE_x\cdot A_{x+n}$.

7-12 Use the group deterministic approach to interpret each of the following expected present value functions as net single premiums.

(a) $A^1_{x:\overline{n}|}$

(b) ${}_{n|}A_x$

(c) $A_{x:\overline{n}|}$

7-13 Calculate A_{77}, given that $A_{76}=.800$, $v\cdot p_{76}=.90$, and $i=.03$.

7-14 A special n-year endowment contract, with net single premium of 600, pays 1000 for survival to time n but pays only the net single premium for failure before time n. Given that $A_{x:\overline{n}|}=.80$, find the value of ${}_nE_x$.

7.3 Continuous Stochastic Models

7-15 A benefit of 50 is paid at the precise time of failure t. The PDF of T_x, the random variable for time of failure, is given by

$$f_x(t) = \begin{cases} \frac{t}{5000} & \text{for } 0 < t \leq 100 \\ 0 & \text{otherwise} \end{cases}$$

Find the APV of the benefit using force of interest $\delta = .10$.

7-16 (a) Define random variable $\bar{Z}^1_{x:\overline{n}|}$ by reference to Equation (7.7).

(b) Give expressions for the first and second moments of $\bar{Z}^1_{x:\overline{n}|}$.

7-17 (a) Define random variable ${}_{n|}\bar{Z}_x$ by reference to Equation (7.11).

(b) Give expressions for the first and second moments of ${}_{n|}\bar{Z}_x$.

(c) Show that ${}_{n|}\bar{A}_x + \bar{A}^1_{x:\overline{n}|} = \bar{A}_x$.

7-18 The random variable ${}_{n|}\bar{Z}_x$ has a mixed distribution. If the future lifetime random variable T_x has PDF given by $(110-x)^{-1}$, describe the discrete part of the mixed distribution of ${}_{20|}\bar{Z}_{40}$.

7-19 Calculate the value of $Var(\bar{Z}_{x:\overline{n}|})$, given the following values:

$$E[\bar{Z}^1_{x:\overline{n}|}] = .23 \qquad v^n = .20 \qquad Var(\bar{Z}^1_{x:\overline{n}|}) = .08 \qquad {}_n p_x = .50$$

7-20 Find an expression for $Var(\bar{Z}_x)$ when the age-at-failure random variable X has an exponential distribution with parameter λ.

7-21 Find an expression for ${}_{n|}\bar{A}_x$ when the age-at-failure random variable X has an exponential distribution with parameter λ.

7-22 Let the age-at-failure random variable X have a uniform distribution with $\omega = 110$. Let $f_Z(z)$ denote the PDF of the random variable $\bar{Z}_{40}$. Calculate the value of $f_Z(.80)$, given also that $\delta = .05$.

7-23 Let $M_{T_x}(r)$ denote the moment generating function of the random variable T_x. Show that $\bar{A}_x = M_{T_x}(-\delta)$.

7.4 Contingent Payment Models with Varying Payments

7-24 Let $\bar{B}_x$ denote the present value random variable for a continuously increasing contingent payment contract with benefit $b_t = 1+.10t$ for failure at time t. Given also that $v^t = (1+.10t)^{-2}$ and the PDF of T_x, the random variable for time of failure, is given by $f_x(t) = .02$ for $0 \leq t \leq 50$, find the variance of $\bar{B}_x$.

7-25 (a) Show that $(IA)_x = A_x + {}_1E_x \cdot (IA)_{x+1}$.

(b) Calculate the value of $(IA)_{36}$, given the following values:

$(IA)_{35} = 3.711$ $\qquad A_{35:\overline{1}|} = .9434$ $\qquad A_{35} = .1300$ $\qquad p_{35} = .9964$

7-26 A student loan of amount 10,000 is amortized over 20 years by continuous payment at $\delta = .08$. The loan is subject to default at constant force of default $\lambda = .01$. A government agency guarantees the outstanding balance of the loan in case of default. Using force of interest .05, calculate the APV of the guarantee.

7-27 A special 10-year endowment contract, with failure benefit paid at the end of the year of failure, has an increasing failure benefit of amount $b_k = (1.06)^{k-1}$ for failure in the kth year and a unit pure endowment benefit paid for survival to time 10. The age-at-failure random variable X is uniformly distributed with $\omega = 100$, and the interest rate is $i = .06$. Let $Z^*_{30:\overline{10}|}$ denote the present value random variable for this contingent contract, issued to a person age 30. Find each of the following.

(a) $Pr[Z^*_{30:\overline{10}|} = (1.06)^{-1}]$

(b) $E[Z^*_{30:\overline{10}|}]$

(c) $Var(Z^*_{30:\overline{10}|})$

7.5 Continuous and m^{thly} Functions Approximated from the Life Table

7-28 Assuming failures are uniformly distributed over each interval $(x, x+1)$, calculate the value of A_{35} given the following values:

$i = .05$ $\qquad q_{35} = .01$ $\qquad \bar{A}_{36} = .185$

7-29 Assuming failures are uniformly distributed over each interval $(x, x+1)$, calculate the value of $\bar{A}^1_{x:\overline{2}|}$ given the following values:

$$i = .10 \qquad q_x = .05 \qquad q_{x+1} = .08$$

7-30 Assuming failures are uniformly distributed over each interval $(x, x+1)$, calculate the value of ${}^2\bar{A}^1_{x:\overline{2}|}$ given the following values:

$$i = .12 \qquad q_x = .10 \qquad q_{x+1} = .20$$

7-31 Assuming failures are uniformly distributed over each interval $(x, x+1)$, show that

$$\frac{(I\bar{A})_x - (\bar{I}\bar{A})_x}{\bar{A}_x} = \frac{1}{d} - \frac{1}{\delta}.$$

7.6 Multi-State Model Representation

7-32 Using the multi-state model notation defined earlier, give APV formulas for each of the following discrete contingent payment models, for a person age x at time 0.

(a) n-year pure endowment

(b) n-year term insurance

(c) n-year deferred insurance

7-33 Using the multi-state model notation defined earlier, give APV formulas for each of the following continuous contingent payment models, for a person age x at time 0.

(a) n-year term insurance

(b) n-year deferred insurance

7-34 Using the multi-state model notation defined earlier, give APV formulas for each of the following contingent payment models with varying payments, for a person age x at time 0.

(a) The increasing insurance whose APV is given by $(IA)_x$ in actuarial notation

(b) The increasing insurance whose APV is given by $(IA)^1_{x:\overline{n}|}$ in actuarial notation

(c) The increasing insurance whose APV is given by $(\bar{I}\bar{A})_x$ in actuarial notation

(d) The decreasing insurance whose APV is given by $(\bar{D}\bar{A})^1_{x:\overline{n}|}$ in actuarial notation

CHAPTER EIGHT

CONTINGENT ANNUITY MODELS (LIFE ANNUITIES)

In this chapter we consider annuity models under which the making of each scheduled payment is *contingent* upon some random event. The reader will note a degree of similarity in notation and terminology with our discussion of interest-only annuities in Chapter 1. In fact, interest-only annuities can be viewed as special cases of contingent annuities where the scheduled payments are made with probability 1. In other words, the making of the payments is not contingent on any probabilistic event.

Generally the random event upon which each payment is contingent is the continued *survival* of a defined entity of interest, such as the continued survival of an identified person. (In this case, contingent annuities are called *life annuities*.) Other examples of contingent annuities could be a sequence of costs incurred (due to lost revenue) as long as a labor strike continues, or a sequence of coupon payments made as long as a particular corporate bond remains in good standing.

Contingent annuities are closely related to the contingent payment models of Chapter 7. In the prior chapter, a *single payment* is made at the time of the *failure* of the entity of interest; in this chapter, a *sequence of payments* is made during the *continued survival* of the entity of interest, up until the failure occurs.

There are many contingent annuity models we wish to present in this chapter, and the reader will need to go over this material several times in order to grasp all the different cases. To help with this sorting task, we will start with an overview of the contents of the chapter.

First, we can separate all contingent annuity models in two groups according to whether the payments in the sequence are level or non-level. Most of our attention will be given to the level payment case, presented in Sections 8.1 - 8.4. Our somewhat abbreviated presentation of the non-level case will all be contained in Section 8.5.

Level payment contingent annuities will be discussed in both discrete and continuous contexts. In the discrete case, we further distinguish between annuities with annual payments and those with payments scheduled more frequently than annual, say m times per year, such as annuities with scheduled (albeit contingent) monthly payments $(m=12)$.

Furthermore, discrete payment annuities, whether annual or m^{thly}, can be of either the immediate type (payments made at ends of payment periods) or the due type (payments made at beginnings of payment periods), as described in Section 1.2.

Within all three categories of discrete annual, discrete m^{thly}, and continuous we will define three different contingent annuity models, namely the whole life, temporary, and deferred whole life models. (The significance of these model names will become clearer as the discussion unfolds.) Furthermore, we will present several different approaches to defining and analyzing these models.

The whole life model, in the annual immediate, annual due, and continuous cases, is presented in Section 8.1, the temporary model, in the same three cases, is presented in Section 8.2, and the deferred whole life model, again in the same three cases, is presented in Section 8.3. The nine models from these three sections are summarized in Section 8.4. The m^{thly} case, both immediate and due, is presented in Section 8.5.

8.1 WHOLE LIFE ANNUITY MODELS

In nearly all cases, discrete contingent annuity models are evaluated from a discrete survival model (life table), such as that presented in Chapter 6 of this text. Here we assume that time is measured in years in the life table, so a contingent annuity with annual payments can be directly evaluated from the table. In this section we will present the whole life model, in each of the immediate, due, and continuous cases, and will analyze the model from several perspectives.

8.1.1 THE IMMEDIATE CASE

We begin by recalling the n-year pure endowment model with present value random variable $Z_{x:\overline{n}|}^{\;\;1}$ defined by Equation (7.20), and expected present value (or actuarial present value) denoted by $A_{x:\overline{n}|}^{\;\;1}$ or ${}_nE_x$. Suppose we have a status with identifying characteristic (x) as of time 0, such as a person alive at time 0 at age x, and a sequence of unit payments scheduled to be made at the end of each year *as long as the status continues to survive.* Such a model is called a *whole life* contingent annuity-immediate model, since the payment sequence will continue for the *whole of life* of the status of interest. It is easy to see that this arrangement is merely a series of t-year pure endowments for $t=1,2,\ldots$. If we let Y_x denote the present value random variable for this model, then we have

$$Y_x = \sum_{t=1}^{\infty} Z_{x:\overline{t}|}^{\;\;1}. \tag{8.1}$$

The expected value of the present value random variable Y_x is denoted a_x, so we have

$$a_x = E[Y_x] = \sum_{t=1}^{\infty} E\left[Z_{x:\overline{t}|}^{\;\;1}\right] = \sum_{t=1}^{\infty} A_{x:\overline{t}|}^{\;\;1} = \sum_{t=1}^{\infty} {}_tE_x, \tag{8.2a}$$

by using results and notation developed in Chapter 7. Furthermore, since $Pr(K_x \geq t) = {}_tp_x$, then from Equation (7.21) we have $A_{x:\overline{t}|}^{\;\;1} = v^t \cdot {}_tp_x$ so that Equation (8.2a) can also be written as

$$a_x = \sum_{t=1}^{\infty} v^t \cdot {}_tp_x. \tag{8.2b}$$

As in the case of single contingent payment models in Chapter 7, we refer to the expected value of the contingent annuity present value random variable as, interchangeably, the expected present value (EPV), or the actuarial present value (APV), or the net single premium (NSP).

This model has a group deterministic interpretation, similar to that presented for the whole life insurance in Section 7.2. Suppose l_x persons each purchase a whole life annuity with unit payments at the end of each year, with each person paying amount X to purchase the annuity. Then we have an initial fund of $X \cdot l_x$ dollars at time 0. According to the life table model, l_{x+1} persons survive to the end of the first year, l_{x+2} survive to the end of the second year, and so on, until there are no more survivors. Then the sequence $l_{x+1}, l_{x+2}, \ldots$ represents the sequence of payments made under the annuities in total. This is illustrated in the following figure.

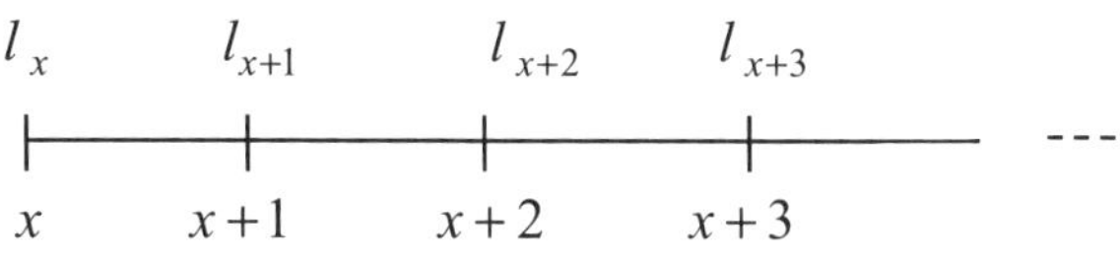

FIGURE 8.1

The total present value at time 0 (age x) of all annuity payments made is

$$v \cdot l_{x+1} + v^2 \cdot l_{x+2} + v^3 \cdot l_{x+3} + \cdots,$$

which is set equal to the initial fund. That is,

$$X \cdot l_x = v \cdot l_{x+1} + v^2 \cdot l_{x+2} + v^3 \cdot l_{x+3} + \cdots. \tag{8.3}$$

If we divide both sides of Equation (8.3) by l_x we obtain

$$X = v \cdot \frac{l_{x+1}}{l_x} + v^2 \cdot \frac{l_{x+2}}{l_x} + v^3 \cdot \frac{l_{x+3}}{l_x} + \cdots, \tag{8.4a}$$

where X represents each person's share of the total present value of all annuity payments made. Thus X is the *net single premium* that each of the l_x persons should pay to purchase the annuity. But the general term in Equation (8.4a), namely $\frac{l_{x+t}}{l_x}$, is simply ${}_tp_x$, the probability of survival to time t. Thus we have

$$X = \sum_{t=1}^{\infty} v^t \cdot {}_tp_x, \tag{8.4b}$$

already identified as the EPV of the annuity by Equation (8.2b). Thus we have established that the expected value of the present value random variable (EPV) and the net single premium (NSP) are the same.

EXAMPLE 8.1

Using the annual interest rate $i = .05$ and the life table values $l_{95}=100$, $l_{96}=70$, $l_{97}=40$, $l_{98}=20$, $l_{99}=4$, and $l_{100}=0$, determine the value of a_{95}.

SOLUTION

Using either the EPV approach of Equation (8.2b) or the NSP approach of Equation (8.4a) we have

$$\begin{aligned} a_{95} &= \left(\frac{1}{1.05}\right)\left(\frac{70}{100}\right)+\left(\frac{1}{1.05}\right)^2\left(\frac{40}{100}\right)+\left(\frac{1}{1.05}\right)^3\left(\frac{20}{100}\right)+\left(\frac{1}{1.05}\right)^4\left(\frac{4}{100}\right) \\ &= .6667+.3628+.1728+.0329 = 1.2352. \end{aligned}$$

❐

There is another, very important, random variable approach to understanding the whole life contingent annuity. If the status of interest fails in the kth time interval, denoted by the event $K_x = k-1$, then exactly $k-1$ annuity payments are made, since no payment would be made at time k (age $x+k$). This is represented in the following diagram.

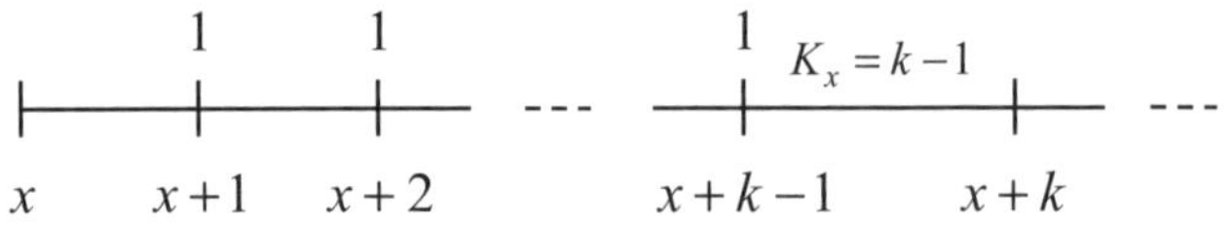

$$\begin{array}{ccccccc} & 1 & 1 & \cdots & 1 \quad K_x=k-1 & & \cdots \\ x & x+1 & x+2 & & x+k-1 & x+k & \end{array}$$

FIGURE 8.2

Thus if $K_x = k-1$, the present value of the annuity is $a_{\overline{k-1}|}$, so, in general, the present value is a random variable denoted by $Y_x = a_{\overline{K_x}|}$. The expected value of this present value random variable is then

$$E[Y_x] = E\left[a_{\overline{K_x}|}\right] = \sum_{k=0}^{\infty} a_{\overline{k}|} \cdot Pr(K_x = k) = \sum_{k=0}^{\infty} \frac{1-v^k}{i} \cdot {}_{k|}q_x, \tag{8.5a}$$

using Equation (1.13) for $a_{\overline{k}|}$ and the actuarial notation ${}_{k|}q_x$ to represent $Pr(K_x = k)$. Then by using ${}_{k|}q_x = {}_kp_x - {}_{k+1}p_x$ (see Example 6.5), we have

$$\begin{aligned} E[Y_x] &= \frac{1}{i}\sum_{k=0}^{\infty}\left[{}_{k|}q_x - v^k({}_kp_x - {}_{k+1}p_x)\right] \\ &= \frac{1}{i}\left[\sum_{k=0}^{\infty} {}_{k|}q_x - \sum_{k=0}^{\infty} v^k \cdot {}_kp_x + (1+i)\sum_{k=0}^{\infty} v^{k+1} \cdot {}_{k+1}p_x\right]. \end{aligned}$$

(Note that we want the third summand to involve v^{k+1}, so we must factor $1+i = v^{-1}$ outside the summation.) The first summation clearly evaluates to 1 (since (x) must fail sometime), the second summation evaluates to $1+a_x$ (from Equation (8.2b) and the fact that ${}_0p_x=1$), and the third summation evaluates to $(1+i)a_x$, again from Equation (8.2b). Thus we have

$$E[Y_x] = \tfrac{1}{i}\left[1-(1+a_x)+(1+i)a_x\right] = a_x, \tag{8.5b}$$

as already established by Equation (8.2a).

This random variable approach to the whole life contingent annuity is particularly useful in finding higher moments of the present value random variable Y_x. First we note that

$$Y_x = a_{\overline{K_x}|} = \tfrac{1}{i}\left[1-v^{K_x}\right] = \tfrac{1}{i}\left[1-(1+i)\cdot v^{K_x+1}\right] = \tfrac{1}{i}\left[1-(1+i)\cdot Z_x\right], \tag{8.6}$$

where $Z_x=v^{K_x+1}$ is defined by Equation (7.1a). We can now use this relationship between the random variables Y_x and Z_x to find the variance of Y_x. We have

$$Var(Y_x) = Var\left[\frac{1-(1+i)\cdot Z_x}{i}\right] = \frac{(1+i)^2\cdot Var(Z_x)}{i^2} = \frac{Var(Z_x)}{d^2}, \tag{8.7a}$$

since $d=\frac{i}{1+i}$. Then using Equation (7.5) for $Var(Z_x)$ we have

$$Var(Y_x) = \frac{{}^2A_x - A_x^{\,2}}{d^2}, \tag{8.7b}$$

where A_x and ${}^2A_x$ are defined in Section 7.1.2.

The relationship between Y_x and Z_x can also be used to develop other relationships between insurance and annuity functions, as shown in the following example and also in the exercises.

EXAMPLE 8.2

Show that $A_x = v-d\cdot a_x$.

SOLUTION

Taking the expectation in Equation (8.6) we obtain

$$a_x = E[Y_x] = E\left[\frac{1-(1+i)\cdot Z_x}{i}\right] = \frac{1-(1+i)\cdot A_x}{i} = \frac{v-A_x}{d}.$$

Rearrangement yields the requested identity. ❐

EXAMPLE 8.3

Using the values given in Example 8.1, find $Var(Y_{95})$.

SOLUTION

Recall that $\delta' = 2\delta$ implies $i' = (1+i)^2 - 1$, so with $i = .05$ we have $i' = (1.05)^2 - 1 = .1025$. Furthermore, $v' = (1+i')^{-1} = (1.05)^{-2} = .90702$ and $d' = i'v' = .09297$. Calculating the annuity APV at rate i' we find

$$\begin{aligned} {}^2a_{95} &= \left(\frac{1}{1.1025}\right)\left(\frac{70}{100}\right)+\left(\frac{1}{1.1025}\right)^2\left(\frac{40}{100}\right)+\left(\frac{1}{1.1025}\right)^3\left(\frac{20}{100}\right)+\left(\frac{1}{1.1025}\right)^4\left(\frac{4}{100}\right) \\ &= .6349+.3291+.1492+.0271 = 1.1403. \end{aligned}$$

(The symbol ${}^2a_x$ denotes the APV calculated at double the force of interest, so that ${}^2a_x$ is related to a_x in the same manner as ${}^2A_x$ is related to A_x. Note, however, that ${}^2A_x$ is also the second moment of Z_x, but ${}^2a_x$ is *not* the second moment of Y_x. We did not need $E[Y_x^2]$, the second moment of Y_x, in order to find $Var(Y_x)$. However, for additional insight, we will develop $E[Y_x^2]$ in Example 8.19.)

Using the identity derived in Example 8.2 and the value of a_{95} from Example 8.1, we find

$$A_{95} = (1.05)^{-1} - \left(\frac{.05}{1.05}\right)(1.2352) = .8936$$

and using the values developed above we find

$${}^2A_{95} = (1.1025)^{-1} - \left(\frac{.1025}{1.1025}\right)(1.1403) = .8010.$$

Finally we find

$$Var(Y_{95}) = \frac{{}^2A_{95} - A_{95}^2}{d^2} = \frac{.8010-(.8936)^2}{\left(\frac{.05}{1.05}\right)^2} = 1.0933. \qquad \square$$

8.1.2 THE DUE CASE

In this section we will essentially repeat the presentation given in Section 8.1.1, but this time with contingent payments made at the *beginning* of each year instead of the end of each year. Recall from Chapter 1 that such annuities are called *annuities-due*. Because the mathematics is totally parallel to that used in Section 8.1.1, we can present it here in a more streamlined fashion.

In the annuity-due case, the whole life contingent annuity model is the same as in the annuity-immediate case, except that payments are scheduled at the beginning of each year instead of the end. Since the status (x) is known to exist at time 0, then the payment scheduled at time 0 (age x) is certain to be made. Thus we have the same series of contingent payments as in the immediate case, plus the certain payment of 1 at time 0. If we let $\ddot{Y}_x$ denote the present value random variable in the annuity-due case, then we have

$$\ddot{Y}_x = 1+Y_x = 1+\sum_{t=1}^{\infty} Z_{x:\overline{t|}}^{\;\;1}. \tag{8.8}$$

Then the expected value of $\ddot{Y}_x$, denoted $\ddot{a}_x$, is easily found as

$$\begin{aligned} \ddot{a}_x &= E[\ddot{Y}_x] = 1+E[Y_x] \\ &= 1+\sum_{t=1}^{\infty} {}_tE_x \\ &= \sum_{t=0}^{\infty} {}_tE_x \\ &= \sum_{t=0}^{\infty} v^t \cdot {}_tp_x, \end{aligned} \tag{8.9}$$

where we note that ${}_0E_x = v^0 \cdot {}_0p_x = 1$. Furthermore, since $E[Y_x] = a_x$ we have the important relationship

$$\ddot{a}_x = a_x + 1. \tag{8.10}$$

Again we note that $\ddot{a}_x = E[\ddot{Y}_x]$ is called the EPV or APV or NSP for the whole life contingent annuity-due.

The group deterministic interpretation is parallel to that in the immediate case, except that there will be a payment of l_x dollars at time 0 (age x) itself. Thus we would modify Equation (8.3) to read

$$X \cdot l_x = l_x + v \cdot l_{x+1} + v^2 \cdot l_{x+2} + \cdots \tag{8.11}$$

and Equation (8.4a) to read

$$X = \frac{l_x}{l_x} + v \cdot \frac{l_{x+1}}{l_x} + v^2 \cdot \frac{l_{x+2}}{l_x} + \cdots. \tag{8.12a}$$

Substituting ${}_tp_x$ for $\frac{l_{x+t}}{l_x}$, for $t = 1,2,\ldots$, and $v^0 \cdot {}_0p_x = 1$ for $\frac{l_x}{l_x}$, we reach

$$X = \sum_{t=0}^{\infty} v^t \cdot {}_tp_x, \tag{8.12b}$$

showing again that the NSP and the EPV are the same.

With respect to the random variable approach in the case of the annuity-due, we note that if failure occurs in the kth time interval, as indicated by the event $K_x = k-1$, then exactly k annuity payments are made since a payment is made at the beginning of the kth year itself (at age $x+k-1$). This is illustrated in the following diagram.

1	1	1		1 ($K_x = k-1$)	
x	$x+1$	$x+2$	---	$x+k-1$	$x+k$ ---

FIGURE 8.3

Then, in general, the present value is a random variable denoted by

$$\ddot{Y}_x = \ddot{a}_{\overline{K_x+1|}} = \frac{1-v^{K_x+1}}{d}, \tag{8.13}$$

with expected value given by

$$E[\ddot{Y}_x] = E\left[\ddot{a}_{\overline{K_x+1|}}\right] = \sum_{k=1}^{\infty} \ddot{a}_{\overline{k|}} \cdot Pr(K_x = k-1). \tag{8.14}$$

In steps parallel to those taken in Section 8.1.1 to show that the right side of Equation (8.5a) reduced to a_x, we can similarly show that the right side of Equation (8.14) reduces to $\ddot{a}_x$. The details are left to the reader as Exercise 8-9.

Since $\ddot{Y}_x = 1+Y_x$, it follows immediately that

$$Var(\ddot{Y}_x) = Var(Y_x) = \frac{Var(Z_x)}{d^2} = \frac{{}^2A_x - A_x^2}{d^2}, \tag{8.15}$$

as established by Equation (8.7b).

EXAMPLE 8.4

Use Equation (8.13) to derive the useful relationship $A_x = 1 - d \cdot \ddot{a}_x$.

SOLUTION

Equation (8.13) can be rearranged as

$$v^{K_x+1} = Z_x = 1 - d \cdot \ddot{Y}_x.$$

Taking the expectation yields the desired relationship. ❐

8.1.3 THE CONTINUOUS CASE

In this section we return to the abstract notion of continuous payment, introduced in Section 1.2.3 in the case of interest-only annuities. Although continuous payment annuities cannot exist in practice, there is some theoretical value in studying them. Furthermore, continuous annuities might be considered good approximations to annuities payable very frequently, such as weekly or even monthly.

For the continuous case, we return to the future lifetime random variable T_x, defined in Section 7.3.1, in place of the discrete duration at failure random variable K_x used thus far in this chapter. If failure occurs at precise time t, which is measured in years and denoted by the event $T_x = t$, for the status of interest with identifying characteristic (x) at time 0, then continuous annuity payment (at an annual rate of 1 unit of money) will be made for exactly t years. The present value of this continuous annuity is $\bar{a}_{\overline{t|}}$, so, in general, the present value is a random variable which we denote by

$$\bar{Y}_x = \bar{a}_{\overline{T_x|}} = \frac{1-v^{T_x}}{\delta}. \tag{8.16}$$

The expected value of this present value random variable, denoted $\bar{a}_x$, is given by

$$\bar{a}_x = E[\bar{Y}_x] = E\left[\bar{a}_{\overline{T_x|}}\right] = \int_0^\infty \bar{a}_{\overline{t|}} \cdot f_x(t)\, dt, \tag{8.17a}$$

where $f_x(t)$ is the probability density function of the random variable T_x. Recall from Section 5.3 that this PDF is given by $f_x(t) = {}_tp_x \cdot \mu_{x+t}$. (See Equation 5.46.) Then we can write Equation (8.17a) as

$$\bar{a}_x = \int_0^\infty \bar{a}_{\overline{t|}} \cdot {}_tp_x \mu_{x+t}\, dt. \tag{8.17b}$$

We evaluate the integral using integration by parts to obtain

$$\int_0^\infty \frac{\bar{a}_{\overline{t|}} \;\Big|\; {}_tp_x\mu_{x+t}\,dt}{v^t\,dt \;\Big|\; -{}_tp_x} = -\bar{a}_{\overline{t|}} \cdot {}_tp_x \Big|_0^\infty + \int_0^\infty v^t \cdot {}_tp_x\, dt = \int_0^\infty v^t \cdot {}_tp_x\, dt,$$

since $\bar{a}_{\overline{t|}} \cdot {}_tp_x \Big|_0^\infty$ is 0 at both the upper and lower limits. Thus we have

$$\bar{a}_x = \int_0^\infty v^t \cdot {}_tp_x\, dt, \tag{8.17c}$$

a convenient form for evaluating $\bar{a}_x$ from some parametric survival models with known conditional survival function ${}_tp_x = \frac{S_0(x+t)}{S_0(x)}$. This is illustrated in the following example.

EXAMPLE 8.5

Evaluate $\bar{a}_x$ from an exponential survival model.

SOLUTION

We know that ${}_tp_x = e^{-\mu t}$ under an exponential survival model. Furthermore we know that $v^t = e^{-\delta t}$, so we have

$$\bar{a}_x = \int_0^\infty e^{-\delta t} \cdot e^{-\mu t}\, dt = \frac{e^{-(\mu+\delta)t}}{-(\mu+\delta)}\bigg|_0^\infty = \frac{1}{\mu+\delta}.$$ ❐

In most practical cases we will not have a convenient parametric survival model from which to evaluate $\bar{a}_x$. Instead it will be evaluated approximately from a discrete survival model in life table form. We will explore this in Section 8.4.4 and the exercises.

Returning to the random variable $\bar{Y}_x$, we observe that it is closely related to the random variable $\bar{Z}_x = v^{T_x}$ defined by Equation (7.34). We have

$$\bar{Y}_x = \bar{a}_{\overline{T_x|}} = \frac{1-v^{T_x}}{\delta} = \frac{1-\bar{Z}_x}{\delta}, \tag{8.18a}$$

which we can also write as

$$\bar{Z}_x + \delta \cdot \bar{Y}_x = 1. \tag{8.18b}$$

Equation (8.18a) enables us to easily find the variance of $\bar{Y}_x$ as

$$Var(\bar{Y}_x) = Var\left(\frac{1-\bar{Z}_x}{\delta}\right) = \frac{Var(\bar{Z}_x)}{\delta^2} = \frac{{}^2\bar{A}_x - \bar{A}_x^{\,2}}{\delta^2} \tag{8.19}$$

from Equation (7.37).

The relationship between $\bar{Y}_x$ and $\bar{Z}_x$ can be used to develop other relationships between continuous insurance and annuity functions, which will be pursued in the exercises.

EXAMPLE 8.6

It is useful to determine the probability that a present value random variable will exceed its own expected value. Consider the present value random variable $\bar{Y}_x = \bar{a}_{\overline{T_x|}}$, where T_x has an exponential distribution with parameter $\lambda = .06$ and interest is $\delta = .04$. Find

$$Pr(\bar{Y}_x > E[\bar{Y}_x]).$$

SOLUTION

We know that $E[\bar{Y}_x] = \bar{a}_x = \frac{1}{\lambda+\delta} = 10$ in this case. Then

$$\begin{aligned} Pr(\bar{Y}_x > 10) &= Pr\left(\frac{1-v^{T_x}}{.04} > 10\right) \\ &= Pr(1-v^{T_x} > .40) \\ &= Pr(v^{T_x} < .60) \\ &= Pr(T_x \cdot \ln v < \ln .60) \\ &= Pr(T_x \cdot -\delta < -.51083) = Pr(T_x > 12.77075). \end{aligned}$$

Since T_x is exponential, then

$$Pr(T_x > 12.77075) = e^{-12.77075(.06)} = .46475.$$ ❐

8.2 TEMPORARY LIFE ANNUITY MODELS

As the name implies, temporary life annuities are payable as long as the status of interest continues to survive, but not beyond a predetermined temporary period of n years.

8.2.1 THE IMMEDIATE CASE

The *immediate n-year temporary life annuity*, payable to a status with identifying characteristic (x) at time 0, will make a payment at the end of each year for n years at the most, provided the status continues to survive. If we let $Y_{x:\overline{n|}}$ denote the present value random variable for this model, then in terms of a series of t-year pure endowments we have

$$Y_{x:\overline{n|}} = \sum_{t=1}^{n} Z_{x:\overline{t|}}^{\;\;1}. \tag{8.20}$$

The expected value of this present value random variable (EPV) is denoted $a_{x:\overline{n|}}$, and is given by

$$\begin{aligned} a_{x:\overline{n|}} &= E\left[Y_{x:\overline{n|}}\right] \\ &= \sum_{t=1}^{n} E\left[Z_{x:\overline{t|}}^{\;\;1}\right] \\ &= \sum_{t=1}^{n} A_{x:\overline{t|}}^{\;\;1} = \sum_{t=1}^{n} {}_tE_x = \sum_{t=1}^{n} v^t \cdot {}_tp_x, \end{aligned} \tag{8.21}$$

using results developed earlier in the text.

The group deterministic interpretation for the temporary annuity-immediate is the same as that presented for the whole life annuity-immediate in Section 8.1.1, except that all series are finite with final term involving l_{x+n}. The derivation is left to the reader as Exercise 8-20.

To analyze the random variable approach to the temporary immediate annuity, consider the following diagram.

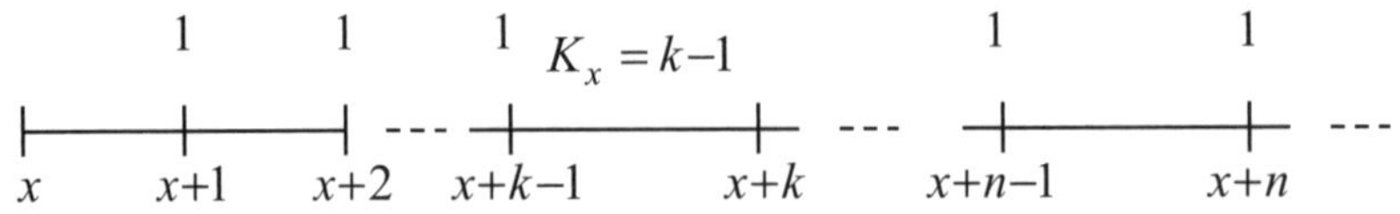

1 1 1 $K_x = k-1$ 1 1

x $x+1$ $x+2$ $x+k-1$ $x+k$ $x+n-1$ $x+n$

FIGURE 8.4

If failure occurs in the kth time interval, where $k \leq n$, then $k-1$ payments are made, with the last payment made at the end of the interval preceding the interval of failure, so the present value of payments will be $a_{\overline{k-1}|}$. But if failure occurs after age $x+n$, so that $K_x \geq n$, then n payments will be made and the present value of payments will be $a_{\overline{n}|}$. Therefore the present value random variable $Y_{x:\overline{n}|}$ is defined as

$$Y_{x:\overline{n}|} = \begin{cases} a_{\overline{K_x}|} & \text{for } K_x < n \\ a_{\overline{n}|} & \text{for } K_x \geq n \end{cases}, \tag{8.22}$$

with expected value given by

$$E\left[Y_{x:\overline{n}|}\right] = \sum_{k=0}^{n-1} a_{\overline{k}|} \cdot Pr(K_x = k) + \sum_{k=n}^{\infty} a_{\overline{n}|} \cdot Pr(K_x = k). \tag{8.23}$$

As we did for the whole life model in Section 8.1.1, we now want to show that the right side of Equation (8.23) reduces to $a_{x:\overline{n}|}$, as defined by Equation (8.21). The details are left to the reader as Exercise 8-21.

Finding the variance of $Y_{x:\overline{n}|}$ directly from its definition is a bit of a challenge. Consequently we defer this task to Section 8.2.2.

Recall from Chapter 1 that the n-payment interest-only annuity-immediate has present value given by $a_{\overline{n}|}$ and accumulated value given by $s_{\overline{n}|} = a_{\overline{n}|} \cdot (1+i)^n$ (see Equation (1.15b). In contingent annuities-immediate we have the analogous concept of the *actuarial accumulated value* (AAV), which is denoted by $s_{x:\overline{n}|}$ and is related to the actuarial present value (APV) $a_{x:\overline{n}|}$ by

$$s_{x:\overline{n}|} = a_{x:\overline{n}|} \cdot \frac{1}{{}_nE_x} = a_{x:\overline{n}|} \cdot \frac{1}{v^n \, {}_np_x} = a_{x:\overline{n}|} \cdot \frac{(1+i)^n \cdot l_x}{l_{x+n}}. \tag{8.24}$$

To get some understanding of what $s_{x:\overline{n}|}$ represents, we will make use of our group deterministic interpretation. Consider the following diagram, where each l_{x+t} value represents the number of survivors at age $x+t$.

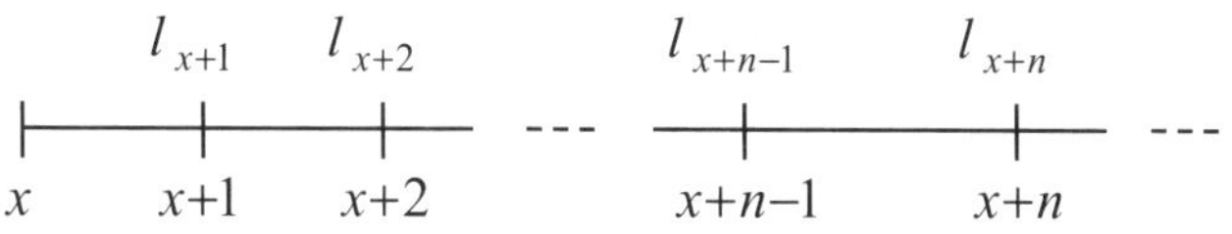

$$
\begin{array}{ccccccc}
 & l_{x+1} & l_{x+2} & \cdots & l_{x+n-1} & l_{x+n} & \\
x & x+1 & x+2 & \cdots & x+n-1 & x+n & \cdots
\end{array}
$$

FIGURE 8.5

Suppose each of the l_{x+1} survivors deposits one unit of money in a fund at time $t=1$, each of the l_{x+2} survivors do the same at time $t=2$, and so on, with each of the l_{x+n} survivors doing the same at time $t=n$. Suppose the fund accumulates at compound interest rate i, and the total accumulated fund is then distributed equally among the l_{x+n} survivors at time n. The share of each of the l_{x+n} survivors would then be

$$
\begin{aligned}
X &= \frac{l_{x+1}(1+i)^{n-1}+l_{x+2}(1+i)^{n-2}+\cdots+l_{x+n}}{l_{x+n}} \\
&= \frac{(1+i)^n\cdot l_x}{l_{x+n}}\left[\frac{l_{x+1}(1+i)^{n-1}+l_{x+2}(1+i)^{n-2}+\cdots+l_{x+n}}{(1+i)^n\cdot l_x}\right] \\
&= \frac{(1+i)^n\cdot l_x}{l_{x+n}}\left[\frac{v\cdot l_{x+1}+v^2\cdot l_{x+2}+\cdots+v^n\cdot l_{x+n}}{l_x}\right] \\
&= \frac{(1+i)^n\cdot l_x}{l_{x+n}}\left[v\cdot p_x+v^2\cdot {}_2p_x+\cdots+v^n\cdot {}_np_x\right] = \frac{(1+i)^n\cdot l_x}{l_{x+n}}\cdot a_{x:\overline{n}|},
\end{aligned}
$$

from Equation (8.21). This establishes Equation (8.24).

EXAMPLE 8.7

An investor wishes to purchase a 10-year corporate bond with annual coupons of \$40.00 each. The investor estimates that each year there is a 2% chance that the bond will default and no further coupons would be paid. At a yield rate of $i=.06$, find the expected present value of the coupons.

SOLUTION

If the coupons were certain to be paid, the present value would be $40a_{\overline{10}|.06}=294.40$. By introducing the default consideration, we now have a 10-year temporary contingent annuity with probability of survival to time t given by ${}_tp_x=(.98)^t$. Then the expected present value of the coupons is

$$
EPV = 40\sum_{t=1}^{10} v^t\cdot {}_tp_x = 40\sum_{t=1}^{10}\left(\frac{.98}{1.06}\right)^t = 40\left(\frac{.98}{1.06}\right)\left[\frac{1-\left(\frac{.98}{1.06}\right)^{10}}{1-\left(\frac{.98}{1.06}\right)}\right] = 266.44. \quad \square
$$

8.2.2 THE DUE CASE

If contingent payments are made at the beginning of each year instead of the end, but for n years at the most and contingent on the continued survival of (x), then we have the *n-year temporary annuity-due* model. It can be analyzed in a manner totally parallel to the immediate annuity case.

The present value random variable is denoted $\ddot{Y}_{x:\overline{n}|}$ and is given as a series of pure endowments by

$$\ddot{Y}_{x:\overline{n}|} = \sum_{t=0}^{n-1} Z_{x:\overline{t}|}^{\;\;1}. \tag{8.25}$$

The expected value of $\ddot{Y}_{x:\overline{n}|}$, denoted $\ddot{a}_{x:\overline{n}|}$, is then given by

$$\begin{aligned} \ddot{a}_{x:\overline{n}|} = E\left[\ddot{Y}_{x:\overline{n}|}\right] &= \sum_{t=0}^{n-1} E\left[Z_{x:\overline{t}|}^{\;\;1}\right] \\ &= \sum_{t=0}^{n-1} {}_tE_x = \sum_{t=0}^{n-1} v^t \cdot {}_tp_x. \end{aligned} \tag{8.26}$$

Comparing Equations (8.20) and (8.25) it is easy to see that $\ddot{Y}_{x:\overline{n}|}$ is related to $Y_{x:\overline{n}|}$ by

$$\ddot{Y}_{x:\overline{n}|} = Y_{x:\overline{n}|} + 1 - Z_{x:\overline{n}|}^{\;\;1}, \tag{8.27}$$

since $Z_{x:\overline{0}|}^{\;\;1} = 1$. Then it follows that

$$\ddot{a}_{x:\overline{n}|} = E\left[\ddot{Y}_{x:\overline{n}|}\right] = E\left[Y_{x:\overline{n}|} + 1 - Z_{x:\overline{n}|}^{\;\;1}\right] = a_{x:\overline{n}|} + 1 - {}_nE_x. \tag{8.28}$$

(Note the similarity of Equation (8.28) to the interest-only relationship $\ddot{a}_{\overline{n}|} = a_{\overline{n}|} + 1 - v^n$.)

The group deterministic interpretation for the temporary annuity-due is left to the reader as Exercise 8-22.

For the random variable approach in the annuity-due case we have

$$\ddot{Y}_{x:\overline{n}|} = \begin{cases} \ddot{a}_{\overline{K_x+1}|} & \text{for } K_x < n \\ \ddot{a}_{\overline{n}|} & \text{for } K_x \geq n \end{cases}, \tag{8.29a}$$

with expected value given by

$$E\left[\ddot{Y}_{x:\overline{n}|}\right] = \sum_{k=0}^{n-1} \ddot{a}_{\overline{k+1}|} \cdot Pr(K_x = k) + \sum_{k=n}^{\infty} \ddot{a}_{\overline{n}|} \cdot Pr(K_x = k). \tag{8.30}$$

As with the temporary annuity-immediate case, we can show that the right side of Equation (8.30) reduces to $\ddot{a}_{x:\overline{n}|}$, as defined by Equation (8.26). The details are left as Exercise 8-23.

By writing Equation (8.29a) as

$$\ddot{Y}_{x:\overline{n}|} = \begin{cases} \dfrac{1-v^{K_x+1}}{d} & \text{for } K_x < n \\ \dfrac{1-v^n}{d} & \text{for } K_x \geq n \end{cases}, \tag{8.29b}$$

it then follows that

$$\ddot{Y}_{x:\overline{n}|} = \frac{1-Z_{x:\overline{n}|}}{d}, \tag{8.31}$$

where

$$Z_{x:\overline{n}|} = \begin{cases} v^{K_x+1} & \text{for } K_x < n \\ v^n & \text{for } K_x \geq n \end{cases}$$

was given by Equation (7.24). Taking the expectation in Equation (8.31) we obtain

$$\ddot{a}_{x:\overline{n}|} = E\left[\ddot{Y}_{x:\overline{n}|}\right] = \frac{1-E\left[Z_{x:\overline{n}|}\right]}{d} = \frac{1-A_{x:\overline{n}|}}{d}, \tag{8.32a}$$

which is often stated as

$$A_{x:\overline{n}|} = 1-d\cdot\ddot{a}_{x:\overline{n}|}. \tag{8.32b}$$

Taking the variance in Equation (8.31) we find

$$Var\left(\ddot{Y}_{x:\overline{n}|}\right) = \frac{Var\left(Z_{x:\overline{n}|}\right)}{d^2} = \frac{{}^2A_{x:\overline{n}|} - A_{x:\overline{n}|}^2}{d^2}. \tag{8.33}$$

Returning now to the temporary annuity-immediate case, we see that

$$Y_{x:\overline{n}|} = \ddot{Y}_{x:\overline{n+1}|} - 1 \tag{8.34}$$

(see Exercise 8-24), where $Y_{x:\overline{n}|}$ is defined by Equation (8.20) and $\ddot{Y}_{x:\overline{n+1}|}$ is defined by Equation (8.25). Therefore $Var(Y_{x:\overline{n}|}) = Var(\ddot{Y}_{x:\overline{n+1}|})$, so $Var(Y_{x:\overline{n}|})$ can be found from Equation (8.33) with n replaced by $n+1$.

Finally, the actuarial accumulated value in the annuity-due case is denoted by $\ddot{s}_{x:\overline{n}|}$ and is given by

$$\ddot{s}_{x:\overline{n}|} = \ddot{a}_{x:\overline{n}|}\cdot\frac{1}{{}_nE_x} = \frac{(1+i)^n\cdot l_x}{l_{x+n}}\cdot\ddot{a}_{x:\overline{n}|}. \tag{8.35}$$

The derivation by the group deterministic interpretation is left as Exercise 8-25.

EXAMPLE 8.8

Find the variance of the present value random variable for the 5-year temporary annuity-due model, given the following information:

$$\ddot{a}_{x:\overline{5}|.05} = 4.13038$$

$$\ddot{a}_{x:\overline{5}|.1025} = 3.79209$$

SOLUTION

First we use Equation (8.32b) to calculate

$$A_{x:\overline{5}|} = 1-\left(\frac{.05}{1.05}\right)(4.13038) = .80331$$

and

$${}^2A_{x:\overline{5}|} = 1-\left(\frac{.1025}{1.1025}\right)(3.79209) = .64744.$$

Then from Equation (8.33) we find

$$Var\left(\ddot{Y}_{x:\overline{5}|}\right) = \frac{.64744-(.80331)^2}{\left(\frac{.05}{1.05}\right)^2} = .94067. \quad \square$$

8.2.3 THE CONTINUOUS CASE

As with the whole life continuous model in Section 8.1.3, we return to the future lifetime random variable T_x in place of the discrete duration at failure random variable K_x used thus far in this section. We consider that annuity payment is made continuously at annual rate 1 up to the time of failure of status (x), but for n years at the most. Then if $T_x = t$, for $t \le n$, the present value of payment is $\bar{a}_{\overline{t}|}$. If $T_x = t$ for $t > n$, then the present value of payment is $\bar{a}_{\overline{n}|}$. Together we have

$$\bar{Y}_{x:\overline{n}|} = \begin{cases} \bar{a}_{\overline{T_x}|} & \text{for } T_x \le n \\ \bar{a}_{\overline{n}|} & \text{for } T_x > n \end{cases}. \tag{8.36}$$

The expected value of the continuous present value random variable, denoted $\bar{a}_{x:\overline{n}|}$, is therefore

$$\bar{a}_{x:\overline{n}|} = E\left[\bar{Y}_{x:\overline{n}|}\right] = \int_0^n \bar{a}_{\overline{t}|} \cdot {}_tp_x\mu_{x+t}\, dt + \bar{a}_{\overline{n}|} \cdot Pr(T_x > n). \tag{8.37a}$$

Substituting $\bar{a}_{\overline{t}|} = (1-v^t)/\delta$ and $Pr(T_x > n) = {}_np_x$, we have

$$\begin{aligned}\bar{a}_{x:\overline{n}|} &= \frac{1}{\delta}\left[\int_0^n (1-v^t)\cdot {}_tp_x\mu_{x+t}\,dt + (1-v^n)\cdot {}_np_x\right] \\ &= \frac{1}{\delta}\left[{}_np_x - v^n\cdot {}_np_x + \int_0^n {}_tp_x\mu_{x+t}\,dt - \int_0^n v^t\cdot {}_tp_x\mu_{x+t}\,dt\right].\end{aligned}$$

The first integral inside the bracket evaluates to

$${}_nq_x = 1 - {}_np_x$$

and the second integral evaluates (using integration by parts) to

$$1 - v^n\cdot {}_np_x - \delta\int_0^n v^t\cdot {}_tp_x\,dt.$$

Substituting we have

$$\bar{a}_{x:\overline{n}|} = \frac{1}{\delta}\left[{}_np_x - v^n\cdot {}_np_x + 1 - {}_np_x - 1 + v^n\cdot {}_np_x + \delta\int_0^n v^t\cdot {}_tp_x\,dt\right] = \int_0^n v^t\cdot {}_tp_x\,dt, \quad (8.37b)$$

a convenient form for $\bar{a}_{x:\overline{n}|}$ that is analogous to Equation (8.17c) for the whole life case.

We recall from Equation (7.38a) and the exercises associated with Section 7.3.3 that

$$\bar{Z}_{x:\overline{n}|} = \bar{Z}^1_{x:\overline{n}|} + Z_{x:\overset{1}{\overline{n}|}} = \begin{cases} v^{T_x} & \text{for } T_x \le n \\ v^n & \text{for } T_x > n \end{cases}.$$

Comparing this with Equation (8.36) for $\bar{Y}_{x:\overline{n}|}$ we observe that

$$\bar{Y}_{x:\overline{n}|} = \frac{1 - \bar{Z}_{x:\overline{n}|}}{\delta}. \quad (8.38)$$

Taking the expectation in Equation (8.38) we obtain

$$\bar{a}_{x:\overline{n}|} = E\left[\bar{Y}_{x:\overline{n}|}\right] = \frac{1 - E\left[\bar{Z}_{x:\overline{n}|}\right]}{\delta} = \frac{1 - \bar{A}_{x:\overline{n}|}}{\delta}, \quad (8.39a)$$

which is often stated as

$$\bar{A}_{x:\overline{n}|} = 1 - \delta\cdot\bar{a}_{x:\overline{n}|}. \quad (8.39b)$$

Taking the variance in Equation (8.38) we find

$$Var\left(\bar{Y}_{x:\overline{n}|}\right) = \frac{Var\left(\bar{Z}_{x:\overline{n}|}\right)}{\delta^2} = \frac{{}^2\bar{A}_{x:\overline{n}|} - \bar{A}_{x:\overline{n}|}^2}{\delta^2}. \quad (8.40)$$

Finally, the actuarial accumulated value in the continuous case is denoted by $\bar{s}_{x:\overline{n}|}$ and is given by

$$\begin{aligned}\bar{s}_{x:\overline{n}|} &= \bar{a}_{x:\overline{n}|}\cdot\frac{1}{{}_nE_x}\\ &= \frac{(1+i)^n\cdot l_x}{l_{x+n}}\int_0^n v^t\cdot{}_tp_x\,dt\\ &= \int_0^n(1+i)^{n-t}\cdot\frac{l_{x+t}}{l_{x+n}}\,dt\\ &= \int_0^n\frac{(1+i)^{n-t}}{{}_{n-t}p_{x+t}}\,dt. \qquad (8.41)\end{aligned}$$

EXAMPLE 8.9

Show that

$$\frac{\partial}{\partial x}\bar{a}_{x:\overline{n}|} = \bar{a}_{x:\overline{n}|}(\mu_x+\delta)-(1-{}_nE_x).$$

SOLUTION

Working from Equation (8.37b) we have

$$\begin{aligned}\frac{\partial}{\partial x}\bar{a}_{x:\overline{n}|} = \frac{\partial}{\partial x}\int_0^n v^t\cdot{}_tp_x\,dt &= \int_0^n v^t\cdot\frac{\partial}{\partial x}{}_tp_x\,dt\\ &= \int_0^n v^t\left[{}_tp_x(\mu_x-\mu_{x+t})\right]dt = \mu_x\cdot\bar{a}_{x:\overline{n}|}-\bar{A}^1_{x:\overline{n}|}.\end{aligned}$$

Then we use Equation (8.39b) to substitute

$$\bar{A}^1_{x:\overline{n}|} = \bar{A}_{x:\overline{n}|}-{}_nE_x = 1-\delta\cdot\bar{a}_{x:\overline{n}|}-{}_nE_x,$$

obtaining

$$\frac{\partial}{\partial x}\bar{a}_{x:\overline{n}|} = \mu_x\cdot\bar{a}_{x:\overline{n}|}-1+\delta\cdot\bar{a}_{x:\overline{n}|}+{}_nE_x.$$

Rearrangement yields the desired result. ❒

8.3 DEFERRED WHOLE LIFE ANNUITY MODELS

In this section we consider whole life annuities that make no payments for the first n years, and then make payments in the $(n+1)^{st}$ and subsequent years provided the status (x) has not yet failed. Once begun, payments then continue as long as the status continues to survive. We consider the same three cases of immediate, due, and continuous as in prior sections.

8.3.1 THE IMMEDIATE CASE

Payments under the *n-year deferred whole life annuity-immediate* are illustrated in the following diagram.

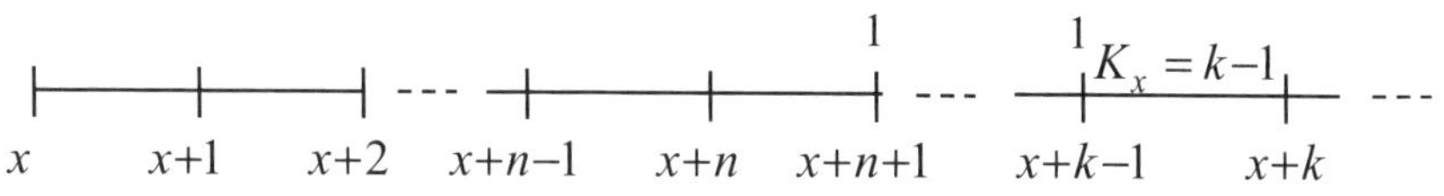

$$\begin{array}{cccccccccc} & & & & & 1 & & 1 \quad K_x = k-1 & & \\ x & x+1 & x+2 & x+n-1 & x+n & x+n+1 & & x+k-1 & x+k & \end{array}$$

FIGURE 8.6

Note that the first payment is at time $t=n+1$, provided (x) has not yet failed. The payments are deferred for n years, so the first payment is for the $(n+1)^{st}$ year. Since the annuity is immediate, the first payment is therefore at $t=n+1$. The last payment is at the end of the year preceding the year of failure, provided failure does not occur so early that payment never begins at all.

It is clear from Figure 8.6 that the present value random variable for this model, which we denote by ${}_{n|}Y_x$, is given by

$$ {}_{n|}Y_x = \sum_{t=n+1}^{\infty} Z_{x:\overset{1}{\overline{t|}}}, \tag{8.42}$$

in terms of a series of pure endowments. It is also easy to see from Figures 8.4 and 8.6 that the temporary annuity provides payments over the first n years and the deferred annuity provides payments after the first n years, contingent on the survival of (x) in all cases, of course. Together these two models provide the same payments as the whole life model of Section 8.1. Therefore it follows that

$$Y_x = Y_{x:\overline{n|}} + {}_{n|}Y_x \tag{8.43a}$$

or

$$ {}_{n|}Y_x = Y_x - Y_{x:\overline{n|}}. \tag{8.43b}$$

Then the expected present value of the immediate deferred model is

$$ {}_{n|}a_x = E\left[{}_{n|}Y_x\right] = E\left[Y_x - Y_{x:\overline{n|}}\right] = a_x - a_{x:\overline{n|}} = \sum_{t=n+1}^{\infty} v^t \cdot {}_tp_x, \tag{8.44}$$

using results developed earlier in the chapter.

Using the change of variable $s=t-n$, so that $t=s+n$, we can rewrite Equation (8.44) as

$$ {}_{n|}a_x = \sum_{s=1}^{\infty} v^{s+n} \cdot {}_{s+n}p_x = v^n \cdot {}_np_x \sum_{s=1}^{\infty} v^s \cdot {}_sp_{x+n} = {}_nE_x \cdot a_{x+n}. \tag{8.45}$$

Note the analogy with annuities-certain, where we have ${}_{n|}a_{\overline{m|}} = v^n \cdot a_{\overline{m|}}$. There we discount the value $a_{\overline{m}|}$ back n years at interest only. Here we discount a_{x+n} back n years for both interest and probability of survival.

EXAMPLE 8.10

Use Equation (8.43b) to show that

$$_{n|}Y_x = \begin{cases} 0 & \text{for } K_x < n \\ v^n \cdot a_{\overline{K_x - n}|} & \text{for } K_x \geq n \end{cases}. \tag{8.46}$$

SOLUTION

Since $_{n|}Y_x = Y_x - Y_{x:\overline{n}|}$, then for $K_x < n$ we have $_{n|}Y_x = a_{\overline{K_x}|} - a_{\overline{K_x}|} = 0$, and for $K_x \geq n$ we have $_{n|}Y_x = a_{\overline{K_x}|} - a_{\overline{n}|} = v^n \cdot a_{\overline{K_x - n}|}$, as required. ❐

From Equation (8.46) we can write

$$_{n|}a_x = E\left[_{n|}Y_x\right] = \sum_{k=n}^{\infty} v^n \cdot a_{\overline{k-n}|} \cdot Pr(K_x = k), \tag{8.47}$$

and can show that the right side of Equation (8.47) reduces to the right side of Equation (8.45). The details are left as Exercise 8-30.

8.3.2 THE DUE CASE

For the *n-year deferred whole life annuity-due*, the first payment is at $t = n$, provided (x) has survived to that point. The present value random variable is

$$_{n|}\ddot{Y}_x = \sum_{t=n}^{\infty} Z_{x:\overline{t}|}^{\;\;1}, \tag{8.48a}$$

with expected value given by

$$_{n|}\ddot{a}_x = E\left[_{n|}\ddot{Y}_x\right] = \sum_{t=n}^{\infty} E\left[Z_{x:\overline{t}|}^{\;\;1}\right] = \sum_{t=n}^{\infty} v^t \cdot {}_tp_x. \tag{8.48b}$$

It should

$$_{n|}\ddot{Y}_x = \ddot{Y}_x - \ddot{Y}_{x:\overline{n}|}, \tag{8.49}$$

so that

$$_{n|}\ddot{a}_x = \ddot{a}_x - \ddot{a}_{x:\overline{n}|}. \tag{8.50}$$

EXAMPLE 8.11

Show that $_{n|}\ddot{a}_x = {}_nE_x \cdot \ddot{a}_{x+n}$.

SOLUTION

If we let $s=t-n,$ so that $t=s+n,$ in Equation (8.48b) we have

$$_{n|}\ddot{a}_x = \sum_{s=0}^{\infty} v^{s+n} \cdot {}_{s+n}p_x = v^n \cdot {}_np_x \sum_{s=0}^{\infty} v^s \cdot {}_sp_{x+n} = {}_nE_x \cdot \ddot{a}_{x+n}, \tag{8.51}$$

as required. ❒

8.3.3 THE CONTINUOUS CASE

If failure occurs at time $T_x=t,$ for $t>n,$ then continuous payment (at annual rate 1) will be made from time n to time t. The present value of this payment stream at $t=0$ is $v^n \cdot \bar{a}_{\overline{t-n}|}$. (If failure is at time $T_x=t$ for $t \leq n,$ no payment is made.) Then the present value random variable is

$$_{n|}\bar{Y}_x = \begin{cases} 0 & \text{for } T_x \leq n \\ v^n \cdot \bar{a}_{\overline{T_x-n}|} & \text{for } T_x > n \end{cases}, \tag{8.52a}$$

with expected value given by

$$_{n|}\bar{a}_x = E\left[{}_{n|}\bar{Y}_x\right] = \int_n^{\infty} v^n \cdot \bar{a}_{\overline{t-n}|} \cdot {}_tp_x\mu_{x+t}\, dt. \tag{8.52b}$$

Using the variable change $s=t-n,$ so that $t=s+n,$ we have

$$_{n|}\bar{a}_x = \int_0^{\infty} v^n \cdot \bar{a}_{\overline{s}|} \cdot {}_{s+n}p_x\mu_{x+s+n}\, ds = v^n \cdot {}_np_x \int_0^{\infty} \bar{a}_{\overline{s}|} \cdot {}_sp_{x+n}\mu_{x+n+s}\, ds = {}_nE_x \cdot \bar{a}_{x+n}, \tag{8.53}$$

from Equation (8.17a).

Returning to Equation (8.52b) we can write

$$\begin{aligned} _{n|}\bar{a}_x &= \frac{1}{\delta}\int_n^{\infty} v^n(1-v^{t-n}) \cdot {}_tp_x\mu_{x+t}\, dt \\ &= \frac{1}{\delta}\left[v^n \int_n^{\infty} {}_tp_x\mu_{x+t}\, dt - \int_n^{\infty} v^t \cdot {}_tp_x\mu_{x+t}\, dt\right] \\ &= \frac{1}{\delta}\left[v^n \cdot {}_np_x - v^n \cdot {}_np_x + \delta\int_n^{\infty} v^t \cdot {}_tp_x\, dt\right] \\ &= \int_n^{\infty} v^t \cdot {}_tp_x\, dt, \end{aligned} \tag{8.54}$$

from the now-familiar integration by parts technique. It is clear that

$$_{n|}\bar{Y}_x = \bar{Y}_x - \bar{Y}_{x:\overline{n}|} \tag{8.55}$$

so that

$$_{n|}\bar{a}_x = \bar{a}_x - \bar{a}_{x:\overline{n}|} \tag{8.56}$$

upon taking the expectation in Equation (8.55).

To find the variance of the continuous deferred annuity present value random variable ${}_{n|}\overline{Y}_x$, we first find its second moment. We have

$$E\left[{}_{n|}\overline{Y}_x^{\,2}\right] = \int_n^\infty v^{2n}\cdot\left(\overline{a}_{\overline{t-n|}}\right)^2\cdot{}_tp_x\mu_{x+t}\,dt$$

$$= \int_0^\infty v^{2n}\cdot\left(\overline{a}_{\overline{s|}}\right)^2\cdot{}_{s+n}p_x\mu_{x+s+n}\,ds = \frac{v^{2n}\cdot{}_np_x}{\delta^2}\int_0^\infty (1-v^s)^2\cdot{}_sp_{x+n}\mu_{x+n+s}\,ds.$$

Now we use integration by parts to evaluate the integral. We have

$$\int_0^\infty \begin{array}{c|c} (1-v^s)^2 & {}_sp_{x+n}\mu_{x+n+s}\,ds \\ \hline 2(1-v^s)\cdot\delta v^s & -{}_sp_{x+n} \end{array} = -(1-v^s)^2\cdot{}_sp_{x+n}\Big|_0^\infty + 2\delta\int_0^\infty (v^s-v^{2s})\cdot{}_sp_{x+n}\,ds.$$

The first term is zero at both limits, so we have

$$E\left[{}_{n|}\overline{Y}_x^{\,2}\right] = \frac{v^{2n}\cdot{}_np_x}{\delta^2}\left[2\delta\int_0^\infty (v^s-v^{2s})\cdot{}_sp_{x+n}\,ds\right] = \frac{2}{\delta}\cdot v^{2n}\cdot{}_np_x(\overline{a}_{x+n}-{}^2\overline{a}_{x+n}).$$

(The observation made in Footnote 1 on page 154 applies here in the continuous case as well.) Then the variance of ${}_{n|}\overline{Y}_x$ is given by

$$Var\left({}_{n|}\overline{Y}_x\right) = E\left[{}_{n|}\overline{Y}_x^{\,2}\right]-\left(E\left[{}_{n|}\overline{Y}_x\right]\right)^2 = \frac{2}{\delta}\cdot v^{2n}\cdot{}_np_x\left(\overline{a}_{x+n}-{}^2\overline{a}_{x+n}\right)-\left({}_{n|}\overline{a}_x\right)^2. \quad (8.57)$$

EXAMPLE 8.12

Show that $\frac{\partial}{\partial n}\,{}_{n|}\overline{a}_x = -{}_nE_x$.

SOLUTION

Working from Equation (8.54) we have

$$\frac{\partial}{\partial n}\,{}_{n|}\overline{a}_x = \frac{\partial}{\partial n}\int_n^\infty v^t\cdot{}_tp_x\,dt = -v^n\cdot{}_np_x = -{}_nE_x,$$

by the fundamental theorem of calculus. ❐

EXAMPLE 8.13

An important annuity form is one for which the first n years of payments are guaranteed to be made, with all payments after the first n years made only if the annuitant continues to survive. Such annuities are referred to as *n-year certain and continuous*, meaning that the payments can continue after the first n years. (This phrase is used even though the payments are not being made continuously.)[1] Consider a person age 40 who wins 10,000 in the lottery and elects to receive payments of P at the beginning of each year for 10 years certain and continuous thereafter for life. Calculate P, given the values $A_{40}=.30$, $A_{50}=.35$, $A^{\;1}_{40:\overline{10|}}=.09$, and $i=.04$.

[1] The phrase *n-year certain and life* is also used to describe this annuity. Its standard actuarial symbol is defined in Section 12.2.

SOLUTION

The guaranteed payments constitute an annuity-certain and the non-guaranteed payments constitute a deferred whole life annuity. The equation of value is

$$10{,}000 = P(\ddot{a}_{\overline{10}|} + {}_{10|}\ddot{a}_{40}) = P(\ddot{a}_{\overline{10}|} + {}_{10}E_{40} \cdot \ddot{a}_{50}).$$

To calculate ${}_{10}E_{40}$, note that

$$A_{40} - A^{\ 1}_{40:\overline{10}|} = .21 = {}_{10}E_{40} \cdot A_{50},$$

so ${}_{10}E_{40} = \frac{.21}{.35} = .60$. We also have

$$\ddot{a}_{50} = \frac{1-A_{50}}{d} = \frac{1-.35}{.04/1.04} = 16.90,$$

and

$$\ddot{a}_{\overline{10}|} = \frac{1-(1.04)^{-10}}{.04/1.04} = 8.43533.$$

Then

$$P = \frac{10{,}000}{8.43533+(.60)(16.90)} = 538.35.$$ ❐

8.4 SUMMARY OF ANNUAL PAYMENT ANNUITIES

The twelve annuity functions presented in Sections 8.1 - 8.3 are summarized in the following table.

TABLE 8.1

Annuity Function	Immediate	Due	Continuous
Whole Life APV	a_x	$\ddot{a}_x$	$\bar{a}_x$
Temporary APV	$a_{x:\overline{n}|}$	$\ddot{a}_{x:\overline{n}|}$	$\bar{a}_{x:\overline{n}|}$
Temporary AAV	$s_{x:\overline{n}|}$	$\ddot{s}_{x:\overline{n}|}$	$\bar{s}_{x:\overline{n}|}$
Deferred APV	${}_{n|}a_x$	${}_{n|}\ddot{a}_x$	${}_{n|}\bar{a}_x$

8.5 LIFE ANNUITIES PAYABLE m^{thly}

In this section we consider the case of life annuities with payments made more often than once per year, such as semiannually, quarterly, or monthly. In general we consider payments made m^{thly}. Note that the special case of $m=1$ returns the general model to the annual model described earlier in this chapter.

When payments are made m^{thly} the standard actuarial convention and notation considers a unit annual payment, but paid m times within the year so that each actual payment is of size

$1/m$. Note that payments, being contingent on the continued survival of the status of interest, can cease somewhere within a year, and not just at a year-end point.

As in prior sections of this chapter, we will consider both the annuity-immediate and annuity-due cases, and all three of the whole life, temporary, and deferred whole life models.

8.5.1 THE IMMEDIATE CASE

The whole life m^{thly} annuity-immediate pays an amount $1/m$ at the end of each $(1/m)^{th}$ of a year, provided the status (x) continues to survive. This is illustrated in the following diagram specifically for $m=4$.

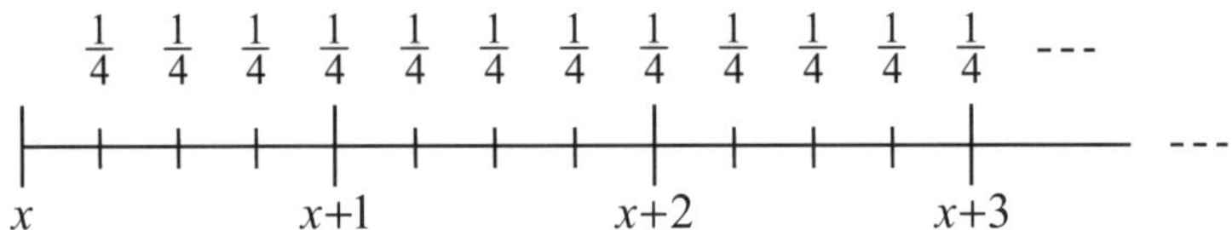

FIGURE 8.7

Generalizing from the annual payment cases presented earlier in the chapter, it is clear that the actuarial present value of the annuity, which we denote by $a_x^{(m)}$, is given by

$$a_x^{(m)} = \frac{1}{m} \cdot \sum_{t=1}^{\infty} v^{t/m} \cdot {}_{t/m}p_x. \tag{8.58}$$

Remember that the base symbol for the APV, $a_x^{(m)}$ in this case, represents a payment amount of one unit per year, but payable m^{thly} within the year, so that each actual payment is amount $1/m$.

For the temporary m^{thly} annuity-immediate, payment is made at one unit per year for n years at the most, but payable m^{thly} within the year. The APV is denoted by $a_{x:\overline{n}|}^{(m)}$, and is given by

$$a_{x:\overline{n}|}^{(m)} = \frac{1}{m} \cdot \sum_{t=1}^{mn} v^{t/m} \cdot {}_{t/m}p_x. \tag{8.59}$$

Note that the final payment (contingent on survival) is made at time $t=n$ years, or $t=mn$ m^{ths} of a year. As before, the actuarial accumulated value is

$$s_{x:\overline{n}|}^{(m)} = a_{x:\overline{n}|}^{(m)} \cdot \frac{1}{{}_nE_x}. \tag{8.60}$$

The n-year deferred whole life m^{thly} annuity-immediate would make its first payment at the end of the first m^{th} following the n-year deferral period, contingent on the survival of (x), of course. Its actuarial present value would therefore be

$${}_{n|}a_x^{(m)} = \frac{1}{m} \cdot \sum_{t=mn+1}^{\infty} v^{t/m} \cdot {}_{t/m}p_x. \tag{8.61}$$

8.5.2 THE DUE CASE

In the whole life m^{thly} annuity-due case, the first payment of $1/m$ is made at time 0 (age x) itself, and is made with probability 1 since the status (x) is known to exist at that time. For the temporary m^{thly} annuity-due, the final payment (contingent on the survival of (x), of course) is at the beginning of the final m^{th} in the nth year. For the deferred m^{thly} annuity-due, the first payment is at time n, the beginning of the first m^{th} following the deferral period. Thus the APVs in the annuity-due case are

$$\ddot{a}_x^{(m)} = \frac{1}{m} \cdot \sum_{t=0}^{\infty} v^{t/m} \cdot {}_{t/m}p_x, \tag{8.62}$$

$$\ddot{a}_{x:\overline{n}|}^{(m)} = \frac{1}{m} \cdot \sum_{t=0}^{mn-1} v^{t/m} \cdot {}_{t/m}p_x, \tag{8.63}$$

and

$$_{n|}\ddot{a}_x^{(m)} = \frac{1}{m} \cdot \sum_{t=mn}^{\infty} v^{t/m} \cdot {}_{t/m}p_x, \tag{8.64}$$

for the whole life, temporary, and deferred whole life models, respectively. As before, the actuarial accumulated value of the temporary m^{thly} annuity-due is

$$\ddot{s}_{x:\overline{n}|}^{(m)} = \ddot{a}_{x:\overline{n}|}^{(m)} \cdot \frac{1}{{}_nE_x}. \tag{8.65}$$

An analogous set of identities to those developed in the annual payment case exist in the m^{thly} payment case as well, such as

$$_{n|}a_x^{(m)} = {}_nE_x \cdot a_{x+n}^{(m)}, \tag{8.66}$$

$$_{n|}\ddot{a}_x^{(m)} = {}_nE_x \cdot \ddot{a}_{x+n}^{(m)}, \tag{8.67}$$

$$a_x^{(m)} = a_{x:\overline{n}|}^{(m)} + {}_{n|}a_x^{(m)}, \tag{8.68}$$

and

$$\ddot{a}_x^{(m)} = \ddot{a}_{x:\overline{n}|}^{(m)} + {}_{n|}\ddot{a}_x^{(m)}. \tag{8.69}$$

It should also be clear that

$$\ddot{a}_x^{(m)} = a_x^{(m)} + \frac{1}{m}. \tag{8.70}$$

8.5.3 RANDOM VARIABLE ANALYSIS

Contingent m^{thly} annuity models can be analyzed in a random variable framework totally parallel to that presented for the annual payment cases. Recall the random variable $K_x^{(m)}$

defined in Section 7.3.4 as the m^{thly} curtate duration at which the status of interest fails. Then the event $K_x^{(m)}=k$ denotes failure in the $(k+1)^{st}$ m^{thly} time interval. In this case, k m^{thly} payments are made under an annuity-immediate and $(k+1)$ m^{thly} payments are made under an annuity-due, and the present value of the payments is then $(1/m)\cdot a_{\overline{k}|}$ or $(1/m)\cdot \ddot{a}_{\overline{k+1}|}$, respectively. Note that the interest rate contained in $a_{\overline{k}|}$ and $\ddot{a}_{\overline{k+1}|}$ is effective over $(1/m)^{th}$ of a year.

Proceeding in a manner totally parallel to the annual payment case, we define, in the immediate case, the present value random variable

$$Y_x^{(m)} = \frac{1}{m}\cdot a_{\overline{K_x^{(m)}}|} = \frac{1}{m}\left(\frac{1-v^{K_x^{(m)}}}{i},\right) \tag{8.71}$$

where i is an effective m^{thly} interest rate, with expected value

$$a_x^{(m)} = E\left[Y_x^{(m)}\right] = \frac{1}{m}\cdot\sum_{k=0}^{\infty}\frac{1-v^k}{i}\cdot Pr(K_x^{(m)}=k), \tag{8.72}$$

for $K_x^{(m)}=0,1,2,\cdots$. Note that

$$Y_x^{(m)} = \frac{1}{m}\left(\frac{1-(1+i)\cdot v^{K_x^{(m)}+1}}{i}\right) = \left(\frac{1}{m}\right)\left(\frac{1}{i}\right)\left[1-(1+i)\cdot Z_x^{(m)}\right], \tag{8.73}$$

where $Z_x^{(m)} = v^{K_x^{(m)}+1}$ is defined by Equation (7.39), with expected value

$$a_x^{(m)} = E\left[Y_x^{(m)}\right] = \left(\frac{1}{m}\right)\left(\frac{1}{i}\right)\left[1-(1+i)\cdot A_x^{(m)}\right] \tag{8.74}$$

and variance

$$Var\left(Y_x^{(m)}\right) = Var\left[\frac{1-(1+i)\cdot Z_x^{(m)}}{m\cdot i}\right] = \frac{(1+i)^2\cdot Var\left(Z_x^{(m)}\right)}{m^2\cdot i^2} = \frac{Var\left(Z_x^{(m)}\right)}{m^2\cdot d^2},$$

where d is the effective m^{thly} discount rate so that $m\cdot d$ is the nominal annual discount rate $d^{(m)}$. Thus we can write the variance of $Y_x^{(m)}$ as

$$Var\left(Y_x^{(m)}\right) = \frac{Var\left(Z_x^{(m)}\right)}{\left(d^{(m)}\right)^2} = \frac{{}^2A_x^{(m)} - A_x^{(m)\,2}}{\left(d^{(m)}\right)^2}. \tag{8.75}$$

Note the parallels between the annual payment and m^{thly} payment models. In particular, observe the similarity of Equation (8.72) to Equation (8.5a), of Equation (8.73) to Equation (8.6), of Equation (8.74) to Example 8.2, and of Equation (8.75) to Equation (8.7b).

In the annuity-due case the present value random variable is

$$\ddot{Y}_x^{(m)} = \frac{1}{m} \cdot \ddot{a}_{\overline{K_x^{(m)}+1}|} = Y_x^{(m)} + \frac{1}{m}, \tag{8.76}$$

from which, by taking expectations, we verify that

$$\ddot{a}_x^{(m)} = a_x^{(m)} + \frac{1}{m}, \tag{8.70}$$

and also that

$$Var\left(\ddot{Y}_x^{(m)}\right) = Var\left(Y_x^{(m)}\right),$$

as given by Equation (8.75).

8.5.4 NUMERICAL EVALUATION IN THE m^{thly} AND CONTINUOUS CASES

If annuity functions are being evaluated from a parametric survival model, then it is no more difficult to evaluate the m^{thly} functions than to evaluate the annual functions, since ${}_rp_x$ can be calculated for fractional as well as integral values of r. The challenge arises when we seek to evaluate the m^{thly} annuity functions from a life table showing values of ${}_rp_x$ only for integral values of r. In this case we must resort to an approximate approach. Two such approximations are presented in this section.

As we did in Section 7.5.2 for the m^{thly} life insurance models, we will first show how to approximate m^{thly} life annuity functions from a life table under the UDD assumption.

Along with the identities $A_x = 1 - d \cdot \ddot{a}_x$ (in the discrete annual case) and $\overline{A}_x = 1 - \delta \cdot \overline{a}_x$ (in the continuous case), we also have

$$A_x^{(m)} = 1 - d^{(m)} \cdot \ddot{a}_x^{(m)} \tag{8.77}$$

in the discrete m^{thly} case. Then we can obtain the UDD-based approximation for the APV of the m^{thly} whole life annuity-due as

$$\begin{aligned}
\ddot{a}_x^{(m)} &= \frac{1 - A_x^{(m)}}{d^{(m)}} \\
&= \frac{1 - \frac{i}{i^{(m)}} \cdot A_x}{d^{(m)}} \\
&= \frac{1 - \frac{i}{i^{(m)}}(1 - d \cdot \ddot{a}_x)}{d^{(m)}} \\
&= \frac{1}{d^{(m)}}\left(1 - \frac{i}{i^{(m)}}\right) + \frac{id}{i^{(m)}d^{(m)}} \cdot \ddot{a}_x \\
&= \frac{id}{i^{(m)}d^{(m)}} \cdot \ddot{a}_x - \frac{i - i^{(m)}}{i^{(m)}d^{(m)}}.
\end{aligned} \tag{8.78a}$$

For convenience of notation, let $\alpha(m) = \frac{id}{i^{(m)}d^{(m)}}$ and $\beta(m) = \frac{i-i^{(m)}}{i^{(m)}d^{(m)}}$. The we have

$$\ddot{a}_x^{(m)} = \alpha(m) \cdot \ddot{a}_x - \beta(m). \tag{8.78b}$$

The UDD-based approximations for ${}_{n|}\ddot{a}_x^{(m)}$, $\ddot{a}_{x:\overline{n}|}^{(m)}$, and $\ddot{s}_{x:\overline{n}|}^{(m)}$ are found from Equation (8.78b) by utilizing relationships established earlier, and are left as Exercise 8-38.

UDD-based approximations for the m^{thly} annuities-immediate can be found by first expressing the m^{thly} annuity-immediate functions in terms of the corresponding m^{thly} annuity-due functions and then substituting the UDD-based approximations for the m^{thly} annuity-due functions. These are left as Exercise 8-39, where $\gamma(m) = \frac{d^{(m)}-d}{i^{(m)}d^{(m)}}$.

The continuous annuity functions are limiting cases of the corresponding m^{thly} functions as $m \to \infty$, so the UDD-based approximations for the continuous functions follow from the approximations for the corresponding m^{thly} functions. This is pursued in Exercise 8-40.

An alternative to the UDD-based approximations is supplied by the Woolhouse formula, which expresses the sum of a function over m^{thly} steps in terms of the sum of the function over unit steps plus adjustment terms.[2]

Consider a continuous function $g(t)$ for which a number of successive derivatives exist. The Woolhouse formula states that

$$\sum_{t=1}^{\infty} g(t/m) = m\left[\sum_{t=1}^{\infty} g(t) - \frac{m-1}{2m} \cdot g(t)\Big|_0^{\infty} - \frac{m^2-1}{12m^2} \cdot g'(t)\Big|_0^{\infty} + \cdots\right], \tag{8.79}$$

where $g'(t)$ denotes the first derivative of $g(t)$.

To apply this formula to m^{thly} annuity functions, we let $g(t) = v^t \cdot {}_tp_x$ so that

$$\begin{aligned} g'(t) &= \frac{d}{dt}\left(v^t \cdot {}_tp_x\right) \\ &= v^t \cdot \frac{d}{dt}\,{}_tp_x + {}_tp_x \cdot \frac{d}{dt}v^t \\ &= v^t\left(-{}_tp_x\mu_{x+t}\right) + {}_tp_x\left(-\delta \cdot v^t\right) \\ &= -v^t \cdot {}_tp_x\left(\mu_{x+t} + \delta\right). \end{aligned} \tag{8.80}$$

Then

$$g(t)\big|_0^{\infty} = v^t \cdot {}_tp_x\big|_0^{\infty} = 0 - 1 = -1$$

[2] The original presentation is found in Woolhouse [24]. The formula is also derived in standard textbooks on numerical analysis.

and

$$g'(t)\Big|_0^\infty = -v^t \cdot {}_tp_x\left(\mu_{x+t}+\delta\right)\Big|_0^\infty = 0-\left[-(\mu_x+\delta)\right] = \mu_x+\delta,$$

so we have

$$\sum_{t=1}^{\infty} v^{t/m} \cdot {}_{t/m}p_x = m\left[\sum_{t=1}^{\infty} v^t \cdot {}_tp_x + \frac{m-1}{2m} - \frac{m^2-1}{12m^2}(\mu_x+\delta)+\cdots\right] \tag{8.81a}$$

or

$$\frac{1}{m}\cdot\sum_{t=1}^{\infty} v^{t/m} \cdot {}_{t/m}p_x = \sum_{t=1}^{\infty} v^t \cdot {}_tp_x + \frac{m-1}{2m} - \frac{m^2-1}{12m^2}(\mu_x+\delta)+\cdots, \tag{8.81b}$$

which, by Equations (8.58) and (8.2b), gives

$$a_x^{(m)} = a_x + \frac{m-1}{2m} - \frac{m^2-1}{12m^2}(\mu_x+\delta)+\cdots. \tag{8.81c}$$

We show the application of the Woolhouse formula only as far as three terms, since, in practice, it is seldom applied using more than three terms. In fact, historically the formula has often been applied using only two terms, so that

$$a_x^{(m)} \approx a_x + \frac{m-1}{2m} \tag{8.82a}$$

and

$$\begin{aligned}\ddot{a}_x^{(m)} &= a_x^{(m)} + \frac{1}{m} \\ &\approx a_x + \frac{m-1}{2m} + \frac{1}{m} \\ &\approx \ddot{a}_x - 1 + \frac{m-1}{2m} + \frac{1}{m} \\ &\approx \ddot{a}_x - \frac{m-1}{2m}.\end{aligned} \tag{8.82b}$$

From Equation (8.81c) we can find the Woolhouse three-term approximations for ${}_{n|}a_x^{(m)}$, $a_{x:\overline{n}|}^{(m)}$, and $s_{x:\overline{n}|}^{(m)}$ (see Exercise 8-41). Similarly, from Equation (8.81c) we can find the Woolhouse three-term approximation for $\ddot{a}_x^{(m)}$, and then those for ${}_{n|}\ddot{a}_x^{(m)}$, $\ddot{a}_{x:\overline{n}|}^{(m)}$, and $\ddot{s}_{x:\overline{n}|}^{(m)}$ (see Exercise 8-42). Finally, from Equations (8.82a) and (8.82b) we can find the Woolhouse two-term approximations for ${}_{n|}\ddot{a}_x^{(m)}$, $\ddot{a}_{x:\overline{n}|}^{(m)}$, $\ddot{s}_{x:\overline{n}|}^{(m)}$, ${}_{n|}a_x^{(m)}$, $a_{x:\overline{n}|}^{(m)}$, and $s_{x:\overline{n}|}^{(m)}$ (see Exercise 8-43).

In light of the relationship previously established between m^{thly} annuities and insurances, we can develop Woolhouse approximations for $A_x^{(m)}$ and $\bar{A}_x$. This is pursued in Exercise 8-46.

8.5.5 SUMMARY OF m^{thly} PAYMENT ANNUITIES

The eight m^{thly} annuity functions presented in this section are summarized in Table 8.2 on the following page:

TABLE 8.2

Annuity Function	Immediate	Due
Whole Life APV	$a_x^{(m)}$	$\ddot{a}_x^{(m)}$
Temporary APV	$a_{x:\overline{n}\rceil}^{(m)}$	$\ddot{a}_{x:\overline{n}\rceil}^{(m)}$
Temporary AAV	$s_{x:\overline{n}\rceil}^{(m)}$	$\ddot{s}_{x:\overline{n}\rceil}^{(m)}$
Deferred APV	${}_{n\mid}a_x^{(m)}$	${}_{n\mid}\ddot{a}_x^{(m)}$

8.6 NON-LEVEL PAYMENT ANNUITY FUNCTIONS

The level annuity-immediate APVs given by Equation (8.2b) in the whole life case and Equation (8.21) in the temporary case can be modified to incorporate the case of non-level payment. If the payment made at time t is denoted by r_t, then we have, in general,

$$APV = \sum_{t=1}^{\infty} r_t \cdot v^t \cdot {}_tp_x \tag{8.83}$$

in the whole life case and

$$APV = \sum_{t=1}^{n} r_t \cdot v^t \cdot {}_tp_x \tag{8.84}$$

in the n-year temporary case. In particular if $r_t = t$, so the payment sequence is increasing, we have

$$(Ia)_x = \sum_{t=1}^{\infty} t \cdot v^t \cdot {}_tp_x \tag{8.85}$$

and

$$(Ia)_{x:\overline{n}\rceil} = \sum_{t=1}^{n} t \cdot v^t \cdot {}_tp_x. \tag{8.86}$$

(Note the notational similarity with the interest-only increasing annuity defined by Equation (1.34).)

The unit decreasing n-year temporary life annuity-immediate has APV given by

$$(Da)_{x:\overline{n}\rceil} = \sum_{t=1}^{n} (n+1-t) \cdot v^t \cdot {}_tp_x. \tag{8.87}$$

The comparable expressions in the annuity-due case would be

$$(I\ddot{a})_x = \sum_{t=0}^{\infty} (t+1) \cdot v^t \cdot {}_tp_x, \tag{8.88}$$

$$(I\ddot{a})_{x:\overline{n}|} = \sum_{t=0}^{n-1} (t+1) \cdot v^t \cdot {}_tp_x, \tag{8.89}$$

and

$$(D\ddot{a})_{x:\overline{n}|} = \sum_{t=0}^{n-1} (n-t) \cdot v^t \cdot {}_tp_x. \tag{8.90}$$

In the case of continuous payment, with payment made at rate $r(t)$ at time t, we would have

$$APV = \int_0^\infty r(t) \cdot v^t \cdot {}_tp_x \, dt \tag{8.91}$$

in the whole life case and

$$APV = \int_0^n r(t) \cdot v^t \cdot {}_tp_x \, dt \tag{8.92}$$

in the n-year temporary case. In particular, if $r(t) = t$ we have the increasing continuous models with

$$(\bar{I}\bar{a})_x = \int_0^\infty t \cdot v^t \cdot {}_tp_x \, dt \tag{8.93}$$

in the whole life case and

$$(\bar{I}\bar{a})_{x:\overline{n}|} = \int_0^n t \cdot v^t \cdot {}_tp_x \, dt \tag{8.94}$$

in the n-year temporary case. If $r(t) = n-t$ we have the decreasing n-year temporary case with

$$(\bar{D}\bar{a})_{x:\overline{n}|} = \int_0^n (n-t) \cdot v^t \cdot {}_tp_x \, dt. \tag{8.95}$$

Another type of non-level payment annuity is one in which the payments vary in a geometric, rather than arithmetic, pattern. This type of annuity is explored in Example 8.19 in Section 8.9.

Just as with the insurance functions of Chapter 7, if annuity APVs are calculated from a select life table the age subscript x is placed in brackets, as in $a_{[x]}$, $\ddot{a}_{[x]:\overline{n}|}$, ${}_{n|}\bar{a}_{[x]}$, and so on, with no change in the calculation process.

8.7 MULTI-STATE MODEL REPRESENTATION

We return to the idea presented earlier whereby we represent the survival model as a simple, two-state Markov model, where State 0 denotes survival and State 1 denotes failure (death). The life annuities presented in this chapter can now be described as a sequence of payments made while the process remains in State 0.

As with the insurance models of Chapter 7, we emphasize that no new concepts arise here; we will merely write annuity APVs using multi-state model notation rather than standard actuarial notation, with the multi-state model notation reflecting the fact that the annuity is payable only while the process remains in State 0.

In the discrete case, a payment is made at time k if the process, known to have started in State 0 at time 0 for a person age x, is still in State 0. The probability of this is ${}_kp_x^{00}$ or ${}_kp_x^{\overline{00}}$, which are the same because State 1 is an absorbing state. Then the APV for a whole life annuity-due is

$$\ddot{a}_x^{00} = \sum_{k=0}^{\infty} v^k \cdot {}_kp_x^{00}, \tag{8.96}$$

where ${}_kp_x^{00} = {}_kp_x$. In the continuous case, the probability of still being in State 0 at time r is ${}_rp_x^{00}$ or ${}_rp_x^{\overline{00}}$, and the APV for a whole life continuous annuity is

$$\bar{a}_x^{00} = \int_0^{\infty} v^r \cdot {}_rp_x^{00}\,dr, \tag{8.97}$$

where ${}_rp_x^{00} = {}_rp_x$ and the usual assumption is made that the entity is known to begin in State 0 at age x at time 0.

A general case arises when the model has more than two states, which we will encounter in Chapters 12 and 14.

8.8 MORTALITY IMPROVEMENT PROJECTION

As mentioned in Section 6.8, age-specific survival rates tend to improve (increase) over time, due primarily to improvements in hygiene, nutrition, health care, and general living standards.

Survival rate improvement is of particular concern in pricing annuity contracts. If the APV of an annuity has been calculated from a model that reflects current survival rates, but those rates then increase over time so that annuitants live longer than contemplated by the model, the price of the annuity would turn out to be inadequate and the insurer would lose money on the annuity contracts. To guard against this, the annuity price could be calculated using a survival model that reflects a projected mortality improvement. Note that "mortality improvement" means increased values of p_x and decreased, or reduced, values of q_x.

There are two different ways to define the mortality improvement projection factors. In both cases we begin with the values of p_x and q_x assumed to apply to a person age x in Year M, denoted by p_x^M and q_x^M. Then we could define *either* a constant annual *survival increase factor* or a constant annual *mortality reduction factor*. (The latter case seems to be the more common approach in actuarial practice.)

For example, if the mortality reduction factor for age x is denoted f_x, then we would calculate

$$q_x^{M+1} = q_x^M \cdot f_x, \tag{8.98a}$$

$$q_x^{M+2} = q_x^M \cdot f_x^{\,2}, \tag{8.98b}$$

and, in general,

$$q_x^{M+k} = q_x^M \cdot f_x^{\,k}. \tag{8.98c}$$

A mortality reduction factor of f_x is sometimes stated as a mortality improvement projection factor of $1-f_x$. The results are the same under each way of defining the factor, of course, but readers of the literature should take care to note the form of the presentation.

EXAMPLE 8.14

Suppose a recent mortality study suggests that $q_{60}^{1990} = .00895$ and $q_{80}^{1990} = .05105$. Assuming a constant annual mortality improvement factor of .005, find the survival rate expected to apply in 2010 to a person who is age 60 in 1990.

SOLUTION

A mortality improvement factor of .005 implies a mortality reduction factor of .995. Then

$$q_{80}^{2010} = (.995)^{20} \cdot q_{80}^{1990} = .04618,$$

so the expected survival rate is $p_{80}^{2010} = .95382$. ☐

It is important to note that a mortality improvement factor of .005 does *not* mean that

$$p_{80}^{2010} = (1.005)^{20} \cdot p_{80}^{1990} = 1.04849!$$

The factors are applied as reduction factors on q_x. It is better if the reduction factors are given directly, so any confusion regarding the meaning of "mortality improvement factor" is eliminated.

To calculate an annuity APV using mortality improvement projection, consider again a person who is age 60 in 1990. The APV for an annuity-immediate issued in 1990 to this person would be

$$\begin{aligned} a_{60}^{1990} &= v \cdot p_{60}^{1990} + v^2 \cdot p_{60}^{1990} \cdot p_{61}^{1991} + v^3 \cdot p_{60}^{1990} \cdot p_{61}^{1991} \cdot p_{62}^{1992} + \cdots \\ &= v \cdot \left(1-q_{60}^{1990}\right) + v^2 \cdot \left(1-q_{60}^{1990}\right)\left(1-q_{61}^{1991}\right) \\ &\qquad + v^3 \cdot \left(1-q_{60}^{1990}\right)\left(1-q_{61}^{1991}\right)\left(1-q_{62}^{1992}\right) + \cdots \\ &= v \cdot \left(1-q_{60}^{1990}\right) + v^2 \cdot \left(1-q_{60}^{1990}\right)\left(1-q_{61}^{1990} \cdot f_{61}\right) \\ &\qquad + v^3 \cdot \left(1-q_{60}^{1990}\right)\left(1-q_{61}^{1990} \cdot f_{61}\right)\left(1-q_{62}^{1990} \cdot f_{62}^{2}\right) + \cdots \end{aligned} \tag{8.99}$$

The APV with mortality improvement projection is calculated from the set of q_x values that apply in 1990, along with the set of mortality reduction factors f_x, for $x = 61, 62, \cdots$.

Further practice with mortality improvement projection is provided in Exercises 8-51 and 8-52.

8.9 WRITTEN-ANSWER QUESTION EXAMPLES

EXAMPLE 8.15

The idea introduced in Example 7.12 of investigating the aggregate outcome for a group of contracts is continued here in the case of annuities. A fund is established to pay continuous whole life annuities to 100 independent lives all age x at annual payment rate 10,000. Using the normal approximation, determine the initial size of the fund such that all payments can be made with probability .90, given the values $\bar{A}_x = .40$, ${}^2\bar{A}_x = .25$, and $\delta = .06$.

SOLUTION

Let F denote the initial fund and let $\bar{Y}_{Agg}$ denote the present value random variable for the aggregate annuity payments. We seek $Pr(\bar{Y}_{Agg} \leq F)$. We have

$$\bar{Y}_{Agg} = \bar{Y}_1 + \bar{Y}_2 + \cdots + \bar{Y}_{100},$$

where $\bar{Y}_i = 10{,}000\bar{Y}_x$. Then

$$\begin{aligned} E[\bar{Y}_{Agg}] = 100 \cdot E[\bar{Y}_i] &= (100)(10{,}000) \cdot E[\bar{Y}_x] \\ &= 1{,}000{,}000\left(\frac{1-\bar{A}_x}{\delta}\right) \\ &= 1{,}000{,}000\left(\frac{1-.40}{.06}\right) = 10{,}000{,}000. \end{aligned}$$

Similarly, because the $\bar{Y}_i$'s are independent, we have

$$\begin{aligned} Var(\bar{Y}_{Agg}) &= 100 \cdot Var(\bar{Y}_i) \\ &= (100)(10{,}000)^2\left(\frac{{}^2\bar{A}_x - \bar{A}_x^{\,2}}{\delta^2}\right) \\ &= (100)(10{,}000)^2\left(\frac{.25-.16}{.0036}\right) = 2.5\times 10^{11}, \end{aligned}$$

and therefore $SD(\bar{Y}_{Agg}) = \sqrt{Var(\bar{Y}_{Agg})} = 500{,}000$. Then, assuming that $\bar{Y}_{Agg}$ is approximately normal, we have

$$Pr(\bar{Y}_{Agg} \leq F) = Pr\left(Z \leq \frac{F-10{,}000{,}000}{500{,}000}\right) = .90,$$

which tells us that

$$\frac{F-10{,}000{,}000}{500{,}000} = 1.282,$$

and therefore $F = (1.282)(500{,}000)+10{,}000{,}000 = 10{,}641{,}000.$ ❐

EXAMPLE 8.16

Explain, by logic, without calculating numerical values, the order of size (from smallest to largest) of the five life annuity APVs $\ddot{a}_x$, a_x, $\ddot{a}_x^{(m)}$, $a_x^{(m)}$, and $\overline{a}_x$.

SOLUTION

Each APV is based on a payment of one unit of money each year, but with the location of that unit payment differing within the year.

Under $\ddot{a}_x$ the entire unit is paid at the beginning of the year, and under a_x it is paid at the end of the year. Then a_x must be smaller than $\ddot{a}_x$ due to greater discounting, and also because the unit gets paid in the year of death in the due case but not in the immediate case. Therefore $a_x < \ddot{a}_x$.

Similarly, considering $\ddot{a}_x^{(m)}$ and $a_x^{(m)}$ the payments are made later under $a_x^{(m)}$, so there is more interest discounting. As well, in the mth of the year of death a payment of $\frac{1}{m}$ is made under the due case but not under the immediate case. Therefore $a_x^{(m)} < \ddot{a}_x^{(m)}$.

Furthermore, by making the entire unit payment at the beginning of the year, rather than in m^{thly} installments throughout the year, we find $\ddot{a}_x > \ddot{a}_x^{(m)}$. Similar reasoning leads to the relationship $a_x < a_x^{(m)}$.

The common limit of $a_x^{(m)}$ and $\ddot{a}_x^{(m)}$, as $m \to \infty$, is $\overline{a}_x$, so it follows that $\overline{a}_x$ must lie between them, and therefore $a_x^{(m)} < \overline{a}_x < \ddot{a}_x^{(m)}$.

Putting all the inequalities together, we conclude that

$$a_x \; < \; a_x^{(m)} \; < \; \overline{a}_x \; < \; \ddot{a}_x^{(m)} \; < \; \ddot{a}_x.$$ ❐

EXAMPLE 8.17

(a) Identify three approximate formulas for evaluating the continuous life annuity APV, $\overline{a}_x$, from the life annuity-due APV, $\ddot{a}_x$.

(b) A natural question to ask is whether any one of the approximations is "more accurate." The answer would be revealed by comparing the approximate values of $\overline{a}_x$ with its exact value, which, in some cases, can be obtained from the assumed underlying survival function.

(i) Assume an exponential survival model with mean 100, force of interest $\delta = .04$, and issue age $x = 50$. Calculate, to five decimal places, the exact values of $\bar{a}_{50}$ and $\ddot{a}_{50}$, and then calculate the approximate value of $\bar{a}_{50}$, using each of the three approximate formulas identified in part (a).

(ii) Repeat part (i), this time assuming a uniform survival model with $\omega = 100$, $\delta = .04$, and $x = 50$.

(iii) Explain the properties of an underlying survival model that would lead you to conclude that the UDD approximation is the "most accurate" one for any value of x.

SOLUTION

(a) The three formulas (see Section 8.4.4 and its associated exercises) are as follows:

(i) Uniform Distribution of Deaths (UDD):

$$\bar{a}_x \approx \frac{id}{\delta^2} \cdot \ddot{a}_x - \frac{i - \delta}{\delta^2}$$

(ii) Two-Term Woolhouse (W_2):

$$\bar{a}_x \approx \ddot{a}_x - \frac{1}{2}$$

(iii) Three-Term Woolhouse (W_3):

$$\bar{a}_x \approx \ddot{a}_x - \frac{1}{2} - \frac{1}{12}(\mu_x + \delta)$$

(b) (i) When the survival model is exponential, then the force of mortality is constant with value equal to the reciprocal of the mean of the exponential distribution, in this case $\mu = .01$. Then we know (see Example 8.5) that

$$\bar{a}_{50} = \frac{1}{\mu + \delta} = \frac{1}{.05} = 20.00000.$$

The value of $\ddot{a}_{50}$ can be found as

$$\begin{aligned}
\ddot{a}_{50} &= \sum_{t=0}^{\infty} v^t \cdot {}_tp_{50} \\
&= \sum_{t=0}^{\infty} e^{-\delta t} \cdot e^{-\mu t} \\
&= \sum_{t=0}^{\infty} \left[e^{-(\mu+\delta)}\right]^t = \frac{1}{1 - e^{-.05}} = 20.50417.
\end{aligned}$$

With $\delta = .04$ we find

$$i = e^{.04} - 1 = .04081077$$

and

$$d = 1 - e^{-.04} = .03921056.$$

Then under UDD we find

$$\begin{aligned}\bar{a}_{50} &\approx \frac{(.04081077)(.03921056)}{.0016} \cdot \ddot{a}_{50} - \frac{.04081077 - .04}{.0016} \\ &= (1.00013324)(20.50417) - .50673125 = 20.00017.\end{aligned}$$

Under W_2 we find

$$\bar{a}_{50} \approx \ddot{a}_{50} - \frac{1}{2} = 20.50417 - .50 = 20.00417.$$

Under W_3 we find

$$\bar{a}_{50} = 20.00417 - \frac{1}{12}(.05) = 20.00000.$$

Clearly the W_3 approximation is better in this case.

(ii) When the survival model is uniform, with $\omega = 100$ and $x = 50$, then we know (see Exercise 8-12) that

$$\bar{a}_{50} = \frac{50 - \bar{a}_{\overline{50|}}}{50\delta} = \frac{50 - \left(\frac{1 - e^{-50\delta}}{\delta}\right)}{50\delta} = 14.19169$$

when evaluated at $\delta = .04$. The value of $\ddot{a}_{50}$ can be found as

$$\begin{aligned}\ddot{a}_{50} &= \sum_{t=0}^{49} v^t \cdot {}_t p_{50} \\ &= \sum_{t=0}^{49} v^t \cdot \left(1 - \frac{t}{50}\right) = \ddot{a}_{\overline{50|}i} - \frac{1}{50} \cdot (Ia)_{\overline{49|}i},\end{aligned}$$

where $i = e^{.04} - 1 = .04081077$. By financial calculator we find $\ddot{a}_{\overline{50|}i} = 22.05183$ and $(Ia)_{\overline{49|}i} = 367.76854$, so that

$$\ddot{a}_{50} = 22.05183 - \frac{367.76854}{50} = 14.69646.$$

Then under UDD we find

$$\bar{a}_{50} \approx \frac{(.04081077)(.03921056)}{.0016} \cdot \ddot{a}_{50} - \frac{.04081077 - .04}{.0016}$$
$$= (1.00013324)(14.69646) - .50673125 = 14.19169.$$

Under W_2 we find

$$\bar{a}_{50} \approx \ddot{a}_{50} - \frac{1}{2} = 14.19646.$$

Under W_3 we find

$$\bar{a}_{50} \approx 14.19646 - \frac{1}{12}(\mu_{50} + .04).$$

Under the uniform distribution with $\omega = 100$, we have $\mu_{50} = \frac{1}{50}$ (see Equation (5.27)). Then

$$\bar{a}_{50} \approx 14.19646 - \frac{1}{12}(.06) = 14.19146.$$

Clearly the UDD approximation is better in this case.

(iii) The UDD approximation assumes a piecewise-linear survival function, so under any survival function meeting that criterion the UDD-based approximation will exactly match the exact value of $\bar{a}_x$ for all x. (The uniform distribution of part (ii) is also piecewise-linear, so the result in part (ii) comes as no surprise.) ❑

EXAMPLE 8.18

Consider a non-level whole life annuity with unit payment in the first year, and with each subsequent payment being $(1+r)$ times the previous payment.

(a) Define the APV for a life annuity-due with this payment pattern.

(b) Show that the APV can be represented by $\ddot{a}'_x$ evaluated at special interest rate i'. Define i'.

(c) Find the APV in the special case where $r = i$. Explain the logic of this result.

(d) Repeat part (a) and part (c) assuming a life annuity-immediate.

SOLUTION

(a) Using Equation (8.83), adapted to the annuity-due case, we have

$$APV = \sum_{t=0}^{\infty}(1+r)^t \cdot v^t \cdot {}_tp_x.$$

(b) The APV can be written as

$$APV = \sum_{t=0}^{\infty}\left(\frac{1+r}{1+i}\right)^t \cdot {}_tp_x.$$

Then if we let $v' = \frac{1+r}{1+i}$, we have

$$APV = \sum_{t=0}^{\infty} v'^t \cdot {}_tp_x = \ddot{a}'_x,$$

as required. The rate i' is found as

$$i' = \frac{1}{v'} - 1 = \frac{1+i}{1+r} - 1 = \frac{i-r}{1+r}.$$

(c) If $r = i$, then $v' = 1$ so the APV is

$$APV = \sum_{t=0}^{\infty} {}_tp_x = 1 + e_x.$$

The logic is that the growth in the payment exactly offsets the effect of discounting, so each payment has present value 1.

(d) For an annuity-immediate, the APV is

$$APV = \sum_{t=1}^{\infty}(1+r)^{t-1} \cdot v^t \cdot {}_tp_x.$$

If $r = i$, we have

$$APV = \frac{1}{1+r} \cdot \sum_{t=1}^{\infty}\left(\frac{1+r}{1+i}\right)^t \cdot {}_tp_x = \frac{e_x}{1+r},$$

since $\left(\frac{1+r}{1+i}\right)^t = 1$ for all *t*. ❑

EXAMPLE 8.19

Consider the random variable $Y_x = a_{\overline{K_x}|}$.

(a) What is $E[Y_x]$ in terms of $\ddot{a}_x$?

(b) Use an approach similar to the one used to developed Equation (8.5b) from Equation (8.5a) to show that the second moment of Y_x is

$$E[Y_x^{\,2}] = \frac{1}{d^2}\left[v^2 - 2v \cdot A_x + {}^2A_x\right].$$

(c) Show that $a_x = \frac{v-A_x}{d}$.

(d) Use the relationship $Var(Y_x) = E\left[Y_x^2\right]-(E[Y_x])^2$ to reach the known result

$$Var(Y_x) = \frac{{}^2A_x - A_x^2}{d^2}.$$

SOLUTION

(a) $E[Y_x] = a_x = \ddot{a}_x - 1$, as derived for Equation (8.5b).

(b) From first principles,

$$\begin{aligned}
E\left[Y_x^{\,2}\right] &= \sum_{k=0}^{\infty}(a_{\overline{k}|})^2 \cdot Pr(K_x = k) \\
&= \sum_{k=0}^{\infty}\left(\frac{1-v^k}{i}\right)^2 \cdot {}_{k|}q_x \\
&= \frac{1}{i^2}\left[\sum_{k=0}^{\infty}(1-2v^k+v^{2k}) \cdot {}_{k|}q_x\right] \\
&= \frac{1}{i^2}\left[\sum_{k=0}^{\infty} {}_{k|}q_x - 2\sum_{k=0}^{\infty} v^k \cdot {}_{k|}q_x + \sum_{k=0}^{\infty} v^{2k} \cdot {}_{k|}q_x\right] \\
&= \frac{1}{i^2}\left[\sum_{k=0}^{\infty} {}_{k|}q_x - 2(1+i) \cdot \sum_{k=0}^{\infty} v^{k+1} \cdot {}_{k|}q_x + (1+i)^2 \cdot \sum_{k=0}^{\infty} (v^2)^{k+1} \cdot {}_{k|}q_x\right] \\
&= \frac{1}{i^2}\left[1-2(1+i) \cdot A_x + (1+i)^2 \cdot {}^2A_x\right] \\
&= \frac{1}{d^2}\left[v^2 - 2v \cdot A_x + {}^2A_x\right],
\end{aligned}$$

as required, since $d^2 = i^2v^2$.

(c) We have

$$a_x = \ddot{a}_x - 1 = \frac{1-A_x}{d} - 1 = \frac{1-A_x-d}{d} = \frac{v-A_x}{d}.$$

(d) Now we can write

$$\begin{aligned}
Var(Y_x) &= E\left[Y_x^{\,2}\right]-(E[Y_x])^2 \\
&= \frac{1}{d^2}\left[v^2 - 2v \cdot A_x + {}^2A_x\right] - \left(\frac{v-A_x}{d}\right)^2 \\
&= \frac{1}{d^2}\left[v^2 - 2v \cdot A_x + {}^2A_x - v^2 + 2v \cdot A_x - A_x^2\right] \\
&= \frac{{}^2A_x - A_x^2}{d^2},
\end{aligned}$$

as required. ❑

8.10 EXERCISES

8.1 Whole Life Annuity Models

8-1 Derive the identity $i \cdot a_x + (1+i)A_x = 1$.

8-2 Use a group deterministic interpretation to show that $\sum_{t=1}^{\infty} l_{x+t} \cdot A_{x+t} = l_x \cdot a_x$.

8-3 Show that $a_x = v \cdot p_x(1+a_{x+1})$. (Note that when $i=0$ this equation reduces to that shown in Exercise 6-15.)

8-4 Calculate the value of $Var(\ddot{Y}_x)$, given the values $\ddot{a}_x = 10$, ${}^2\ddot{a}_x = 6$, and $i = \frac{1}{24}$.

8-5 Show that $A_x = v \cdot \ddot{a}_x - a_x$.

8-6 Show that $\ddot{a}_x = 1 + v \cdot p_x \cdot \ddot{a}_{x+1}$.

8-7 After calculating the value of $\ddot{a}_x$ at interest rate $i = .05$, a student discovers that the value of p_{x+1} is larger by .03 than the value used in the initial calculation. Find the amount by which the value of $\ddot{a}_x$ is increased when the correct value of p_{x+1} is used, given the following values used in the initial calculation:

$q_x = .01$ $\qquad$ $q_{x+1} = .05$ $\qquad$ $\ddot{a}_{x+1} = 6.951$

8-8 A whole life annuity product pays the contract holder 12,000 at the beginning of each year. It is suggested that a death benefit, payable at the end of the year of death, be added to the product. Find the size of the death benefit that will minimize the variance of the present value random variable of the new product, given $d = .08$.

8-9 Show that the right side of Equation (8.14) reduces to $\ddot{a}_x$, as defined by Equation (8.9).

8-10 Use Equation (8.18) to derive the useful relationship $\bar{A}_x = 1 - \delta \cdot \bar{a}_x$.

8-11 Show that $\frac{d}{dx}\bar{a}_x = \bar{a}_x(\mu_x + \delta) - 1$.

8-12 Show that if the age-at-failure random variable has a uniform distribution with parameter ω, then the expected value of $\overline{Y}_x$ is given by

$$E[\overline{Y}_x] = \frac{(\omega-x)-\overline{a}_{\overline{\omega-x}|}}{\delta(\omega-x)}.$$

8-13 Find the value of $\overline{A}_x$, given the following values:

$$\overline{a}_x = 10 \qquad {}^2\overline{a}_x = 7.375 \qquad Var(\overline{a}_{\overline{T_x}|}) = 50$$

8-14 Given that $Var(\overline{a}_{\overline{T_x}|}) = \frac{100}{9}$, $\delta = 4k$, and $\mu_{x+t} = k$ for all t, find the value of k.

8-15 If $\delta = .03$ and $\mu_{x+t} = .025$ for all t, calculate the probability that $\overline{Y}_x = \overline{a}_{\overline{T_x}|}$ will exceed 20.

8-16 Show that

$$Cov(\overline{Y}_x, \overline{Z}_x) = \frac{\overline{A}_x^{\,2} - {}^2\overline{A}_x}{\delta}.$$

8-17 $\overline{a}_x$ is calculated using force of failure μ_{x+t} and force of interest δ. $\overline{a}'_x$ is calculated using force of failure μ'_{x+t} and force of interest δ'. Given that $\delta' = 3\delta$ and $\overline{a}'_x = \overline{a}_x$ for all x, show that $\mu'_{x+t} = \mu_{x+t} - 2\delta$.

8-18 A group of persons all age x is made up of 50% females and 50% males. Find the value of $Var(\overline{Y}_x)$ for a person chosen at random from the group, given $\delta = .10$ and the following values:

	Female	**Male**
$E[\overline{Z}_x]$	0.09	0.15
$Var(\overline{Y}_x)$	4.00	5.00

8.2 Temporary Annuity Models

8-19 Show that $i \cdot a_{x:\overline{n}|} + i \cdot A^{1}_{x:\overline{n}|} + A_{x:\overline{n}|} = 1.$

8-20 Repeat the group deterministic demonstration, presented in Section 8.1.1 for the whole life case, to show that the APV and the NSP for the temporary immediate annuity are equal.

8-21 Show that the right side of Equation (8.23) reduces to $a_{x:\overline{n}|}$, as defined by Equation (8.21).

8-22 Repeat Exercise 8-20 to show that the APV and the NSP for the temporary annuity-due are equal.

8-23 Show that the right side of Equation (8.30) reduces to $\ddot{a}_{x:\overline{n}|}$, as defined by Equation (8.26).

8-24 Derive Equation (8.34).

8-25 Repeat the group deterministic demonstration, presented in Section 8.2.1 for the temporary immediate case, to derive Equation (8.35) for the actuarial accumulated value in the annuity-due case.

8-26 Calculate the value of $\ddot{a}_{x:\overline{4}|}$, given the following values:

k	$\ddot{a}_{\overline{k}|}$	${}_{k-1|}q_x$
1	1.00	.33
2	1.93	.24
3	2.80	.16
4	3.62	.11

8-27 Calculate the value of $Var(\ddot{Y}_{x:\overline{3}|})$, given ${}_tp_x = (.90)^t$ for $t \geq 0$ and the following values of $\ddot{Y}_{x:\overline{3}|}$, for given values of K_x, the random variable for the curtate duration at failure of (x):

K_x	$\ddot{Y}_{x:\overline{3}|}$
0	1.00
1	1.87
2	2.62

8-28 Show that $Var(\overline{Y}_{x:\overline{n}|})$ in terms of annuity functions is given by

$$Var(\overline{Y}_{x:\overline{n}|}) = \frac{2}{\delta}(\bar{a}_{x:\overline{n}|} - {}^2\bar{a}_{x:\overline{n}|}) - \bar{a}_{x:\overline{n}|}^2.$$

8-29 Show that $\int_0^n \bar{a}_{\overline{t}|} \cdot {}_tp_x\mu_{x+t}\,dt = \bar{a}_{x:\overline{n}|} - {}_np_x \cdot \bar{a}_{\overline{n}|}$.

8.3 Deferred Whole Life Annuity Models

8-30 Show that the right side of Equation (8.47) reduces to ${}_{n|}a_x$, as defined by Equation (8.45).

8-31 Show that

$${}_{n|}\ddot{Y}_x = \begin{cases} 0 & \text{for } K_x < n \\ v^n \cdot \ddot{a}_{\overline{K_x-n+1}|} & \text{for } K_x \geq n \end{cases}.$$

Then show that $E[{}_{n|}\ddot{Y}_x] = {}_nE_x \cdot \ddot{a}_{x+n} = {}_{n|}\ddot{a}_x$.

8-32 Let S denote the number of annuity payments actually made under a unit 5-year deferred whole life annuity-due. Find the value of $Pr(S > {}_{5|}\ddot{a}_x)$, given the following values:

$\ddot{a}_{x:\overline{5}|} = 4.542$ $\qquad$ $i = .04$ $\qquad$ $\mu_{x+t} = .01$, for all t

8-33 A 30-year unit deferred whole life annuity-due is issued to (35), with the extra feature that the net single premium is refunded without interest if (35) dies during the deferred period. Calculate the net single premium, given the following values:

$\ddot{a}_{65} = 9.90$ $\qquad$ $A_{35:\overline{30}|} = .21$ $\qquad$ $A^{\;1}_{35:\overline{30}|} = .07$

8-34 A present value random variable $\overline{Y}$ is defined by

$$\overline{Y} = \begin{cases} \bar{a}_{\overline{n}|} & \text{for } T_x \leq n \\ \bar{a}_{\overline{T_x}|} & \text{for } T_x > n \end{cases}.$$

Show that $E[\overline{Y}] = \bar{a}_{\overline{n}|} + {}_{n|}\bar{a}_x$.

8.4 Summary of Annual Payment Annuities
8.5 Contingent Annuities Payable m^{thly}

8-35 Derive each of Equations (8.66) through (8.70).

8-36 (a) Show that $\ddot{a}^{(m)}_{x:\overline{n}|} = a^{(m)}_{x:\overline{n}|} + \frac{1}{m}(1 - {}_nE_x)$.

(b) Show that ${}_{n|}\ddot{a}^{(m)}_x = {}_{n|}a^{(m)}_x + \frac{1}{m} \cdot {}_nE_x$.

(c) Show that $a^{(m)}_x = \frac{1}{m} \cdot v^{1/m} \cdot {}_{1/m}p_x + v^{1/m} \cdot {}_{1/m}p_x \cdot a^{(m)}_{x+1/m}$.

8-37 Derive Equation (8.77).

8-38 Derive the following UDD-based approximations.

(a) ${}_{n|}\ddot{a}^{(m)}_x \approx \alpha(m) \cdot {}_{n|}\ddot{a}_x - \beta(m) \cdot {}_nE_x$

(b) $\ddot{a}^{(m)}_{x:\overline{n}|} \approx \alpha(m) \cdot \ddot{a}_{x:\overline{n}|} - \beta(m) \cdot (1 - {}_nE_x)$

(c) $\ddot{s}^{(m)}_{x:\overline{n}|} \approx \alpha(m) \cdot \ddot{s}_{x:\overline{n}|} - \beta(m) \cdot \left(\frac{1}{{}_nE_x} - 1\right)$

8-39 Derive the following UDD-based approximations, where $\gamma(m) = \frac{d^{(m)} - d}{i^{(m)} d^{(m)}}$.

(a) $a^{(m)}_x \approx \alpha(m) \cdot a_x + \gamma(m)$

(b) ${}_{n|}a^{(m)}_x \approx \alpha(m) \cdot {}_{n|}a_x + \gamma(m) \cdot {}_nE_x$

(c) $a^{(m)}_{x:\overline{n}|} \approx \alpha(m) \cdot a_{x:\overline{n}|} + \gamma(m) \cdot (1 - {}_nE_x)$

(d) $s^{(m)}_{x:\overline{n}|} \approx \alpha(m) \cdot s_{x:\overline{n}|} + \gamma(m) \cdot \left(\frac{1}{{}_nE_x} - 1\right)$

8-40 (a) By taking the limit as $m \rightarrow \infty$ in Equation (8.78a), derive the UDD-based approximation

$$\bar{a}_x \approx \frac{id}{\delta^2} \cdot \ddot{a}_x - \frac{i - \delta}{\delta^2}.$$

(b) By taking the limit as $m \rightarrow \infty$ in Exercise 8-39(a), derive the alternative UDD-based approximation

$$\bar{a}_x \approx \frac{id}{\delta^2} \cdot a_x + \frac{\delta - d}{\delta^2}.$$

(c) Show that the right sides in parts (a) and (b) are equal.

8-41 Derive the following Woolhouse three-term approximations.

(a) $_{n|}a_x^{(m)} \approx {}_{n|}a_x + {}_nE_x\left[\frac{m-1}{2m} - \frac{m^2-1}{12m^2}(\mu_{x+n}+\delta)\right]$

(b) $a_{x:\overline{n|}}^{(m)} \approx a_{x:\overline{n|}} + \frac{m-1}{2m}(1-{}_nE_x) - \frac{m^2-1}{12m^2}\left[\mu_x - {}_nE_x\cdot\mu_{x+n} + \delta(1-{}_nE_x)\right]$

(c) $s_{x:\overline{n|}}^{(m)} \approx s_{x:\overline{n|}} + \frac{m-1}{2m}\left(\frac{1}{{}_nE_x}-1\right) - \frac{m^2-1}{12m^2}\left[\frac{\mu_x}{{}_nE_x} - \mu_{x+n} + \delta\left(\frac{1}{{}_nE_x}-1\right)\right]$

8-42 Derive the following Woolhouse three-term approximations.

(a) $\ddot{a}_x^{(m)} \approx \ddot{a}_x - \frac{m-1}{2m} - \frac{m^2-1}{12m^2}(\mu_x+\delta)$

(b) $_{n|}\ddot{a}_x^{(m)} \approx {}_{n|}\ddot{a}_x - {}_nE_x\left[\frac{m-1}{2m} + \frac{m^2-1}{12m^2}(\mu_{x+n}+\delta)\right]$

(c) $\ddot{a}_{x:\overline{n|}}^{(m)} \approx \ddot{a}_{x:\overline{n|}} - \frac{m-1}{2m}(1-{}_nE_x) - \frac{m^2-1}{12m^2}\left[\mu_x - {}_nE_x\cdot\mu_{x+n} + \delta(1-{}_nE_x)\right]$

(d) $\ddot{s}_{x:\overline{n|}}^{(m)} \approx \ddot{s}_{x:\overline{n|}} - \frac{m-1}{2m}\left(\frac{1}{{}_nE_x}-1\right) - \frac{m^2-1}{12m^2}\left[\frac{\mu_x}{{}_nE_x} - \mu_{x+n} + \delta\left(\frac{1}{{}_nE_x}-1\right)\right]$

8-43 Derive the following Woolhouse two-term approximations.

(a) $_{n|}\ddot{a}_x^{(m)} \approx {}_{n|}\ddot{a}_x - \frac{m-1}{2m}\cdot {}_nE_x$

(b) $\ddot{a}_{x:\overline{n|}}^{(m)} \approx \ddot{a}_{x:\overline{n|}} - \frac{m-1}{2m}(1-{}_nE_x)$

(c) $\ddot{s}_{x:\overline{n|}}^{(m)} \approx \ddot{s}_{x:\overline{n|}} - \frac{m-1}{2m}\left(\frac{1}{{}_nE_x}-1\right)$

(d) $_{n|}a_x^{(m)} \approx {}_{n|}a_x + \frac{m-1}{2m}\cdot {}_nE_x$

(e) $a_{x:\overline{n|}}^{(m)} \approx a_{x:\overline{n|}} + \frac{m-1}{2m}(1-{}_nE_x)$

(f) $s_{x:\overline{n|}}^{(m)} \approx s_{x:\overline{n|}} + \frac{m-1}{2m}\left(\frac{1}{{}_nE_x}-1\right)$

8-44 Show that the approximations given by Equations (8.82a) and (8.82b), applied to continuous annuity models, lead to

$$\bar{a}_x \approx \ddot{a}_x - \frac{1}{2} = a_x + \frac{1}{2}.$$

8-45 Show that, under the UDD assumption,

$$\bar{A}_x = \frac{i}{\delta} - \frac{(i-d)\ddot{a}_x}{\delta}.$$

8-46 Derive the following Woolhouse three-term approximations.

(a) $\bar{a}_x \approx \ddot{a}_x - \frac{1}{2} - \frac{1}{12}(\mu_x + \delta) = a_x + \frac{1}{2} - \frac{1}{12}(\mu_x + \delta)$

(b) $\bar{A}_x = 1 - \delta\left[\ddot{a}_x - \frac{1}{2} - \frac{1}{12}(\mu_x + \delta)\right]$

(c) $\mathring{e}_x = e_x + \frac{1}{2} - \frac{1}{12}\mu_x$

8.6 Non-Level Payment Annuity Functions

8-47 Calculate the probability that the present value of payments actually made under a unit 3-year temporary increasing annuity-due will exceed the APV of the annuity contract, given the following values:

$p_x = .80$ $p_{x+1} = .75$ $p_{x+2} = .50$ $v = .90$

8-48 An increasing temporary annuity-due pays 2 in the first year, 3 in the second year, and 4 in the third year. Using the values given in Exercise 8-47, calculate the variance of the present value random variable for this annuity.

8-49 (a) Show that $(IA)_x = \ddot{a}_x - d \cdot (I\ddot{a})_x$.

(b) Show that $(\bar{I}\bar{A})_x = \bar{a}_x - \delta \cdot (\bar{I}\bar{a})_x$.

8.7 Multi-State Model Representation

8-50 Using the multi-state model notation defined in Section 8.6 and earlier, give APV formulas for each of the following, for a person age x at time 0

(a) Whole life annuity-immediate

(b) n-year temporary annuity-due

(c) n-year deferred annuity-immediate

(d) n-year temporary continuous annuity

8.8 Mortality Improvement Projection

8-51 A person currently age 60 wishes to purchase a unit 20-year deferred, 2-year temporary annuity-immediate, with net single premium given by ${}_{20|}a_{60:\overline{2}|}$. Current survival rates are $p_{80} = .9521$ and $p_{81} = .9461$ and the rate of interest is $i = .06$. Let X denote the NSP with no mortality improvement projection. Let Y denote the NSP with 1% annual mortality improvement projection for the payout period of the annuity, but no mortality improvement projection during the deferred period. Find the value of $\frac{Y}{X}$.

8-52 A mortality table is projected from Base Year 2000 to future Year Y by the relationship

$$q_x^{[Y]} = q_x^{[2000]} \cdot (1 - AA_x)^{Y-2000},$$

where AA_x denotes the mortality improvement projection factor for age x. The following values are given:

x	$q_x^{[2000]}$	AA_x
35	.000475	.011
36	.000514	.012
37	.000554	.013
38	.000598	.014
39	.000648	.015

Find the value of ${}_5q_{35}^{[2008]}$.

CHAPTER NINE

FUNDING PLANS FOR CONTINGENT CONTRACTS (ANNUAL PREMIUMS)

Suppose a small mining company wishes to operate only one mine at a time. While still working a particular mine, it begins to look ahead to the next time it will need to explore for a new mining location when the current mine is no longer productive. The company wishes to accumulate, out of current revenue, a fund to finance these future exploration costs. From past experience the company has a good idea of how much will be needed, but does not know *when* the future exploration costs will arise.

Similarly, an insurance company that has sold a whole life insurance contract to a person age x at issue of the contract knows how much will be needed to pay the eventual death benefit under the contract, but does not know *when* the death benefit cost will occur.

How should these businesses go about the task of *funding* these eventual costs?

Suppose the uncertainty regarding time of future payment did not exist. That is, suppose we know that we will need amount X at time k, and we wish to fund this eventual need by accumulating deposits of size P each made at the beginning of each time interval from now (which we denote as time 0) until time k.

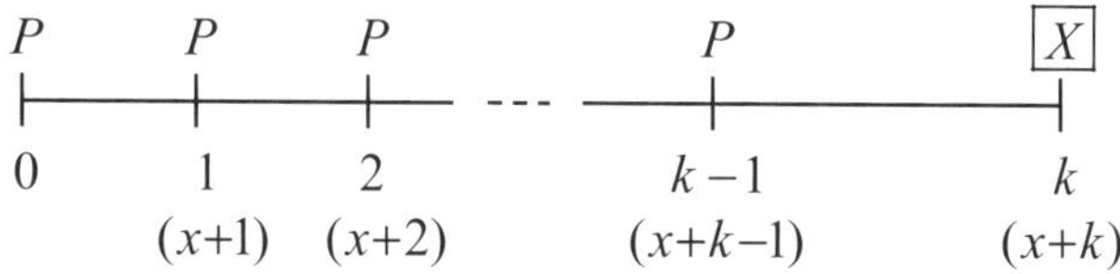

FIGURE 9.1

If the deposits will earn effective interest rate i per period, then we might determine P so that the accumulated fund at time k will provide exactly the needed amount X. Thus we have

$$P \cdot \ddot{s}_{\overline{k}|i} = X, \tag{9.1a}$$

which we can also write as

$$P \cdot \ddot{a}_{\overline{k}|i} = X \cdot v^k. \tag{9.1b}$$

Equation (9.1b) defines the periodic deposit by equating the present value of the funding scheme to the present value of the amount to be needed at time k, where each present value is taken at interest only.

With contingent payment models, including insurance contracts, the time at which amount X is needed is stochastic rather than fixed. The analogy to Equation (9.1b) is that the periodic funding payment is found by equating the *actuarial present value* (APV) of the funding scheme to the APV of the contingent payment. Funding payments determined in this manner are said to satisfy the *equivalence principle*.[1] Specifically in the case of insurance contracts, the equivalence principle would be

$$APV(Premiums) = APV(Benefit\ Payments). \tag{9.1c}$$

9.1 ANNUAL FUNDING SCHEMES FOR CONTINGENT PAYMENT MODELS

In this section we consider funding schemes for various types of contingent contracts, wherein the funding pattern is represented by a series of discrete annual funding payments.

9.1.1 DISCRETE CONTINGENT PAYMENT MODELS

Consider the whole life contingent payment model, as developed in Section 7.1, under which a payment of X will be made at time k if the status of interest, which we denote by (x), fails in the interval $(k-1,k]$. If this contingent payment is funded under the equivalence principle, then the periodic funding payment P is determined from

$$P\cdot\ddot{a}_x = X\cdot A_x, \tag{9.2}$$

where $X\cdot A_x$ is the APV of the contingent payment and $P\cdot\ddot{a}_x$ is the APV of the funding scheme. Note that funding payments are made at the *beginning* of each time interval including the beginning of the interval of failure.

To define the standard actuarial terminology and notation for contingent payment funding schemes, we consider the eventual contingent payment to be of unit amount. For a whole life contingent model, with time measured in years, the periodic funding payment is denoted by P_x. Thus we have

$$P_x\cdot\ddot{a}_x = A_x \tag{9.3a}$$

or

$$P_x = \frac{A_x}{\ddot{a}_x}, \tag{9.3b}$$

from which P_x can be calculated from values of A_x and $\ddot{a}_x$ defined in Chapters 7 and 8, respectively.

Using the identity $A_x = 1-d\cdot\ddot{a}_x$ (see Example 8.4), we can write

$$P_x = \frac{1-d\cdot\ddot{a}_x}{\ddot{a}_x} = \frac{1}{\ddot{a}_x}-d, \tag{9.4}$$

[1] See Section 9.3 for an alternative method of determining funding payments.

which allows us to calculate the funding payment from the contingent annuity APV only.

For any of the n-year term insurance, n-year pure endowment, or n-year endowment insurance models, the contingent payment will be made at time n at the latest (if, in fact, ever made at all). Clearly it would not be reasonable to fund one of these contingent benefits *beyond* time n, the point at which the benefit either has already been paid or it has become clear that the benefit will never be paid. Of course funding does not extend beyond the time of failure of (x) in any case. This suggests that the APV of the funding scheme for these n-year contracts is represented by the temporary n-year annuity-due. Thus we have

$$P^{1}_{x:\overline{n|}} = \frac{A^{1}_{x:\overline{n|}}}{\ddot{a}_{x:\overline{n|}}} \tag{9.5}$$

for the n-year term insurance model,

$$P_{x:\overline{n|}}^{\;\;\;1} = \frac{A_{x:\overline{n|}}^{\;\;\;1}}{\ddot{a}_{x:\overline{n|}}} \tag{9.6}$$

for the n-year pure endowment model, and

$$P_{x:\overline{n|}} = \frac{A_{x:\overline{n|}}}{\ddot{a}_{x:\overline{n|}}} \tag{9.7a}$$

for the n-year endowment insurance model. If we substitute for $A_{x:\overline{n|}}$ using Equation (7.26), we then have

$$P_{x:\overline{n|}} = P^{1}_{x:\overline{n|}} + P_{x:\overline{n|}}^{\;\;\;1}. \tag{9.7b}$$

Note the notational principle used to define the symbol for the annual funding payment: in the above cases the annual funding payment symbol is the same as the APV symbol, with A replaced by P.

In the life insurance context, annual funding payments are called *annual premiums*. To clarify that these funding payments provide *only* for the contingent benefit payment, and not for such things as profit margins or expenses of operation, they are referred to as *net annual premiums*.[2] Recall from Chapter 7 that the APV of the benefit payment is also called the *net single premium* (NSP). Thus we see that a contingent benefit could be funded by a net single premium, which is the APV of the contingent benefit, or by a sequence of net annual premiums whose APV is equal to the APV of the benefit and therefore equal to the NSP.[3]

We have established that funding should not extend beyond the occurrence of the contingent event that triggers the payment, nor beyond the duration of a contract with a maximum term.

---

[2] The issue of adjusting net premiums to cover expenses and profit margins will be addressed in Section 9.6.

[3] In certain property/casualty insurance arrangements, the term *pure premium* is used in place of net premium. Some texts also use the term *benefit premium*.

However it is possible to plan the funding scheme over a *shorter* period than the term of the contract. In general, if the funding scheme is confined to the first t years of a contract, where $t<n$ in the case of n-year contracts and $t<\infty$ in the case of whole life contracts, then the APV of the funding scheme is given by $P\cdot\ddot{a}_{x:\overline{t|}}$. Such funding schemes are referred to as *limited payment funding patterns* and the resulting net premium is called the *limited payment net premium* or the *t-pay net premium*. In general, the interval over which premiums are to be paid is called the *premium paying period.*

The standard actuarial notation for all limited payment net premiums involves the use of a pre-subscript t on the basic P symbol. Thus we have, for example,

$$ {}_tP_x = \frac{A_x}{\ddot{a}_{x:\overline{t|}}} \tag{9.8a}$$

for limited payment whole life (or t-pay whole life),

$$ {}_tP^1_{x:\overline{n|}} = \frac{A^1_{x:\overline{n|}}}{\ddot{a}_{x:\overline{t|}}} \tag{9.8b}$$

for limited payment n-year term insurance,

$$ {}_tP_{x:\overline{n|}}^{\ \ 1} = \frac{A_{x:\overline{n|}}^{\ \ 1}}{\ddot{a}_{x:\overline{t|}}} \tag{9.8c}$$

for limited payment n-year pure endowment, and

$$ {}_tP_{x:\overline{n|}} = \frac{A_{x:\overline{n|}}}{\ddot{a}_{x:\overline{t|}}} \tag{9.8d}$$

for t-pay n-year endowment insurance. Note that $t<n$ in Equations (9.8b), (9.8c), and (9.8d).

In the special case of n-year deferred insurance, as defined in Section 7.1, if the funding scheme continues until the failure of (x) the net premium is defined by

$$ P({}_{n|}A_x) = \frac{{}_{n|}A_x}{\ddot{a}_x}, \tag{9.9a}$$

and if the funding is limited to the first t years (contingent on the survival of (x), of course) the net premium is defined by

$$ {}_tP({}_{n|}A_x) = \frac{{}_{n|}A_x}{\ddot{a}_{x:\overline{t|}}}, \tag{9.9b}$$

where logically $t\leq n$.

EXAMPLE 9.1

A special 10-year contingent contract issued to (30) will pay a unit benefit at the end of the year of failure, if failure occurs during the 10-year period, or will refund the net annual premiums paid if (30) survives to the end of the 10-year period. Calculate the net annual premium, using the equivalence principle, given the following values:

$$A_{30:\overline{10}|} = .60 \qquad A_{30:\overline{10}|}^{\;\;\;\;\;1} = .47 \qquad d = .05$$

SOLUTION

Under the equivalence principle we equate the APV of the funding scheme to the APV of the contingent benefits. Let P denote the net level annual premium. We have

$$P \cdot \ddot{a}_{30:\overline{10}|} = A^{1}_{30:\overline{10}|} + 10P \cdot A_{30:\overline{10}|}^{\;\;\;\;\;1}.$$

Then

$$P = \frac{A^{1}_{30:\overline{10}|}}{\ddot{a}_{30:\overline{10}|} - 10A_{30:\overline{10}|}^{\;\;\;\;\;1}},$$

where

$$A^{1}_{30:\overline{10}|} = A_{30:\overline{10}|} - A_{30:\overline{10}|}^{\;\;\;\;\;1} = .60 - .47 = .13$$

and

$$\ddot{a}_{30:\overline{10}|} = \frac{1 - A_{30:\overline{10}|}}{d} = \frac{1 - .60}{.05} = 8.$$

Then

$$P = \frac{.13}{8 - (10)(.47)} = .03939.$$ ❐

9.1.2 CONTINUOUS CONTINGENT PAYMENT MODELS

Recall the continuous contingent payment models developed in Section 7.3, which are referred to as *immediate payment of claims models* in the life insurance context. Here we consider such contingent payment contracts funded by net annual premiums that have been determined by the equivalence principle. The notation for the net annual premium is different from that defined in Section 9.1.1 to reveal the immediate payment of claims feature. Here we have

$$P(\bar{A}_x) = \frac{\bar{A}_x}{\ddot{a}_x} \tag{9.10a}$$

for the whole life model,

$$P(\bar{A}^{1}_{x:\overline{n}|}) = \frac{\bar{A}^{1}_{x:\overline{n}|}}{\ddot{a}_{x:\overline{n}|}} \tag{9.10b}$$

for the n-year term insurance model, and

$$P(\bar{A}_{x:\overline{n}|}) = \frac{\bar{A}_{x:\overline{n}|}}{\ddot{a}_{x:\overline{n}|}} \tag{9.10c}$$

for the n-year endowment insurance model. (Recall that there is no continuous version of the pure endowment model with APV given by $A_{x:\overline{n}|}^{\ \ 1} = {}_nE_x$.) If these immediate payment of claims models are funded by t-year limited payment plans, then each P symbol carries the pre-subscript t and each $\ddot{a}$ function in the denominator is replaced by $\ddot{a}_{x:\overline{t}|}$, where $t < n$.[4]

The net annual premiums in this section can be evaluated from a life table by approximating the continuous functions in the numerator under the UDD assumption, as described in Section 7.5.1.

9.1.3 CONTINGENT ANNUITY MODELS

An n-year deferred life annuity contract, with net single premium given by ${}_{n|}a_x$ in the immediate case, ${}_{n|}\ddot{a}_x$ in the due case, and ${}_{n|}\bar{a}_x$ in the continuous case, is often funded by annual premiums paid over the n-year deferred period, subject to the continued survival of (x), of course. The net annual premiums are defined by

$$P({}_{n|}a_x) = \frac{{}_{n|}a_x}{\ddot{a}_{x:\overline{n}|}}, \tag{9.11a}$$

$$P({}_{n|}\ddot{a}_x) = \frac{{}_{n|}\ddot{a}_x}{\ddot{a}_{x:\overline{n}|}}, \tag{9.11b}$$

and

$$P({}_{n|}\bar{a}_x) = \frac{{}_{n|}\bar{a}_x}{\ddot{a}_{x:\overline{n}|}}, \tag{9.11c}$$

respectively.

The annual premiums defined by Equations (9.11a), (9.11b), and (9.11c) provide *only* for the deferred annuity payments, which are made only if (x) survives through the n-year deferred period. This implies that no benefit is paid, and premiums are therefore forfeited, in the case of failure during the deferred period. In practice this is not the case, and a failure benefit is paid in the event of failure during the deferred period. Suppose the deferred period failure benefit is the return of net annual premiums paid, with interest at the same rate i as is used to discount the benefit back to issue, and the unit annuity payments begin at age $x+n$. What would the net annual premium be in this case?

---

[4] These insurances involving net annual premiums and immediate payment of claims are referred to as *semicontinuous insurances*, and the premiums are called *semicontinuous net premiums*. When the premium is paid annually, and the benefit is paid at the end of the year of failure (as in Section 9.1.1), the insurances are called *fully discrete* and the premiums are called *fully discrete net annual premiums*.

If the net annual premium is P, then the failure benefit is $P\cdot\ddot{s}_{\overline{1}|}$ for failure in the first year, $P\cdot\ddot{s}_{\overline{2}|}$ for failure in the second year, and so on. The equation of value is therefore

$$P\cdot\ddot{a}_{x:\overline{n}|} = {}_{n|}\ddot{a}_x + \sum_{t=1}^{n} P\cdot\ddot{s}_{\overline{t}|}\cdot v^t\cdot {}_{t-1|}q_x,$$

for an n-year deferred annuity-due. The summation term is evaluated as

$$\begin{aligned}
P\sum_{t=1}^{n}\ddot{s}_{\overline{t}|}\cdot v^t\cdot {}_{t-1|}q_x &= \frac{P}{d}\sum_{t=1}^{n}\left[(1+i)^t-1\right]\cdot v^t\cdot {}_{t-1|}q_x \\
&= \frac{P}{d}\left[\sum_{t=1}^{n}{}_{t-1|}q_x - \sum_{t=1}^{n}v^t\cdot {}_{t-1|}q_x\right] \\
&= \frac{P}{d}\left[{}_nq_x - A^{\ 1}_{x:\overline{n}|}\right] \\
&= \frac{P}{d}\left[1-{}_np_x-(1-d\cdot\ddot{a}_{x:\overline{n}|}-{}_nE_x)\right] \\
&= P\cdot\ddot{a}_{x:\overline{n}|}+\frac{P}{d}({}_nE_x-{}_np_x).
\end{aligned}$$

Recall that ${}_nE_x = v^n\cdot{}_np_x$, so ${}_np_x = {}_nE_x\cdot(1+i)^n$. Substituting for ${}_np_x$ in the last line of the summation evaluation yields

$$P\cdot\ddot{a}_{x:\overline{n}|}-\frac{P}{d}[(1+i)^n-1]\cdot{}_nE_x.$$

Then the equation of value becomes

$$P\cdot\ddot{a}_{x:\overline{n}|} = {}_{n|}\ddot{a}_x + P\cdot\ddot{a}_{x:\overline{n}|} - P\cdot\ddot{s}_{\overline{n}|}\cdot{}_nE_x,$$

which leads to

$$P\cdot\ddot{s}_{\overline{n}|}\cdot{}_nE_x = {}_{n|}\ddot{a}_x$$

and finally to

$$P = \frac{1}{\ddot{s}_{\overline{n}|}}\cdot\frac{1}{{}_nE_x}\cdot{}_{n|}\ddot{a}_x = \frac{\ddot{a}_{x+n}}{\ddot{s}_{\overline{n}|}}, \tag{9.12}$$

since ${}_{n|}\ddot{a}_x = {}_nE_x\cdot\ddot{a}_{x+n}$. This result shows that the net premium in this case is the amount that accumulates, at interest only, to the amount needed at the start of the benefit period, which is $\ddot{a}_{x+n}$.[5] Because the premium is an interest-only function, and does not depend on the survival/failure rates, we say there is no *cost of insurance* under such a contract. We will later encounter deferred annuities that do involve a cost of insurance.

[5] We will derive this result again in Chapter 10 using reserves (see Example 10.5).

9.1.4 NON-LEVEL PREMIUM CONTRACTS

Contingent payment contracts can be funded by a non-level sequence of net premiums. To find the sequence of net premiums under the equivalence principle would require that the net premiums in the sequence bear a known relationship to each other, for otherwise the equivalence principle relationship would contain several unknowns.

For example, suppose a 5-year increasing term insurance contract, with benefit $1000k$ for failure in the kth year, for $k=1,2,3,4,5,$ is funded by a net premium sequence of P, $2P$, $3P$, $4P$, $5P$, paid at the beginning of each year. Then the equivalence principle states that

$$P\cdot(I\ddot{a})_{x:\overline{5|}} = 1000(IA)^{1}_{x:\overline{5|}},$$

where the two increasing functions are defined by Equations (8.89) and (7.52), respectively.

EXAMPLE 9.2

A special whole life contingent contract, with benefit paid at the end of the year of failure, pays a benefit of 1 for failure in the first year and a benefit increasing by 4% per year for failure thereafter. The net premium increases by 4% per year as well. Using a 4% interest rate, find an expression for the initial net premium.

SOLUTION

The APV of the net premium stream is

$$P_1[1+(1.04)\cdot v\cdot p_x+(1.04)^2\cdot v^2\cdot {}_2p_x+\cdots] = P_1(1+p_x+{}_2p_x+\cdots) = P_1(1+e_x),$$

where P_1 denotes the initial net premium. The APV of the benefit is

$$\sum_{k=1}^{\infty} b_k\cdot v^k\cdot {}_{k-1|}q_x = \sum_{k=1}^{\infty}(1.04)^{k-1}\cdot v^k\cdot {}_{k-1|}q_x = v\sum_{k=1}^{\infty} {}_{k-1|}q_x = v,$$

since $\sum_{k=1}^{\infty} {}_{k-1|}q_x=1$. Then by the equivalence principle we have

$$P_1 = \frac{v}{1+e_x}.$$ ❐

EXAMPLE 9.3

In Example 7.11 we considered a contingent payment contract with failure benefit including a return of the net *single* premium with interest. Now we consider the case where the failure benefit includes a return of the net *annual* premiums, this time without interest. For a fully discrete whole life insurance issued to (35), the failure benefit is 1000 plus the return of net annual premiums without interest. Calculate the net annual premium for this contract, given the values $A_{35}=.42898$, $(IA)_{35}=6.16761$, and $i=.05$.

SOLUTION

If the net annual premium is P, then the benefit is $1000+P$ for failure in the first year, $1000+2P$ for failure in the second year, and so on. Then the equation of value is

$$P \cdot \ddot{a}_{35} = 1000A_{35} + P \cdot (IA)_{35},$$

where

$$\ddot{a}_{35} = \frac{1-A_{35}}{d} = \frac{1-.42898}{.05/1.05} = 11.99142.$$

Then we have

$$\begin{aligned} P &= \frac{1000A_{35}}{\ddot{a}_{35}-(IA)_{35}} \\ &= \frac{(1000)(.42898)}{11.99142-6.16761} = 73.66. \end{aligned}$$

❒

9.2 RANDOM VARIABLE ANALYSIS

The topic of determining annual funding payments for contingent contracts can be approached in a stochastic manner, building on the discussion and results presented in Chapters 7 and 8. Suppose a unit payment will be made at time k if the status of interest (x) fails in the kth time interval, and this contingent payment arrangement is funded by payments of P at the beginning of each time interval until failure occurs. This familiar model is illustrated in the following figure.

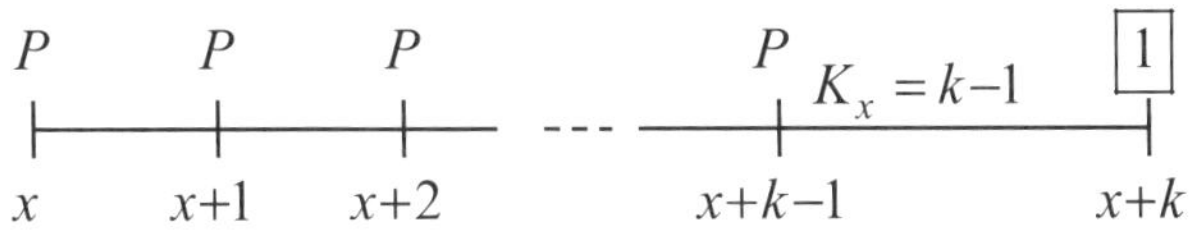

FIGURE 9.2

If the payment is made at time k, then v^k is the present value of the payment, and $P \cdot \ddot{a}_{\overline{k}|}$ is the present value of the associated premium income. The excess of v^k over $P \cdot \ddot{a}_{\overline{k}|}$ would represent the insurer's *present value of the loss* occurring under this arrangement if, specifically, $K_x = k-1$. In general, we let ${}_0L_x$ denote the random variable for the present value, at time 0, of loss under this whole life contingent payment model. Then we have

$${}_0L_x = v^{K_x+1} - P \cdot \ddot{a}_{\overline{K_x+1}|} = Z_x - P \cdot \ddot{Y}_x, \tag{9.13}$$

using notation defined in Chapters 7 and 8. Note that ${}_0L_x$ could turn out to be either positive or negative, with a negative loss interpreted as a gain under the arrangement.

The expected value of ${}_0L_x$ is given by

$$E[{}_0L_x] = E[Z_x - P\cdot \ddot{Y}_x] = A_x - P\cdot \ddot{a}_x. \tag{9.14}$$

If we adopt the rule that the net annual premium will be selected so that $E[{}_0L_x]=0$, then we have $E[{}_0L_x]=A_x - P\cdot \ddot{a}_x = 0$, which leads to

$$P = \frac{A_x}{\ddot{a}_x} = P_x, \tag{9.15}$$

as already defined by Equation (9.3b). Thus we see that determining the net annual premium by setting the expected value of the present-value-of-loss random variable equal to zero is identical to the equivalence principle used throughout Section 9.1. This is true for all of the contingent payment models we have defined, not just for the whole life model illustrated here.

Recall that

$$\ddot{Y}_x = \ddot{a}_{\overline{K_x+1}|} = \frac{1-v^{K_x+1}}{d} = \frac{1-Z_x}{d},$$

so we can write the present-value-of-loss random variable as

$${}_0L_x = Z_x - P\cdot \ddot{Y}_x = Z_x - P\left(\frac{1-Z_x}{d}\right) = Z_x\left(1+\frac{P}{d}\right)-\frac{P}{d}. \tag{9.16}$$

Equation (9.16) enables us to find the variance of ${}_0L_x$. Since the variance of the constant P/d is zero, we then have

$$\begin{aligned} Var({}_0L_x) &= Var\left[Z_x\left(1+\frac{P}{d}\right)\right] = \left(1+\frac{P}{d}\right)^2 \cdot Var(Z_x) \\ &= \left(1+\frac{P}{d}\right)^2 \cdot ({}^2A_x - A_x^2), \end{aligned} \tag{9.17a}$$

by using Equation (7.5) for the variance of Z_x. In the special case of net annual premium determined by the equivalence principle, which implies $E[{}_0L_x]=0$, we have $P=P_x$. Then Equation (9.17a) can be written as

$$\begin{aligned} Var({}_0L_x) &= \left(1+\frac{P_x}{d}\right)^2 \cdot ({}^2A_x - A_x^2) \\ &= \left(\frac{P_x+d}{d}\right)^2 \cdot ({}^2A_x - A_x^2) \\ &= \left(\frac{1}{d\cdot \ddot{a}_x}\right)^2 \cdot ({}^2A_x - A_x^2), \end{aligned} \tag{9.17b}$$

from Equation (9.4).

If $E[{}_0L_x]=0$ it follows that $Var({}_0L_x)=E[{}_0L_x{}^2]$. For the fully discrete whole life contingent payment model, with $P=P_x$ under the equivalence principle, we have

$$_0L_x{}^2 = \left[Z_x\left(1+\frac{P_x}{d}\right)-\frac{P_x}{d}\right]^2. \tag{9.18}$$

It can then be shown that $E[{}_0L_x{}^2]$, with ${}_0L_x{}^2$ given by Equation (9.18), reduces to the expression for $Var({}_0L_x)$ given by Equation (9.17b). The details are left as Exercise 9-9.

EXAMPLE 9.4

Let ${}_0L^1_{x:\overline{2}|}$ denote the present-value-of-loss random variable for a two-year term insurance with unit benefit paid at the end of the year of failure, and net annual premium determined by the equivalence principle. Given the values $q_x=.10$, $q_{x+1}=.20$, and $v=.90$, calculate the value of $Var({}_0L^1_{x:\overline{2}|})$.

SOLUTION

The net annual premium is

$$P^1_{x:\overline{2}|} = \frac{A^1_{x:\overline{2}|}}{\ddot{a}_{x:\overline{2}|}} = \frac{v\cdot q_x+v^2\cdot p_x\cdot q_{x+1}}{1+v\cdot p_x} = \frac{(.90)(.10)+(.90)^2(.90)(.20)}{1+(.90)(.90)} = .13027.$$

If failure occurs in the first year, which happens with probability .10, one premium will have been paid, and the present value of loss will be

$$v-P^1_{x:\overline{2}|} = .90-.13027 = .76973.$$

If failure occurs in the second year, which happens with probability $(.90)(.20)=.18$, two premiums will have been paid, and the present value of loss will be

$$v^2-P^1_{x:\overline{2}|}-v\cdot P^1_{x:\overline{2}|} = (.90)^2-.13027-.13027(.90) = .56249.$$

If failure does not occur in the first two years at all, which happens with probability $(.90)(.80)=.72$, two premiums *but no benefit* will have been paid, and the present value of loss will be

$$0-P^1_{x:\overline{2}|}-v\cdot P^1_{x:\overline{2}|} = -.24751.$$

Since $E[{}_0L^1_{x:\overline{2}|}]=0$, by the equivalence principle, then we have

$$\begin{aligned} Var({}_0L^1_{x:\overline{2}|}) &= E[{}_0L^1_{x:\overline{2}|}{}^2] \\ &= (.76973)^2(.10)+(.56249)^2(.18)+(-.24751)^2(.72) = .16030. \end{aligned}$$

❐

We can observe from Example 9.4 that the insurer sustains a loss on this particular contract if failure occurs in either of the two contract years, which happens with probability .28, and enjoys a gain if failure does not occur, which happens with probability .72. Although the expected loss (and hence the expected gain) is zero, we see that the probability of gain exceeds the probability of loss.

This notion of gain or loss on a single contract can be explored for contracts that are more extensive than the simple two-year term insurance of Example 9.4. Consider a unit fully discrete whole life contract issued at age 40, with net annual premium determined by the equivalence principle using the life table of Appendix A and 6% interest. The life table gives the value $A_{40} = .12401$, so we have

$$\ddot{a}_{40} = \frac{1-A_{40}}{d} = \frac{1-.12401}{.06/1.06} = 15.47582,$$

and therefore

$$P_{40} = \frac{A_{40}}{\ddot{a}_{40}} = \frac{.12401}{15.47582} = .00801.$$

Then we can calculate the possible values of ${}_0L_{40}$ as follows:

If $K_{40} = 0$, then

$${}_0L_{40} = v - P_{40} = .93539;$$

if $K_{40} = 1$, then

$${}_0L_{40} = v^2 - P_{40} \cdot \ddot{a}_{\overline{2}|} = .87443;$$

$$\vdots$$

if $K_{40} = 34$, then

$${}_0L_{40} = v^{35} - P_{40} \cdot \ddot{a}_{\overline{35}|} = .00701;$$

if $K_{40} = 35$, then

$${}_0L_{40} = v^{36} - P_{40} \cdot \ddot{a}_{\overline{36}|} = -.00140.$$

This shows us that the insurer sustains a loss on this contract if failure occurs within the first 35 years, and enjoys a gain if failure occurs in the 36th year or later. Then the probability of gain, from Table A.2, is ${}_{35}p_{40} = \frac{69,287}{97,033} = .71406$, and the probability of loss is .28594, notwithstanding that the expected gain (and therefore expected loss) is zero.

Note that the gain/loss analysis presented here is on a *net premium basis*. We will revisit this issue in Section 9.6 where we consider the gain/loss issue on a *gross premium basis*.

The variance of the present-value-of-loss random variable can be found for other than the whole life contingent payment model, as illustrated in the following example.

EXAMPLE 9.5

Find the variance of the present-value-of-loss random variable for an n-year endowment model, with net premium determined by the equivalence principle.

SOLUTION

The loss random variable is

$$ {}_0L_{x:\overline{n}|} = Z_{x:\overline{n}|} - P_{x:\overline{n}|} \cdot \ddot{Y}_{x:\overline{n}|}, \tag{9.19a}$$

where $Z_{x:\overline{n}|}$ is given by Equation (7.24) and $\ddot{Y}_{x:\overline{n}|}$ is given by Equation (8.29a). But from Equation (8.31) we know that

$$\ddot{Y}_{x:\overline{n}|} = \frac{1-Z_{x:\overline{n}|}}{d},$$

so we can write

$$ {}_0L_{x:\overline{n}|} = Z_{x:\overline{n}|}\left(1+\frac{P_{x:\overline{n}|}}{d}\right) - \frac{P_{x:\overline{n}|}}{d}. \tag{9.19b}$$

Then the variance of ${}_0L_{x:\overline{n}|}$ follows directly as

$$Var\left({}_0L_{x:\overline{n}|}\right) = \left(1+\frac{P_{x:\overline{n}|}}{d}\right)^2 \cdot Var\left(Z_{x:\overline{n}|}\right) = \left(1+\frac{P_{x:\overline{n}|}}{d}\right)^2 \cdot \left({}^2A_{x:\overline{n}|} - A_{x:\overline{n}|}^2\right). \tag{9.20}$$

❐

EXAMPLE 9.6

We know that if the net annual premium is determined by the equivalence principle, then the expected value of the present-value-of-loss random variable is zero. Here we consider the case where the premium is determined from a selected survival model, but the contingent contract is issued on a risk with an elevated failure probability in a particular year. Suppose an insurance of 1000 is issued to (60) at the standard premium rate, but this person is expected to experience a first-year failure probability that is ten times the standard value, with all other probabilities at the standard rates. Find the expected value of the present-value-of-loss random variable in this case, given the values $i=.06$, $A_{60}=.36933$, $A_{61}=.38300$, and $q_{60}=.01376$.

SOLUTION

The original net premium is

$$1000P_{60} = \frac{1000A_{60}}{\ddot{a}_{60}} = \frac{369.33}{11.14184} = 33.15,$$

where

$$\ddot{a}_{60} = \frac{1-A_{60}}{d} = \frac{.63067}{.06/1.06} = 11.14184.$$

For this particular insured the present-value-of-loss random variable is

$$_0L = 1000Z'_{60} - 33.15\ddot{Y}'_{60},$$

where Z'_{60} and $\ddot{Y}'_{60}$ denote the present value random variables based on $q'_{60} = 10 \cdot q_{60} = .13760$.

Then

$$E[_0L] = 1000A'_{60} - 33.15\ddot{a}'_{60},$$

where

$$A'_{60} = v \cdot q'_{60} + v \cdot p'_{60} \cdot A_{61} = \frac{.13760}{1.06} + \frac{.86240}{1.06}(.38300) = .44141,$$

so

$$\ddot{a}'_{60} = \frac{1-A'_{60}}{d} = \frac{.55859}{.06/1.06} = 9.86840.$$

Finally

$$E[_0L] = (1000)(.44141) - (33.15)(9.86840) = 114.27.$$ ❐

9.3 THE PERCENTILE PREMIUM PRINCIPLE[6]

As an alternative to determining net annual premiums by the equivalence principle, we might select the premium such that the probability of a positive loss is less than some tolerance limit. For example, let us find the premium for a unit discrete whole life insurance issued to (40) such that $Pr(_0L_{40} > 0) < .25$, where $_0L_{40}$ is the present-value-of-loss random variable defined in Section 9.2, assuming $i = .05$ and a uniform distribution of future lifetime with $\omega = 110$.

First we recall that

$$_0L_{40} = Z_{40} - P \cdot \ddot{Y}_{40} = Z_{40}\left(1+\frac{P}{d}\right) - \frac{P}{d},$$

so

$$Pr(_0L_{40} = 0) = Pr\left[v^{K_{40}+1}\left(1+\frac{P}{d}\right) = \frac{P}{d}\right]. \tag{9.21}$$

The future lifetime random variable T_{40} has a uniform distribution over the interval $(0,70)$, so the 25th percentile of the distribution of T_{40} is at $t = 17.50$. Therefore the premium is set so that $_0L_{40} = 0$ for failure in the 18th year, which is denoted by $K_{40} = 17$. That is,

[6] Some texts prefer the name *portfolio percentile premium principle.*

$$v^{18}\left(1+\frac{P}{d}\right) = \frac{P}{d},$$

which solves for

$$P = \frac{d \cdot v^{18}}{1-v^{18}} = \frac{1}{\ddot{s}_{\overline{18}|.05}} = .03385.$$

Note that, at this premium rate, if failure occurs earlier than in the 18th year a positive loss will result and if failure occurs later than in the 18th year the loss will be negative. If the premium rate is higher than .03385, then $Pr({}_0L_{40} > 0)$ is even smaller than .25. Premiums determined by this method are called *percentile premiums* (the 25th percentile premium in this case).

The above application of the percentile premium principle was done with respect to a single contract. In practice, the insurer is less likely to be concerned with the probability of gain/loss on a single contract, and more likely to examine the probability of gain/loss on a block, or portfolio, of identical and independent policies. This is explored in the following example.

EXAMPLE 9.7

Continuing the concept explored in Examples 7.12 and 8.15, we will now investigate the aggregate outcome for a group of annual premium contracts. Consider the present-value-of-loss random variable for a fully discrete whole life insurance, introduced in Section 9.2, with annual premium $P = .025$. (Note that the premium has not necessarily been determined by the equivalence principle.) Using the normal approximation, determine the minimum number of contracts to be issued to independent lives all age x so that the probability of a positive loss on the collection of contracts does not exceed .05, given the values $A_x = .24905$, ${}^2A_x = .09476$, and $i = .06$.

SOLUTION

The aggregate loss at issue is

$${}_0L_{Agg} = {}_0L_1 + {}_0L_2 + \cdots + {}_0L_n,$$

where each ${}_0L_i$ is the same as ${}_0L_x$ defined earlier, and n, the number of contracts to be issued, is the value we seek. The criterion for determining n is

$$Pr({}_0L_{Agg} > 0) \le .05.$$

Recall (see Section 9.2) that

$$\begin{aligned} {}_0L_x &= Z_x - P \cdot \ddot{Y}_x \\ &= \left(1+\frac{P}{d}\right) \cdot Z_x - \frac{P}{d} \\ &= \left(1+\frac{.025}{.06/1.06}\right) \cdot Z_x - \frac{.025}{.06/1.06}. \end{aligned}$$

Then

$$E[{}_0L_x] = 1.44167A_x - .44167$$
$$= (1.44167)(.24905) - .44167 = -.08262$$

and

$$Var({}_0L_x) = (1.44167)^2 \cdot ({}^2A_x - A_x{}^2)$$
$$= (1.44167)^2 \cdot [.09476 - (.24905)^2] = .06803.$$

Then

$$E[{}_0L_{Agg}] = n \cdot E[{}_0L_x] = -.08262n$$

and

$$Var({}_0L_{Agg}) = n \cdot Var({}_0L_x) = .06803n,$$

so $SD({}_0L_{Agg}) = \sqrt{Var({}_0L_{Agg})} = .26084\sqrt{n}$. Then, assuming that ${}_0L_{Agg}$ is approximately normal, we have

$$Pr({}_0L_{Agg} > 0) = Pr\left(Z > \frac{0-(-.08262n)}{.26084\sqrt{n}}\right) = .05,$$

where Z is the unit normal random variable. This tells us that

$$1.645 = \frac{0-(-.08262n)}{.26084\sqrt{n}} = \frac{.08262n}{.26084\sqrt{n}}.$$

This leads to

$$.42907\sqrt{n} = .08262n,$$

which solves for $n = 26.97$, or $n = 27$. ❐

The same analysis as in Example 9.5 could be used to determine the percentile premium, with the value of n given. This is pursued in Exercise 9-13. Note how the premium in the $n = 100$ case is lower than in the $n = 27$ case. This illustrates how the mortality risk is diversified over the group of contracts. The risk declines as the size of the group increases.

Does this mean that the premium approaches zero as $n \to \infty$? Of course not; even for an infinitely large group of policies, the insurance cannot be free. The limiting value of the premium as $n \to \infty$ is discovered in Exercise 9-14.

9.4 CONTINUOUS PAYMENT FUNDING SCHEMES

In this section we consider a funding scheme for a contingent payment model wherein the funding payments are made continuously. As we have noted before, the notion of continuous payment is totally abstract and does not occur in practice, but the mathematics of continuous payment models is sufficiently interesting to merit at least a brief study. We will consider in detail only the whole life insurance model; the extension to certain other models by analogous steps will be clear.

9.4.1 DISCRETE CONTINGENT PAYMENT MODELS

If a unit contingent payment is made at the end of the time interval of failure, its APV is given by A_x. If the funding payment, which we call the net annual premium, is made continuously at annual rate P, then the APV of the funding scheme is $P \cdot \bar{a}_x$. Equating the two APVs gives the net continuous annual premium rate, which is denoted by $\bar{P}_x$. Thus we have

$$\bar{P}_x = \frac{A_x}{\bar{a}_x}. \tag{9.22a}$$

By similar reasoning we obtain

$$\bar{P}^1_{x:\overline{n}|} = \frac{A^1_{x:\overline{n}|}}{\bar{a}_{x:\overline{n}|}} \tag{9.22b}$$

for n-year term insurance with continuous premium,

$$\bar{P}_{x:\overline{n}|}^{\;\;1} = \frac{A_{x:\overline{n}|}^{\;\;1}}{\bar{a}_{x:\overline{n}|}} \tag{9.22c}$$

for n-year pure endowment with continuous premium,

$$\bar{P}_{x:\overline{n}|} = \frac{A_{x:\overline{n}|}}{\bar{a}_{x:\overline{n}|}} \tag{9.22d}$$

for n-year endowment insurance with continuous premium, and

$$\bar{P}({}_{n|}A_x) = \frac{{}_{n|}A_x}{\bar{a}_{x:\overline{n}|}} \tag{9.22e}$$

for n-year deferred insurance with continuous premium paid during the deferred period as long as (x) continues to survive.

The net annual premiums in this section can be evaluated from a life table by approximating the continuous annuity functions in the denominator under one of the two assumptions described in Section 8.4.4 and its associated exercises.

9.4.2 CONTINUOUS CONTINGENT PAYMENT MODELS

Of greater theoretical interest than the Section 9.4.1 models involving continuous funding but benefit payment at the end of the interval of failure would be those with continuous funding and benefit payment at the precise time point of failure. (Recall that in the insurance context this is referred to as immediate payment of claims.[7]) The annual net premium rate for the whole life model in this case is denoted by $\bar{P}(\bar{A}_x)$. By the now-familiar equivalence principle we have

$$\bar{A}_x = \bar{P}(\bar{A}_x)\cdot\bar{a}_x \tag{9.23a}$$

or

$$\bar{P}(\bar{A}_x) = \frac{\bar{A}_x}{\bar{a}_x}. \tag{9.23b}$$

Using the result of Exercise 8-10 we can write

$$\bar{P}(\bar{A}_x) = \frac{1-\delta\cdot\bar{a}_x}{\bar{a}_x} = \frac{1}{\bar{a}_x}-\delta, \tag{9.24a}$$

or

$$\frac{1}{\bar{a}_x} = \bar{P}(\bar{A}_x)+\delta. \tag{9.24b}$$

EXAMPLE 9.8

If the age-at-failure random variable has an exponential distribution with mean $\frac{1}{\lambda}$, show that $\bar{P}(\bar{A}_x)=\lambda$, and explain why the net premium rate does not depend on the issue age of the insurance.

SOLUTION

From Equation (7.44) we have $\bar{A}_x=\frac{\lambda}{\lambda+\delta}$, where δ is the force of interest, and from Example 8.5 we have $\bar{a}_x=\frac{1}{\lambda+\delta}$. Then

$$\bar{P}(\bar{A}_x) = \frac{\lambda}{\lambda+\delta}\div\frac{1}{\lambda+\delta} = \lambda.$$

Due to the memoryless property of the exponential distribution, the future lifetime random variable T_x has the same distribution for all x, so the net premium rate is the same for all issue ages. (As mentioned in Section 5.2.2, this distribution is often used to model certain types of mechanical failure.) ❐

The stochastic approach, using the present-value-of-loss random variable, extends nicely to these fully continuous premium models. By analogy to the discrete case presented in Section 9.2, we define the present value of loss to be

$${}_0\bar{L}(\bar{A}_x) = v^{T_x}-\bar{P}\cdot\bar{a}_{\overline{T_x|}} \tag{9.25a}$$

[7] These models of continuous funding coupled with immediate payment of claims are called *fully continuous premium models*, and the premium rate is called the *fully continuous net premium rate*.

for an arbitrary continuous premium rate. But under the equivalence principle, which implies $E\left[{}_0\bar{L}(\bar{A}_x)\right]=0$, we have $\bar{P}=\bar{P}(\bar{A}_x)$ as already defined by Equation (9.23b). Thus we have

$$\begin{aligned} {}_0\bar{L}(\bar{A}_x) &= v^{T_x} - \bar{P}(\bar{A}_x)\cdot \bar{a}_{\overline{T_x}|} \\ &= \bar{Z}_x - \bar{P}(\bar{A}_x)\cdot \bar{Y}_x \\ &= \bar{Z}_x - \bar{P}(\bar{A}_x)\cdot\left(\frac{1-\bar{Z}_x}{\delta}\right) \\ &= \bar{Z}_x\left(1+\frac{\bar{P}(\bar{A}_x)}{\delta}\right)-\frac{\bar{P}(\bar{A}_x)}{\delta}, \end{aligned} \tag{9.25b}$$

which leads directly to

$$\begin{aligned} Var\left[{}_0\bar{L}(\bar{A}_x)\right] &= \left(1+\frac{\bar{P}(\bar{A}_x)}{\delta}\right)^2\cdot Var(\bar{Z}_x) \\ &= \left(1+\frac{\bar{P}(\bar{A}_x)}{\delta}\right)^2\cdot({}^2\bar{A}_x-\bar{A}_x{}^2) \\ &= \left(\frac{1}{\delta\cdot\bar{a}_x}\right)^2\cdot({}^2\bar{A}_x-\bar{A}_x{}^2), \end{aligned} \tag{9.26a}$$

by use of Equation (9.24b). Then using the result of Exercise 8-10 we also have

$$Var\left[{}_0\bar{L}(\bar{A}_x)\right] = \frac{{}^2\bar{A}_x-\bar{A}_x{}^2}{(1-\bar{A}_x)^2}. \tag{9.26b}$$

EXAMPLE 9.9

Let ${}_0\bar{L}(\bar{A}_x)$ denote the present-value-of-loss random variable under a fully continuous whole life model with continuous annual premium rate determined by the equivalence principle. Let L^* denote the present-value-of-loss random variable under a similar model with continuous annual premium rate .05. Find the value of $Var(L^*)$, given the following values:

$$Var[{}_0\bar{L}(\bar{A}_x)]=.25 \qquad \bar{A}_x=.40 \qquad \delta=.06$$

SOLUTION

From Equation (9.25a) we have

$${}_0\bar{L}(\bar{A}_x) = \bar{Z}_x-P\cdot\bar{Y}_x = \bar{Z}_x-P\left(\frac{1-\bar{Z}_x}{\delta}\right) = \bar{Z}_x\left(1+\frac{P}{\delta}\right)-\frac{P}{\delta}.$$

When the premium rate is determined from the equivalence principle, we have

$$P = \frac{\bar{A}_x}{\bar{a}_x} = \frac{.40}{\frac{1-.40}{.06}} = .04.$$

Then the variance is

$$Var[{}_0\bar{L}(\bar{A}_x)] = \left(1+\frac{P}{\delta}\right)^2 \cdot Var(\bar{Z}_x) = \left(1+\frac{.04}{.06}\right)^2 \cdot Var(\bar{Z}_x) = .25,$$

which solves for $Var(\bar{Z}_x) = .09$. Similarly,

$$Var(L^*) = \left(1+\frac{P^*}{\delta}\right)^2 \cdot Var(\bar{Z}_x) = \left(1+\frac{.05}{.06}\right)^2 (.09) = .3025.$$ ❐

9.5 FUNDING SCHEMES WITH m^{thly} PAYMENTS

In many applications, such as with insurance contracts, periodic funding payments are made at m^{thly} intervals within the year, such as semiannually, quarterly, or monthly. In general, if funding payments are made m times within a year, at the beginning of each mth of the year, the annual rate of funding will be denoted by the symbol $P^{(m)}$, with additional notation to identify the particular model being funded. It is important to remember that $P^{(m)}$ denotes the *net annual funding rate*, with funding payments made m times within the year, so that each actual funding payment is $\frac{P^{(m)}}{m}$. In the insurance context, $P^{(m)}$ is called a *true fractional premium.*

As before, the net annual funding rate will be determined by the equivalence principle, with the actuarial present value of the funding scheme found by using the m^{thly} annuity-due function developed in Section 8.4.2. Thus we would have

$$P_x^{(m)} = \frac{A_x}{\ddot{a}_x^{(m)}} \tag{9.27a}$$

for the whole life contingent payment model with m^{thly} funding,

$$P^{(m)}{}^{1}_{x:\overline{n}|} = \frac{A^{1}_{x:\overline{n}|}}{\ddot{a}^{(m)}_{x:\overline{n}|}} \tag{9.27b}$$

for the n-year term insurance model,

$$P^{(m)}{}_{x:\overset{\;1}{\overline{n}|}} = \frac{A_{x:\overset{\;1}{\overline{n}|}}}{\ddot{a}^{(m)}_{x:\overline{n}|}} \tag{9.27c}$$

for the n-year pure endowment model,

$$P^{(m)}_{x:\overline{n}|} = \frac{A_{x:\overline{n}|}}{\ddot{a}^{(m)}_{x:\overline{n}|}} \tag{9.27d}$$

for the n-year endowment insurance model, and

$$P^{(m)}({}_{n|}a_x) = \frac{{}_{n|}a_x}{\ddot{a}^{(m)}_{x:\overline{n}|}} \tag{9.27e}$$

for the n-year deferred immediate annuity model.

Under the immediate payment of claims models, where the contingent payment is made at the moment of failure rather than the end of the interval of failure, the APV in the numerator of the premium formula is replaced by its continuous counterpart and the premium symbol is adjusted as well. We would have

$$P^{(m)}\left(\bar{A}_x\right) = \frac{\bar{A}_x}{\ddot{a}^{(m)}_x} \tag{9.28a}$$

for the whole life model,

$$P^{(m)}\left(\bar{A}^{1}_{x:\overline{n}|}\right) = \frac{\bar{A}^{1}_{x:\overline{n}|}}{\ddot{a}^{(m)}_{x:\overline{n}|}} \tag{9.28b}$$

for the n-year term insurance model, and

$$P^{(m)}\left(\bar{A}_{x:\overline{n}|}\right) = \frac{\bar{A}_{x:\overline{n}|}}{\ddot{a}^{(m)}_{x:\overline{n}|}} \tag{9.28c}$$

for the n-year endowment insurance model.

If the funding scheme is limited to t years, where $t<n$, then the APV of the m^{thly} annuity in the denominator of the premium formula becomes $\ddot{a}^{(m)}_{x:\overline{t}|}$ and the premium symbol is adjusted to include the pre-subscript t as in the Equation (9.8) set. For example, for t-pay n-year term insurance with immediate payment of claims we would have

$${}_tP^{(m)}\left(\bar{A}^{1}_{x:\overline{n}|}\right) = \frac{\bar{A}^{1}_{x:\overline{n}|}}{\ddot{a}^{(m)}_{x:\overline{t}|}}. \tag{9.29}$$

The numerical calculation of m^{thly} net premiums follows directly from the approximate calculation of the associated m^{thly} annuity-due in the denominator of the premium formula. The details of such calculations are presented in Section 8.4.4 and its associated exercises.

9.6 FUNDING PLANS INCORPORATING EXPENSES

Recall the observation made earlier in this chapter that the annual funding payments determined by the equivalence principle, which we called net annual premiums in the life insurance context, provide only for the contingent benefit payment. In practice, of course, the price of an insurance (or other contingent payment) product must be set higher than the net premium in order to generate revenue to pay expenses of operation and the contingent benefit payments, as well as providing a profit margin to the insurer. The total annual premium actually paid for an insurance product, determined to cover benefits, expenses, and profit, is called the *gross annual premium*,[8] and is denoted by G.

Allowance for profit can be incorporated into the gross premium either implicitly or explicitly. The *implicit approach* is to use pricing assumptions that are more conservative than those actually expected to occur. This could include using an interest rate lower than that actually expected to be earned, or using a life table with higher-than-expected mortality rates (for an insurance contract) or with higher-than-expected survival rates (for an annuity contract). The *explicit approach* is to use specific profit factors in the premium calculation that are analogous to expense factors as described below.

If the explicit approach is used, it is then possible to view the total gross premium in three components: (1) the portion that provides for the benefit only, (2) the portion that provides for the expenses only, and (3) the portion that provides for the profit only. We recognize Component (1) as the net premium defined earlier. Some texts, as well as earlier editions of this text, focused attention on Components (1) and (2) together (i.e., the annual premium to cover benefits and expenses, but not profit), and referred to this amount as the *expense-augmented premium*.

If the implicit approach to incorporating profit in the gross premium is used, then a separate "profit premium" is not determined and the gross premium would be the same as the expense-augmented premium defined above. In this edition, we will consistently assume the implicit approach and therefore have no need to distinguish between the gross premium and the expense-augmented premium.[9] Only the term gross premium will be used henceforth in this text.[10]

It is a simple matter to extend the equivalence principle to incorporate expenses and therefore to calculate gross premiums. For ease of illustration we assume that the expenses allocated to a particular contingent contract are fixed costs known in advance. Then the *gross premium equivalence principle* states that the APV of the gross premiums equals the APV of the benefit payment plus the APV of the expense charges allocated to the contract.

9.6.1 EXPENSE CHARGES

For illustration we assume that expense charges allocated to a contract are of the following four types:

(1) A percentage of the gross premium itself.

[8] Other synonymous terms used in the actuarial literature include *contract premium*, *office premium*, and *expense-loaded premium*. In this text, and on Exam MLC, only the term gross premium will be used.

[9] The usefulness of making a gross premium vs. expense-augmented premium distinction is revealed when doing gross premium gain and loss analysis. (See Section 17.1.)

[10] In addition, it is likely that only the term gross premium will be used on Exam MLC.

(2) A fixed amount per unit of face value.

(3) A fixed (or percentage of benefit) amount incurred when the benefit payment is made.

(4) A fixed amount for the contract itself, regardless of benefit amount.

The analysis of corporate operational expenses leading to the determination of expense charges to be included in the price of each product is a complex issue that will vary according to the type of business under discussion. In any case the mechanics of this expense analysis are beyond the scope of this text.

We will, however, illustrate the four types of expense charges listed above under a typical life insurance policy, since the pricing of life insurance is a common example of this type of actuarial analysis.

Percent of premium expenses arise as commissions paid to sales agents and state premium taxes. It is customary for sales commissions to be larger for the first several years of a contract and then smaller in later years. The premium tax is likely to be level over all years.

The amount per unit of insurance might be expected to cover such things as underwriting (i.e., risk classification) expense, policy issue expenses, and subsequent policy maintenance expenses. Again it would be customary for these per unit expenses to be higher in the first year than in subsequent years of the policy. In our illustration we will consider the unit of insurance to be $1000.

The expense associated with making the benefit payment, called the *settlement expense*, is a one-time charge incurred at the same time as the benefit is paid. Therefore it can be introduced into the gross premium calculation by simply adding it to the benefit payment amount.

Since premiums need to be calculated per unit of benefit, such as per $1000, it is convenient to convert the fixed amount per policy expenses to the fixed amount per unit of insurance type by assuming an average policy size.[11] We illustrate the above discussion with the following example, and with the exercises associated with this section.

EXAMPLE 9.10

Assume that all per policy expenses have been converted to the per $1000 of benefit type. Assume a fully discrete whole life insurance contract issued to (x), with the following expenses: 75% of the first premium and 10% of all premiums thereafter; $10 at the beginning of the first year and $2 at the beginning of each year thereafter; $20 settlement expense. Find an expression for the gross premium of a $1000 benefit contract.

SOLUTION

If we let G denote the gross premium, then the APV of the premium income is $G \cdot \ddot{a}_x$. The APV of the percent of premium expense charges is $.75G + .10G \cdot a_x$, since the 10% charge is

[11] An alternative approach is to determine an annual policy fee that is independent of policy size. Actuaries who specialize in life insurance pricing will study this issue far more deeply than the introductory level presented here. In particular, they will explore this issue of policy fee determination and the important topic of expense analysis mentioned earlier.

incurred at the beginning of each year after the first only if the contract is still in force. The APV of the fixed per \$1000 of benefit expense charges is $10+2a_x$, by the same reasoning. The APV of the settlement expense is $20A_x$, since it is incurred at the same time as the benefit payment. Of course the APV of the benefit payment itself is $1000A_x$. Then the equivalence principle states that

$$G \cdot \ddot{a}_x = .75G + .10G \cdot a_x + 10 + 2a_x + 1020A_x$$

so

$$G = \frac{1020A_x + 10 + 2a_x}{\ddot{a}_x - .75 - .10a_x}.$$

Since $\ddot{a}_x = a_x + 1$, this can also be written as

$$G = \frac{1020A_x + 8 + 2\ddot{a}_x}{.90\ddot{a}_x - .65}.$$ ❐

9.6.2 RANDOM VARIABLE ANALYSIS

Recall the present value of payment random variable Z_x, defined in Section 7.1.2, and the present value of an immediate contingent unit payment stream random variable Y_x, as defined in Section 8.1.1. We can use Z_x and Y_x to now define a *present value of expenses random variable*, which we denote by H_x. The definition of H_x will depend on the specific pattern of expenses in each case. For the contract described in Example 9.10, for example, it would be defined as

$$H_x = (.75G+10) + (.10G+2) \cdot Y_x + 20Z_x, \tag{9.30}$$

which the reader is asked to verify in Exercise 9-28.

Recall the whole life net premium present-value-of-loss random variable ${}_0L_x$, defined by Equation (9.13). We can now define a *gross premium present-value-of-loss random variable*, which we denote by ${}_0L_x^G$, as the excess of the present value of benefits and expenses over the present value of gross premiums. For the whole life contract described in Example 9.10, we have

$${}_0L_x^G = 1000Z_x + H_x - G \cdot \ddot{Y}_x, \tag{9.31}$$

where H_x is defined by Equation (9.30), which the reader is asked to verify in Exercise 9-29.

The gross premium equivalence principle applied to determine the gross premium would then solve for G such that $E[{}_0L_x^G] = 0$. For the contract of Example 9.10 we have

$$\begin{aligned} {}_0L_x^G &= 1000Z_x + H_x - G \cdot \ddot{Y}_x \\ &= 1020Z_x + (.75G+10) + (.10G+2) \cdot Y_x - G \cdot \ddot{Y}_x. \end{aligned}$$

Then

$$E[{}_0L_x^G] = 1020A_x + (.75G+10) + (.10G+2)\cdot a_x - G\cdot \ddot{a}_x = 0$$

implies

$$G\cdot \ddot{a}_x = .75G + .10G\cdot a_x + 10 + 2a_x + 1020A_x,$$

as already established in Example 9.10.

9.7 WRITTEN-ANSWER QUESTION EXAMPLES

EXAMPLE 9.11

You are given $i = .06$ and the following survival probabilities:

n	1	2	3	4	5
${}_np_x$	.99105	.98143	.97107	.95994	.94800

(a) Calculate the values of $\ddot{a}_{x:\overline{5}|}$, $A^{1}_{x:\overline{5}|}$, and $P^{1}_{x:\overline{5}|}$.

(b) Suppose an impaired life is subject to a force of mortality given by $\mu'_x = \mu_x + .002$, where μ_x denotes the standard force of mortality. Let $\ddot{a}'_{x:\overline{n}|}$ denote the APV of the temporary annuity-due for this life.

(i) Intuitively, should $\ddot{a}'_{x:\overline{n}|}$ be larger or smaller than $\ddot{a}_{x:\overline{n}|}$? Why?

(ii) Show that $\ddot{a}'_{x:\overline{n}|}$ can be calculated from standard survival rates but using interest rate i'. What is the value of i'?

(iii) Calculate the values of $\ddot{a}'_{x:\overline{5}|}$, $A'^{1}_{x:\overline{5}|}$, and $P'^{1}_{x:\overline{5}|}$.

SOLUTION

(a) From first principles we find

$$\ddot{a}_{x:\overline{5}|} = 1 + \frac{.99105}{1.06} + \frac{.98143}{(1.06)^2} + \frac{.97107}{(1.06)^3} + \frac{.95994}{(1.06)^4} = 4.38411.$$

Then

$$
\begin{aligned}
A^{\;1}_{x:\overline{5}|} &= 1-d\cdot\ddot{a}_{x:\overline{5}|}-{}_5E_x \\
&= 1-\left(\frac{.06}{1.06}\right)(4.38411)-\frac{.94800}{(1.06)^5} = .04344.
\end{aligned}
$$

Finally,

$$P^{\;1}_{x:\overline{5}|} = \frac{.04344}{4.38411} = .00991.$$

(b) (i) $\ddot{a}'_{x:\overline{5}|}$ will be smaller than $\ddot{a}_{x:\overline{5}|}$; the greater mortality implies a smaller probability for each payment, so a smaller APV.

(ii) We know that

$${}_tp'_x = {}_tp_x\cdot e^{-.002t}$$

(see Exercise 6-18). Then

$$\ddot{a}'_{x:\overline{5}|} = \sum_{t=0}^{4} v^t\cdot{}_tp'_x = \sum_{t=0}^{4} e^{-\delta t}\cdot{}_tp_x\cdot e^{-.002t} = \sum_{t=0}^{4} e^{-\delta' t}\cdot{}_tp_x,$$

where $\delta'=\delta+.002$. Interest rate $i=.06$ implies $\delta=\ln(1.06)=.058268908$, so we have $\delta'=\delta+.002=.060268908$, and therefore $i'=e^{\delta'}-1=.06212$.

(iii) Then

$$\ddot{a}'_{x:\overline{5}|} = 1+\frac{.99105}{1.06212}+\frac{.98143}{(1.06212)^2}+\frac{.97107}{(1.06212)^3}+\frac{.95994}{(1.06212)^4} = 4.36785,$$

which is less that $\ddot{a}_{x:\overline{5}|}=4.38411$, as expected. Then

$$
\begin{aligned}
A'^{\;1}_{x:\overline{5}|} &= 1-d\cdot\ddot{a}'_{x:\overline{5}|}-{}_5E'_x \\
&= 1-\left(\frac{.06}{1.06}\right)(4.36785)-\frac{.94800}{(1.06212)^5} = .05140,
\end{aligned}
$$

and finally

$$P'^{\;1}_{x:\overline{5}|} = \frac{.05140}{4.36785} = .01177.$$

❐

9.8 EXERCISES

9.1 Annual Funding Schemes for Contingent Payment Models

9-1 Show that $P_{x:\overline{n}|} = \dfrac{1}{\ddot{a}_{x:\overline{n}|}}-d.$

9-2 Show that

$$_tP^1_{x:\overline{n}|} = P^1_{x:\overline{t}|} + P_{x:\overline{t}|}^{\ \ 1} \cdot A^1_{x+t:\overline{n-t}|}.$$

9-3 A 10-pay limited-payment whole life contract issued to (30) pays a benefit at the end of the year of failure of amount 1000 plus a refund of all net level premiums paid, without interest. Show that the net level annual premium, determined by the equivalence principle, is

$$P = \frac{1000A_{30}}{\ddot{a}_{30:\overline{10}|} - (IA)^1_{30:\overline{10}|} - 10 \cdot {}_{10|}A_{30}}.$$

9-4 A whole life contingent contract issued to (75) pays 1000 at the end of the interval of failure. The net premium paid at the beginning of the kth year is $P_k = P_1(1+i)^{k-1}$. The interest rate is 5% and the age-at-failure random variable has a uniform distribution with $\omega = 105$. Using the equivalence principle, find the value of P_1.

9-5 A 40-year-old home buyer takes out a 25-year mortgage of 100,000 at interest rate 5%, and purchases a 25-year decreasing term insurance contract with a death benefit that will exactly pay off the mortgage at the end of the year of death of the borrower. Calculate the net level annual premium for the term insurance, given the following values:

$$\ddot{a}_{40:\overline{25}|} = 14 \qquad {}_{25}p_{40} = .80$$

9-6 Calculate the value of $1000P(\bar{A}_{x:\overline{n}|})$, assuming UDD over each interval $(x, x+1)$ and the following values:

$$\bar{A}_{x:\overline{n}|} = .804 \qquad {}_nE_x = .600 \qquad i = .04$$

9-7 A 10-year deferred annuity-due with annual payment 10,000 is issued to (55), with net annual premiums paid during the deferred period. In addition to the annuity payments, the contract also provides for the return of all net premiums paid, without interest, if death occurs during the deferred period. Find the net level annual premium, given the following values:

$$\ddot{a}_{55:\overline{10}|} = 8 \qquad \ddot{a}_{55} = 12 \qquad (IA)^1_{55:\overline{10}|} = 2.50$$

9-8 Show that

$$\ddot{s}_{x:\overline{n}|} = \frac{1}{P_{x:\overline{n}|}^{\ \ 1}}.$$

9.2 Random Variable Analysis

9-9 Show that $E[{}_0L_x^{\,2}]$, where ${}_0L_x^{\,2}$ is defined by Equation (9.18), simplifies to the expression for $Var({}_0L_x)$ given by Equation (9.17b).

9-10 Recall that $E[{}_0L_x]=0$ only if the net premium is determined by the equivalence principle. Find the value of $E[{}_0L_{49}]$, given the following values:

$$A_{49}=.29224 \qquad Var({}_0L_{49})=.10$$
$$^2A_{49}=.11723 \qquad i=.05$$

9-11 For a unit whole life insurance, let ${}_0L_x$ denote the present-value-of-loss random variable when the premium is chosen such that $E[{}_0L_x]=0$, and let ${}_0L_x^*$ denote the present-value-of-loss random variable when the premium is chosen such that $E[{}_0L_x^*] = -.20$. Given that $Var({}_0L_x)=.30$, find the value of $Var({}_0L_x^*)$.

9-12 Let π denote the annual premium for a whole life contingent contract of benefit amount 10,000 issued to (30), and let ${}_0L(\pi)$ denote the present value of loss random variable for this contract. The interest rate is $i=.06$. Find the smallest value of π such that $Pr[{}_0L(\pi) > 0] < .50$, given the following values from the life table survival model to which (30) is subject:

$$l_{30}=9{,}501{,}382 \qquad l_{77}=4{,}828{,}285 \qquad l_{78}=4{,}530{,}476$$

9.3 The Percentile Premium Principle

9-13 Rework Example 9.7 to solve for the annual premium so that the probability of a positive loss on a collection of 100 identical and independent contracts does not exceed .05.

9-14 Rework Exercise 9-13 to find the annual premium as the number of contracts approaches infinity. (Note that this is the same as the net premium determined by the equivalence principle.)

9-15 Rework Example 9.7 with $P=.024$ and $n=100$ to find the probability of a positive loss on the collection of contracts.

9.4 Continuous Payment Funding Schemes

9-16 Find the value of $1000[\bar{P}(\bar{A}_x)-P_x]$, given the following values:

$$_{k|}q_x = \frac{.90^{k+1}}{9} \text{ for } k=0,1,2,\ldots \qquad \mu_{x+t}=\mu, \text{ for all } t \qquad i=.08$$

9-17 A fully continuous whole life model has an increasing benefit function of amount $b_t=(1+i)^t$ for failure at time t. If the premium is determined by the equivalcnce principle, show that the present-value-of-loss random variable is $\frac{\bar{Z}_x-\bar{A}_x}{1-\bar{A}_x}$.

9-18 If the force of interest is δ and the force of failure is $\lambda(x)=\lambda$ for all x, show that $Var[{}_0\bar{L}(\bar{A}_x)]=\frac{\lambda}{\lambda+2\delta}$, with continuous premium rate determined by the equivalence principle.

9-19 Let L denote the present-value-of-loss random variable under a fully continuous whole life model with continuous net annual premium rate determined by the equivalence principle. Let L^* denote the present-value-of-loss random variable under a similar model with continuous annual premium rate $\frac{4}{3}$ times the rate in L. Find the sum of the expected value and standard deviation of L^*, given the following values:

$$Var(L)=.5652 \qquad \bar{a}_x=5 \qquad \delta=.08$$

9-20 Let L denote the present-value-of-loss random variable under a fully continuous whole life model with continuous annual premium rate .09, and with a benefit of 2 paid at the precise instant of failure. Given that $\delta=.06$ and $\mu_{x+t}=.04$ for all t, find the value of $Var(L)$.

9-21 Let L denote the present-value-of-loss random variable under a fully continuous whole life model with continuous net annual premium rate determined by the equivalence principle. Find the value of $\bar{P}(\bar{A}_x)$, given the following values:

$$\frac{Var(\bar{Z}_x)}{Var(L)}=.36 \qquad \bar{a}_x=10$$

9-22 Let L denote the present-value-of-loss random variable under a fully continuous whole life contract issued to (40), with continuous net annual premium rate determined by the equivalence principle. The applicable survival model is uniform with $\omega=100$. Given also that $\delta=.02$ and ${}^2\bar{A}_{40}=.379$, find the value of $Var(L)$.

9-23 Show that $\bar{P}(\bar{A}_x)=\frac{\delta\cdot\bar{A}_x}{1-\bar{A}_x}$.

9-24 Find the CDF of ${}_0\bar{L}(\bar{A}_x)$, as defined by Equation (9.25a), if T_x has an exponential distribution with mean $\frac{1}{\lambda}$.

9.5 Funding Schemes with m^{thly} Payments

9-25 A 10-year term insurance issued to (30) for amount 10,000 has benefit paid at the end of the year of failure. Level true fractional premiums are determined under the equivalence principle and the UDD assumption. Calculate the difference (accurate to two decimals) between the annual premium rates if premiums are paid monthly versus semiannually, given the following values:

$$A^{1}_{30:\overline{10|}}=.015 \qquad \ddot{a}_{30:\overline{10|}}=8 \qquad {}_{10}E_{30}=.604 \qquad i=.05$$

9.6 Funding Plans Incorporating Expenses

9-26 A special endowment contract issued to (25) pays a pure endowment of 150,000 for survival to age 65, and a refund of all gross annual premiums paid, with interest, at the end of the year of failure, for failure before age 65. The gross annual premium is 1.20 times the net level annual premium. Calculate the net level annual premium, given the values $P_{25:\overline{40|}}=.008$, ${}_{40}p_{25}=.80$, and $i=.06$.

9-27 Consider a 20-pay unit discrete whole life insurance, with expense factors of a flat amount .02 each year, plus an additional .05 in the first year only, plus 3% of each premium paid. Find the gross annual premium for this contract, given the values $\ddot{a}_x=20$, $\ddot{a}_{x:\overline{20|}}=10$, and $d=.04$.

9-28 Verify Equation (9.30).

9-29 Verify Equation (9.31).

CHAPTER TEN

CONTINGENT CONTRACT RESERVES (NET LEVEL PREMIUM RESERVES)

We introduce the very important concept of reserves under contingent contracts by returning to the simple funding arrangement presented at the beginning of Chapter 9. Recall that the periodic funding payment was determined such that the present value at time 0 (at interest only) of the funding scheme was equal to the present value at time 0 of the payment needed at time k.

Now we consider time t, where $0<t<k$, and analyze the status of our funding arrangement at that time. (For convenience we assume that both t and k are integers.) This is illustrated in Figure 10.1, where the payments denoted by P have been made and those denoted by (P) are scheduled but have not yet been made.

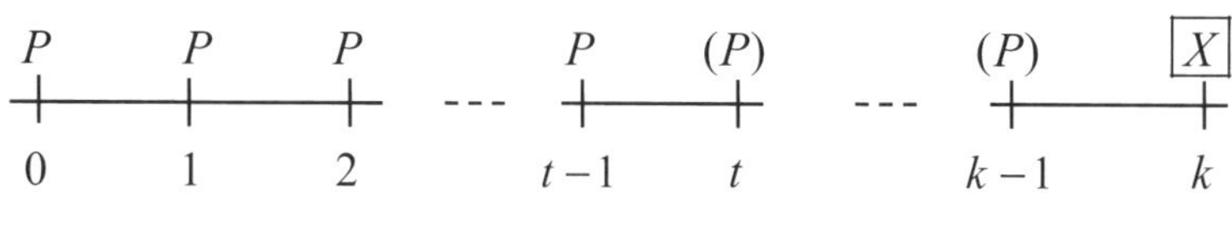

FIGURE 10.1

If we multiply both sides of Equation (9.1b) by $(1+i)^t$ we obtain

$$P \cdot \ddot{a}_{\overline{k}|i}(1+i)^t = X \cdot v^{k-t}, \tag{10.1a}$$

which equates the value at time t of the funding scheme to the value at time t of the future payment being funded. But the value at time t of the funding scheme can be separated into the value of the payments already made and the value of those yet to be made. When we do this, Equation (10.1a) becomes

$$P \cdot \ddot{s}_{\overline{t}|i} + P \cdot \ddot{a}_{\overline{k-t}|i} = X \cdot v^{k-t}, \tag{10.1b}$$

where $t<k$, or

$$P \cdot \ddot{s}_{\overline{t}|i} = X \cdot v^{k-t} - P \cdot \ddot{a}_{\overline{k-t}|i}. \tag{10.1c}$$

The left side of Equation (10.1c) gives the balance at time t of the fund being accumulated to provide the needed amount X at time k, and therefore represents the *financial status of the funding arrangement* as of time t. The right side of Equation (10.1c) represents the same concept and quantity, of course, but expresses the status of the funding arrangement as the excess of the present value of the future needed payment over the present value of the future funding payments yet to be made.

In general, we refer to the financial status of a funding arrangement as the *reserve* associated with that funding arrangement. Note that the reserve is measured at the *end* of the tth time interval, *just before* the funding payment for the $(t+1)^{st}$ interval is made. For this reason we refer to the reserve as a *terminal reserve*.[1] Note also that the reserve is different for different values of t, so we view the reserve as a function of t. In general we will use the symbol ${}_tV$ to denote the tth *terminal reserve* of a funding plan, with additional notation to describe the nature of the arrangement being funded.

(Viewing the reserve as the financial status of a funding arrangement is only applicable from the perspective of the party funding the future payment, not the party receiving the funding payments. The latter's perspective is explained more fully in the next chapter.)

With contingent payment models, including insurance contracts, the future time k at which amount X is paid out is stochastic rather than fixed and the future funding stream is stochastic as well. The analogy to the right side of Equation (10.1c) is that the reserve in the contingent payment case will be found as the excess of the APV of the future contingent payment over the APV of the future funding stream. In light of this use of *future* activity only, we say the reserve is determined by the *prospective method*.[2]

In the insurance context, the contingent payment is called the *benefit* under the insurance contract and the funding payments are therefore called the *benefit premiums* or the *net premiums*.[3] Therefore the general idea of the tth terminal net premium reserve, determined by the prospective method, under an insurance contract can be expressed as

$$ {}_tV = (APV\ of\ future\ benefits) - (APV\ of\ future\ net\ premiums). \tag{10.2} $$

In the sections that follow, we will analyze the terminal net premium reserve concept for various types of contingent contracts. Because the tth reserve is fundamentally just the status of the funding scheme at duration t of the contingent contract, the format of this chapter will closely follow that of Chapter 9 where the funding payments themselves were defined. Furthermore, we will be assuming that the net premium used in the funding scheme has been determined by the equivalence principle, and the same interest rate and life table that were used to determine the net premium in the first place are also used to determine the net premium reserves. Therefore, if a level net premium has been determined by the equivalence principle, and used to calculate a reserve according to Equation (10.2), the resulting reserve is called the *net level premium reserve*; we will refer to such reserves as *NLP reserves*.

Chapter 10 is concerned with NLP terminal reserves only. We wish to emphasize that the NLP terminal reserve is simply a mathematical function of the insurance contract. Its practical significance is somewhat limited; this will become clearer when we consider other important types of reserves, and other contract values, in Chapters 11 and 14.

---

[1] An alternative measure of the funding status, called the *initial reserve*, will arise in Section 10.1.3.

[2] The alternative, of determining the reserve at duration t from *past* activity only, is called the *retrospective method*, and will be introduced in Section 10.1.2. This will be the contingent payment analogy to the left side of Equation (10.1c).

[3] Although both terms "benefit premium" and "net premium" are used in other texts, and in practice, we will use only net premium henceforth in this text. (The Society of Actuaries uses net premium, rather than benefit premium, on Exam MLC.) Similarly, this text, as well as Exam MLC, uses the term "net premium reserve" rather than "benefit reserve."

10.1 NLP RESERVES FOR CONTINGENT PAYMENT MODELS WITH ANNUAL PAYMENT FUNDING

In this section we consider NLP reserves for various types of contingent payment models being funded by a series of discrete level annual premiums, as identified in Section 9.1. We will also analyze the reserve from the random variable perspective introduced in Section 9.2. Throughout Sections 10.1.1 - 10.1.5, we will be assuming that the single contingent payment is made at the end of the time interval (e.g., year) of failure. The alternative case of immediate payment of claims is treated in Section 10.1.6, and the case of contingent annuities is treated in Section 10.1.7.

Note that t is necessarily an integer throughout this section. This restriction is then relaxed for the fully continuous models of Section 10.2.

10.1.1 NLP RESERVES BY THE PROSPECTIVE METHOD

The following diagram provides an orientation for much of the discussion in this section.

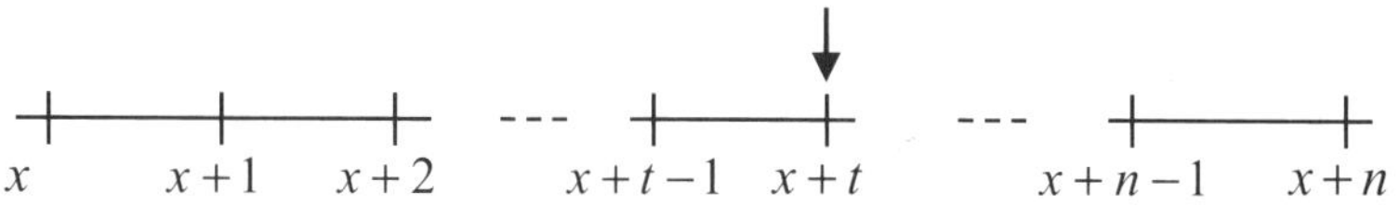

$$x \quad x+1 \quad x+2 \quad \cdots \quad x+t-1 \quad x+t \quad \cdots \quad x+n-1 \quad x+n$$

FIGURE 10.2

Consider the unit whole life insurance contract, with benefit payable at the end of the year in which the status of interest (x) fails, being funded by discrete level annual premiums of P_x paid at the beginning of each year. Given that the contract is still in effect at duration t (i.e., given that (x) has not yet failed at time t), the tth NLP terminal reserve by the prospective method is given by Equation (10.2) as

$$_tV_x = A_{x+t} - P_x \cdot \ddot{a}_{x+t}. \tag{10.3}$$

For n-year term insurance, with $t < n$, we have

$$_tV^1_{x:\overline{n}|} = A^{\ 1}_{x+t:\overline{n-t}|} - P^1_{x:\overline{n}|} \cdot \ddot{a}_{x+t:\overline{n-t}|}, \tag{10.4}$$

for n-year pure endowment we have

$$_tV_{x:\overline{n}|}^{\ \ 1} = A_{x+t:\overline{n-t}|}^{\ \ \ \ 1} - P_{x:\overline{n}|}^{\ \ 1} \cdot \ddot{a}_{x+t:\overline{n-t}|}, \tag{10.5}$$

and for n-year endowment insurance we have

$$_tV_{x:\overline{n}|} = A_{x+t:\overline{n-t}|} - P_{x:\overline{n}|} \cdot \ddot{a}_{x+t:\overline{n-t}|}. \tag{10.6}$$

All of Equations (10.4), (10.5) and (10.6) presume $t < n$. For $t = n$ the term insurance NLP reserve is $_nV^1_{x:\overline{n}|} = 0$, because the contract has expired without value. In the case of both pure endowment and endowment insurance we have ${}_nV_{x:\overline{n}|}^{\;\;1} = {}_nV_{x:\overline{n}|} = 1,$ because the contract matures at duration n for the amount of the unit endowment benefit.

In the case of limited payment funding patterns, such as h-pay whole life, we have

$${}_t^hV_x = A_{x+t} - {}_hP_x \cdot \ddot{a}_{x+t:\overline{h-t}|}, \tag{10.7a}$$

for $t < h$, since the future premium stream continues only to the hth year.[4]

For $t \geq h$ there are no future premiums so the prospective NLP reserve is simply

$${}_t^hV_x = A_{x+t}. \tag{10.7b}$$

Prospective NLP reserve expressions for other types of contingent payment contracts with limited payment funding patterns will be pursued in the exercises.

In the special case of the n-year deferred insurance defined in Section 7.1.3, the prospective NLP reserve expression will depend on the duration of the funding scheme. For example, if the funding is limited to the first n years (i.e., the deferred period), then we have

$${}_t^nV({}_{n|}A_x) = {}_{n-t|}A_{x+t} - {}_nP({}_{n|}A_x) \cdot \ddot{a}_{x+t:\overline{n-t}|}, \tag{10.8a}$$

for $t < n$, and

$${}_t^nV({}_{n|}A_x) = A_{x+t}, \tag{10.8b}$$

for $t \geq n$. NLP reserve expressions resulting from other assumptions about the funding pattern will be pursued in the exercises.

EXAMPLE 10.1

Find the value of ${}_{n-1}V_{x:\overline{n}|}$, given $A_{x:\overline{n}|} = .20$ and $d = .08$.

SOLUTION

Prospectively we have

$${}_{n-1}V_{x:\overline{n}|} = A_{x+n-1:\overline{1}|} - P_{x:\overline{n}|} \cdot \ddot{a}_{x+n-1:\overline{1}|}.$$

But $A_{x+n-1:\overline{1}|} = v$, since payment is certain at age $x+n$ under the endowment contract, and $\ddot{a}_{x+n-1:\overline{1}|} = 1$, so we have

$${}_{n-1}V_{x:\overline{n}|} = v - P_{x:\overline{n}|}.$$

[4] Note the notational rules. The parameter for number of premiums, h, occupies the pre-subscript position in the premium symbol ${}_hP_x$. But that position is reserved for the duration in the NLP reserve symbol, so the number-of-premiums parameter h is moved to the pre-superscript position in ${}_t^hV_x$.

Recall that

$$P_{x:\overline{n}|} = \frac{A_{x:\overline{n}|}}{\ddot{a}_{x:\overline{n}|}} = \frac{A_{x:\overline{n}|}}{\frac{1-A_{x:\overline{n}|}}{d}} = \frac{.20}{\frac{.80}{.08}} = .02.$$

Then

$${}_{n-1}V_{x:\overline{n}|} = (1-.08)-.02 = .90.$$ ❐

10.1.2 NLP RESERVES BY THE RETROSPECTIVE METHOD

As mentioned in the introductory section of this chapter, we can develop an expression for the NLP terminal reserve at duration t by considering only the past activity in the interval $(x, x+t]$, which we refer to as the *retrospective method*. For the whole life insurance model, we begin with the equivalence relationship between benefits and premiums stated as of time 0 and given by Equation (9.3a). Then we focus our attention at time t, and assume the contract is still in force at that time. We can separate the APV of the contingent annuity into the part addressing payments over the first t years and the part addressing payments after the first t years. From Equation (8.50) and Example 8.10 we have

$$\ddot{a}_x = \ddot{a}_{x:\overline{t}|} + {}_{t|}\ddot{a}_x = \ddot{a}_{x:\overline{t}|} + {}_tE_x \cdot \ddot{a}_{x+t}. \tag{10.9}$$

Similarly, we can separate the APV of the contingent benefit payment into the part addressing payment if the contingent event occurs within the first t years and the part addressing payment if the contingent event occurs after the first t years. From Equation (7.16) and Exercise 7-11 we have

$$A_x = A^1_{x:\overline{t}|} + {}_{t|}A_x = A^1_{x:\overline{t}|} + {}_tE_x \cdot A_{x+t}. \tag{10.10}$$

Now we use Equations (10.9) and (10.10) to substitute for $\ddot{a}_x$ and A_x, respectively, in Equation (9.3a) to obtain

$$P_x(\ddot{a}_{x:\overline{t}|} + {}_tE_x \cdot \ddot{a}_{x+t}) = A^1_{x:\overline{t}|} + {}_tE_x \cdot A_{x+t}$$

or

$$P_x \cdot \ddot{a}_{x:\overline{t}|} - A^1_{x:\overline{t}|} = {}_tE_x\left(A_{x+t} - P_x \cdot \ddot{a}_{x+t}\right)$$

or

$$\left(P_x \cdot \ddot{a}_{x:\overline{t}|} - A^1_{x:\overline{t}|}\right) \cdot \frac{1}{{}_tE_x} = A_{x+t} - P_x \cdot \ddot{a}_{x+t}. \tag{10.11a}$$

Recall from Equation (8.35) that

$$\ddot{s}_{x:\overline{t}|} = \ddot{a}_{x:\overline{t}|} \cdot \frac{1}{{}_tE_x}$$

gives the accumulated actuarial value of the temporary annuity-due. Finally we define

$$_tk_x = A^1_{x:\overline{t}|} \cdot \frac{1}{_tE_x} \tag{10.12}$$

to be the *accumulated cost of insurance* over the age interval $(x, x+t]$. Substituting in Equation (10.11a) we have

$$P_x \cdot \ddot{s}_{x:\overline{t}|} - {}_tk_x = A_{x+t} - P_x \cdot \ddot{a}_{x+t}. \tag{10.11b}$$

We recognize the right side of Equation (10.11b) as $_tV_x$ by the prospective method, so the left side must be $_tV_x$ as well. Thus we have

$$_tV_x = P_x \cdot \ddot{s}_{x:\overline{t}|} - {}_tk_x \tag{10.11c}$$

as the tth retrospective reserve for the whole life insurance model.

EXAMPLE 10.2

Find the value of $P^1_{x:\overline{n}|}$, given $P_x = .090$, $_nV_x = .563$, and $P_{x:\overline{n}|}^{\ \ 1} = .00864$.

SOLUTION

Because the value of $P_{x:\overline{n}|}^{\ \ 1}$ is given, and the value of the term insurance premium $P^1_{x:\overline{n}|}$ is sought, the retrospective view of the NLP reserve is suggested. We have

$$\begin{aligned}
_nV_x &= P_x \cdot \ddot{s}_{x:\overline{n}|} - {}_nk_x \\
&= P_x\left(\frac{\ddot{a}_{x:\overline{n}|}}{_nE_x}\right) - \frac{A^1_{x:\overline{n}|}}{_nE_x} \\
&= P_x\left(\frac{\ddot{a}_{x:\overline{n}|}}{_nE_x}\right) - \frac{P^1_{x:\overline{n}|} \cdot \ddot{a}_{x:\overline{n}|}}{_nE_x} \\
&= P_x\left(\frac{1}{P_{x:\overline{n}|}^{\ \ 1}}\right) - \frac{P^1_{x:\overline{n}|}}{P_{x:\overline{n}|}^{\ \ 1}}.
\end{aligned}$$

(See Exercise 9-8.) Then we have

$$_nV_x = \frac{.090}{.00864} - \frac{P^1_{x:\overline{n}|}}{.00864} = .563,$$

which solves for $P^1_{x:\overline{n}|} = .08514$. ❐

We need to get a better understanding about what ${}_tk_x$ actually represents, and we can do this by returning to the deterministic group approach used several times in Chapters 7 and 8. Consider the following diagram, which is an extension of Figure 7.2.

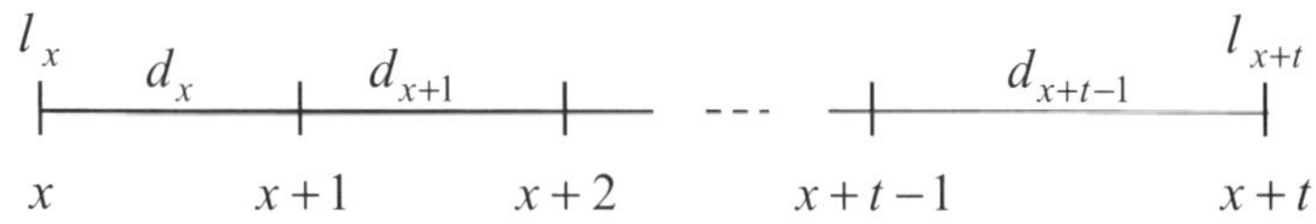

$$\begin{array}{ccccccccc} l_x & d_x & & d_{x+1} & & \cdots & d_{x+t-1} & & l_{x+t} \\ x & & x+1 & & x+2 & \cdots & x+t-1 & & x+t \end{array}$$

FIGURE 10.3

The sequence $d_x, d_{x+1}, \ldots, d_{x+t-1}$ represents the sequence of payments made if each of l_x persons purchases a whole life insurance of unit benefit at age x. The accumulated value at time t (age $x+t$) of the benefit payments is

$$d_x(1+i)^{t-1} + d_{x+1}(1+i)^{t-2} + \cdots + d_{x+t-1},$$

since all payments are made at the end of the interval of failure. There are l_{x+t} survivors in the group at time t. Each survivor's share of this accumulated value of benefit payments is called the *accumulated cost of insurance* and is given by

$$\begin{aligned} {}_tk_x &= \frac{d_x(1+i)^{t-1} + d_{x+1}(1+i)^{t-2} + \cdots + d_{x+t-1}}{l_{x+t}} \\ &= \frac{l_x}{l_{x+t}} \left[\frac{d_x(1+i)^{t-1} + d_{x+1}(1+i)^{t-2} + \cdots + d_{x+t-1}}{l_x} \right] \\ &= \frac{(1+i)^t}{{}_tp_x} \left[\frac{v \cdot d_x + v^2 \cdot d_{x+1} + \cdots + v^t \cdot d_{x+t-1}}{l_x} \right] = \frac{1}{{}_tE_x} \cdot A^1_{x:\overline{t|}}, \end{aligned}$$

as established by Equation (10.12).

Retrospective NLP reserve expressions for other types of insurance models will be developed in the exercises.

10.1.3 ADDITIONAL NLP TERMINAL RESERVE EXPRESSIONS

Starting with the basic prospective reserve expression given by Equation (10.3) for the whole life insurance model, we can develop several additional expressions for the tth NLP terminal reserve under that model. We have

$${}_tV_x = A_{x+t} - P_x \cdot \ddot{a}_{x+t} = (1 - d \cdot \ddot{a}_{x+t}) - P_x \cdot \ddot{a}_{x+t} = 1 - (P_x + d) \cdot \ddot{a}_{x+t} \tag{10.13}$$

by using the result of Example 8.4. Then substituting for (P_x+d) from Equation (9.4) we have the elegant formula

$${}_tV_x = 1 - \frac{\ddot{a}_{x+t}}{\ddot{a}_x}, \tag{10.14}$$

which expresses the NLP reserve in terms of contingent annuity values.

If we substitute for $\ddot{a}_{x+t}$ in Equation (10.13) by again using Equation (9.4) we obtain

$$ {}_tV_x = 1 - \frac{P_x + d}{P_{x+t} + d} = \frac{P_{x+t} - P_x}{P_{x+t} + d}, \tag{10.15} $$

which expresses the NLP reserve in terms of net annual premium values. Conversely, if we substitute $\frac{1-A_x}{d}$ for $\ddot{a}_x$ and $\frac{1-A_{x+t}}{d}$ for $\ddot{a}_{x+t}$ in Equation (10.14), we obtain

$$ {}_tV_x = 1 - \frac{1 - A_{x+t}}{1 - A_x} = \frac{A_{x+t} - A_x}{1 - A_x}, \tag{10.16} $$

which expresses the NLP reserve in terms of net single premium values. By substituting $P_{x+t} \cdot \ddot{a}_{x+t}$ for A_{x+t} in Equation (10.13) we obtain

$$ {}_tV_x = P_{x+t} \cdot \ddot{a}_{x+t} - P_x \cdot \ddot{a}_{x+t} = (P_{x+t} - P_x) \cdot \ddot{a}_{x+t}, \tag{10.17} $$

which is called the *premium difference formula*.

Another expression results if we substitute for $\ddot{a}_{x+t}$ in Equation (10.13) using

$$ \ddot{a}_{x+t} = \frac{A_{x+t}}{P_{x+t}}, $$

which itself comes from Equation (9.3a) with x replaced by $x+t$. Then Equation (10.13) becomes

$$ {}_tV_x = A_{x+t} - P_x \left(\frac{A_{x+t}}{P_{x+t}} \right) = \left(1 - \frac{P_x}{P_{x+t}} \right) \cdot A_{x+t}. \tag{10.18} $$

Equation (10.18) has an important interpretation. If a whole life insurance contract were issued at age $x+t$, then a level annual net premium of P_{x+t} would be sufficient to fund the future unit contingent benefit payment. But instead the contract was issued at age x, with level annual net premium of P_x (where $P_x < P_{x+t}$), so the future premium stream of P_x each will fund a future contingent payment of size $\frac{P_x}{P_{x+t}} < 1$. The remainder of the future contingent payment, which is $1 - \frac{P_x}{P_{x+t}}$, must be funded by the NLP reserve at time t, so the reserve has to be the expected present value of a benefit of that size, which is stated by Equation (10.18). The amount of future benefit funded by the NLP reserve is called the *amount of reduced paid-up insurance*, because this amount of benefit is "paid up" at duration t even if no future premiums are paid. (See also Section 14.3.2.)

NLP reserve expressions similar to those given by Equations (10.13) through (10.18) for the whole life model can also be developed for the endowment insurance model. This is pursued in Exercise 10-5.

10.1.4 RANDOM VARIABLE ANALYSIS

Recall that the present-value-of-loss random variable defined by Equation (9.13) measures the present value of loss at time 0. (Recall that the value of P resulting from setting $E[{}_0L_x]=0$ is the same as the value of P produced by the equivalence principle.) Now suppose the insurance contract is still in effect at time t, which means that the status of interest has not yet failed at time t. This means we are given that $K_x \geq t$. Then conditional on $K_x \geq t$ we can write the present value of future loss at time t as $v^{k-t} - P \cdot \ddot{a}_{\overline{k-t}|}$ for failure occurring in the kth time interval, where $k = t+1, t+2, \cdots$. In general we would have

$$ {}_tL_x = v^{K_x+1-t} - P_x \cdot \ddot{a}_{\overline{K_x+1-t}|} \tag{10.19a} $$

$$ = Z_{x+t} - P_x \cdot \ddot{Y}_{x+t} \tag{10.19b} $$

as the present-value-of-loss random variable measured at time t, given $K_x \geq t$. This is illustrated in the following figure.

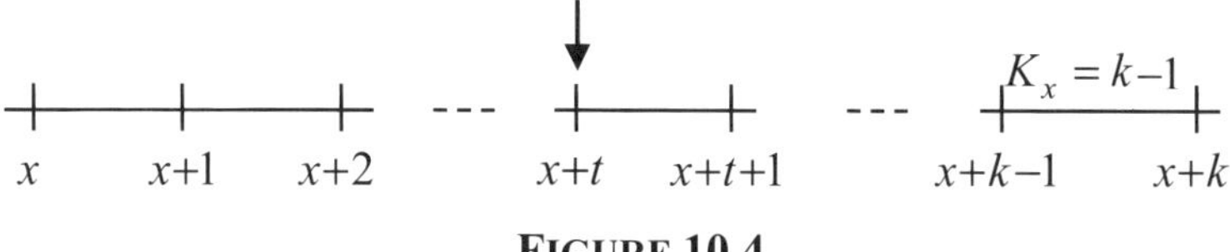

FIGURE 10.4

Taking the conditional expectation in Equation (10.19b), given $K_x \geq t$, we have

$$ E[{}_tL_x \mid K_x \geq t] = A_{x+t} - P_x \cdot \ddot{a}_{x+t}, \tag{10.20} $$

which is the prospective expression for the tth NLP terminal reserve. Thus we conclude that if the level funding payment, or net level premium, is determined by the equivalence principle, then the NLP terminal reserve is given by the conditional expected value of the present-value-of-loss random variable measured at time t.

The conditional variance of the present-value-of-loss random variable ${}_tL_x$ is found in the same way we found $Var({}_0L_x)$ in Section 9.2 (see Equations (9.17a) and (9.17b)), producing

$$ Var\left({}_tL_x \mid K_x \geq t\right) = \left(1+\frac{P_x}{d}\right)^2 \cdot \left({}^2A_{x+t} - A_{x+t}{}^2\right). \tag{10.21} $$

The parallel development of the expected value and variance of ${}_tL_{x:\overline{n}|}$ is left as Exercise 10-8.

EXAMPLE 10.3

Let ${}_2L = 1000 \cdot {}_2L^1_{x:\overline{4}|}$ denote the present-value-of-loss random variable at duration 2 for a 4-year term insurance of amount 1000 issued to (*x*), given $K_x \geq 2$. Find the value of $Var({}_2L)$, given the following values:

$$P^1_{x:\overline{4}|} = .12 \qquad q_{x+2} = .12 \qquad q_{x+3} = .13 \qquad i = 0$$

SOLUTION

Note that $v = 1$ since $i = 0$. We will use *P* in place of $1000P^1_{x:\overline{4}|}$ for notational convenience. ${}_2L$ assumes the value $1000 - P = 880$ if failure occurs in $(x+2, x+3]$, which event happens with probability .12, and ${}_2L$ assumes the value $1000 - 2P = 760$ if failure occurs in $(x+3, x+4]$, which happens with probability $(.88)(.13) = .1144$. If survival to age $x+4$ occurs, which happens with probability $(.88)(.87) = .7656$, then ${}_2L$ assumes the value $0 - 2P = -240$. (Note that ${}_2L$ is defined conditional on $K_x \geq 2$.) Then we find

$$E[{}_2L|K_x \geq 2] = (880)(.12) + (760)(.1144) + (-240)(.7656) = 8.80$$

and

$$E[{}_2L^2|K_x \geq 2] = (880)^2(.12) + (760)^2(.1144) + (-240)^2(.7656) = 203{,}104$$

and therefore

$$Var({}_2L|K_x \geq 2) = 203{,}104 - (8.80)^2 = 203{,}026.56.$$

❐

10.1.5 NLP RESERVES FOR CONTINGENT CONTRACTS WITH IMMEDIATE PAYMENT OF CLAIMS

Recall the continuous contingent payment models developed in Section 7.3, which we also refer to as immediate payment of claims models. The annual funding payments for such models were considered in Section 9.1.2. Prospective expressions for the tth NLP terminal reserve for such models are parallel to those developed earlier in this section for models with benefit paid at the end of the year of failure.[5] Thus, for example, we have

$${}_tV(\bar{A}_x) = \bar{A}_{x+t} - P(\bar{A}_x) \cdot \ddot{a}_{x+t} \tag{10.22}$$

for the whole life model,

$${}_tV(\bar{A}^1_{x:\overline{n}|}) = \bar{A}^{\ 1}_{x+t:\overline{n-t}|} - P(\bar{A}^1_{x:\overline{n}|}) \cdot \ddot{a}_{x+t:\overline{n-t}|} \tag{10.23}$$

for the *n*-year term insurance model, and

[5] Just as the level annual premiums for immediate payment of claims models are called semicontinuous net premiums, just so the associated NLP reserves are called *semicontinuous net premium reserves*.

$$ {}_tV(\bar{A}_{x:\overline{n|}}) = \bar{A}_{x+t:\overline{n-t|}} - P(\bar{A}_{x:\overline{n|}}) \cdot \ddot{a}_{x+t:\overline{n-t|}} \tag{10.24} $$

for the n-year endowment insurance model. If the contract involves a limited funding pattern over the first h years only, then the tth NLP reserve for an n-year term insurance with immediate payment of claims is given by

$$ {}_t^hV(\bar{A}^{1}_{x:\overline{n|}}) = \bar{A}^{\;1}_{x+t:\overline{n-t|}} - {}_hP(\bar{A}^{1}_{x:\overline{n|}}) \cdot \ddot{a}_{x+t:\overline{h-t|}} \tag{10.25a} $$

for $t < h < n$, and

$$ {}_t^hV(\bar{A}^{1}_{x:\overline{n|}}) = \bar{A}^{\;1}_{x+t:\overline{n-t|}} \tag{10.25b} $$

for $h < t < n$.

The retrospective reserve expression for the whole life model is

$$ {}_tV(\bar{A}_x) = P(\bar{A}_x) \cdot \ddot{s}_{x:\overline{t|}} - {}_t\bar{k}_x, \tag{10.26} $$

where

$$ {}_t\bar{k}_x = \bar{A}^{1}_{x:\overline{t|}} \cdot \frac{1}{{}_tE_x}. \tag{10.27} $$

Other NLP terminal reserve expressions for contracts with immediate payment of claims are developed in the exercises. The NLP reserve expressions in this section can be evaluated from a life table by using the UDD assumption to evaluate the various $\bar{A}$ functions.

10.1.6 NLP RESERVES FOR LIFE ANNUITY MODELS

If an n-year deferred life annuity-due contract is funded by level annual premiums over the deferred period, then the tth NLP terminal reserve, for $t < n$, is given by

$$ {}_tV({}_{n|}\ddot{a}_x) = {}_{n-t|}\ddot{a}_{x+t} - P({}_{n|}\ddot{a}_x) \cdot \ddot{a}_{x+t:\overline{n-t|}}, \tag{10.28} $$

since the future benefit is still a deferred annuity-due (deferred for $n-t$ years) and $n-t$ level net annual premiums still remain to be made. The level net premium $P({}_{n|}\ddot{a}_x)$ is defined by Equation (9.11b).

10.2 RECURSIVE RELATIONSHIPS FOR DISCRETE MODELS WITH ANNUAL PREMIUMS

Additional understanding of the NLP reserve concept can be obtained by examining how the reserve evolves from one duration to the next. We will again make use of the group deterministic interpretation as the easiest way to present these ideas for the first time, and then move to a stochastic presentation of the same concepts. We will use the generic symbols P (for the level net premium) and ${}_tV$ (for the NLP terminal reserve at integral duration t), since the presentation here is applicable to any of the whole life, term, or endowment insurance models, including the h-pay limited-payment models provided $t < h$. We also assume a fixed contingent payment benefit amount of B.[6]

We focus on the single year of age from $x+t$ to $x+t+1$, which is the $(t+1)^{st}$ year of the contingent payment contract. This is illustrated in the following figure.

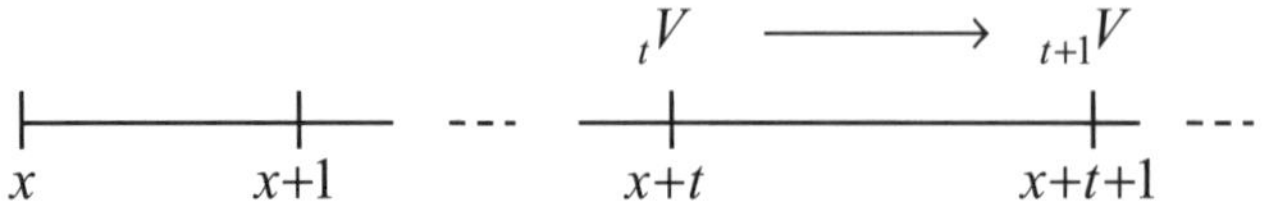

FIGURE 10.5

We will find it useful to begin with the group deterministic approach considered first in Section 7.2 and several places thereafter. Suppose l_x persons each purchase an identical contingent contract of face amount B, with level annual net premium P. At the end of the tth year there are l_{x+t} persons alive (and hence l_{x+t} contracts in force). Each contract carries an NLP terminal reserve of size $_tV$ at that time, so the total aggregate reserve fund is $l_{x+t} \cdot {}_tV$. At the beginning of the $(t+1)^{st}$ year each person pays a premium of P, so the aggregate fund becomes

$$l_{x+t}({}_tV+P) = l_{x+t} \cdot {}_{t+1}I, \tag{10.29}$$

where ${}_{t+1}I = {}_tV+P$ is called the $(t+1)^{st}$ *initial net premium reserve* for the contingent contract. This aggregate initial reserve fund then earns interest at rate i, and therefore grows to amount $l_{x+t}({}_tV+P)(1+i)$ by the end of the $(t+1)^{st}$ year. During that year d_{x+t} contracts fail and l_{x+t+1} contracts survive. The aggregate fund at time $t+1$ must be sufficient to pay the contingent benefit of B to each of the d_{x+t} that fail and establish the $(t+1)^{st}$ NLP terminal reserve for the l_{x+t+1} that survive. Thus we have

$$l_{x+t}({}_tV+P)(1+i) = d_{x+t} \cdot B + l_{x+t+1} \cdot {}_{t+1}V. \tag{10.30a}$$

If we divide both sides of Equation (10.30a) by l_{x+t}, we obtain

$$({}_tV+P)(1+i) = q_{x+t} \cdot B + p_{x+t} \cdot {}_{t+1}V, \tag{10.30b}$$

which expresses the same idea as Equation (10.30a), but on an expected value basis for one particular contract rather than on an aggregate deterministic basis for a collection of similar contracts. If we multiply both sides of Equation (10.30b) by v we obtain

$${}_tV + P = v \cdot q_{x+t} \cdot B + v \cdot p_{x+t} \cdot {}_{t+1}V, \tag{10.30c}$$

---

[6] In Section 11.3 we generalize this development to the case with non-level premiums and/or benefits.

which expresses the initial NLP reserve as an expected present value by considering the two possible uses of the initial reserve at year end, depending on whether the contract fails (with probability q_{x+t}) or survives (with probability p_{x+t}). Next we subtract ${}_tV$ from both sides of Equation (10.30c) and multiply it by $p_{x+t}+q_{x+t} = 1$, obtaining

$$\begin{aligned} P &= v\cdot q_{x+t}\cdot B+v\cdot p_{x+t}\cdot {}_{t+1}V - {}_tV(p_{x+t}+q_{x+t}) \\ &= (v\cdot B-{}_tV)\cdot q_{x+t}+(v\cdot {}_{t+1}V-{}_tV)\cdot p_{x+t}. \end{aligned} \tag{10.30d}$$

Equation (10.30d) expresses the net level premium as an expected present value by considering the two possible roles it could play at year end, namely providing the excess of the present value of benefit over the existing NLP reserve (if the contract fails) or the excess of the present value of the new $(t+1)^{st}$ NLP reserve over the existing reserve (if the contract survives).

Finally, substituting $1-q_{x+t}$ for p_{x+t} in Equation (10.30b) and rearranging we have

$${}_{t+1}V = ({}_tV+P)(1+i) - q_{x+t}(B-{}_{t+1}V). \tag{10.30e}$$

The excess of the benefit over the NLP terminal reserve, $B-{}_{t+1}V$, is called the *net amount at risk*. This is a cost to the insurer at time $t+1$ if the contract fails in $(t,t+1]$, which happens with probability q_{x+t}, so the product $q_{x+t}(B-{}_{t+1}V)$ is called the *expected cost of insurance based on the net amount at risk.*

EXAMPLE 10.4

Use Equation (10.30e), with ${}_0V=0$, to derive the formula

$${}_nV = P\cdot \ddot{s}_{\overline{n}|}-\sum_{k=1}^{n} q_{x+k-1}\cdot(B-{}_kV)(1+i)^{n-k}, \tag{10.30f}$$

which expresses ${}_nV$ in terms of the sequence of annual net amounts at risk.

SOLUTION

Starting with $t=0$ and ${}_0V=0$, we recursively find

$${}_1V = P(1+i)-q_x\cdot(B-{}_1V)$$

and

$$\begin{aligned} {}_2V &= ({}_1V+P)(1+i)-q_{x+1}\cdot(B-{}_2V) \\ &= P\cdot \ddot{s}_{\overline{2}|}-\left[q_x\cdot(B-{}_1V)(1+i)+q_{x+1}\cdot(B-{}_2V)\right]. \end{aligned}$$

Continuing in this manner we obtain the desired result. ❒

EXAMPLE 10.5

Contingent payment contracts sometimes contain a refund of premium feature, with or without interest. Consider an n-year deferred life annuity-due issued to (x), with net level annual premiums paid during the deferred period. The contract includes a benefit of return of net level premiums paid, with interest at rate i, for failure during the deferred period. The net level premium and the NLP reserves are also calculated at rate i. Find expressions for the net level annual premium and the tth NLP terminal reserve, for $t \leq n$.

SOLUTION

This problem is best approached using the recursive relationship of this section. Since ${}_0V = 0$ we have

$$P(1+i) = q_x[P(1+i)] + p_x \cdot {}_1V$$

or

$$P(1+i) \cdot (1-q_x) = p_x \cdot {}_1V,$$

so ${}_1V = P(1+i)$. Thus we see that the first NLP reserve is the same as the failure benefit in the first year, namely the first premium with interest.

Similarly, we have

$$({}_1V+P)(1+i) = q_{x+1}(P \cdot \ddot{s}_{\overline{2}|}) + p_{x+1} \cdot {}_2V.$$

But

$$({}_1V+P)(1+i) = [P(1+i)+P](1+i) = P \cdot \ddot{s}_{\overline{2}|},$$

so we have

$$P \cdot \ddot{s}_{\overline{2}|} \cdot (1-q_{x+1}) = p_{x+1} \cdot {}_2V,$$

so ${}_2V = P \cdot \ddot{s}_{\overline{2}|}$. Continuing in this way we find ${}_tV = P \cdot \ddot{s}_{\overline{t}|}$ for all $t \leq n$. But, prospectively, ${}_nV = \ddot{a}_{x+n}$, so we find $P = \dfrac{\ddot{a}_{x+n}}{\ddot{s}_{\overline{n}|}}$. ❐

Thus we see that if the failure benefit is the return of net premiums with interest at the same rate as that used for premium and reserve calculation, then the NLP reserve is the same as the failure benefit itself. (Recall that we developed this result for the net annual premium only in Section 9.1.3.) When the failure benefit is the reserve, then there is no cost of insurance under the contract, since each contract provides its own failure benefit. In effect, the mortality risk has been transferred from the insurer to the insured. Note that the result ${}_tV = P \cdot \ddot{s}_{\overline{t}|}$ is reached directly from Equation (10.30f), since $B = {}_kV$ in this case.

EXAMPLE 10.6

The matter of a modified parameter in one particular year, already explored in Examples 7.10 and 9.6, can arise in connection with reserves as well. Consider a unit fully discrete whole life insurance issued to (x), with non-level premiums. The insured is expected to experience a higher than standard failure probability at age $x+19$ only. The net premium for the 20th contract year is higher than the standard net annual premium P_x by .01, but all net premium reserves on this contract are identical to those on a standard whole life contract with net level premiums. Calculate the excess of q'_{x+19}, the rate experienced by this insured, over the standard rate q_{x+19}, given the values ${}_{20}V_x = .427$ and $i = .03$.

SOLUTION

Recursively, for a standard policy, we have

$$({}_{19}V_x + P_x)(1.03) = q_{x+19} + p_{x+19} \cdot {}_{20}V_x,$$

and for this particular substandard policy we have

$$({}_{19}V'_x + P_x + .01)(1.03) = q'_{x+19} + p'_{x+19} \cdot {}_{20}V'_x.$$

But ${}_{19}V'_x = {}_{19}V_x$ and ${}_{20}V'_x = {}_{20}V_x$. Subtracting the first equation from the second we find

$$(.01)(1.03) = (q'_{x+19} - q_{x+19}) + {}_{20}V_x \cdot (p'_{x+19} - p_{x+19}) = (q'_{x+19} - q_{x+19})(1 - {}_{20}V_x),$$

so

$$q'_{x+19} - q_{x+19} = \frac{(.01)(1.03)}{1-.427} = .01798.$$ ❐

10.3 NLP RESERVES FOR CONTINGENT PAYMENT MODELS WITH CONTINUOUS PAYMENT FUNDING

Here we return to the concept of funding contingent payment contracts with continuous funding payments, as introduced in Section 9.3. We repeat the observation made in Section 9.3 that this notion is an abstract one, but with some interesting mathematics that justifies a brief study of it. We will consider in detail only the whole life model.

10.3.1 DISCRETE WHOLE LIFE CONTINGENT PAYMENT MODELS

Consider the discrete whole life contingent payment model with continuous funding at annual rate $\overline{P}_x$, as defined by Equation (9.20a). (Recall that the payment model is called discrete because the contingent payment is made at the end of the discrete interval (generally year) of failure, notwithstanding that the funding scheme is continuous.) If the contract has not yet failed at time t, then the tth NLP terminal reserve is given by the prospective method as

$${}_t\overline{V}_x = A_{x+t} - \overline{P}_x \cdot \overline{a}_{x+t}. \tag{10.31}$$

If the continuous funding scheme is limited to the first h years of the contract, then we have

$${}^h_t\overline{V}_x = A_{x+t} - {}_h\overline{P}_x \cdot \overline{a}_{x+t:\overline{h-t}|} \tag{10.32a}$$

if $t < h$, and

$$ {}_t^h\overline{V}_x = A_{x+t} \tag{10.32b}$$

if $t \geq h$, since there are no future funding payments beyond duration h.

The retrospective NLP reserve is given by

$$ {}_t\overline{V}_x = \overline{P}_x \cdot \overline{s}_{x:\overline{t|}} - {}_tk_x, \tag{10.33}$$

which differs from the annual premium case given by Equation (10.11c) in that the accumulation of past premium occurs continuously. The continuous actuarial accumulated value, denoted $\overline{s}_{x:\overline{t|}}$, is defined by Equation (8.41).

The NLP reserve expressions in this section can be evaluated from a life table by using the UDD-based approximations or the Woolhouse approximations described in Chapter 8, to evaluate the various continuous annuity functions.

10.3.2 Continuous Whole Life Contingent Payment Models

Next we consider the whole life model with both continuous funding and immediate payment of claims, as introduced in Section 9.4.2, with annual net premium rate denoted by $\overline{P}(\overline{A}_x)$. Recall that such models are called fully continuous premium models, so their reserves are called *fully continuous net premium reserves*.

By now the reader should understand the principles used to write various NLP reserve expressions. For this model the NLP reserve at duration t is given prospectively as

$$ {}_t\overline{V}(\overline{A}_x) = \overline{A}_{x+t} - \overline{P}(\overline{A}_x) \cdot \overline{a}_{x+t} \tag{10.34}$$

and retrospectively as

$$ {}_t\overline{V}(\overline{A}_x) = \overline{P}(\overline{A}_x) \cdot \overline{s}_{x:\overline{t|}} - {}_t\overline{k}_x, \tag{10.35}$$

where the continuous version of the accumulated cost of insurance, denoted ${}_t\overline{k}_x$, is defined by Equation (10.27).

Additional expressions for the reserve in the fully continuous case, analogous to those presented in Section 10.1.3 in the discrete case, can be developed by steps parallel to those used in Section 10.1.3. Accordingly we will present only a sample of results here, and then invite the reader to derive the continuous version of the rest of the Section 10.1.3 results in the exercises.

Analogous to Equation (10.13) we now have

$$ {}_t\overline{V}(\overline{A}_x) = 1 - \left[\overline{P}(\overline{A}_x) + \delta\right] \cdot \overline{a}_{x+t}, \tag{10.36}$$

analogous to Equation (10.14) we now have

$$ {}_t\bar{V}(\bar{A}_x) = 1-\frac{\bar{a}_{x+t}}{\bar{a}_x}, \tag{10.37}$$

and analogous to Equation (10.17) we now have

$$ {}_t\bar{V}(\bar{A}_x) = \left[\bar{P}(\bar{A}_{x+t})-\bar{P}(\bar{A}_x)\right]\cdot\bar{a}_{x+t}. \tag{10.38}$$

In the fully continuous case, the NLP reserve is defined for all real values of t, rather than being restricted to integral t only. Strictly speaking, ${}_t\bar{V}(\bar{A}_x)$ should be called a "terminal" reserve only for integral t. Since ${}_t\bar{V}(\bar{A}_x)$ is defined for *all* t, we do not refer to it as a terminal reserve.

EXAMPLE 10.7

Show that

$$\frac{d}{dt}\,{}_t\bar{V}(\bar{A}_x) = \frac{\bar{A}_{x+t}-\bar{a}_{x+t}\cdot\mu_{x+t}}{\bar{a}_x}.$$

SOLUTION

Using Equation (10.37) we have

$$\frac{d}{dt}\,{}_t\bar{V}(\bar{A}_x) = \frac{d}{dt}\left(1-\frac{\bar{a}_{x+t}}{\bar{a}_x}\right) = -\frac{1}{\bar{a}_x}\cdot\frac{d}{dt}\,\bar{a}_{x+t} = -\frac{\bar{a}_{x+t}(\mu_{x+t}+\delta)-1}{\bar{a}_x},$$

using the result from Exercise 8-11. Then we have

$$\frac{d}{dt}\,{}_t\bar{V}(\bar{A}_x) = \frac{1-\delta\cdot\bar{a}_{x+t}-\bar{a}_{x+t}\cdot\mu_{x+t}}{\bar{a}_x} = \frac{\bar{A}_{x+t}-\bar{a}_{x+t}\cdot\mu_{x+t}}{\bar{a}_x},$$

as required. ❒

For this fully continuous whole life model, the analogy to the discrete model recursion formula, given in Section 10.2, would be in the form of a differential equation. Using the group deterministic approach of Section 10.2, we observe that the aggregate reserve fund at time t is $l_{x+t}\cdot{}_t\bar{V}(\bar{A}_x)$, for all $t>0$. Due to its continuous nature, this aggregate fund is increasing at time t at rate $l_{x+t}\cdot\bar{P}(\bar{A}_x)$, from the arrival of premium income; it also is increasing at time t at rate $\delta\cdot l_{x+t}\cdot{}_t\bar{V}(\bar{A}_x)$, from interest earnings (assuming a constant rate of interest); and it is decreasing at time t at rate $l_{x+t}\cdot\mu_{x+t}$, from unit benefits paid to those failing at time t. Then the total rate of change of the aggregate reserve fund at time t is

$$l_{x+t}\cdot\bar{P}(\bar{A}_x)+\delta\cdot l_{x+t}\cdot{}_t\bar{V}(\bar{A}_x)-l_{x+t}\cdot\mu_{x+t}.$$

(See also Exercise 10-24.) Since the rate of change is given by the derivative, we can write

$$\tfrac{d}{dt}\left(l_{x+t}\cdot{}_t\bar{V}(\bar{A}_x)\right) = l_{x+t}\cdot\bar{P}(\bar{A}_x)+\delta\cdot l_{x+t}\cdot{}_t\bar{V}(\bar{A}_x)-l_{x+t}\cdot\mu_{x+t}. \tag{10.39}$$

Equation (10.39) is known as Thiele's Equation in the actuarial literature. We encounter it here in the simplified case of a net level premium rate and a fixed unit failure benefit. We will encounter Thiele's Equation again in Chapter 11 in a more general single-decrement setting, again in Section 12.5.6 in a multi-life setting, and again in Section 14.4.5 in a multiple-decrement setting.

To solve this differential equation, we transpose the term involving δ to the left side and multiply both sides by the integrating factor v^t to obtain

$$v^t \cdot \frac{d}{dt}\left(l_{x+t} \cdot {}_t\bar{V}(\bar{A}_x)\right) - \delta \cdot v^t \left(l_{x+t} \cdot {}_t\bar{V}(\bar{A}_x)\right) = v^t \cdot l_{x+t}\left(\bar{P}(\bar{A}_x) - \mu_{x+t}\right). \tag{10.40}$$

Next, recall from interest theory that

$$\frac{d}{dt}v^t = v^t \cdot \ln v = -\delta \cdot v^t.$$

Then using the product rule for differentiation, we recognize the left side of Equation (10.40) as

$$\frac{d}{dt}\left(v^t \cdot l_{x+t} \cdot {}_t\bar{V}(\bar{A}_x)\right) = v^t \cdot \frac{d}{dt}\left(l_{x+t} \cdot {}_t\bar{V}(\bar{A}_x)\right) + \left(l_{x+t} \cdot {}_t\bar{V}(\bar{A}_x)\right) \cdot \frac{d}{dt}v^t,$$

so we have

$$\frac{d}{dt}\left(v^t \cdot l_{x+t} \cdot {}_t\bar{V}(\bar{A}_x)\right) = v^t \cdot l_{x+t}\left(\bar{P}(\bar{A}_x) - \mu_{x+t}\right). \tag{10.41}$$

Now we integrate both sides of Equation (10.41) from $t=0$ to $t=n$, obtaining

$$\int_0^n d\left(v^t \cdot l_{x+t} \cdot {}_t\bar{V}(\bar{A}_x)\right) = \int_0^n v^t \cdot l_{x+t}\left(\bar{P}(\bar{A}_x) - \mu_{x+t}\right) dt. \tag{10.42}$$

Since ${}_0\bar{V}(\bar{A}_x) = 0$, the left side of Equation (10.42) evaluates to $v^n \cdot l_{x+n} \cdot {}_n\bar{V}(\bar{A}_x)$. We divide both sides by l_x to obtain

$$v^n \cdot {}_np_x \cdot {}_n\bar{V}(\bar{A}_x) = \bar{P}(\bar{A}_x) \cdot \int_0^n v^t \cdot {}_tp_x \, dt - \int_0^n v^t \cdot {}_tp_x \mu_{x+t} \, dt = \bar{P}(\bar{A}_x) \cdot \bar{a}_{x:\overline{n}|} - \bar{A}^1_{x:\overline{n}|}. \tag{10.43}$$

Finally, dividing both sides of Equation (10.43) by ${}_nE_x = v^n \cdot {}_np_x$ we have

$${}_n\bar{V}(\bar{A}_x) = \bar{P}(\bar{A}_x) \cdot \bar{s}_{x:\overline{n}|} - {}_n\bar{k}_x,$$

the retrospective NLP reserve expression given by Equation (10.35).

10.3.3 APPROXIMATE VALUES OF FULLY CONTINUOUS RESERVES

If a continuous parametric survival model is adopted, then the exact value of ${}_t\bar{V}$, the fully continuous reserve, can be calculated for any value of t. If the reserve values are to be calculated from a tabular (life table) model, then the values can be approximated by approximating the $\bar{A}, \bar{a},$ and $\bar{P}$ functions contained in the reserve expression using methods presented in Chapters 7 and 8.

Another technique that can be used to approximate values of ${}_t\bar{V}$ in the fully continuous case is a recursive one that utilizes Thiele's Equation and an approximation for the derivative of ${}_t\bar{V}$. This technique is presented in Example 10.11 in Section 10.7.

10.3.4 RANDOM VARIABLE ANALYSIS

Recall the present-value-of-loss random variable defined in the fully continuous case by Equation (9.25a). Recall also that under the equivalence principle we have $E[{}_0\bar{L}(\bar{A}_x)]=0$ and $P=\bar{P}(\bar{A}_x)$. Then given that $T_x > t$, so the contingent contract is still in effect at time t, the present-value-of-loss random variable at time t is given by

$$ {}_t\bar{L}(\bar{A}_x) = v^{T_x-t} - \bar{P}(\bar{A}_x)\cdot \bar{a}_{\overline{T_x-t|}} \tag{10.44a}$$

$$ = \bar{Z}_{x+t} - \bar{P}(\bar{A}_x)\cdot \bar{Y}_{x+t}. \tag{10.44b}$$

Taking the conditional expectation of Equation (10.44b) we find

$$ E\left[{}_t\bar{L}(\bar{A}_x)|T_x > t\right] = \bar{A}_{x+t} - \bar{P}(\bar{A}_x)\cdot \bar{a}_{x+t}, \tag{10.45}$$

which is the prospective expression for the NLP benefit reserve at time t in the fully continuous case. Thus we find that, just as in the discrete case of Section 10.1.4, if the continuous funding rate is determined by the equivalence principle, the NLP benefit reserve is the conditional expected value of the present-value-of-loss random variable measured at time t.

The variance of ${}_t\bar{L}(\bar{A}_x)$ is found from Equation (10.44b) in the same way we found $Var[{}_0\bar{L}(\bar{A}_x)]$ in Section 9.4.2, producing

$$ Var\left[{}_t\bar{L}(\bar{A}_x)|T_x > t\right] = \left(\frac{1}{\delta\cdot\bar{a}_x}\right)^2\cdot\left({}^2\bar{A}_{x+t} - \bar{A}_{x+t}{}^2\right) \tag{10.46a}$$

$$ = \frac{{}^2\bar{A}_{x+t} - \bar{A}_{x+t}{}^2}{(1-\bar{A}_x)^2}. \tag{10.46b}$$

In this section we have presented only the expected value and variance of the random variable ${}_t\bar{L}(\bar{A}_x)$, conditional on $T_x > t$ in both cases. For a more extensive exploration of this random variable, including the development of both its CDF and PDF, the reader is referred to Section 7.2 of Bowers, *et al.* [4].

10.4 NLP RESERVES FOR CONTINGENT PAYMENT MODELS WITH m^{thly} PAYMENT FUNDING

Suppose periodic funding payments are made at m^{thly} intervals within the year, at annual net premium rates defined in Section 9.4. Since the NLP reserve at duration t is merely the status of the funding scheme at that time, then expressions for the prospective NLP reserve follow directly from those for the associated net premium rate. Here we assume that t is an integer, so the reserve is being measured at annual intervals.

For the whole life contingent payment model with m^{thly} funding, the tth NLP terminal reserve is given prospectively by

$$ {}_tV_x^{(m)} = A_{x+t} - P_x^{(m)} \cdot \ddot{a}_{x+t}^{(m)}. \tag{10.47a} $$

For the n-year term insurance model we have

$$ {}_tV^{1\,(m)}_{x:\overline{n|}} = A^{\;1}_{x+t:\overline{n-t|}} - P^{1\,(m)}_{x:\overline{n|}} \cdot \ddot{a}^{(m)}_{x+t:\overline{n-t|}}, \tag{10.47b} $$

for the n-year pure endowment model we have

$$ {}_tV^{(m)}_{x:\overset{\;\,1}{\overline{n|}}} = A_{x+t:\overset{\;\,1}{\overline{n-t|}}} - P^{(m)}_{x:\overset{\;\,1}{\overline{n|}}} \cdot \ddot{a}^{(m)}_{x+t:\overline{n-t|}}, \tag{10.47c} $$

and for the n-year endowment insurance model we have

$$ {}_tV^{(m)}_{x:\overline{n|}} = A_{x+t:\overline{n-t|}} - P^{(m)}_{x:\overline{n|}} \cdot \ddot{a}^{(m)}_{x+t:\overline{n-t|}}. \tag{10.47d} $$

Note that $t < n$ in all three of these n-year models. Similarly, for the n-year deferred annuity-immediate model we have

$$ {}_tV^{(m)}({}_{n|}a_x) = {}_{n-t|}a_{x+t} - P^{(m)}({}_{n|}a_x) \cdot \ddot{a}^{(m)}_{x+t:\overline{n-t|}}, \tag{10.47e} $$

for $t < n$. The premium rates appearing in Equations (10.47a) through (10.47e) are defined by Equations (9.27a) through (9.27e), respectively.

Under the whole life model with immediate payment of claims, with net premium rate defined by Equation (9.28a), the prospective reserve is given by

$$ {}_tV^{(m)}(\bar{A}_x) = \bar{A}_{x+t} - P^{(m)}(\bar{A}_x) \cdot \ddot{a}^{(m)}_{x+t}. \tag{10.48} $$

Retrospective NLP reserve expressions are also easily written by analogy to other cases already discussed. Thus we would have

$$ {}_tV_x^{(m)} = P_x^{(m)} \cdot \ddot{s}^{(m)}_{x:\overline{t|}} - {}_tk_x \tag{10.49a} $$

for the whole life model with m^{thly} premiums and

$$ {}_tV^{(m)}_{x:\overline{n|}} = P^{(m)}_{x:\overline{n|}} \cdot \ddot{s}^{(m)}_{x:\overline{t|}} - {}_tk_x \tag{10.49b}$$

for the n-year endowment insurance model.

As with the continuous payment funding cases of Section 10.2, the NLP reserve expressions in this section can be evaluated from a life table by using one of the approximation methods presented in Chapter 8 for the m^{thly} annuities.

EXAMPLE 10.8

Show that, under the assumption of UDD over each interval $(x, x+1)$,

$$ {}_tV^{(m)}_x = \left[1+\frac{i-i^{(m)}}{i^{(m)}d^{(m)}} \cdot P^{(m)}_x\right] \cdot {}_tV_x. \tag{10.50}$$

SOLUTION

Starting with Equation (10.47a) we have

$$ {}_tV^{(m)}_x = A_{x+t} - P^{(m)}_x \cdot \ddot{a}^{(m)}_{x+t}. $$

Substituting for A_{x+t} from Equation (10.3) and for $\ddot{a}^{(m)}_{x+t}$ from Equation (8.78a) we have

$$ {}_tV^{(m)}_x = {}_tV_x + P_x \cdot \ddot{a}_{x+t} - P^{(m)}_x \left[\frac{id}{i^{(m)}d^{(m)}} \cdot \ddot{a}_{x+t} - \frac{i-i^{(m)}}{i^{(m)}d^{(m)}}\right]. $$

Using $\alpha(m) = \frac{id}{i^{(m)}d^{(m)}}$ and $\beta(m) = \frac{i-i^{(m)}}{i^{(m)}d^{(m)}}$ for notational convenience, we then have

$$ {}_tV^{(m)}_x = {}_tV_x + \beta(m) \cdot P^{(m)}_x - \ddot{a}_{x+t}\left[\alpha(m) \cdot P^{(m)}_x - P_x\right]. $$

Next recall that $P_x = \frac{A_x}{\ddot{a}_x}$ and $P^{(m)}_x = \frac{A_x}{\ddot{a}^{(m)}_x}$, so $P_x = P^{(m)}_x \cdot \frac{\ddot{a}^{(m)}_x}{\ddot{a}_x}$. Substituting this for P_x we have

$$ {}_tV^{(m)}_x = {}_tV_x + \beta(m) \cdot P^{(m)}_x - \ddot{a}_{x+t} \cdot P^{(m)}_x \left[\alpha(m) - \frac{\ddot{a}^{(m)}_x}{\ddot{a}_x}\right]. $$

Since $\ddot{a}^{(m)}_x = \alpha(m) \cdot \ddot{a}_x - \beta(m)$, the last term becomes $\frac{\ddot{a}_{x+t}}{\ddot{a}_x} \cdot P^{(m)}_x \cdot \beta(m)$, which leads finally to

$$ {}_tV^{(m)}_x = {}_tV_x + \beta(m) \cdot P^{(m)}_x\left(1 - \frac{\ddot{a}_{x+t}}{\ddot{a}_x}\right) = \left[1+\beta(m) \cdot P^{(m)}_x\right] \cdot {}_tV_x, $$

as required. ❐

10.5 MULTI-STATE MODEL REPRESENTATION

In Chapters 9 and 10 we have defined notation and formulas used to express net premiums and net level premium reserves in standard actuarial notation for a variety of contingent payment contract models. All such formulas evolved from the notation used for insurance and annuity models as presented in Chapters 7 and 8, respectively.

Similarly, we can express net premiums and net level premium reserves in multi-state model notation, using the notation defined for the insurance and annuity models in Sections 7.6 and 8.6, respectively. This is pursued in Exercises 10-27 and 10-28.

10.6 GAIN AND LOSS ANALYSIS

An important actuarial activity is the analysis of contingent contracts to determine financial gain or loss under such contracts, and, in certain cases, to identify the source of the gain or loss. We choose to introduce this topic here in the simplified setting of net level premium reserves, so the reader can understand the basic idea. We then return to the topic in Section 11.5.

We explore this analysis separately for contingent insurance and contingent annuity contracts.

10.6.1 CONTINGENT INSURANCE CONTRACTS

The recursive relationships of Section 10.2 are particularly useful for this analysis. In Equations (10.30a) through (10.30e), the symbols i, q_{x+t}, and p_{x+t} refer to the interest and mortality *assumed* in the calculation of the net premium and the net premium reserves. Equation (10.30b) shows that if the interest and mortality *actually experienced* in the $(t+1)^{st}$ contract year are the same as that assumed in premium and reserve calculation, then there is neither gain nor loss to the insurer in that year under that contract. This is illustrated as well if we rewrite Equation (10.30b) as

$$({}_tV+P)(1+i)-(q_{x+t}+p_{x+t}\cdot{}_{t+1}V) = 0. \tag{10.51}$$

Now suppose the interest and mortality actually experienced in the $(t+1)^{st}$ contract year are denoted by i', q'_{x+t}, and p'_{x+t}. In particular, suppose $i'>i$ and $q'_{x+t}<q_{x+t}$. Then the amount on hand at time $t+1$ would be

$$G^T = ({}_tV+P)(1+i')-(q'_{x+t}+p'_{x+t}\cdot{}_{t+1}V), \tag{10.52}$$

which would be a positive quantity and would represent a gain in the $(t+1)^{st}$ contract year for the insurer. We denote this gain by G^T. (If $i'<i$ and/or $q'_{x+t}>q_{x+t}$, then we would find $G^T<0$ and interpret the negative gain as a loss to the insurer.)

We can define

$$G^M = ({}_tV+P)(1+i)-(q'_{x+t}+p'_{x+t}\cdot{}_{t+1}V) \tag{10.53}$$

to be the *gain from mortality*. Note that i is used in Equation (10.53) rather than i', even in cases where $i'\neq i.$ Similarly, we can define

$$G^I = ({}_tV+P)(1+i')-(q_{x+t}+p_{x+t}\cdot{}_{t+1}V) \tag{10.54}$$

to be the *gain from interest*, where q_{x+t} and p_{x+t} are used rather than q'_{x+t} and p'_{x+t}.

In this setting of net premium and net premium reserves, it follows that $G^M+G^I=G^T$, when G^T, G^M, and G^I are calculated by Equations (10.52), (10.53), and (10.54), respectively. (See Exercise 10-29.)

EXAMPLE 10.9

Consider a unit fully discrete whole life insurance issued at age 40 with net premium and net premium reserves given by $P_{40}=.008013$, ${}_{10}V_{40}=.085697$, and ${}_{11}V_{40}=.096115$. (These values were calculated from the life table in Appendix A at 6% interest.) Suppose, in the eleventh contract year, the actual earned interest rate is $i'=.065$ and the actual experienced mortality rate is $q'_{50}=.00300$. Calculate each of G^T, G^M and G^I, and show that $G^M+G^I=G^T$.

SOLUTION

We calculate G^T from Equation (10.52) as

$$\begin{aligned} G^T &= (.085697+.008013)(1.065)-[.00300+(.99700)(.096115)] \\ &= .099801150-.098826655 = .000974495, \end{aligned}$$

we calculate G^M from Equation (10.53) as

$$\begin{aligned} G^M &= (.085697+.008013)(1.06)-[.00300+(.99700)(.096115)] \\ &= .099332600-.098826655 = .000505945, \end{aligned}$$

and we calculate G^I from Equation (10.54) as

$$\begin{aligned} G^I &= (.085697+.008013)(1.065)-[.00356+(.99644)(.096115)] \\ &= .099801150-.099332831 = .000468319. \end{aligned}$$

Then

$$G^M+G^I = .000505945+.000468319 = .000974264,$$

which is the same as G^T, within rounding error. ❒

In practice, of course, contingent insurance contracts are not issued on a net premium and net premium reserve basis. We have chosen to introduce the topic of gain and loss analysis in this environment of only two factors (interest and mortality) for simplicity and ease of understanding. We will revisit this notion of gain or loss by source in a more advanced setting in Section 11.5.

10.6.2 CONTINGENT ANNUITY CONTRACTS

In the case of an annual premium deferred annuity contract, we distinguish the two subcases of (a) the contract being within the deferred period, and (b) the contract being after the deferred period (i.e., during the payout period when there are no further premiums). Again we are considering here the simpler net premium case, with the more realistic gross premium case considered in Section 11.5.

The simplest case is the contingent annuity model presented in Section 9.1.3 and revisited in Example 10.5, where the failure benefit during the deferred period is the year-end reserve. We have seen that mortality is not a factor under such a contract, so any gain or loss during the deferred period can be due to interest only. If the interest rate anticipated (or assumed) to be earned in the $(t+1)^{st}$ contract year is i, and the rate actually earned is i', then the interest gain in that year is

$$G^I = (i'-i)\cdot({}_tV+P), \tag{10.55}$$

where ${}_tV$ is the contract reserve at the beginning of the $(t+1)^{st}$ year.

Next we consider an annual premium deferred annuity-due which is in its payout period. If the annual annuity benefit is B, then the recursive relationship for the $(t+1)^{st}$ contract year is

$$({}_tV-B)(1+i) = p_{x+t}\cdot {}_{t+1}V,$$

since there are no premiums, the benefit is paid at the beginning of the year under an annuity-due, and the year-end reserve needs to be established only if the contract holder survives the year. Then, just as for an insurance contract in Section 10.6.1, if i and p_{x+t} refer to the interest and mortality assumed in the reserve calculation, we have

$$({}_tV-B)(1+i)-p_{x+t}\cdot {}_{t+1}V = 0. \tag{10.56}$$

The total gain would be given by

$$G^T = ({}_tV-B)(1+i')-p'_{x+t}\cdot {}_{t+1}V, \tag{10.57}$$

the gain from mortality would be given by

$$G^M = ({}_tV-B)(1+i)-p'_{x+t}\cdot {}_{t+1}V, \tag{10.58}$$

and the gain from interest would be given by

$$G^I = ({}_tV - B)(1+i') - p_{x+t} \cdot {}_{t+1}V. \tag{10.59}$$

Again we see that $G^M + G^I = G^T$ (see Exercise 10-32).

10.7 WRITTEN-ANSWER QUESTION EXAMPLES

EXAMPLE 10.10

Consider a 5-year fully discrete unit endowment insurance issued to (50). Using the mortality rates given in Appendix A and interest rate $i = .06$, the net level premium is .16902. (The reader should verify this calculation.) Suppose 100,000 identical contracts are issued. Then if the premium assumptions are realized (i.e., if 6% interest is earned and the survival pattern follows the table exactly), the aggregate NLP reserve fund at time $t = 5$ should be the exact amount needed to pay the unit pure endowment benefit to each survivor at that time. Show that this is so.

SOLUTION

We use the recursive method for determining the reserves. The calculations are shown in the following table:

t	Survivors $(2)_t = (2)_{t-1} - (4)_{t-1}$	Premiums $(3)_t = .16902(2)_t$	Failures $(4)_t = (2)_t \cdot q_{50+t}$	NLP Reserve Fund $(5)_t = [(5)_{t-1} + (3)_t](1.06) - (4)_t$
0	100,000	16,902	356	17,560
1	99,644	16,842	392	36,074
2	99,252	16,776	431	55,590
3	98,821	16,703	469	76,162
4	98,352	16,623	512	97,840
5	97,840			

Thus we see that there are 97,840 survivors at age 55, and the aggregate NLP reserve fund holds the exact amount needed to pay the unit pure endowment benefit to the survivors, as expected. ❑

EXAMPLE 10.11

(a) State the definition of $\frac{d}{dx}f(x)$. Explain how this definition could be modified to provide an approximation to the derivative of $f(x)$.

(b) Consider a fully continuous 20-year endowment insurance of face amount 1000, issued at age $x = 25$. Using the life table in Appendix A, an interest rate of $i = .06$, and the UDD assumption, calculate each of the following:

(i) The value of 1000 $\bar{P}(\bar{A}_{25:\overline{20}|})$.

(ii) The value of 1000 ${}_{19}\bar{V}(\bar{A}_{25:\overline{20}|})$, given $K_{25} \geq 19$.

(c) State Thiele's Equation for this policy, using $\bar{P}$ and ${}_t\bar{V}$ for 1000 $\bar{P}(\bar{A}_{25:\overline{20}|})$ and for 1000 ${}_t\bar{V}(\bar{A}_{25:\overline{20}|})$, respectively, for notational convenience.

(d) Using part (a), state an approximation for $\frac{d}{dt}\,{}_t\bar{V}\big|_{t=19}$.

(e) Using $h=1$, use the results of parts (c) and (d) to approximate the value of ${}_{19}\bar{V}$.

(f) Explain how the approximation could be improved.

SOLUTION

(a) The definition of the derivative is

$$\frac{d}{dx}f(x) = \lim_{h\to 0}\frac{f(x+h)-f(x)}{h}.$$

If h is "small," then the derivative can be approximated by the value of

$$\frac{f(x+h)-f(x)}{h},$$

and the quality of the approximation increases as the value of h decreases (since the "approximation" is exact as $h \to 0$).

(b) (i) From Table A.2 we find

$${}_{20}E_{25} = v^{20}\cdot {}_{20}p_{25} = \frac{l_{45}}{l_{25}(1.06)^{20}} = .30514$$

and

$$A^{\;1}_{25:\overline{20}|} = A_{25} - {}_{20}E_{25}\cdot A_{45} = .01086.$$

Then

$$\bar{A}^{\;1}_{25:\overline{20}|} = \frac{i}{\delta}\cdot A^{\;1}_{25:\overline{20}|} = \left(\frac{.06}{.0582689}\right)(.01086) = .01118,$$

so

$$\bar{A}_{25:\overline{20}|} = \bar{A}^{\;1}_{25:\overline{20}|} + {}_{20}E_{25} = .31632,$$

so

$$\bar{a}_{25:\overline{20}|} = \frac{1-\bar{A}_{25:\overline{20}|}}{\delta} = 11.73314,$$

and finally

$$1000\bar{P}\left(\bar{A}_{25:\overline{20}|}\right) = \frac{1000\bar{A}_{25:\overline{20}|}}{\bar{a}_{25:\overline{20}|}} = 26.96.$$

(ii) Given that the policyholder is surviving at $t=19$, which is age 44, the prospective reserve is

$$1000_{19}\bar{V}\left(\bar{A}_{25:\overline{20}|}\right) = 1000\bar{A}_{44:\overline{1}|} - \bar{P}\cdot\bar{a}_{44:\overline{1}|}.$$

We first find

$$\bar{A}^{1}_{44:\overline{1}|} = \frac{i}{\delta}\cdot A^{1}_{44:\overline{1}|} = \frac{iv}{\delta}\cdot q_{44} = \frac{(.06)(.00197)}{(1.06)(.0582689)} = .00191.$$

Then

$$\bar{A}_{44:\overline{1}|} = \bar{A}^{1}_{44:\overline{1}|} + v\cdot p_{44} = .94345$$

and

$$\bar{a}_{44:\overline{1}|} = \frac{1-\bar{A}_{44:\overline{1}|}}{\delta} = .97054.$$

Then

$$1000_{19}\bar{V}\left(\bar{A}_{25:\overline{20}|}\right) = 943.45-(26.96)(.97054) = 917.28.$$

(c) Thiele's Equation is

$$\frac{d}{dt}\,{}_t\bar{V} = \bar{P}+\delta\cdot{}_t\bar{V} - \mu_{25+t}(1000-{}_t\bar{V}).$$

(d) The derivative at $t=19$ can be approximated by $\frac{{}_{19+h}\bar{V}-{}_{19}\bar{V}}{h}$.

(e) With $t=19$ and $h=1$, from parts (c) and (d) we have

$$\bar{P}+\delta\cdot{}_{19}\bar{V} - \mu_{44}(1000-{}_{19}\bar{V}) \approx {}_{20}\bar{V} - {}_{19}\bar{V},$$

which solves for

$${}_{19}\bar{V} \approx \frac{{}_{20}\bar{V}-\bar{P}+1000\mu_{44}}{(1+\delta+\mu_{44})}.$$

Because the contract is an endowment, we know that ${}_{20}\bar{V}=1000$. By assuming UDD, we find $\mu_{44}=q_{44}=.00197$ (see Equation (6.37)). Then

$${}_{19}\bar{V} = \frac{1000-26.96+1.97}{1.0602389} = 919.61.$$

(f) To improve the approximation, we could use a smaller value of h. For example, if we use $h=.25$, then starting with the boundary value ${}_{20}\bar{V}=1000$ we would recursively calculate ${}_{19.75}\bar{V}$, ${}_{19.50}\bar{V}$, ${}_{19.25}\bar{V}$, and finally ${}_{19}\bar{V}$. As the value of h is made even smaller, the number of recursive calculations increases and greater accuracy results.

(Note: The recursive technique described here is called *Euler's Method.* We do not need to use this method to approximate ${}_t\bar{V}$ in the net premium reserve case, since we can just as easily calculate ${}_t\bar{V}$ exactly. In later chapters, however, we will encounter more complex models where Euler's Method of approximating ${}_t\bar{V}$ will be quite useful.) ❑

EXAMPLE 10.12

Consider a 20-year discrete endowment policy issued to (45) with face amount 1000.

(a) Using the life table in Appendix A, with $i=.06$, calculate the net annual premium for this policy.

(b) Suppose the death benefit is the return of net premiums paid, with interest at 6%, instead of the fixed face amount of 1000. The pure endowment benefit remains 1000. Calculate the net annual premium in this case.

(c) Now suppose the death benefit is the face amount of 1000 *plus* the terminal reserve at the end of the year of death, with the pure endowment benefit remaining at 1000. Calculate the net annual premium in this case.

(d) Explain, by logic, the order of magnitude of the premiums calculated in parts (a), (b), and (c).

(e) Write the retrospective reserve expression for ${}_5V$ for each of the three contracts.

(f) Explain why ${}_5V^{(a)}$ accumulates the net premiums using $\ddot{s}_{x:\overline{5}|}$ but ${}_5V^{(b)}$ accumulates the net premiums using $\ddot{s}_{\overline{5}|}$. Which produces the larger accumulation of the premiums?

(g) Intuitively, which of part (a) or part (c) has the greater cost of insurance? Verify the intuitive answer by an algebraic demonstration.

SOLUTION

(a) Using Table A.2 we first find

$$ {}_{20}E_{45} = v^{20}\cdot {}_{20}p_{45} = \frac{l_{65}}{(1.06)^{20}\cdot l_{45}} = \frac{85{,}075}{(3.20714)(96{,}222)} = .27568. $$

Then

$$\begin{aligned} A_{45:\overline{20|}} &= A_{45} - {}_{20}E_{45} \cdot A_{65} + {}_{20}E_{45} \\ &= .15794 + (.27568)(1-.36778) = .33223 \end{aligned}$$

and

$$\ddot{a}_{45:\overline{20|}} = \frac{1-A_{45:\overline{20|}}}{d} = \frac{1-.33223}{.06/1.06} = 11.79726,$$

so

$$1000P_{45:\overline{20|}} = \frac{1000A_{45:\overline{20|}}}{\ddot{a}_{45:\overline{20|}}} = \frac{332.23}{11.79726} = 28.16.$$

(b) When the death benefit is the return of net premiums with interest at the same rate used to calculate the premium and the reserves, then the reserve is simply the accumulation of the net premiums at interest only. (This result was developed earlier in Section 9.1.3 and in Example 10.5.) In this case we have, retrospectively,

$${}_{20}V = P \cdot \ddot{s}_{\overline{20|}.06}.$$

But it must be true that ${}_{20}V = 1000$ to provide the pure endowment benefit upon survival to age 65, so we find

$$P = \frac{1000}{\ddot{s}_{\overline{20|}.06}} = \frac{1000}{38.99273} = 25.65.$$

(c) We again use the recursive relationship given in Section 10.2. We have

$$\begin{aligned} ({}_tV+P)(1+i) &= (1000+{}_{t+1}V)\cdot q_{45+t} + {}_{t+1}V \cdot p_{45+t} \\ &= 1000q_{45+t} + {}_{t+1}V, \end{aligned}$$

since $q_{45+t} + p_{45+t} = 1$. Then with the initial condition of ${}_0V = 0$, we find

$${}_1V = P(1+i) - 1000q_{45}.$$

Then, recursively, we find

$$\begin{aligned} {}_2V &= ({}_1V+P)(1+i) - 1000q_{46} \\ &= \left[P(1+i) - 1000q_{45} + P\right](1+i) - 1000q_{46} \\ &= P \cdot \ddot{s}_{\overline{2|}} - 1000\left[q_{45}(1+i) + q_{46}\right], \end{aligned}$$

and eventually

$${}_{20}V = P \cdot \ddot{s}_{\overline{20|}} - 1000\left[q_{45}(1+i)^{19} + q_{46}(1+i)^{18} + \cdots + q_{64}\right].$$

(Note that this result is reached directly from Equation (10.30f), where $B = 1000 + {}_kV$ in this case.) But we also know that ${}_{20}V = 1000$, so we have

$$P = \frac{1000+1000\left[q_{45}(1+i)^{19}+q_{46}(1+i)^{18}+\cdots+q_{64}\right]}{\ddot{s}_{\overline{20}|}}.$$

A simple program in Excel, or other software, will produce .18987 as the value of the quantity in brackets in the numerator. Then we finally have

$$P = \frac{1000(1+.18987)}{38.99273} = 30.52.$$

(d) The death benefit in part (c) is the greatest of the three, and the death benefit in part (b) is the smallest of the three. That is

$$DB^{(b)} < DB^{(a)} < DB^{(c)}.$$

The pure endowment benefit is the same in all three cases, so the net annual premium will be smallest for the contract with the smallest death benefit. Therefore we have

$$P^{(b)} < P^{(a)} < P^{(c)},$$

which is verified by

$$25.65 < 28.16 < 30.52.$$

(e) For parts (a), (b), and (c), the respective reserves at $t=5$ are

$${}_5V^{(a)} = P^{(a)}\cdot\ddot{s}_{45:\overline{5}|}-1000\,{}_5k_{45},$$

$${}_5V^{(b)} = P^{(b)}\cdot\ddot{s}_{\overline{5}|},$$

and

$${}_5V^{(c)} = P^{(c)}\ddot{s}_5-1000\left[q_{45}(1+i)^4+q_{46}(1+i)^3+\cdots+q_{49}\right].$$

(f) $\ddot{s}_{45:\overline{5}|}$ accumulates to a larger amount than does $\ddot{s}_{\overline{5}|}$, as explained in Section 8.2.1, because it includes not only the accumulation of each $t=5$ survivor's own premiums, but also the survivor's share of premiums paid by those who died before $t=5$. In part (a), this premium accumulation is then reduced by the survivor's share of the death benefits paid to those who died before $t=5$ to reach the reserve value.

In part (b), each death provides its own death benefit via the return of premium feature, so each survivor gets no share of those premiums but also has no cost of insurance to pay. (Each death provides fully for its own death benefit.) This is why ${}_5V^{(b)}$ shows accumulation of premium at interest only.

(g) The cost of insurance in part (c) will be smaller because each death uses its own premiums to pay part of its death benefit, as reflected by the fact that the survivor's reserve accumulates only its own premiums. To verify algebraically, the part (a) cost of insurance is

$$\begin{aligned}1000\,{}_5k_{45} &= 1000\left[\frac{d_{45}(1+i)^4 + d_{46}(1+i)^3 + \cdots + d_{49}}{l_{50}}\right] \\ &= 1000\left[\frac{l_{45}\cdot q_{45}(1+i)^4 + l_{46}\cdot q_{46}(1+i)^3 + \cdots + l_{49}\cdot q_{49}}{l_{50}}\right] \\ &= 1\ 000\left[\frac{q_{45}(1+i)^4}{{}_5p_{45}} + \frac{q_{46}(1+i)^3}{{}_4p_{46}} + \cdots + \frac{q_{49}}{p_{49}}\right].\end{aligned}$$

Each term inside the brackets is the same as the corresponding term for cost of insurance in part (c), except that it is divided by a survival probability which is less than one. This makes each term in part (a) larger than each corresponding term in part (c), so the total part (a) cost of insurance exceeds the total part (c) cost of insurance. ❐

10.8 EXERCISES

10.1 NLP Reserves for Contingent Payment Models with Annual Payment Funding

10-1 Write prospective NLP reserve expressions for the following:

(a) ${}^h_tV^1_{x:\overline{n}|}$ (b) ${}^h_tV_{x:\overline{n}|}$

10-2 Write the prospective NLP reserve expression for an h-pay n-year deferred insurance, where $h<n$.

10-3 Calculate ${}_{20}V_{45}$, given the following values:

$$P_{45}=.014 \qquad P_{45:\overline{20}|}=.030 \qquad P_{45:\overline{20}|}^{\ \ \ 1}=.022$$

10-4 Write retrospective NLP reserve expressions for the following:

(a) ${}_tV^1_{x:\overline{n}|}$, for $t<n$

(b) ${}_tV_{x:\overline{n}|}$, for $t<n$

(c) ${}_tV_{x:\overline{n}|}^{\ \ \ 1}$, for $t<n$

(d) ${}^h_tV_x$, for $t>h$

10-5 Derive each of the following expressions for ${}_tV_{x:\overline{n}|}$, for $t<n$:

(a) $1-(P_{x:\overline{n}|}+d)\cdot\ddot{a}_{x+t:\overline{n-t}|}$

(b) $1-\frac{\ddot{a}_{x+t:\overline{n-t}|}}{\ddot{a}_{x:\overline{n}|}}$

(c) $\frac{P_{x+t:\overline{n-t}|}-P_{x:\overline{n}|}}{P_{x+t:\overline{n-t}|}+d}$

(d) $\frac{A_{x+t:\overline{n-t}|}-A_{x:\overline{n}|}}{1-A_{x:\overline{n}|}}$

(e) $(P_{x+t:\overline{n-t}|}-P_{x:\overline{n}|})\cdot\ddot{a}_{x+t:\overline{n-t}|}$

(f) $A_{x+t:\overline{n-t}|}\left(1-\frac{P_{x:\overline{n}|}}{P_{x+t:\overline{n-t}|}}\right)$

10-6 Calculate the value of $1000({}_2V_{x:\overline{3}|}-{}_1V_{x:\overline{3}|})$, given the following values:

$$P_{x:\overline{3}|}=.33251 \qquad i=.06 \qquad l_x=100 \qquad l_{x+1}=90$$

10-7 Let ${}_{10}V$ denote the net premium reserve at duration 10 for a special whole life insurance contract issued to (x) that pays nothing for failure in the first year and 5000, paid at the end of the year of failure, for failure after the first year. Net level premiums, determined by the equivalence principle, are payable for the life of the contract. Calculate the value of ${}_{10}V$, given the following values:

$${}_{10}V_x=.20 \qquad \ddot{a}_x=5 \qquad q_x=.05 \qquad v=.90$$

10-8 Consider the n-year endowment contract, with net premium determined by the equivalence principle.

(a) Define the random variable for the present value of loss at duration t, denoted by ${}_tL_{x:\overline{n}|}$, where $t<n$.

(b) Give an expression for the conditional expected value of ${}_tL_{x:\overline{n}|}$, given $K_x\geq t$.

(c) Give an expression for the conditional variance of ${}_tL_{x:\overline{n}|}$, given $K_x\geq t$.

10-9 A 2-year term insurance of amount 400 is issued to (x), with net premium determined by the equivalence principle. Find the probability that the loss at issue is less than 190, given the following values:

$$P^1_{x:\overline{2}|}=.185825 \qquad {}_1V^1_{x:\overline{2}|}=.04145 \qquad i=.10$$

10-10 Show that ${}_t\bar{k}_x=\frac{i}{\delta}\cdot{}_tk_x$, under the assumption of UDD over each separate interval $(x+j,x+j+1)$, for $j=0,1,\ldots,t-1$.

10-11 Derive the reserve formula

$$_tV(\bar{A}_x) = [P(\bar{A}_{x+t}) - P(\bar{A}_x)] \cdot \ddot{a}_{x+t}.$$

10-12 A single-premium 10-year temporary continuous life annuity, with unit annual benefit rate, is issued to (80). The applicable survival model is uniform with $\omega = 100$. Given $\delta - \frac{1}{15}$, find the value of $Var({}_5L)$.

10.2 Recursive Relationships for Discrete Models with Annual Premiums

10-13 A contingent contract issued to (35) has a benefit of 2500 for failure in the 10th year. The interest rate is $i = .10$. The net annual premium is P. Given that ${}_9V + P = {}_{10}V = 500$, find the value of q_{44}.

10-14 Calculate p_{38}, given the following values:

$${}^{20}_{23}V_{15} = .585 \qquad {}^{20}_{24}V_{15} = .600 \qquad i = .04$$

10-15 A 10-pay whole life contract of face amount 1000 is issued to (x). The net annual premium is 32.88 and the NLP reserve at the end of year 9 is 322.87. Given $i = .06$ and $q_{x+9} = .01262$, find the value of P_{x+10}.

10-16 A 10-year deferred annuity-due issued to (x) includes a failure benefit during the deferred period that is a refund of the net single premium with interest at the same rate i used to calculate the premium. The terminal reserve at the end of year 9 is 15.238 and the interest rate is $i = .05$. Calculate the net single premium.

10-17 A single premium 25-year deferred annuity-due, with unit annual benefit, is issued to (40). The applicable survival model is uniform with $\omega = 100$. The interest rate is $i = .05$. The single premium is refunded with interest at 5% at the end of the year of failure if failure occurs during the deferred period. Find the value of the reserve at duration 20.

10-18 Beginning with Equation (10.30b), derive the recursive reserve formula[7]

$${}_{t+1}V = \frac{{}_tV + P}{{}_1E_{x+t}} - \frac{A^{\;1}_{x+t:\overline{1}|}}{{}_1E_{x+t}}.$$

[7] This relationship is known in the actuarial literature as the Fackler recursive formula. It was quite useful for calculating reserves in the days before computerization.

10.3 NLP Reserves for Contingent Payment Models with Continuous Payment Funding

10-19 Derive each of the following expressions for ${}_t\bar{V}(\bar{A}_x)$.

(a) $\frac{\bar{A}_{x+t}-\bar{A}_x}{1-\bar{A}_x}$ (b) $\left(1-\frac{\bar{P}(\bar{A}_x)}{\bar{P}(\bar{A}_{x+t})}\right)\cdot\bar{A}_{x+t}$

10-20 Let ${}_0\bar{L}(\bar{A}_x)$ denote the present value of loss at issue for a fully continuous whole life contract issued to (x). Find the value of ${}_{20}\bar{V}(\bar{A}_x)$, given the following values:

$$Var[{}_0\bar{L}(\bar{A}_x)]=.20 \qquad {}^2\bar{A}_x=.30 \qquad \bar{A}_{x+20}=.70$$

10-21 Calculate $\bar{a}_{x+t}$, given the following values:

$${}_t\bar{V}(\bar{A}_x)=.1000 \qquad \bar{P}(\bar{A}_x)=.0105 \qquad \delta=.03$$

10-22 If the survival model is uniform with $\omega=100$ and the interest rate is $i=.05$, calculate the value of ${}_{10}\bar{V}(\bar{A}_{40})$.

10-23 If the survival model is exponential with failure rate λ and the force of interest is δ, calculate the value of ${}_t\bar{V}(\bar{A}_x)$. Explain the logic behind the result.

10-24 Equation (10.39) gives Thiele's differential equation in the context of the aggregate reserve fund. From it, derive the result

$$\frac{d}{dt}\,{}_t\bar{V}(\bar{A}_x) = \bar{P}(\bar{A}_x)+\delta\cdot{}_t\bar{V}(\bar{A}_x)-\mu_{x+t}\left(1-{}_t\bar{V}(\bar{A}_x)\right),$$

which is Thiele's differential equation in the context of a single whole life policy.

10.4 NLP Reserves for Contingent Payment Models with m^{thly} Payment Funding

10-25 Assuming UDD over each interval $(x, x+1)$, calculate (accurate to two decimals) the value of $1000({}_5V_{35}^{(4)}-{}_5V_{35})$, given the following values:

$${}_5V_{35}=.04471 \qquad A_{35}=.17092 \qquad i=.05$$

10-26 Instead of approximating $\ddot{a}_x^{(m)}$ using UDD, use the Woolhouse approximation given by Equation (8.82b). Find the value of ${}_4V_x^{(2)}$ accurate to five decimal places, given the values $\ddot{a}_x=20$, ${}_4V_x=.06$, and $d=.026$.

10.5 Multi-State Model Representation

10-27 Using the multi-state model notation defined earlier, give the prospective formula for the reserve represented in standard actuarial notation by ${}_{20}V_{30}$.

10-28 Using the multi-state model notation defined earlier, give the prospective formula for the reserve represented in standard actuarial notation by ${}_{10}V^{\,1}_{30:\overline{20|}}$.

10.6 Gain and Loss Analysis

10-29 Show that $G^M + G^I = G^T$, where the three gains are calculated by Equations (10.53), (10.54), and (10.52), respectively.

10-30 Show that the gain from mortality, as given by Equation (10.53), can also be written as

$$G^M = (q_{x+t} - q'_{x+t})(1 - {}_{t+1}V).$$

10-31 Similarly, show that the gain from interest, as given by Equation (10.54), can also be written as

$$G^I = ({}_tV + P)(i' - i).$$

10-32 Show that the gains from mortality and interest, given by Equations (10.58) and (10.59), respectively, sum to the total gain, as given by Equation (10.57).

CHAPTER ELEVEN

CONTINGENT CONTRACT RESERVES (RESERVES AS FINANCIAL LIABILITIES)

In Chapter 10 we presented an extensive analysis of the concept of net level premium reserves, pointing out that the NLP reserve is a mathematical function of the contingent contract under consideration. In this chapter we describe several reserve concepts beyond that of the NLP reserve.

A basic new idea in this chapter is the recognition that the contingent contract reserve constitutes a *financial liability* for the institution, such as a life insurer, that has issued the contingent contract.[1] When a life insurance policy provides for a benefit payment at some unknown time in the future, with the benefit funded by level annual premium payments, the premiums paid in the early contract years generally exceed the cost of insurance in those years. The fund accumulated as a result of this cannot be considered profit to the insurer; its value must be retained *as an accounting liability* and eventually used to pay the contingent benefit when it arises.

Along with its role on the liability side of the balance sheet, the contract reserve plays an important role in the determination of annual net income.

Consider a whole life insurance contract with level annual gross premium G and associated expense amount E_t in the tth contract year.[2] If the reserve concept were ignored, the stream of annual contributions to net income would be $G-E_t$ in the tth year, for each year that the failure benefit is not paid, and $G-E_n-B$ if the benefit is paid in the nth year. This stream of small positive contributions to net income each year, along with the large negative contribution in the year of failure, does not represent an appropriate accounting for the contract. It represents, in effect, a reported income stream generated by cash accounting, which gives an overly positive view of the contract's financial status.

When the reserve concept is recognized, the contribution to net income each year is reduced by the increase in reserve for that year. Then the stream of (usually positive) contributions to net income is $G-E_1-{}_1V$ in the first year and $G-E_t-({}_tV-{}_{t-1}V)$ in the tth year in general. If failure occurs in the nth year, the benefit is paid and the reserve is released so the contribution to net income is $G-E_n-(B-{}_{n-1}V)$, which is generally negative. By reporting the

[1] We assume here that the reader has had (at least) a one-semester university course in financial accounting, and understands such basic accounting concepts as assets, liabilities, and net worth, and the summary accounting reports of income statement and balance sheet.

[2] For convenience, we assume that the gross premium and the expense-augmented premium (see Section 9.6) are the same, and denoted by G.

annual reserve increase as an expense item, the pattern of annual contributions to net income has been placed on an accrual, rather than cash, accounting basis.

In Chapter 10 we developed formulas for determining this accounting liability under the assumption that it would be defined as the NLP reserve, using the net level premium developed by the equivalence principle. In practice, the financial liability held by the insurer, and reported on its balance sheet, is not normally the NLP reserve. In this chapter we develop several alternatives to NLP reserves that might be calculated by the insurer and held as the financial liability associated with a particular contingent contract. These alternatives include modified reserves (in Section 11.1), net premium reserves at non-integral durations of the contingent contract (in Section 11.2), net premium reserves using non-level net premiums (in Section 11.3), and reserves incorporating expenses (in Section 11.4).

An insurer is likely to determine reserves of more than one type for use in more than one set of financial statements. Statements produced for the insurance regulatory authorities have traditionally used modified reserves.[3] Statements produced for internal company management purposes are more likely to use gross premium reserves (see Section 11.4). Still a third set of financial reports, meeting requirements set by the applicable taxing authority, might be maintained for income tax purposes.

At the time of this writing, the insurance industry and its regulators in the United States are discussing a new concept known as *principle-based reserving*. The basic idea is that reserves should be principles-driven, rather than formula-driven, and each insurer would set its contingent contract reserves at levels appropriate for that company, rather than have such levels prescribed by the regulators. To guard against the possibility of insurers setting their reserve levels too low, a mechanism for testing the reserves for adequacy (most likely by stochastic simulation) would be established.

Similar considerations apply to the question of how much *surplus* should be retained by an insurer, versus the alternative of paying larger dividends to shareholders or policyholders. This is a corporate accounting issue, rather than a contingent contract issue, and is not discussed further in this text.

11.1 MODIFIED RESERVES

Consider a contingent contract with level annual gross premium (or contract premium) G, as described in Section 9.6. If the level net premium P is used to provide cost of coverage and reserve accumulation, as discussed throughout Chapter 10, then it follows that the level amount $G-P$ is available each year to cover expenses of operation and a contribution to profit. In reality, for the type of contingent contracts considered in this text, such as insurance policies, the pattern of expenses each year is not level. Expenses are much greater in the first year, due to the cost of underwriting and issuing the contract, plus the practice of paying a larger commission to the sales agent in the first year.

[3] In the United States, the business of insurance is regulated by the states. Each state has a Commissioner of Insurance, and these commissioners work together through the National Association of Insurance Commissioners (NAIC). The regulatory financial reporting and reserving requirements are recommended by the NAIC, and generally implemented in each state.

11.1.1 RESERVE MODIFICATION IN GENERAL

In light of the greater first year expenses, we consider that a *smaller* portion of the gross premium be used for cost of coverage plus reserve accumulation in the first year, with a *larger* portion used in subsequent years, than would be the case under the NLP reserve system. To quantify this idea, let α denote the net premium in the first year and β denote the net premium in all years after the first (also called the *renewal* years), where $\alpha < P < G$ and $P < \beta < G$.[4] Then the amount available for expenses and profit is $G-\alpha$ in the first year and $G-\beta$ in all subsequent years. The *modified reserve* at the end of the first year for a unit insurance can be calculated from Equation (10.30b), using α in place of P and ${}_0V = 0$, obtaining

$$\alpha(1+i) = q_x + p_x \cdot {}_1V^M \tag{11.1a}$$

or

$${}_1V^M = \frac{\alpha(1+i)-q_x}{p_x}. \tag{11.1b}$$

Then for a contract still in force at duration t, for $t \geq 1$, the modified reserve can be calculated prospectively as

$$\begin{aligned} {}_tV^M &= (APV\ of\ future\ benefits) \\ &\quad -(APV\ of\ future\ modified\ premiums). \end{aligned} \tag{11.2}$$

The modified premiums (or valuation premiums) α and β are determined at issue so that the APV of all modified premiums will equal the APV of future benefits. Of course this will also be the APV of the net level premiums, so we have

$$\alpha + \beta \cdot a_x = P_x \cdot \ddot{a}_x \tag{11.3a}$$

for a whole life contract, and

$$\alpha + \beta \cdot a_{x:\overline{n-1}|} = P \cdot \ddot{a}_{x:\overline{n}|} \tag{11.3b}$$

for a contract with premium paying period limited to n years.

It is also possible to use modified premiums over only the first k years of a contract, where $k < n$. In this case, α is used in the first year, β is used in years 2 through k, and the net level premium P is used in all years thereafter. Then Equation (11.3b) would be altered to read

$$\alpha + \beta \cdot a_{x:\overline{k-1}|} = P \cdot \ddot{a}_{x:\overline{k}|}, \tag{11.3c}$$

which is the more general case.

[4] As mentioned earlier, the process of determining reserves for contingent contracts is called *valuation of liabilities*. When NLP reserves are calculated, the net level premium P is also called the *level valuation premium*; when modified reserves are calculated, α is called the *first-year valuation premium* and β is called the *renewal-year valuation premium*.

The solution of Equation (11.3c) for α and β is not unique, of course, so it follows that either α or β (or possibly the quantity $\beta-\alpha$) must be defined in each specific case. This is illustrated in the examples and exercises that follow.

EXAMPLE 11.1

Show that

$$\beta = P+\frac{\beta-\alpha}{\ddot{a}_{x:\overline{k}|}}. \tag{11.4}$$

SOLUTION

In Equation (11.3c) we substitute the identity

$$a_{x:\overline{k-1}|} = \ddot{a}_{x:\overline{k}|}-1,$$

obtaining

$$\alpha+\beta\left(\ddot{a}_{x:\overline{k}|}-1\right) = P\cdot\ddot{a}_{x:\overline{k}|}$$

or

$$(\beta-P)\cdot\ddot{a}_{x:\overline{k}|} = \beta-\alpha,$$

from which the desired formula immediately follows. (Equation (11.4) is useful in cases where the modified reserve system is defined by specifying the excess of β over α.) ❐

A theoretical fully continuous whole life contract funded by a continuous net level premium $\bar{P}(\bar{A}_x)$ will generate fully continuous NLP reserves, denoted by ${}_t\bar{V}(\bar{A}_x)$, as described in Section 10.3.2. If such a contract were to use modified continuous premiums in lieu of the level $\bar{P}(\bar{A}_x)$, then modified fully continuous reserves would result. In this case, the discrete modified premium structure of α in the first year and β in the renewal years, described earlier in this section, would be replaced by a continuous premium rate of $\bar{\alpha}(r)$ at time r, increasing continuously to a level continuous premium rate of $\bar{\beta}$ after some defined length of time. This notion is further explored in Exercise 11-2.

11.1.2 FULL PRELIMINARY TERM MODIFIED RESERVES

Many specific modified reserve systems have been defined over the years.[5] In this section we consider one special case of modified reserves.

As a minimum, we consider that the first year modified premium α should be no less than the cost of insurance coverage in the first year. For a unit insurance contract, this would be $v\cdot q_x = A^{\,1}_{x:\overline{1}|}$, which is also denoted by c_x in the actuarial literature. If β is then the renewal modified premium for the remainder of the premium-paying period n, then we have

[5] The details of these systems are beyond the scope of this introductory text. Actuarial readers eventually specializing in life insurance reserving (also called *valuation*) will study these methods in detail at a later time. In particular, the reader will learn the importance of the *Commissioners Reserve Valuation Method* (CRVM).

$$\alpha^F = v \cdot q_x = c_x \tag{11.5a}$$

and

$$\beta^F = \frac{P \cdot \ddot{a}_{x:\overline{n}|} - c_x}{a_{x:\overline{n-1}|}}, \tag{11.5b}$$

from Equation (11.3b). This modified reserve system is called the *full preliminary term* (FPT) *method*, which explains the use of the superscript F on α and β.

EXAMPLE 11.2

Show that for a whole life unit insurance issued at age x, under the FPT reserving method, the first year terminal reserve is ${}_1V^F = 0$ and the renewal modified premium is $\beta^F = P_{x+1}$.

SOLUTION

The first result follows from Equation (10.30b) with $P = \alpha^F = v \cdot q_x$ and ${}_0V = 0$. We have

$$\alpha^F(1+i) = q_x + p_x \cdot {}_1V^F,$$

or

$$v \cdot q_x(1+i) = q_x = q_x + p_x \cdot {}_1V^F,$$

from which the result ${}_1V^F = 0$ follows since $p_x \neq 0$. Then from Equation (11.3a) we have

$$\alpha^F + \beta^F \cdot a_x = P_x \cdot \ddot{a}_x = A_x.$$

Substituting $\alpha^F = v \cdot q_x$ we have

$$\beta^F \cdot a_x = A_x - v \cdot q_x$$

or

$$\beta^F(v \cdot p_x \cdot \ddot{a}_{x+1}) = v \cdot p_x \cdot A_{x+1},$$

from which the result $\beta^F = P_{x+1}$ follows. ❐

The results of Example 11.2 can be generalized to other insurance coverages. Since the first year FPT reserve is zero and the modified renewal premium is the same as the net level premium at the attained age, then an insurance contract known to be in force at duration $t = 1$ (age $x+1$) will have FPT reserves that are the same as the NLP reserves for a similar contract issued at one age higher with one year less to run. This idea is further explored in Exercise 11-3.

A natural extension of the FPT method is the *two-year full preliminary term method*, whereby the modified premiums are $\alpha_1 = c_x$ in the first year, $\alpha_2 = c_{x+1}$ in the second year, and β in all years after the second. This method is further explored in Exercise 11-4.

Example 11.2 and Exercise 11-4 show that when the net premium for a particular year equals the cost of insurance for that year, the terminal net premium reserve is zero. This shows us that long-term insurance coverage could be provided by a sequence of one-year term insurances, and no terminal net premium reserve would ever develop. This is a basic characteristic of a contract of universal life insurance, which we explore in Chapter 16.

11.1.3 DEFICIENCY RESERVES

On rare occasion, it might turn out that $\beta > G$ (i.e., that the modified premium exceeds the gross premium). In that case, G is used in place of β in the prospective reserve formula. The excess of the reserve using G over the reserve using β is called a *deficiency reserve.*

11.1.4 NEGATIVE RESERVES

Another unusual situation would arise if, at any duration t, the APV of future modified premiums was to exceed the APV of future benefits, which would produce a *negative reserve.* Since the reserve represents a liability that the insurer eventually owes to the insured, a negative reserve would suggest a liability that the insured eventually owes to the insurer. But the insured could terminate the contract at any time, and escape paying this accrued liability. In light of this, insurers take care to avoid the kind of policy structure that could create a negative reserve.

11.2 NET PREMIUM RESERVES AT FRACTIONAL DURATIONS

In Chapter 10, and thus far in this chapter, all the discussion regarding reserves for contingent contracts with annual payment funding had assumed the parameter t to be an integer, so that the reserve was being measured at the end of the tth contract year. (For contracts with continuous payment funding, on the other hand, the reserve is defined for all values of t on the real number axis.) Now in this section we address the practical issue of defining the net premium reserve at a non-integral duration for annual payment funding contracts, as illustrated in the following figure.

$$
\begin{array}{ccc}
({}_tV+P) & {}_{t+s}V & {}_{t+1}V \\
\hline
x+t & x+t+s & x+t+1
\end{array}
$$

FIGURE 11.1

Using the basic prospective approach, we can write the fractional duration reserve ${}_{t+s}V$ as the actuarial present value of future benefits (APVB) minus the actuarial present value of future net premiums (APVP) as of duration $t+s$. We have

$$
\begin{aligned}
{}_{t+s}V &= v^{1-s} \cdot {}_{1-s}q_{x+t+s} + v^{1-s} \cdot {}_{1-s}p_{x+t+s} \cdot APVB_{t+1} - v^{1-s} \cdot {}_{1-s}p_{x+t+s} \cdot APVP_{t+1} \\
&= v^{1-s} \cdot {}_{1-s}q_{x+t+s} + v^{1-s} \cdot {}_{1-s}p_{x+t+s} \cdot {}_{t+1}V. \qquad (11.6)
\end{aligned}
$$

Now we multiply both sides of Equation (11.6) by $v^s \cdot {}_sp_{x+t}$, obtaining

$$v^s \cdot {}_sp_{x+t} \cdot {}_{t+s}V = v \cdot {}_{s|1-s}q_{x+t} + v \cdot p_{x+t} \cdot {}_{t+1}V. \tag{11.7}$$

Next we take Equation (10.30c), rewrite it as $v = \frac{{}_tV + P - v \cdot p_{x+t} \cdot {}_{t+1}V}{q_{x+t}}$, and substitute the right side for the first value of v on the right side of Equation (11.7), obtaining

$$v^s \cdot {}_sp_{x+t} \cdot {}_{t+s}V = ({}_tV+P)\left(\frac{{}_{s|1-s}q_{x+t}}{q_{x+t}}\right) + (v \cdot p_{x+t} \cdot {}_{t+1}V)\left(1 - \frac{{}_{s|1-s}q_{x+t}}{q_{x+t}}\right). \tag{11.8}$$

Equation (11.8) shows us that the expected present value at duration t of the fractional duration reserve ${}_{t+s}V$ is a weighted average of the initial reserve $({}_tV+P)$ and the expected present value of the terminal reserve ${}_{t+1}V$, with weights r and $1-r$, respectively, where

$$r = \frac{{}_{s|1-s}q_{x+t}}{q_{x+t}}. \tag{11.9}$$

Next we evaluate r under the UDD assumption over the age interval $(x+t, x+t+1)$, obtaining $r = 1-s$ (see Exercise 11-5), which allows us to write

$$v^s \cdot {}_sp_{x+t} \cdot {}_{t+s}V = ({}_tV+P)(1-s) + (v \cdot p_{x+t} \cdot {}_{t+1}V)(s). \tag{11.10}$$

A more intuitive approach to the fractional duration net premium reserve is suggested by the graph shown in Figure 11.2.

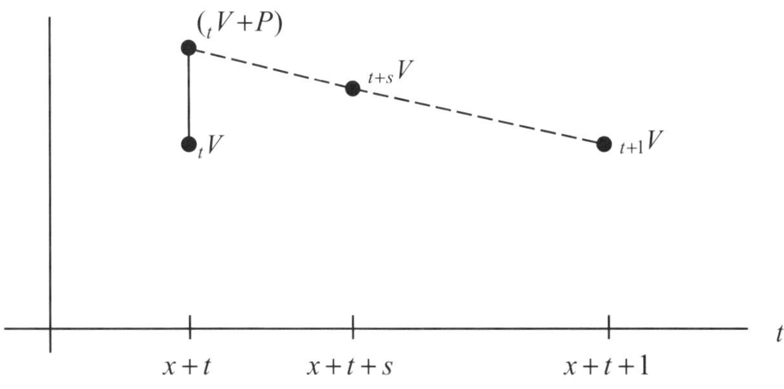

Figure 11.2

In practice the net premium reserve at fractional duration $t+s$ is often found by linear interpolation between the initial reserve $({}_tV+P)$ and the terminal reserve ${}_{t+1}V$, producing

$${}_{t+s}V = ({}_tV+P)(1-s) + ({}_{t+1}V)(s). \tag{11.11}$$

Equation (11.11) is reached from Equation (11.10) by assuming that $i = q_{x+t} = 0$ over the interval $(x+t, x+t+1)$. Finally, we can write Equation (11.11) as

$$_{t+s}V = ({}_tV)(1-s)+({}_{t+1}V)(s)+(P)(1-s). \tag{11.12}$$

In Equation (11.12), the interpolated reserve $(1-s)({}_tV)+(s)({}_{t+1}V)$ is called the *mid-terminal reserve factor* and the final term is called the *unearned net premium reserve*. In particular, when $s=\frac{1}{2}$ the interim reserve $_{t+1/2}V$ is called the *mean reserve*.

The development of $_{t+s}V^{(m)}$, the fractional duration reserve for a contingent contract funded by m^{thly} premiums, is a bit more complex, and is not pursued in this text. The interested reader is referred to pages 240-241 of Bowers, et al. [4] or pages 112-113 of Jordan [13].

11.3 GENERALIZATION TO NON-LEVEL BENEFITS AND NON-LEVEL NET PREMIUMS

In this section we consider cases where the benefit payment and/or the funding payment stream are not level. Clearly the level models considered earlier are special cases of the more general non-level models considered in this section.

11.3.1 DISCRETE MODELS

Let the benefit payment for failure in the kth year, payable at the end of that year, be denoted by b_k, and let the net premium for the kth year, payable at the beginning of that year, be denoted by P_k. This is illustrated in the following diagram.

P_1	b_1 P_2	b_2 P_3	b_3	
x	$x+1$	$x+2$	$x+3$	---

FIGURE 11.3

Then the APV of benefit for a whole life model is given by Equation (7.50) as

$$APVB = \sum_{k=0}^{\infty} b_{k+1}\cdot v^{k+1}\cdot Pr(K_x=k) = \sum_{k=0}^{\infty} b_{k+1}\cdot v^{k+1}\cdot {}_kp_x\cdot q_{x+k}. \tag{11.13a}$$

Similarly, the APV of the net premium stream is given by an adaptation of Equation (8.83) as

$$APVP = \sum_{k=0}^{\infty} P_{k+1}\cdot v^k\cdot {}_kp_x. \tag{11.13b}$$

We then use the basic equivalence principle at time 0 to write

$$\sum_{k=0}^{\infty} b_{k+1} \cdot v^{k+1} \cdot {}_k p_x \cdot q_{x+k} = \sum_{k=0}^{\infty} P_{k+1} \cdot v^k \cdot {}_k p_x. \tag{11.14}$$

Of course there is no unique solution to Equation (11.14) for the sequence of net premiums, given the sequence of benefit payment amounts. In practice we might solve for the $\{P_k\}$ sequence by establishing a relationship among the terms in the sequence. For example, we might let the net premium sequence vary in a geometric pattern with $P_k = P_1(1+r)^{k-1}$, where $r>0$ provides a pattern of increasing premiums, $r<0$ provides a pattern of decreasing premiums, and $r=0$ provides a pattern of level premiums as in Chapter 9.

Once the sequence of net premiums is established, the terminal net premium reserve at integral duration t, given that the contract has not yet failed, is easily written by again invoking the equivalence principle. By the prospective method we have

$${}_tV = \sum_{k=0}^{\infty} b_{t+k+1} \cdot v^{k+1} \cdot {}_k p_{x+t} \cdot q_{x+t+k} - \sum_{k=0}^{\infty} P_{t+k+1} \cdot v^k \cdot {}_k p_{x+t}. \tag{11.15}$$

In Exercise 11-7 the reader will be asked to write the general retrospective formula. Note that the other formulas for the whole life case, presented in Section 10.1.3, do not extend to the general case. We can, however, easily adapt the recursive relationships, presented in Section 10.2 in the level benefit and level net premium case, to the general case. Focusing on the $(t+1)^{st}$ contract year (see Figure 10.5), with benefit premium P_{t+1} paid at the beginning of the year and benefit b_{t+1} paid at the end of the year if failure occurs in that year, Equation (10.30a) now becomes

$$l_{x+t}({}_tV+P_{t+1})(1+i) = b_{t+1} \cdot d_{x+t} + l_{x+t+1} \cdot {}_{t+1}V, \tag{11.16a}$$

Equation (10.30b) now becomes

$$({}_tV+P_{t+1})(1+i) = b_{t+1} \cdot q_{x+t} + p_{x+t} \cdot {}_{t+1}V, \tag{11.16b}$$

and Equation (10.30e) now becomes

$${}_{t+1}V = ({}_tV+P_{t+1})(1+i) - q_{x+t}(b_{t+1} - {}_{t+1}V), \tag{11.16e}$$

where $b_{t+1} - {}_{t+1}V$ is the net amount at risk for the $(t+1)^{st}$ year.

The derivation of Equation (10.30c) by the use of random variables in the level benefit and level net premium case is also easily extended to derive its counterpart in the general case, which would be

$${}_tV+P_{t+1} = v \cdot b_{t+1} \cdot q_{x+t} + v \cdot p_{x+t} \cdot {}_{t+1}V. \tag{11.16c}$$

EXAMPLE 11.3

A 20-year endowment contract issued to (55) has a decreasing failure benefit, paid at the end of the year of failure, of $b_k = (21-k)$ for failure in the kth year and a pure endowment benefit of 1. The annual net premium is level. Find the value of ${}_{11}V,$ given the following values:

$${}_{10}V = 5.00 \qquad {}_{19}V = .60 \qquad q_{65} = .10 \qquad i = .08$$

SOLUTION

First we look at the last year, where we have

$$({}_{19}V+P)(1+i) = b_{20} \cdot q_{74} + 1 \cdot p_{74},$$

under the endowment insurance. But $b_{20} = 1,$ so we have

$$(.60+P)(1.08) = 1$$

which solves for $P = .32592.$ Then we look at the eleventh year, where we have

$$({}_{10}V+P)(1+i) = b_{11} \cdot q_{65} + {}_{11}V \cdot p_{65},$$

or

$$(5.00+.32592)(1.08) = (10)(.10) + {}_{11}V(.90),$$

which solves for ${}_{11}V = 5.28.$ ❒

11.3.2 CONTINUOUS MODELS

In the fully continuous general whole life model, with payment of benefit amount b_r for failure at precise time r and net premium at rate $\overline{P}(r)$ at time r, the prospective net premium reserve at time t, given that the contract has not yet failed at that time, is given by

$${}_t\overline{V} = \int_0^\infty b_{t+s} \cdot v^s \cdot {}_sp_{x+t}\mu_{x+t+s}\, ds - \int_0^\infty \overline{P}(t+s) \cdot v^s \cdot {}_sp_{x+t}\, ds. \tag{11.17}$$

Similarly, the retrospective reserve at time t would be

$${}_t\overline{V} = \int_0^t \overline{P}(r) \cdot \frac{1}{{}_{t-r}E_{x+r}}\, dr - \int_0^t b_r \cdot \mu_{x+r} \cdot \frac{1}{{}_{t-r}E_{x+r}}\, dr. \tag{11.18}$$

EXAMPLE 11.4

A fully continuous whole life contract issued to (65) has continuous level net premiums. The survival model is exponential with hazard rate .02 and the force of interest is .04. The failure benefit rate is $b_t = 1000e^{.04t}$ for failure at time $t > 0$. Given that survival to duration 2 has occurred, calculate the value of ${}_2\bar{V}$.

SOLUTION

The continuous net premium rate $\bar{P}$ is found as

$$\begin{aligned} \bar{P} \cdot \bar{a}_{65} &= \int_0^\infty b_t \cdot v^t \cdot {}_tp_{65}\mu_{65+t}\, dt \\ &= (1000)(.02) \int_0^\infty e^{.04t} \cdot e^{-.04t} \cdot e^{-.02t}\, dt \;=\; 1000. \end{aligned}$$

Under the exponential survival model the value of $\bar{a}_{65}$ is $\frac{1}{\lambda+\delta} = \frac{1}{.06}$, so the net premium rate is $\bar{P} = 60$. At duration $t = 2$ the APV of future premium is $\bar{P} \cdot \bar{a}_{67}$, which is still 1000 under this survival model. The APV of future benefit at $t = 2$ is given by

$$\begin{aligned} \int_0^\infty b_{s+2} \cdot v^s \cdot {}_sp_{67}\mu_{67+s}\, ds &= (1000)(.02)\int_0^\infty e^{.04(s+2)} \cdot e^{-.04s} \cdot e^{-.02s}\, ds \\ &= 20e^{.08} \int_0^\infty e^{-.02s}\, ds \\ &= \frac{20e^{.08}}{.02} \;=\; 1083.29. \end{aligned}$$

Then the continuous net premium reserve, by the prospective method, is

$${}_2\bar{V} \;=\; 1083.29 - 1000.00 \;=\; 83.29. \qquad \square$$

The analysis at the end of Section 10.3.2 involving Thiele's differential equation can be modified to apply to the fully continuous general whole life model with benefit amount b_r and net premium rate $\bar{P}(r)$. In the general case, the aggregate reserve fund at time t is $l_{x+t} \cdot {}_t\bar{V}$ and its total rate of change at time t is

$$l_{x+t} \cdot \bar{P}(t) + \delta \cdot l_{x+t} \cdot {}_t\bar{V} - b_t \cdot l_{x+t} \cdot \mu_{x+t},$$

which is the derivative of the aggregate reserve fund. Then the general form of the differential equation, analogous to Equation (10.39) in Section 10.3.2, is

$$\frac{d}{dt}\left(l_{x+t} \cdot {}_t\bar{V}\right) = l_{x+t} \cdot \bar{P}(t) + \delta \cdot l_{x+t} \cdot {}_t\bar{V} - b_t \cdot l_{x+t} \cdot \mu_{x+t}. \tag{11.19}$$

The differential equation is solved by steps parallel to those used in Section 10.3.2 for the level-premium, level-benefit case, to reach the general retrospective reserve expression given by Equation (11.18). The details are left for the reader as Exercise 11-12.

11.4 INCORPORATION OF EXPENSES

Recall that all reserve expressions developed in Chapter 10 and thus far in this chapter are for *net premium reserves* only, by which we mean that they are based on net premiums. In Section 9.6 we saw how to incorporate expense factors into a gross premium equivalence principle to determine gross premiums.

It is now a simple matter to include the expense factors, along with the gross premium, to determine *gross premium reserves*. The general prospective formula for the tth net premium reserve, given by Equation (10.2), is now modified to read

$$
\begin{aligned}
{}_tV^G &= (APV\ of\ future\ benefits\ and\ expenses) \\
&\quad - (APV\ of\ future\ gross\ premiums),
\end{aligned}
\tag{11.20}
$$

where the symbol ${}_tV^G$ denotes the tth terminal gross premium reserve. This is illustrated in the following example.

EXAMPLE 11.5

Give an expression for the tth prospective gross premium reserve for the whole life contract described in Example 9.10.

SOLUTION

At duration t, given that the contingent contract is still in effect, the APV of the future gross premium income is $G \cdot \ddot{a}_{x+t}$, where G is defined in Example 9.10. The APV of the future percent of premium expense charges is $.10G \cdot \ddot{a}_{x+t}$, and the APV of the future fixed per \$1000 of benefit expense charges is $2\ddot{a}_{x+t}$. The APV of the benefit payment itself plus the settlement expense together is $1020A_{x+t}$. Thus we have

$$
{}_tV^G = 1020A_{x+t} + (.10G+2)\ddot{a}_{x+t} - G \cdot \ddot{a}_{x+t} = 1020A_{x+t} - (.90G-2)\ddot{a}_{x+t}. \quad \square
$$

Returning to Section 9.6, we can separate the amount of the level net premium P from the gross premium G. The remainder of G represents the amount of annual premium needed to fund the expenses of administering the contract. In other words, we define

$$
EP = G - P \tag{11.21}
$$

to be the annual *expense premium* for the contract.

The notion of separating the gross premium into net premium and expense premium components naturally extends to the reserve. As already covered extensively in Chapter 10, the prospective net premium reserve is the APV of future benefits minus the APV of future net premiums. Similarly we define the tth prospective *expense reserve* to be

$$ {}_tV^E = (APV \text{ of future expenses}) - (APV \text{ of future expense premiums}). \quad (11.22) $$

It should be clear that

$$ {}_tV^G = {}_tV^N + {}_tV^E, \quad (11.23) $$

where ${}_tV^N$ is the tth net premium reserve previously denoted by simply ${}_tV$.

EXAMPLE 11.6

Give an expression for the tth prospective expense reserve for the whole life contract described in Example 9.10.

SOLUTION

First we find the level expense premium as

$$ EP \cdot \ddot{a}_x = .75G + .10G \cdot a_x + 10 + 2a_x + 20A_x, $$

where G is defined in Example 9.10. Then the expense reserve is

$$ {}_tV^E = 20A_{x+t} + (.10G+2)\ddot{a}_{x+t} - EP \cdot \ddot{a}_{x+t}. $$ ❐

Recall how the concept of the present-value-of-loss (at issue) random variable, ${}_0L_x$, introduced in Section 9.2, was easily extended to the present-value-of-loss (at duration t) random variable, ${}_tL_x$, defined in Section 10.1.4. In the same way, the gross premium present-value-of-loss (at issue) random variable, ${}_0L_x^G$, defined in Section 9.6, is easily extended to the gross premium present-value-of-loss (at duration t) random variable, which we denote by ${}_tL_x^G$. This is pursued in Exercise 11-16.

Recall that we expanded Equation (10.30b), which had presumed level net premiums and a level failure benefit, into Equation (11.16b), which generalized Equation (10.30b) for non-level benefits and net premium. Now we generalize further to include expenses.

Let G_t denote the gross premium for the tth contract year, r_t denote the percent-of-premium expense factor for that year, e_t denote the fixed expense for that year, and s_t denote the settlement expense associated with a benefit paid at the end of the tth contract year. Then Equation (11.16b) is generalized to

$$ [{}_tV^G + G_{t+1}(1-r_{t+1}) - e_{t+1}](1+i_{t+1}) = (b_{t+1}+s_{t+1}) \cdot q_{x+t} + p_{x+t} \cdot {}_{t+1}V^G. \quad (11.24) $$

Note that Equation (11.24) allows for the reserve interest rate to also vary by contract year, for maximum generality. In many applications, i_{t+1} will be set as a constant.

Next we consider the fully continuous model including expenses. In Section 10.3 we presented Thiele's differential equation in the context of level net premium and level benefit, and expanded it in Section 11.3 in the context of non-level net premium and non-level benefit. Now we expand Thiele's equation to include expenses.

Modifying earlier notation to be appropriate for a fully continuous model, we let $\bar{G}_t$ denote the gross premium rate at time t (which would often be a constant), r_t denote the percent-of-premium expense factor at time t, $\bar{e}_t$ denote the annual rate of per policy expenses, paid continuously, δ_t denote the force of interest at time t (generally a constant), b_t denote the failure benefit at time t, and s_t denote the settlement expense associated with a benefit paid at time t. Then we can write Thiele's equation as

$$\frac{d}{dt}\,{}_t\bar{V}^G = \bar{G}_t(1-r_t)-\bar{e}_t+\delta_t\cdot {}_t\bar{V}^G-\mu_{x+t}\left(b_t+s_t-{}_t\bar{V}^G\right). \tag{11.25}$$

In Example 11.11 we consider the use of Euler's Method to approximate values of ${}_t\bar{V}^G$, as a minor extension of Example 10.15 where we defined this technique in the context of a fully continuous net premium model.

11.5 GAIN AND LOSS ANALYSIS

We now continue our analysis of financial gain or loss under a contingent contract which we began in Section 10.6, this time in the more realistic environment of gross premiums and gross premium reserves.

We begin with Equation (11.24), found in Section 11.4, and modify it to read

$$[{}_tV^G+G_{t+1}(1-r_{t+1})-e_{t+1}](1+i_{t+1})-[(b_{t+1}+s_{t+1})\cdot q_{x+t}+p_{x+t}\cdot {}_{t+1}V^G], \tag{11.30a}$$

which uses the gross premium and gross premium reserves. Recall that this expression is written with maximum generality to allow the benefit, gross premium, interest rate, and all expense factors to vary by contract year. In practice, many of these parameters would be constant over contract years.

Mimicking the discussion in Section 10.6.1 in the net premium case, if the interest, mortality, and expenses *actually experienced* in the $(t+1)^{st}$ contract year are the same as those assumed in the gross premium and gross premium reserve calculations, then there would be neither gain nor loss in that year. That is,

$$[{}_tV^G+G_{t+1}(1-r_{t+1})-e_{t+1}](1+i_{t+1})-[(b_{t+1}+s_{t+1})\cdot q_{x+t}+p_{x+t}\cdot {}_{t+1}V^G] = 0. \tag{11.30b}$$

But if the factors actually experienced in the $(t+1)^{st}$ year are denoted with primes, with the gross premium, gross premium reserves, and benefit unchanged, then

$$G^T = [{}_tV^G+G_{t+1}(1-r'_{t+1})-e'_{t+1}](1+i'_{t+1})-[(b_{t+1}+s'_{t+1})\cdot q'_{x+t}+p'_{x+t}\cdot {}_{t+1}V^G], \tag{11.31}$$

represents a gain in the $(t+1)^{st}$ year if $G^T > 0$ and a loss if $G^T < 0$.

EXAMPLE 11.9

Consider a block of fully discrete whole life policies issued at age 40 with face amount 50,000. On the assumed mortality, interest, and expense bases, the gross annual premium per policy is 685.00, the tenth-year gross premium reserve is 3950.73, and the eleventh-year gross premium reserve is 4607.07. The assumed interest rate is 6%, the assumed mortality rate for the eleventh year is $q_{50} = .00592$, and the assumed expenses are 5% of the gross premium and 300 to process a death claim. In the eleventh year, there are 1000 policies in force at the beginning of that year and five deaths occur in the year. Actual expenses in the eleventh year are 6% of the gross premium and 100 to process each death claim, and the actual earned interest rate is 6.5%. Calculate the total gain on a single policy.

SOLUTION

Note first that the beginning-of-year expense is percent of premium only, so the term e_{t+1} can be ignored. Substituting the actually experienced factors for the assumed factors, we have

$$\begin{aligned} G^T &= [3950.73 + 685.00(1-.06)](1.065) - [(50,100)(.005) + (.995)(4607.07)] \\ &= (4594.63)(1.065) - (250.50+4584.03) = 58.75. \end{aligned}$$ ❑

In Section 10.6.1 we analyzed the gain by source (mortality or interest) in the net premium case. Now we can similarly analyze the gain by source (mortality, interest, or expense) here in the gross premium case, but with an important difference. In the net premium case, the interest and mortality gains could be calculated independently and they would sum to the total gain (see Example 10.9). In the gross premium case, we find interest and expense terms multiplied together and also mortality and expense terms multiplied together (see Equation (11.30b)). A consequence of this is that if the three gains by source are calculated independently, they will not sum to the total gain (see Example 11.12).

To correct this, we first choose an order for calculating the three gains by source. (The order is arbitrary, but different gain-by-source values will be obtained depending on the chosen order.) The process is illustrated in the following example.

EXAMPLE 11.10

Using the data given in Example 11.9, calculate, in order, the gains from interest, mortality, and expenses.

SOLUTION

The gain from interest is calculated by using the actual interest rate $i' = .065$ in Expression (11.30a), but still using the assumed values for mortality and expense. Then the gain from interest is

$$
\begin{aligned}
G^I &= [3950.73+685.00(1-.05)](1.065)-[(50{,}300)(.00592)+(.99408)(4607.07)] \\
&= (4601.48)(1.065)-(297.776+4579.796) = 23.00.
\end{aligned}
$$

The gain from mortality is calculated by using the actual mortality rate $q'_{50}=.005$ and the actual interest rate $i'=.065$, but still using the assumed values for expenses. This gives the combined gain from interest and mortality, so the previously-calculated gain from interest is subtracted to reach the gain from mortality. Then the gain from mortality is

$$
\begin{aligned}
G^M &= [3950.73+685.00(.95)](1.065)-[(50{,}300)(.005)+(.995)(4607.07)]-23.00 \\
&= (4601.48)(1.065)-(251.50+4584.03)-23.00 = 42.05.
\end{aligned}
$$

The gain from expenses, being calculated last, is the balancing item. That is,

$$G^E = G^T - G^I - G^M,$$

so it is obvious that the three gains by source sum to the total gain. In this example,

$$G^E = 58.75-23.00-42.05 = -6.30,$$

showing a loss, rather than gain, from expenses. □

Further practice with the gain-by-source calculations is provided in Example 11.12 and the exercises associated with this section.

11.6 WRITTEN-ANSWER QUESTION EXAMPLES

EXAMPLE 11.11

This example builds on Example 10.15, which introduced Euler's method in the net premium reserve case. Now consider a warranty contract on an electronic device that pays 100 at the moment of failure, or at the end of five years if failure has not yet occurred. The gross annual premium, paid continuously, is 20, percent-of-premium expense is 2%, failure settlement expense is 10 (but there is no settlement expense if failure does not occur), the force of interest is .04, and the force of failure for this device is $\mu_t = .01t^2$.

(a) State Thiele's equation for this contract.

(b) What are two possible boundary conditions for using Euler's method?

(c) Use Euler's method to approximate ${}_4\bar{V}^G$, with $h=.50$. Use the approximate derivatives at $t=4.5$ and $t=4.0$.

(d) Repeat part (c) using the approximate derivatives at $t=5.0$ and $t=4.5$.

SOLUTION

(a) There is no per-contract expense, so the $\bar{e}_t$ term in Equation (11.25) is zero. We have

$$\begin{aligned}\frac{d}{dt}\,{}_t\bar{V}^G &= \bar{G}_t(1-r_t)+\delta_t\cdot{}_t\bar{V}^G-\mu_t\left(b_t+s_t-{}_t\bar{V}^G\right)\\ &= 19.60+.04\,{}_t\bar{V}^G-.01t^2\left(110-{}_t\bar{V}^G\right).\end{aligned}$$

(b) The possible boundary conditions are ${}_0\bar{V}^G=0$ and ${}_5\bar{V}^G=100.$

(c) As in Example 10.15, we can approximate the derivative by

$$\frac{d}{dt}\,{}_t\bar{V}^G \approx \frac{{}_{t+h}\bar{V}^G-{}_t\bar{V}^G}{h}.$$

Since we seek the value of ${}_4\bar{V}^G,$ it is easier to do backward recursion from ${}_5\bar{V}^G=100$ than to do forward recursion from ${}_0\bar{V}^G=0.$ With $h=.50$ and $t=4.5,$ we have

$$19.60+.04\,{}_{4.5}\bar{V}^G-(.01)(4.5)^2\left(110-{}_{4.5}\bar{V}^G\right) \approx \frac{{}_5\bar{V}^G-{}_{4.5}\bar{V}^G}{.50},$$

or

$${}_{4.5}\bar{V}^G+.50\left[19.60+.04\,{}_{4.5}\bar{V}^G-.2025\left(110-{}_{4.5}\bar{V}^G\right)\right] \approx {}_5\bar{V}^G,$$

which solves for

$${}_{4.5}\bar{V}^G \approx \frac{100-(.50)(19.60)+(.50)(.2025)(110)}{1+(.50)(.04)+(.50)(.2025)} = 90.38.$$

Then with $t=4.0,$ we have

$$19.60+.04\,{}_{4.0}\bar{V}^G-(.01)(4.0)^2\left(110-{}_{4.0}\bar{V}^G\right) \approx \frac{{}_{4.5}\bar{V}^G-{}_{4.0}\bar{V}^G}{.50},$$

which solves for

$${}_{4.0}\bar{V}^G = \frac{90.38-(.50)(19.60)+(.50)(.16)(110)}{1+(.50)(.04)+(.50)(.16)} = 81.25.$$

(d) Instead of using $\frac{d}{dx}f(x)\approx\frac{f(x+h)-f(x)}{h},$ we could use the equally-acceptable approximation $\frac{d}{dx}f(x)\approx\frac{f(x)-f(x-h)}{h}.$ Adapted to this question, we have

$$\frac{d}{dt}\,{}_t\bar{V}^G \approx \frac{{}_t\bar{V}^G-{}_{t-h}\bar{V}^G}{h}.$$

Now with $h=.50$ and $t=5.0$, we have

$$19.60+.04\,{}_{5.0}\bar{V}^G-(.01)(5.0)^2\left(110-{}_{5.0}\bar{V}^G\right)\approx\frac{{}_{5.0}\bar{V}^G-{}_{4.5}\bar{V}^G}{.50},$$

where ${}_{5.0}\bar{V}^G=100$ is still our boundary condition. We then have

$${}_{4.5}\bar{V}^G\approx 100-.50(19.60+4-2.50)=89.45.$$

Then with $t=4.5$, we have

$$19.60+.04\,{}_{4.5}\bar{V}^G-(.01)(4.5)^2\left(110-{}_{4.5}\bar{V}^G\right)\approx\frac{{}_{4.5}\bar{V}^G-{}_{4.0}\bar{V}^G}{.50},$$

which solves for

$${}_{4.0}\bar{V}^G\approx 89.45-.50(19.60+3.578-4.161375)=79.94.$$ ❑

EXAMPLE 11.12

Refer to the information presented in Example 11.9.

(a) Calculate each of G^I, G^M, and G^E independently. Show that they do not sum to $G^T=58.75$.

(b) Repeat Example 11.10, this time calculating the gains in the order mortality, expenses, and interest.

SOLUTION

(a) We already have $G^I=23.00$ from Example 11.10, since G^I was calculated first, using $i'=.065$ in place of $i=.06$. To calculate G^M independently, we use the actual $q'_{50}=.00500$ in place of the assumed $q_{50}=.00592$, but revert to the assumed $i=.06$. This gives us

$$\begin{aligned}G^M &= [3950.73+685.00(.95)](1.06)-[(50{,}300)(.005)+(.995)(4607.07)]\\ &= (4601.48)(1.06)-(251.50+4584.03)=42.04.\end{aligned}$$

To calculate G^E independently, we use $r'=6\%$ and $s'=100$ in place of $r=.05$ and $s=300$, but revert to $i=.06$ and $q_{50}=.00592$. This gives us

$$\begin{aligned}G^E &= [3950.73+685.00(.94)](1.06)-[(50{,}100)(.00592)+(.99408)(4607.07)]\\ &= (4594.63)(1.06)-(296.59+4579.80)=-6.08.\end{aligned}$$

Then we have

$$G^I + G^M + G^E \;=\; 23.00 + 42.04 - 6.08 \;=\; 58.96,$$

which does not sum to $G^T = 58.75$.

(b) The gain from mortality will be $G^M = 42.02$ from part (a), since it is calculated first. The gain from expenses will be

$$\begin{aligned} G^E &= [3950.73 + 685.00(.94)](1.06) - \big[(50{,}100)(.005) + (.995)(4607.07)\big] - G^M \\ &= (4594.63)(1.06) - (250.50 + 4584.03) - 42.02 \;=\; -6.24, \end{aligned}$$

where we use the e' and s' factors as well as q'_{60} and p'_{60}, but subtract the value of G^M. Then G^I is the balancing item of

$$G^I \;=\; G^T - G^M - G^E \;=\; 58.75 - 42.02 - (-6.24) \;=\; 22.97.$$

The three gains-by-source values sum to the total gain, as in Example 11.10, but each is slightly different than its value in Example 11.10 due to the altered order of calculation. ❑

11.7 EXERCISES

11.1 Modified Benefit Reserves

11-1 If net premiums are modified for the entire premium paying period of n years, show each of the following:

(a) ${}_tV^{NLP}_{x:\overline{n}|} - {}_tV^{M}_{x:\overline{n}|} = (\beta - P)\cdot \ddot{a}_{x+t:\overline{n-t}|}$ (b) ${}_tV^{M}_{x:\overline{n}|} = 1 - (\beta + d)\cdot \ddot{a}_{x+t:\overline{n-t}|}$

11-2 Consider a fully continuous unit whole life insurance issued at age x, under which modified continuous reserves accumulate using modified premium rate $\overline{\alpha}(r)$ at time r, for $0 < r \leq 5$, and modified premium rate $\overline{\beta}$ at time $r \geq 5$. The premium rate $\overline{\alpha}(r)$ is defined as $\overline{\alpha}(0) = .25\overline{\beta}$, increasing linearly to $\overline{\alpha}(5) = \overline{\beta}$. Show that

$$\overline{\beta} \;=\; \frac{\overline{A}_x}{\overline{a}_x - .75\overline{a}_{x:\overline{5}|} + .15(\overline{I}\overline{a})_{x:\overline{5}|}}.$$

11-3 For an h-pay, n-year unit endowment insurance issued at age x, with reserves calculated by the FPT method, show that

$$ {}_t^hV_{x:\overline{n}|}^{FPT} = {}_{t-1}^{h-1}V_{x+1:\overline{n-1}|}^{NLP}, $$

where $t < h < n$.

11-4 As an extension of Example 11.2, show that, under the two-year FPT reserving method, ${}_1V^F = {}_2V^F = 0$ and $\beta = P_{x+2}$.

11.2 Net Premium Reserves at Fractional Durations

11-5 Show that the expression for r given in Equation (11.9) reduces to $r = 1-s$ under the UDD assumption.

11-6 Show that the tth year mean reserve for a unit insurance can be written as

$$ {}_{t-1/2}V = \frac{1}{2}\left[(1+v\cdot p_{x+t-1})\cdot {}_tV + v\cdot q_{x+t-1}\right]. $$

11.3 Generalization to Non-Level Benefits and Non-Level Net Premiums

11-7 Write the general retrospective formula which is the counterpart to the prospective formula given by Equation (11.15).

11-8 A 3-year term insurance issued to (x) has a decreasing failure benefit, paid at the end of the year of failure. The interest rate is $i = .06$. Calculate the initial reserve for the second year, given the following values:

$$ b_1 = 200 \qquad b_2 = 150 \qquad b_3 = 100 $$
$$ q_x = .03 \qquad q_{x+1} = .06 \qquad q_{x+2} = .09 $$

11-9 A 2-year endowment contract issued to (x) has a failure benefit of 1000 plus the reserve at the end of the year of failure and a pure endowment benefit of 1000. Given that $i = .10$, $q_x = .10$, and $q_{x+1} = .11$, calculate the net level premium.

11-10 A whole life contract issued to (40) pays a benefit, at the end of the year of failure, of b_k for failure in the kth year. The net premium P is equal to P_{20}, and the net premium reserves satisfy ${}_tV = {}_tV_{20}$, for $t = 0,1,\ldots,19$. Furthermore, $q_{40+k} = q_{20+k} + .01$, for $k = 0,1,\ldots,19$. Given that ${}_{11}V_{20} = .08154$ and $q_{30} = .008427$, calculate b_{11}.

11-11 A continuously decreasing 25-year term insurance issued to (40) has benefit rate $b_t = 1000\bar{a}_{\overline{25-t|}}$ for failure at time t. The continuous net premium rate is $\bar{P} = 200$. Given also that $i = .05$ and $\bar{A}_{50:\overline{15|}} = .60$, find the net premium reserve at time $t = 10$.

11-12 Solve Thiele's differential equation, given by Equation (11.19), to reach the retrospective reserve expression given by Equation (11.18).

11-13 Equation (11.19) gives Thiele's differential equation in the context of the aggregate reserve fund. From it, derive the result

$$\frac{d}{dt}\,{}_t\bar{V} = \bar{P}(t) + \delta \cdot {}_t\bar{V} - \mu_{x+t}(b_t - {}_t\bar{V}),$$

which is Thiele's differential equation in the context of a single policy.

11.4 Incorporation of Expenses

11-14 For the 20-pay whole life insurance described in Exercise 9-27, find the gross premium reserve at (a) duration 10 and (b) duration 20, given the additional values $\ddot{a}_{x+10} = 16.5$, $\ddot{a}_{x+20} = 12.5$, and $\ddot{a}_{x+10:\overline{10|}} = 7$.

11-15 Show that ${}_tV = {}_tV^G - {}_tV^E$, where ${}_tV^G$ is given in Example 11.5 and ${}_tV^E$ is given in Example 11.6.

11-16 We now define ${}_tL_x^G$ as the gross premium present-value-of-loss random variable measured at time t, given that $K_x \geq t$ (i.e., the contract has not yet failed at time t). For the whole life contract described in Example 9.8, show that

$$E\left[{}_tL_x^G \mid K_x \geq t\right] = {}_tV^G,$$

the gross premium reserve, as determined in Example 11.5.

11-17 Consider the gross premium recursion relationship given by Equation (11.24). Suppose the premium is paid continuously at annual rate $\bar{G}_t$ at time t, and fixed expenses are paid continuously at annual rate $\bar{e}_t$ at time t. State Thiele's differential equation in this general case including expenses.

11.5 Gain and Loss Analysis

11-18 Derive each of the following symbolic results, assuming that the gains by source are calculated in the order mortality, then expenses, and then interest. (Note that the subscripts $t+1$ have been omitted on each expense factor.)

(a) $G^M = (q_{x+t} - q'_{x+t})(b+s-{}_{t+1}V^G)$

(b) $G^E = [G(r-r')+(e-e')](1+i)+(s-s')\cdot q'_{x+t}$

(c) $G^I = [{}_tV + G(1-r') - e'](i'-i)$

11-19 A block of 1000 fully discrete 20-year term insurance policies of face amount 10,000 were issued to independent lives all age 40, of which 990 remain in force after three policy years. The gross premium and gross premium reserves are $G=90$, ${}_3V^G = 97.12$, and ${}_4V^G = 164.13$. For the fourth policy year, the anticipated interest rate is $i=.05$, the anticipated mortality rate is $q_{43}=.003$, and the anticipated percent-of-premium expense rate is $r=.03$. In the fourth policy year, the actual interest rate, mortality rate, and percent-of-premium expense rate were .04, .002, and .025, respectively. (There is no per-policy expense or settlement expense.) Calculate, in order, each of the following gains by source for the 990 policies together:

(a) Gain from interest
(b) Gain from mortality
(c) Gain from expenses

11-20 An annual premium deferred annuity is now in its payout phase, paying 10,000 at the end of each year. The contract holder is currently age 70. The only expense is 5% of the benefit payment, payable at the end of the year for surviving contract holders only. The contract reserves are calculated from the life table in Appendix A at $i=.06$. For the year of age from 70 to 71, the anticipated interest and mortality rates are .06 and .02041, respectively, and the actual interest and mortality rates are .055 and .025, respectively. Calculate, in order, (a) the gain from mortality and (b) the gain from interest.

CHAPTER TWELVE

MODELS DEPENDENT ON MULTIPLE SURVIVALS (MULTI-LIFE MODELS)

All the discussion to this point in the text has focused on the complementary concepts of survival and failure of a single entity, such as a single person under a life insurance policy or a life annuity. We consistently referred to the entity whose survival was being observed as our *status of interest*, and we defined what constituted survival (and therefore failure) in each particular case. This generic approach to the concept of survival will be continued in this chapter.

We now consider the case where the status of interest is itself made up of two or more entities, such as two separate individual lives. In actuarial science such models are said to involve multiple lives and are known as *multi-life models*. We will develop the theory of multi-life models in the two-life case first, and then show how it is easily extended to more than two lives.

We will also need to distinguish whether the two individual lives comprising a multi-life status have independent or dependent future lifetimes. The assumption of independence will simplify our work to some extent, and is presumed wherever needed throughout the chapter. Independence is not presumed for the discussion in Sections 12.5 and 12.6.

12.1 THE JOINT-LIFE MODEL

A *joint-life status* is one for which survival of the status requires the survival of *all* (or *both*, in the two-life case) of the individual members making up the status. Accordingly, the status fails upon the *first* failure of its component members.

12.1.1 THE TIME-TO-FAILURE RANDOM VARIABLE FOR A JOINT-LIFE STATUS

Consider a two-life joint status, made up of lives that are ages x and y as of time 0. We use the notation (xy) to denote such a status,[1] and we use T_{xy} to denote the random variable for the future lifetime (or time-to-failure) of the status. From the definition of failure it is clear that T_{xy} will be the *smaller* of the individual future lifetimes denoted by T_x and T_y. That is,

$$T_{xy} = \min(T_x, T_y). \tag{12.1}$$

Our analysis of the future lifetime random variable T_{xy} will parallel that for the individual life T_x presented in Section 5.3. Indeed, by using the generic concept of a status or entity, the two cases of T_{xy} and T_x are really the same except for the different notation.

[1] If numerical ages are used instead of the letters x and y, such as if $x = 20$ and $y = 25$, for example, the status is denoted (20:25). The colon would also be used to denote the status $(x+n:y+n)$.

12.1.2 THE SURVIVAL DISTRIBUTION FUNCTION OF T_{xy}

We begin our analysis of the random variable T_{xy} with its SDF, given by

$$S_{xy}(t) = Pr(T_{xy} > t) \tag{12.2}$$

and denoted by ${}_tp_{xy}$ in standard actuarial notation. Since survival of the status itself requires the survival of both component members of the status, then assuming independence of the individual lifetimes we have

$${}_tp_{xy} = {}_tp_x \cdot {}_tp_y, \tag{12.3}$$

which is the bridge between joint-life and individual life functions. Equation (12.3) will allow us to evaluate many joint-life functions from a single-life tabular survival model.

12.1.3 THE CUMULATIVE DISTRIBUTION FUNCTION OF T_{xy}

The CDF of T_{xy} is given by

$$F_{xy}(t) = 1 - S_{xy}(t) = Pr(T_{xy} \leq t), \tag{12.4}$$

and is denoted by ${}_tq_{xy}$ in actuarial notation. It follows that

$${}_tq_{xy} = 1 - {}_tp_{xy} \tag{12.5a}$$

for all t. If the individual lifetimes are independent, then we can write

$$\begin{aligned} {}_tq_{xy} &= 1 - {}_tp_x \cdot {}_tp_y \\ &= 1 - (1 - {}_tq_x)(1 - {}_tq_y) = {}_tq_x + {}_tq_y - {}_tq_x \cdot {}_tq_y. \end{aligned} \tag{12.5b}$$

Equation (12.5b) illustrates a very basic concept in probability. ${}_tq_{xy}$ denotes the probability that the joint status fails before (or at) time t, which occurs if either or both of the individual lives fail before (or at) time t. Since the events $(T_x \leq t)$ and $(T_y \leq t)$ are not mutually exclusive, the probability of the union event, which is ${}_tq_{xy}$, is given by the general addition rule reflected in Equation (12.5b).

As in the individual life case discussed earlier in the text, the pre-subscript t is suppressed in the special case of $t = 1$. Thus we have

$$p_{xy} = S_{xy}(1) = Pr(T_{xy} > 1) \tag{12.6a}$$

and

$$q_{xy} = 1 - p_{xy} = F_{xy}(1) = Pr(T_{xy} \leq 1). \tag{12.6b}$$

EXAMPLE 12.1

If T_x and T_y are independent, and each is uniformly distributed over each year of age separately, show that, for $0<t<1$,

$$_tq_{xy} = t\cdot q_x(1-t\cdot q_y)+t\cdot q_y(1-t\cdot q_x)+t^2\cdot q_x\cdot q_y.$$

SOLUTION

With independent lifetimes we have, from Equation (12.5b),

$$_tq_{xy} = {}_tq_x + {}_tq_y - {}_tq_x\cdot {}_tq_y.$$

Under UDD this becomes

$$\begin{aligned} _tq_{xy} &= t\cdot q_x + t\cdot q_y - t^2\cdot q_x\cdot q_y \\ &= t\cdot q_x - t^2\cdot q_x\cdot q_y + t\cdot q_y - t^2\cdot q_x\cdot q_y + t^2\cdot q_x\cdot q_y \\ &= t\cdot q_x(1-t\cdot q_y)+t\cdot q_y(1-t\cdot q_x)+t^2\cdot q_x\cdot q_y, \end{aligned}$$

as required. ❒

12.1.4 THE PROBABILITY DENSITY FUNCTION OF T_{xy}

The PDF of T_{xy} is defined by

$$f_{xy}(t) = \frac{d}{dt}F_{xy}(t) = -\frac{d}{dt}S_{xy}(t). \tag{12.7}$$

In the special case of independence, we have

$$\begin{aligned} f_{xy}(t) &= -\frac{d}{dt}S_{xy}(t) \\ &= -\frac{d}{dt}({}_tp_x\cdot {}_tp_y) \\ &= -\left({}_tp_x\cdot\frac{d}{dt}\,{}_tp_y + {}_tp_y\cdot\frac{d}{dt}\,{}_tp_x\right) \\ &= -[{}_tp_x(-{}_tp_y\mu_{y+t}) + {}_tp_y(-{}_tp_x\mu_{x+t})] \\ &= {}_tp_x\cdot {}_tp_y\mu_{y+t} + {}_tp_y\cdot {}_tp_x\mu_{x+t} \\ &= {}_tp_{xy}(\mu_{x+t}+\mu_{y+t}), \end{aligned} \tag{12.8}$$

where we have used Equation (6.21) for $\frac{d}{dt}\,{}_tp_x$ and $\frac{d}{dt}\,{}_tp_y$.

12.1.5 THE HAZARD RATE FUNCTION OF T_{xy}

Recall that a hazard rate function (HRF) measures the conditional instantaneous rate of failure at precise time t, given survival to time t. For individual lives in a life insurance context we refer to the hazard rate as the *force of mortality*; in the context of a joint status it is more appropriate to view the hazard rate as a *force of failure* rather than a force of mortality. Regardless of the terminology used, the HRF is defined as

$$\lambda_{xy}(t) = \frac{f_{xy}(t)}{S_{xy}(t)}. \tag{12.9a}$$

In the special case of independent lives we have

$$\lambda_{xy}(t) = \frac{{}_tp_{xy}(\mu_{x+t}+\mu_{y+t})}{{}_tp_{xy}} = \mu_{x+t}+\mu_{y+t}. \tag{12.9b}$$

In standard actuarial notation the HRF is denoted by $\mu_{x+t:y+t}$,[2] so we have

$$\mu_{x+t:y+t} = \mu_{x+t}+\mu_{y+t}. \tag{12.9c}$$

This shows that the force of failure acting on the joint status is the sum of the forces of failure (or forces of mortality) acting on the individual components (lives) in the case of independent lives.

12.1.6 CONDITIONAL PROBABILITIES

The conditional failure probability, denoted by ${}_{n|}q_x$ in the single-life case, has its counterpart in the joint-life case. We define

$${}_{n|}q_{xy} = Pr(n < T_{xy} \le n+1), \tag{12.10}$$

the probability that the time of failure of the joint status occurs in the $(n+1)^{st}$ time interval.[3] Since failure of the status occurs with the first failure of the individual components, then ${}_{n|}q_{xy}$ denotes the probability that the first failure occurs in the $(n+1)^{st}$ interval. Thus we have

$$\begin{aligned} {}_{n|}q_{xy} &= {}_np_{xy} - {}_{n+1}p_{xy} && (12.11a) \\ &= {}_np_{xy}(1-p_{x+n:y+n}) \\ &= {}_np_{xy} \cdot q_{x+n:y+n}. && (12.11b) \end{aligned}$$

---

[2] Note that the joint status HRF is a function of t, with the identifying characteristics of its component members (x) and (y) fixed at time $t=0$. To reinforce the idea that the joint status HRF is a function of t only, some texts prefer the notation $\mu_{xy}(t)$. (See, for example, Section 9.3 of Bowers, *et al.* [4] .)

[3] Recall the discrete random variable K_x, defined in Chapter 5 as the curtate duration at failure for the status (x). If we now define K_{xy} as the random variable for the curtate duration at failure of the joint status (xy), we have ${}_{n|}q_{xy} = Pr(K_{xy} = n)$.

In the case of independent lives we can evaluate ${}_{n|}q_{xy}$ from the life table using

$$ {}_{n|}q_{xy} = {}_np_x \cdot {}_np_y - {}_{n+1}p_x \cdot {}_{n+1}p_y. \tag{12.12}$$

EXAMPLE 12.2

If T_x and T_y are independent, calculate the value of ${}_{2|}q_{xy}$ given the following values:

$$\begin{array}{lll} q_x = .08 & q_{x+1} = .09 & q_{x+2} = .10 \\ q_y = .10 & q_{y+1} = .15 & q_{y+2} = .20 \end{array}$$

SOLUTION

${}_{2|}q_{xy}$ denotes the probability that the joint-life status fails in the third year, which is also denoted by $Pr(K_{xy} = 2)$. Here we have

$$\begin{aligned} {}_{2|}q_{xy} &= {}_2p_{xy} \cdot q_{x+2:y+2} \\ &= {}_2p_x \cdot {}_2p_y (1 - p_{x+2} \cdot p_{y+2}) \\ &= (.92)(.91)(.90)(.85)[1-(.90)(.80)] = .17932. \end{aligned}$$

❐

12.1.7 MOMENTS OF T_{xy}

The expected value of T_{xy} gives the complete expectation of future "lifetime" of the joint status. It is denoted by $\overset{\circ}{e}_{xy}$ in actuarial notation and defined by

$$\overset{\circ}{e}_{xy} = E[T_{xy}] = \int_0^\infty t \cdot f_{xy}(t)\, dt \tag{12.13a}$$

$$= \int_0^\infty {}_tp_{xy}\, dt, \tag{12.13b}$$

the joint status counterpart to Equation (5.48d). The second moment is given by

$$E[T_{xy}{}^2] = \int_0^\infty t^2 \cdot f_{xy}(t)\, dt, \tag{12.14}$$

and the variance of T_{xy} follows as

$$Var(T_{xy}) = E[T_{xy}{}^2] - \left(E[T_{xy}]\right)^2. \tag{12.15}$$

Similarly, we can define the *curtate expectation of future lifetime for the joint status*, the counterpart to the single-life function of Section 6.3.4, as

$$e_{xy} = \sum_{k=1}^{\infty} {}_kp_{xy} \tag{12.16}$$

and the temporary curtate lifetime as

$$e_{xy:\overline{n}|} = \sum_{k=1}^{n} {}_kp_{xy}. \tag{12.17}$$

Note that $e_{xy:\overline{n}|}$ represents the average number of whole years of survival within the next n years for the joint status (xy).

EXAMPLE 12.3

Let T_x and T_y be independent time-to-failure random variables, each with exponential distributions with hazard rates λ_x and λ_y, respectively. Find an expression for $\overset{\circ}{e}_{xy}$.

SOLUTION

We know that ${}_tp_x = e^{-t\cdot\lambda_x}$ and ${}_tp_y = e^{-t\cdot\lambda_y}$, so under independence we have

$${}_tp_{xy} = {}_tp_x \cdot {}_tp_y = e^{-t(\lambda_x+\lambda_y)}.$$

This shows us that T_{xy} has an exponential distribution with hazard rate $\lambda = \lambda_x + \lambda_y$, so

$$\overset{\circ}{e}_{xy} = E[T_{xy}] = \frac{1}{\lambda_x + \lambda_y}.$$ □

12.2 THE LAST-SURVIVOR MODEL

A *last-survivor status* is one for which survival of the status requires the survival of any one (or more) of its component members. That is, the status is said to survive as long as *at least one* of its members survives, so that it fails only when *all* of its members have failed. Then the time of failure of the status is the time of the *last* failure among its components, or the *second* failure in the two-life case. Note that the n-year certain and continuous annuity, defined in Example 8.14, is a special case of a last-survivor status, since the annuity pays until the second failure out of (40) and $\overline{10}|$. The APV of this annuity is denoted $\ddot{a}_{\overline{40:\overline{10}|}}$ in actuarial notation.

12.2.1 THE TIME-TO-FAILURE RANDOM VARIABLE FOR A LAST-SURVIVOR STATUS

For a two-life last-survivor status composed of the individual lives (x) and (y), we denote the status itself by $(\overline{xy})$ and the random variable for the future lifetime of the status by $T_{\overline{xy}}$. Since the status fails on the last failure, then $T_{\overline{xy}}$ will be the *larger* of the individual future lifetimes T_x and T_y. That is

$$T_{\overline{xy}} = \max(T_x, T_y). \tag{12.18}$$

12.2.2 FUNCTIONS OF THE RANDOM VARIABLE $T_{\overline{xy}}$

If T_x and T_y are independent, then it follows that the CDF of $T_{\overline{xy}}$ is

$$F_{\overline{xy}}(t) = Pr(T_{\overline{xy}} \leq t) = F_x(t) \cdot F_y(t). \tag{12.19a}$$

In actuarial notation we would write

$${}_tq_{\overline{xy}} = {}_tq_x \cdot {}_tq_y. \tag{12.19b}$$

The SDF of $T_{\overline{xy}}$ can then be found as

$$S_{\overline{xy}}(t) = Pr(T_{\overline{xy}} > t) = 1 - F_{\overline{xy}}(t). \tag{12.20a}$$

In actuarial notation, again presuming the independence of T_x and T_y, we have

$$\begin{aligned} {}_tp_{\overline{xy}} &= 1 - {}_tq_{\overline{xy}} \\ &= 1 - {}_tq_x \cdot {}_tq_y \\ &= 1 - (1 - {}_tp_x)(1 - {}_tp_y) \\ &= {}_tp_x + {}_tp_y - {}_tp_x \cdot {}_tp_y \\ &= {}_tp_x + {}_tp_y - {}_tp_{xy}. \end{aligned} \tag{12.20b}$$

Equation (12.20b) is very important, as it allows us to express last-survivor survival probabilities in terms of single-life and joint-life functions, so we will be able to evaluate last-survivor functions from a single-life survival model or life table. Although Equation (12.20b) was derived here assuming the independence of T_x and T_y, the identity is also true for dependent lifetimes T_x and T_y, as we shall see in Section 12.2.3.

The PDF of $T_{\overline{xy}}$ is then found from the SDF as

$$\begin{aligned} f_{\overline{xy}}(t) &= -\frac{d}{dt} S_{\overline{xy}}(t) \\ &= -\frac{d}{dt}({}_tp_x + {}_tp_y - {}_tp_{xy}) \\ &= {}_tp_x\mu_{x+t} + {}_tp_y\mu_{y+t} - {}_tp_{xy}\mu_{x+t:y+t}, \end{aligned} \tag{12.21}$$

and the HRF follows as

$$\lambda_{\overline{xy}}(t) = \frac{f_{\overline{xy}}(t)}{S_{\overline{xy}}(t)} = \frac{{}_tp_x\mu_{x+t} + {}_tp_y\mu_{y+t} - {}_tp_{xy}\mu_{x+t:y+t}}{{}_tp_x + {}_tp_y - {}_tp_{xy}}. \tag{12.22}$$

The conditional probability for failure of the status in the $(n+1)^{st}$ time interval is

$$\begin{aligned} {}_{n|}q_{\overline{xy}} &= Pr(n < T_{\overline{xy}} \leq n+1) \\ &= {}_n p_{\overline{xy}} - {}_{n+1}p_{\overline{xy}} \\ &= ({}_n p_x + {}_n p_y - {}_n p_{xy}) - ({}_{n+1}p_x + {}_{n+1}p_y - {}_{n+1}p_{xy}) \\ &= {}_{n|}q_x + {}_{n|}q_y - {}_{n|}q_{xy}. \end{aligned} \tag{12.23}$$

As with the joint-life function (see Footnote 3), we can define $K_{\overline{xy}}$ as the random variable for the curtate duration at failure of the last-survivor status $(\overline{xy})$, so we have

$$ {}_{n|}q_{\overline{xy}} = Pr(K_{\overline{xy}} = n). \tag{12.24}$$

EXAMPLE 12.4

Find the probability that the second failure out of independent lives (x) and (y) occurs in the fifth year, given the following values:

$${}_4p_x = .85 \qquad {}_4p_y = .68 \qquad {}_5p_x = .81 \qquad {}_5p_y = .60$$

SOLUTION

We seek the value of

$${}_{4|}q_{\overline{xy}} = {}_4p_{\overline{xy}} - {}_5p_{\overline{xy}}.$$

Due to independence we have

$${}_4p_{\overline{xy}} = .85+.68-(.85)(.68) = .952$$

and

$${}_5p_{\overline{xy}} = .81+.60-(.81)(.60) = .924.$$

Then

$${}_{4|}q_{\overline{xy}} = .952-.924 = .028.$$ ❑

The expected value of $T_{\overline{xy}}$ gives the complete expectation of future lifetime for the last-survivor status. We have

$$\overset{\circ}{e}_{\overline{xy}} = E[T_{\overline{xy}}] = \int_0^\infty t \cdot f_{\overline{xy}}(t)\,dt = \int_0^\infty {}_tp_{\overline{xy}}\,dt. \tag{12.25a}$$

Then using Equation (12.20b) for ${}_tp_{\overline{xy}}$ we have

$$\overset{\circ}{e}_{\overline{xy}} = \overset{\circ}{e}_x + \overset{\circ}{e}_y - \overset{\circ}{e}_{xy}. \tag{12.25b}$$

The corresponding curtate expectation is

$$e_{\overline{xy}} = \sum_{k=1}^{\infty} {}_kp_{\overline{xy}} = e_x + e_y - e_{xy} \tag{12.26}$$

and the temporary curtate expectation is

$$e_{\overline{xy}:\overline{n}|} = \sum_{k=1}^{n} {}_kp_{\overline{xy}} = e_{x:\overline{n}|} + e_{y:\overline{n}|} - e_{xy:\overline{n}|}. \tag{12.27}$$

EXAMPLE 12.5

Calculate $\overset{\circ}{e}_{\overline{50:60}}$, given that T_{50} and T_{60} are independent and each follows a survival distribution given by $\lambda(x) = \frac{1}{100-x}$, for $0 < x < 100$.

SOLUTION

We recognize the given survival model to be uniform with $\omega = 100$, so we have ${}_tp_{50} = \frac{50-t}{50}$, for $0 \le t \le 50$, ${}_tp_{60} = \frac{40-t}{40}$, for $0 \le t \le 40$, and ${}_tp_{50:60} = \left(\frac{50-t}{50}\right)\left(\frac{40-t}{40}\right)$, for $0 \le t \le 40$. We also know that $\overset{\circ}{e}_{50} = 25$ and $\overset{\circ}{e}_{60} = 20$. We find $\overset{\circ}{e}_{50:60}$ from

$$\begin{aligned} \overset{\circ}{e}_{50:60} &= \int_0^{40} {}_tp_{50:60}\, dt \\ &= \frac{1}{2000}\int_0^{40} (50-t)(40-t)\, dt \\ &= \frac{1}{2000}\left(2000t - 45t^2 + \tfrac{1}{3}t^3\right)\Big|_0^{40} = 14.67. \end{aligned}$$

Then

$$\overset{\circ}{e}_{\overline{50:60}} = 25 + 20 - 14.67 = 30.33.$$

❒

12.2.3 RELATIONSHIPS BETWEEN T_{xy} AND $T_{\overline{xy}}$

Recall that T_{xy} is the time of the first failure between (x) and (y), and $T_{\overline{xy}}$ is the time of the second failure. Then it follows that T_{xy} is one of T_x or T_y and $T_{\overline{xy}}$ is necessarily the other one. Without knowing which one is which, it will still follow that

$$T_{xy} + T_{\overline{xy}} = T_x + T_y \tag{12.28a}$$

and

$$T_{xy} \cdot T_{\overline{xy}} = T_x \cdot T_y. \tag{12.28b}$$

From Equation (12.28a) we have

$$T_{\overline{xy}} = T_x + T_y - T_{xy}, \tag{12.29}$$

which, upon taking expectations, leads directly to Equation (12.25b). By similar reasoning we have

$${}_tp_{xy} + {}_tp_{\overline{xy}} = {}_tp_x + {}_tp_y, \tag{12.30}$$

from which Equation (12.20b) follows without assuming independence.

Even if T_x and T_y are independent, it should be clear that T_{xy} and $T_{\overline{xy}}$ are not. We can use Equation (12.28b), along with other earlier results, to find the covariance of T_{xy} and $T_{\overline{xy}}$. We have

$$Cov(T_{xy}, T_{\overline{xy}}) = E[T_{xy} \cdot T_{\overline{xy}}] - E[T_{xy}] \cdot E[T_{\overline{xy}}] = E[T_x \cdot T_y] - E[T_{xy}] \cdot E[T_x + T_y - T_{xy}],$$

by use of Equations (12.28b) and (12.29). But if T_x and T_y are independent, then

$$E[T_x \cdot T_y] = E[T_x] \cdot E[T_y],$$

so we have

$$\begin{aligned} Cov(T_{xy}, T_{\overline{xy}}) &= E[T_x] \cdot E[T_y] - E[T_{xy}] \cdot \left(E[T_x] + E[T_y] - E[T_{xy}]\right) \\ &= \mathring{e}_x \cdot \mathring{e}_y - \mathring{e}_{xy}\left(\mathring{e}_x + \mathring{e}_y - \mathring{e}_{xy}\right) \\ &= \mathring{e}_x \cdot \mathring{e}_y - \mathring{e}_x \cdot \mathring{e}_{xy} - \mathring{e}_y \cdot \mathring{e}_{xy} + \mathring{e}_{xy}^{\,2} \\ &= \left(\mathring{e}_x - \mathring{e}_{xy}\right)\left(\mathring{e}_y - \mathring{e}_{xy}\right). \end{aligned} \tag{12.31}$$

Note that this covariance is always positive.

12.3 CONTINGENT PROBABILITY FUNCTIONS

For two individual statuses (x) and (y), we might be interested in the probability that (x) will fail before (y) fails. A probability for an event addressing order of failures is called a *contingent probability*. The event that (x) fails before (y) is represented by the event $T_x < T_y$. If T_x and T_y are independent, then we have

$$Pr(T_x < T_y) = \int_0^\infty f_x(t) \cdot S_y(t)\, dt, \tag{12.32a}$$

since if (x) fails at time t the event $T_x < T_y$ is satisfied if (y) has not yet failed at that time, the probability of which is $S_y(t)$. In actuarial notation we have

$$Pr(T_x < T_y) = {}_{\infty}q_{xy}^{1} = \int_0^{\infty} {}_tp_x\mu_{x+t} \cdot {}_tp_y \, dt = \int_0^{\infty} {}_tp_{xy}\mu_{x+t} \, dt. \tag{12.32b}$$

The "upper one" in ${}_{\infty}q_{xy}^{1}$ is used to denote order of failure ((x) must fail before (y) to satisfy the event), which we saw earlier in the symbol $Z^1_{x:\overline{n}|}$ (see Section 7.1). The pre-subscript ∞ indicates that the event is satisfied if (x) fails before (y) within unlimited time. The probability that (x) fails before (y) and within n years is therefore given by

$${}_nq_{xy}^{1} = \int_0^{n} {}_tp_{xy}\mu_{x+t} \, dt. \tag{12.33a}$$

Similarly we would have

$${}_nq_{x\overset{1}{y}} = \int_0^{n} {}_tp_{xy}\mu_{y+t} \, dt. \tag{12.33b}$$

EXAMPLE 12.6

Show that

$${}_nq_{\overset{1}{x}y} + {}_nq_{x\overset{1}{y}} = {}_nq_{xy}.$$

SOLUTION

The result is intuitive. ${}_nq_{\overset{1}{x}y}$ represents the probability that the first failure occurs before time n and it is (x), and ${}_nq_{x\overset{1}{y}}$ is the same probability with the first failure being (y). Together they represent the probability that the first failure occurs before time n, which is ${}_nq_{xy}$. Mathematically, using Equations (12.33a) and (12.33b) we have

$$\begin{aligned} {}_nq_{\overset{1}{x}y} + {}_nq_{x\overset{1}{y}} &= \int_0^{n} {}_tp_{xy}\mu_{x+t} \, dt + \int_0^{n} {}_tp_{xy}\mu_{y+t} \, dt \\ &= \int_0^{n} {}_tp_{xy}(\mu_{x+t}+\mu_{y+t}) \, dt = \int_0^{n} {}_tp_{xy}\mu_{x+t:y+t} \, dt = {}_nq_{xy}. \end{aligned}$$

❐

The event that (x) fails *after* (y) is represented by $T_x > T_y$, and we have

$$Pr(T_x > T_y) = \int_0^{\infty} f_x(t) \cdot F_y(t) \, dt, \tag{12.34a}$$

since if (x) fails at time t the event $T_x > T_y$ requires that (y) has already failed at that time, the probability of which is $F_y(t)$. In actuarial notation we have

$$Pr(T_x > T_y) = {}_{\infty}q^{\;2}_{xy} = \int_0^{\infty} {}_tp_x\mu_{x+t}(1-{}_tp_y)\,dt$$

$$= \int_0^{\infty} {}_tp_x\mu_{x+t}\,dt - \int_0^{\infty} {}_tp_{xy}\mu_{x+t}\,dt = 1-{}_{\infty}q^{\;1}_{xy}, \tag{12.34b}$$

as expected. The probability that (x) fails after (y) and within n years is then

$${}_nq^{\;2}_{xy} = \int_0^{n} {}_tp_x\mu_{x+t}(1-{}_tp_y)\,dt = {}_nq_x - {}_nq^{\;1}_{xy}. \tag{12.35}$$

EXAMPLE 12.7

Show that

$${}_nq^{\;2}_{xy} + {}_nq^{\;\;2}_{x y} = {}_nq_{\overline{xy}}.$$

SOLUTION

Again the result is intuitive. Mathematically we have

$${}_nq^{\;2}_{xy} + {}_nq^{\;\;2}_{x y} = \int_0^{n} {}_tp_x\mu_{x+t}(1-{}_tp_y)\,dt + \int_0^{n} {}_tp_y\mu_{y+t}(1-{}_tp_x)\,dt$$

$$= \int_0^{n}\left[{}_tp_x\mu_{x+t} + {}_tp_y\mu_{y+t} - {}_tp_{xy}(\mu_{x+t}+\mu_{y+t})\right]dt = {}_nq_x + {}_nq_y - {}_nq_{xy} = {}_nq_{\overline{xy}},$$

since $\mu_{x+t} + \mu_{y+t} = \mu_{x+t:y+t}$. ❐

12.4 CONTINGENT CONTRACTS INVOLVING MULTI-LIFE STATUSES

All the material presented in Chapters 7 - 11 concerning contingent payment models and contingent annuities, including their funding and reserving plans, is applicable to the two-life statuses (joint and last-survivor) defined in this chapter. Indeed, the presentation throughout Chapters 7 - 11 was made in general terms to facilitate its extension to the multi-life case. Thus the general concept of a status with identifying characteristic x now can represent the joint-life status (xy) or the last-survivor status $(\overline{xy})$. Throughout this section we assume the independence of T_x and T_y when needed.

It is therefore unnecessary to duplicate the entire presentation in the earlier chapters simply substituting (xy) or $(\overline{xy})$ for (x). Rather we will list only a very small selection of the relationships we developed earlier, now recast in joint or last-survivor notation, to illustrate this point.

12.4.1 CONTINGENT PAYMENT MODELS (CHAPTER 7 MODELS)

If K_{xy} denotes the random variable for the curtate duration at which the joint status (xy) fails, then

$$Z_{xy} = v^{K_{xy}+1} \tag{12.36}$$

denotes the random variable for the present value of a unit paid at the end of that interval. Further,

$$A_{xy} = E[Z_{xy}] = \sum_{k=0}^{\infty} v^{k+1} \cdot {}_{k|}q_{xy} \tag{12.37}$$

denotes the first moment of Z_{xy} and

$$^{2}A_{xy} = E[Z_{xy}{}^{2}] = \sum_{k=0}^{\infty} (v^{k+1})^{2} \cdot {}_{k|}q_{xy} \tag{12.38}$$

denotes its second moment, from which the variance follows.

The extension to joint-life term insurance, deferred insurance, pure endowment, and endowment insurance all follow directly from their Chapter 7 counterparts.

Similar remarks hold for continuous contingent payment models. We define

$$\bar{Z}_{xy} = v^{T_{xy}} \tag{12.39}$$

as the random variable for the present value of a unit paid at the precise time of failure of (xy), with

$$\bar{A}_{xy} = E[\bar{Z}_{xy}] = \int_{0}^{\infty} v^{t} \cdot {}_{t}p_{xy}\mu_{x+t:y+t}\, dt \tag{12.40}$$

and

$$^{2}\bar{A}_{xy} = E[\bar{Z}_{xy}{}^{2}] = \int_{0}^{\infty} (v^{t})^{2} \cdot {}_{t}p_{xy}\mu_{x+t:y+t}\, dt \tag{12.41}$$

as its first and second moments.

The same definitions apply for the last-survivor status, with some notational adjustments. We have, for example,

$$A_{\overline{xy}} = E[Z_{\overline{xy}}] = \sum_{k=0}^{\infty} v^{k+1} \cdot {}_{k|}q_{\overline{xy}}. \tag{12.42a}$$

Substituting for ${}_{k|}q_{\overline{xy}}$ from Equation (12.23) we then have

$$A_{\overline{xy}} = A_{x} + A_{y} - A_{xy}. \tag{12.42b}$$

In the case of the continuous function we have

$$
\begin{aligned}
\overline{A}_{\overline{xy}} = E[\overline{Z}_{\overline{xy}}] &= \int_0^\infty v^t \cdot f_{\overline{xy}}(t)\,dt \\
&= \int_0^\infty v^t \left({}_tp_x\mu_{x+t} + {}_tp_y\mu_{y+t} - {}_tp_{xy}\mu_{x+t:y+t} \right) dt \\
&= \overline{A}_x + \overline{A}_y - \overline{A}_{xy},
\end{aligned} \tag{12.42c}
$$

using Equation (12.21) for the PDF of $T_{\overline{xy}}$.

12.4.2 CONTINGENT ANNUITY MODELS (CHAPTER 8 MODELS)

We can again substitute the joint-life status (xy) or the last-survivor status $(\overline{xy})$ for the generic status of interest (x) used in Chapter 8 to define annuities payable as long as a joint-life or last-survivor status continues to survive. As in Chapter 8, such annuities can be paid as immediate, due, or continuous. We would have, for example,

$$
a_{xy} = \sum_{k=1}^{\infty} v^k \cdot {}_kp_{xy}, \tag{12.43}
$$

$$
\ddot{a}_{\overline{xy}} = \sum_{k=0}^{\infty} v^k \cdot {}_kp_{\overline{xy}}, \tag{12.44}
$$

$$
\overline{a}_{xy:\overline{n}|} = \int_0^n v^t \cdot {}_tp_{xy}\,dt \tag{12.45}
$$

and

$$
\ddot{s}_{\overline{xy}:\overline{n}|} = \ddot{a}_{\overline{xy}:\overline{n}|} \cdot \frac{1}{{}_nE_{\overline{xy}}}, \tag{12.46}
$$

where

$$
{}_nE_{\overline{xy}} = v^n \cdot {}_np_{\overline{xy}} = {}_nE_x + {}_nE_y - {}_nE_{xy}. \tag{12.47}
$$

The relationship between insurance and annuity functions, presented in Chapter 8, will also hold in the multi-life cases. We would have, for example,

$$
A_{xy} = 1 - d \cdot \ddot{a}_{xy} \tag{12.48}
$$

and

$$
\overline{A}_{\overline{xy}} = 1 - \delta \cdot \overline{a}_{\overline{xy}}. \tag{12.49}
$$

12.4.3 ANNUAL PREMIUMS AND RESERVES

The annual net premium for a whole life joint-life insurance of unit amount is given by the equivalence principle as

$$
P_{xy} = \frac{A_{xy}}{\ddot{a}_{xy}}. \tag{12.50}
$$

Note that since the contingent benefit pays on the first failure, the funding scheme should stop at the first failure as well. In the case of a last-survivor status, we have

$$P_{\overline{xy}} = \frac{A_{\overline{xy}}}{\ddot{a}_{\overline{xy}}} \tag{12.51}$$

if the funding continues until the second failure at which point the benefit is paid.

EXAMPLE 12.8

A contingent contract pays a benefit of amount b at the end of the year of the second failure of independent lives (x) and (y). The net annual premium is 110 paid at the beginning of each year while both (x) and (y) survive and 40 per year after the first failure. Find the value of b, given the following values:

$$A_{xy} = .80 \qquad \ddot{a}_x = 8 \qquad \ddot{a}_y = 7 \qquad d = .05$$

SOLUTION

The APV of the benefit is $b \cdot A_{\overline{xy}}$. The APV of the premium stream is

$$110\ddot{a}_{xy} + 40(\ddot{a}_{\overline{xy}} - \ddot{a}_{xy}).$$

By the equivalence principle we have

$$b(A_x + A_y - A_{xy}) = 40\ddot{a}_x + 40\ddot{a}_y + 30\ddot{a}_{xy}$$

or

$$b[1-(.05)(8)+1-(.05)(7)-.80] = (40)(8)+(40)(7)+(30)\left(\frac{1-.80}{.05}\right),$$

which solves for $b = 1600$. ❐

Net premium terminal reserves can easily be defined by the prospective method. For the joint-life insurance we have

$${}_tV_{xy} = A_{x+t:y+t} - P_{xy} \cdot \ddot{a}_{x+t:y+t} \tag{12.52}$$

if the status has not yet failed as of time t. For the last-survivor status, a bit more care is needed. Although the status $(\overline{xy})$ has not yet failed at time t, it is possible that one of its component members may have already failed. Thus there are three cases for the net premium reserve at duration t, namely

$${}_tV_{\overline{xy}} = A_{\overline{x+t:y+t}} - P_{\overline{xy}} \cdot \ddot{a}_{\overline{x+t:y+t}} \tag{12.53a}$$

if both components (x) and (y) still survive,

$${}_tV_{\overline{xy}} = A_{x+t} - P_{\overline{xy}} \cdot \ddot{a}_{x+t} \tag{12.53b}$$

if (y) has already failed and only (x) survives, or

$$_tV_{\overline{xy}} = A_{y+t} - P_{\overline{xy}} \cdot \ddot{a}_{y+t} \qquad (12.53c)$$

if (x) has already failed and only (y) survives.

12.4.4 REVERSIONARY ANNUITIES

A special type of two-life annuity is one that pays only after one of the lives has failed, and then for as long as the other continues to survive. Such annuities are called *reversionary annuities*.

If payment is made to the status (y), provided it has not failed, but only after the failure of the status (x), then the total condition for payment at time k is that (x) has failed but (y) has not. The probability of this is

$$_kq_x \cdot {}_kp_y = {}_kp_y(1-{}_kp_x) = {}_kp_y - {}_kp_{xy}, \qquad (12.54)$$

so the actuarial present value of a reversionary annuity payable under such circumstances would be

$$a_{x|y} = \sum_{k=1}^{\infty} v^k({}_kp_y - {}_kp_{xy}) = a_y - a_{xy}. \qquad (12.55)$$

The result is intuitive. a_y represents the APV of payment made for the lifetime of (y), and a_{xy} is the APV of payment made for the joint lifetime of (xy). We can read Equation (12.55) as providing payment as long as (y) survives, but taking it away while (x) also survives, with the net effect being payment made while (y) survives but after the failure of (x).

If the payment is made for n years at most, with the requirement that (y) has failed but (x) has not, the APV would be

$$\begin{aligned} a_{y|x:\overline{n}|} &= \sum_{k=1}^{n} v^k \cdot {}_kp_x \cdot {}_kq_y \\ &= \sum_{k=1}^{n} v^k({}_kp_x - {}_kp_{xy}) = a_{x:\overline{n}|} - a_{xy:\overline{n}|}. \qquad (12.56) \end{aligned}$$

In the continuous case we have

$$\begin{aligned} \bar{a}_{x|y} &= \int_0^{\infty} v^t \cdot {}_tp_y \cdot {}_tq_x \, dt \\ &= \int_0^{\infty} v^t({}_tp_y - {}_tp_{xy})\, dt = \bar{a}_y - \bar{a}_{xy}. \qquad (12.57) \end{aligned}$$

If a reversionary annuity is funded by net annual premiums, the length of the premium-paying period would be the joint lifetime, since upon failure of the joint status either payments begin or the contract expires without value. If payments are to be made to (x) after the failure of (y), then use of the equivalence principle leads to the annual net premium

$$P(a_{y|x}) = \frac{a_{y|x}}{\ddot{a}_{xy}} = \frac{a_x - a_{xy}}{\ddot{a}_{xy}}. \tag{12.58}$$

The net premium reserve at duration t would again depend on what combination of (x) and (y) still survive. If both are alive, the reversionary annuity contract is still in premium-paying status so the reserve is

$$_tV(a_{y|x}) = a_{y+t|x+t} - P(a_{y|x}) \cdot \ddot{a}_{x+t:y+t}. \tag{12.59a}$$

If (x) only is alive the contract is beyond the premium-paying period and in payout status, so the reserve is simply

$$_tV(a_{y|x}) = a_{x+t}. \tag{12.59b}$$

If (y) only is alive, no payment will ever be made so the contract has expired and the reserve is zero.

EXAMPLE 12.9

Show that $a_{\overline{xy}} = a_{x|y} + a_{y|x} + a_{xy}$.

SOLUTION

The result is intuitive. $a_{x|y}$ represents payments made if (y) is alive but (x) is not, $a_{y|x}$ represents payments made if (x) is alive but (y) is not, and a_{xy} represents payments made if both are alive. The three cases are mutually exclusive. Together they provide payments if either (x) or (y) is alive, which is represented by $a_{\overline{xy}}$. Mathematically,

$$\begin{aligned} a_{x|y} + a_{y|x} + a_{xy} &= a_y - a_{xy} + a_x - a_{xy} + a_{xy} \\ &= a_x + a_y - a_{xy} \\ &= a_{\overline{xy}}, \end{aligned}$$

as required. ❐

12.4.5 CONTINGENT INSURANCE FUNCTIONS

A *contingent insurance* is one for which payment of the unit benefit depends on the order of failure among its component members. The insurance functions follow from the probability functions introduced in Section 12.3. Here we consider only insurances with immediate payment of claims.

A contingent insurance benefit paid at the failure of (x) only if (x) fails *before* (y) has APV given by

$$\bar{A}^{\,1}_{xy} = \int_0^\infty v^t \cdot {}_tp_{xy}\mu_{x+t}\,dt. \tag{12.60}$$

If the benefit is paid at the failure of (x) only if (x) fails *after* (y), the APV is

$$\bar{A}^{\,2}_{xy} = \int_0^\infty v^t \cdot {}_tp_x\mu_{x+t}(1-{}_tp_y)\,dt = \bar{A}_x - \bar{A}^{\,1}_{xy}. \tag{12.61}$$

EXAMPLE 12.10

Show that

$$\bar{A}^{\,1}_{xy} + \bar{A}_{x\overset{1}{y}} = \bar{A}_{xy}$$

and

$$\bar{A}^{\,2}_{xy} + \bar{A}_{x\overset{2}{y}} = \bar{A}_{\overline{xy}}.$$

SOLUTION

$$\begin{aligned}\bar{A}^{\,1}_{xy} + \bar{A}_{x\overset{1}{y}} &= \int_0^\infty v^t \cdot {}_tp_{xy}\mu_{x+t}\,dt + \int_0^\infty v^t \cdot {}_tp_{xy}\mu_{y+t}\,dt \\ &= \int_0^\infty v^t \cdot {}_tp_{xy}\mu_{x+t:y+t}\,dt = \bar{A}_{xy}\end{aligned}$$

$$\begin{aligned}\bar{A}^{\,2}_{xy} + \bar{A}_{x\overset{2}{y}} &= \left(\bar{A}_x - \bar{A}^{\,1}_{xy}\right) + \left(\bar{A}_y - \bar{A}_{x\overset{1}{y}}\right) \\ &= \bar{A}_x + \bar{A}_y - \left(\bar{A}^{\,1}_{xy} - \bar{A}_{x\overset{1}{y}}\right) \\ &= \bar{A}_x + \bar{A}_y - \bar{A}_{xy} = \bar{A}_{\overline{xy}}\end{aligned}$$

□

12.5 MULTI-STATE MODEL REPRESENTATION

The multi-life models presented thus far in this chapter can be easily represented as multi-state models. We illustrate this idea in the two-life case, with extension to three or more lives being apparent.

12.5.1 THE GENERAL MODEL

Consider two persons alive at ages x and y, respectively, at time 0. The model is in State 0 as long as both lives continue to survive. Since both lives are surviving at time 0, it follows that the process begins in State 0 at that time. The model is illustrated in Figure 12.1 on the following page.

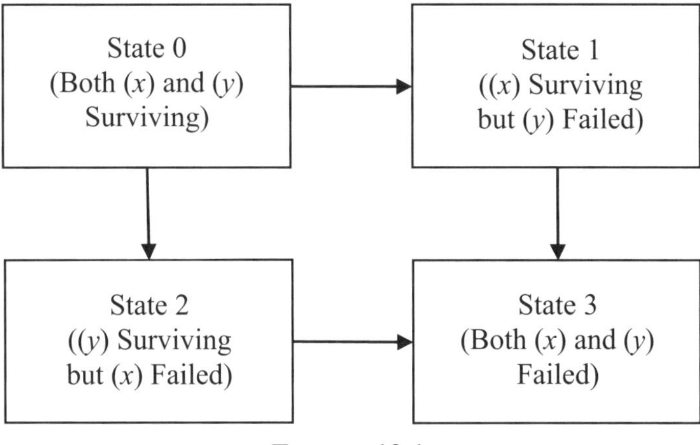

FIGURE 12.1

Since the only decrement is failure, or death, it follows that any state, once left, cannot be reentered. Therefore the event of being in State 0 at time t, given in State 0 at time 0, is the same as the event of never leaving State 0 over that time interval.

Similarly, the event of being in State i, for $i=1$ or 2, at any time after entering that state is the same as the event of never leaving that state once it has been entered. Note that transition from State 1 to State 2, or from State 2 to State 1, is not possible.

Clearly State 3 is an absorbing state, which can never be left once it has been entered. We also assume, in this model, that the simultaneous failure of (x) and (y) is not possible, so direct transition from State 0 to State 3 cannot occur.[4]

12.5.2 NOTATION

Recall our general multi-state model notation defined earlier for single-life functions, where ${}_tp_x^{ij}$ denoted the probability that a life known to be in State i at time 0 at age x would be in State j at time t. For the two-state model, where the process necessarily began in State 0, the only two meaningful probability functions were ${}_tp_x^{00}$ and ${}_tp_x^{01}$.

Now we consider a pair of lives, one age x and one age y with both alive at time 0, to constitute a status known to be in State 0 at time 0. We use ${}_tp_{xy}^{00}$ to denote the probability that the status is still in State 0 at time t (i.e., both are still alive), ${}_tp_{xy}^{01}$ to denote the probability that the status is in State 1 at time t (i.e., (x) only is alive), ${}_tp_{xy}^{02}$ to denote the probability that the status is in State 2 at time t (i.e., (y) only is alive), and ${}_tp_{xy}^{03}$ to denote the probability that the status is in State 3 at time t (neither is alive).

Transition out of State 0 occurs on the first death, with transition to State 1 due to the death of (y) and transition to State 2 due to the death of (x). Then it follows that the force of transition from State 0 to State 1 at time t is the same concept as the force of mortality for

[4] This restriction is relaxed in Section 12.8.

(y) at that time, namely μ_{y+t}. Similarly, the force of transition from State 0 to State 2 at time t is the same as the force of mortality for (x) at that time, which is μ_{x+t}.

We recognize that transition from State 1 to State 3 at time t also occurs due to the death of (x), so this force of transition is also the force of mortality for (x) at that time. However, there is an important distinction to make here. The transition from State 0 to State 2, due to the death of (x), occurs while (y) is still alive; the transition from State 1 to State 3, also due to the death of (x), occurs after (y) has died. If the two lives are independent, then these two notions of μ_{x+t} would be the same. To allow for the possibility that the force of mortality for (x) is different depending on whether (y) is alive, we will use the notation $\mu^{02}_{x+t:y+t}$ and μ^{13}_{x+t} for the forces of transition from State 0 to State 2 and from State 1 to State 3, respectively.[5]

With all of the necessary functions now defined, we can revisit the formulas for the APVs developed earlier in the chapter, using standard actuarial notation, and rewrite them using our multi-state model notation. Recall that we consider two types of contracts, namely annuity contracts (which make payments while the process is in a particular state) and insurance contracts (which make payments when the process transitions from one state to another).

12.5.3 ANNUITY CONTRACTS

We consider here the annuity contracts that make payments while the process is in each of States 0, 1 and 2. (No payments would be made when the process is in State 3.) Our general annuity-immediate symbol will be a^{0j}_{xy} for the APV of payments made while in State j for a status known to be in State 0 at time 0 at ages x and y, where $j=0,1,2$. The following table summarizes these three contracts.

TABLE 12.1

State	Name of Annuity	APV Symbol in Standard Actuarial Notation	APV Symbol in Multi-State Model Notation
0	Joint-Life	a_{xy}	a^{00}_{xy}
1	Reversionary, to (x) after the Death of (y)	$a_{y\|x}$	a^{01}_{xy}
2	Reversionary, to (y) after the Death of (x)	$a_{x\|y}$	a^{02}_{xy}

In addition to these three, which are annuities paid while in one specific state, we also have the last-survivor annuity, which is paid while in any of States 0, 1 or 2. Then it follows that

[5] A possible reason for the distinction is that (x) and (y) are often a married couple. Research shows that the survival pattern of widowed spouses is often different from that of married spouses at the same age.

$$a_{\overline{xy}} = a_{xy}^{00} + a_{xy}^{01} + a_{xy}^{02}, \tag{12.62}$$

which was shown in Example 12.9 using standard actuarial notation. (Note that we do not define a symbol for $a_{\overline{xy}}$ in multi-state model notation.)

Each of these four annuities-immediate has its continuous counterpart; their APV symbols are the same as their annuity-immediate symbols except for placing a bar over the a. The joint-life and last-survivor annuities also have annuity-due counterparts, but the reversionary annuities do not. This makes ten annuity APV symbols in total. Three of these are presented in the following example, with the other seven left to the exercises.

EXAMPLE 12.11

Write, in multi-state model notation, the APV formulas for (a) a joint-life annuity-due, (b) a reversionary annuity to (y) after the death of (x), and (c) a continuous last-survivor annuity.

SOLUTION

(a) The annuity is payable while the process is in State 0, so we have

$$\ddot{a}_{xy}^{00} = \sum_{k=0}^{\infty} v^k \cdot {}_k p_{xy}^{00}, \tag{12.63a}$$

where ${}_k p_{xy}^{00} = {}_k p_{xy} = {}_k p_x \cdot {}_k p_y$, if (x) and (y) are independent.

(b) The annuity is payable while the process is in State 2, so we have

$$a_{xy}^{02} = \sum_{k=1}^{\infty} v^k \cdot {}_k p_{xy}^{02}, \tag{12.63b}$$

where ${}_k p_{xy}^{02} = {}_k p_x \cdot {}_k q_y$, if (x) and (y) are independent.

(c) The annuity is payable continuously while the process is in any one of States 0, 1 or 2, so we have

$$\bar{a}_{\overline{xy}} = \int_0^{\infty} v^t \cdot \left({}_t p_{xy}^{00} + {}_t p_{xy}^{01} + {}_t p_{xy}^{02} \right) dt. \tag{12.63c}$$

(We do not define a symbol for the APV in multi-state model notation.) ❑

12.5.4 INSURANCE CONTRACTS

Here we consider the contracts that make a unit payment upon transition from State i to State j. There are four possible cases, as summarized in the following table.

TABLE 12.2

Case	Transition from State	Transition to State	APV Symbol in Standard Actuarial Notation	APV Symbol in Multi-State Model Notation
1	0	1	$\bar{A}_{x\overset{1}{y}}$	$\bar{A}_{xy}^{01}$
2	0	2	$\bar{A}_{\overset{1}{x}y}$	$\bar{A}_{xy}^{02}$
3	1	3	$\bar{A}_{\overset{2}{x}y}$	---
4	2	3	$\bar{A}_{x\overset{2}{y}}$	---

In addition to these four, which are insurances that pay upon transition from one specific state to another, we also have the joint-life insurance and the last-survivor insurance. The former is made up of Cases 1 and 2 combined, and the latter is made up of Cases 3 and 4 combined.

EXAMPLE 12.12

Write, in multi-state model notation, the APV formulas for a unit paid upon (a) transition from State 0 to State 2, (b) transition from State 1 to State 3, and (c) the failure of the last-survivor status.

SOLUTION

(a) The density function for transition from State 0 to State 2 at time t is ${}_tp_{xy}^{00}\,\mu_{x+t}^{02}$, so the APV is

$$\bar{A}_{xy}^{02} = \int_0^\infty v^t \cdot {}_tp_{xy}^{00}\,\mu_{x+t}^{02}\,dt. \tag{12.64a}$$

(b) The density function for transition from State 1 to State 3 at time t is ${}_tp_{xy}^{01}\mu_{x+t}^{13}$, so the APV is

$$\bar{A}_{\overset{2}{x}y} = \int_0^\infty v^t \cdot {}_tp_{xy}^{01}\,\mu_{x+t}^{13}\,dt. \tag{12.64b}$$

(We do not define a symbol for this APV in multi-state model notation.)

(c) The density function for failure at time t for the last-survivor status is the sum of the density functions for transition in Case 3 and 4, so the APV is

$$\bar{A}_{\overline{xy}} = \int_0^\infty v^t \cdot \left({}_tp_{xy}^{01}\,\mu_{x+t}^{13} + {}_tp_{xy}^{02}\,\mu_{y+t}^{23}\right) dt. \tag{12.64c}$$

(We do not define a symbol for this APV in multi-state model notation.) ❑

12.5.5 SOLVING THE KOLMOGOROV FORWARD EQUATION

In this section we consider the Kolmogorov differential equation presented in Section 3.2.2 as it applies to the multi-life model of Section 12.5.1. As shown by the arrows in Figure 12.1, not all transitions between states are possible, so the only non-zero forces of transition are μ_{y+t}^{01}, μ_{x+t}^{02}, μ_{x+t}^{13}, and μ_{y+t}^{23}.

Suppose (x) and (y) are both alive at those ages at time 0, so that the process is in State 0. Then ${}_t p_{xy}^{00}$ denotes the probability that the process is still in State 0 (i.e., both are still surviving) at time t, and ${}_t p_{xy}^{01}$ denotes the probability that the process is in State 1 (i.e., (x) is surviving but (y) has failed) at time t. (Note that ${}_t p_{xy}^{02}$ is the same as ${}_t p_{xy}^{01}$, with the roles of (x) and (y) reversed.)

If the process is in State 1 at a reset time 0, then both ${}_t p_x^{11}$ and ${}_t p_x^{13}$ denote concepts of interest to us. (Note that ${}_t p_x^{10} = {}_t p_x^{12} = 0$.) These symbols are subscripted with x only, because, by definition of State 1, (x) only is alive. These functions are then the same as those denoted ${}_t p_x^{00}$ and ${}_t p_x^{01}$ in earlier chapters. Similarly, both ${}_t p_y^{22}$ and ${}_t p_y^{23}$ are also concepts of interest, but they are the same nature as ${}_t p_x^{11}$ and ${}_t p_x^{13}$.

It is clear that, for a process in State 3 at reset time 0, the probability of remaining in State 3 is one and the probability of transitioning to any other state is zero.

The above analysis suggests that we need solve the Kolmogorov equation only for ${}_n p_{xy}^{00}$, and for ${}_n p_{xy}^{01}$ or ${}_n p_{xy}^{02}$ (since they are the same with (x) and (y) reversed). We do this for ${}_n p_{xy}^{01}$ in Example 12.17, and leave the solution for ${}_n p_{xy}^{00}$ to Exercise 12-22.

12.5.6 THIELE'S EQUATION IN THE MULTI-LIFE MODEL

Recall Thiele's differential equation in the context of a single-life model, as discussed in Section 10.3.2, Example 10.11, Exercise 10-24, Section 11.3.2, Section 11.4, and Example 11.11. In the net premium single-life case, the subtractive term represented the rate at which cost of insurance was being deducted from the continuous reserve at time t, and was always of the form $\mu_{x+t}(B - {}_t\bar{V})$, where B denotes the benefit payable for death at time t.

In the multi-life model, the form of Thiele's equation will depend on the state in which the process is located at time t, as well as the type of insurance contract whose continuous reserve is being analyzed. If we restrict our multi-life model to the two-life model of Figure 12.1, we can then consider the form of Thiele's equation for any of the following combinations of states and contracts:

(a) A joint-life insurance located in State 0. (If the process is in any of States 1, 2, or 3, a joint-life insurance can no longer be in force.)

(b) A first-to-die insurance located in State 0. (If the process is in any of States 1, 2, or 3, a first-to-die insurance can no longer be in force.)

(c) An insurance paid on the death of (x) provided it occurs after the death of (y) located in State 0 or 1. (If the process is in State 2, the insurance can no longer be in force.)

(d) Symmetrically, an insurance paid on the death of (y) provided it occurs after the death of (x) located in State 0 or 2. (If the process is in State 1, the insurance can no longer be in force.)

(e) A last-survivor insurance located in any of States 0, 1, or 2.

We will examine the form of the Thiele equations for several of these multi-life insurances in Example 12.18, and the remainder of them in Exercises 12-24 and 12-25.

12.6 GENERAL RANDOM VARIABLE ANALYSIS

Consider again the case of two individual lives (x) and (y), with time-to-failure (or future lifetime) random variables T_x and T_y, respectively. When T_x and T_y are independent, we have seen how all discrete multi-life functions can ultimately be evaluated from a single-life survival model, usually in life table form. But how do we evaluate multi-life functions if independence does not hold?

In theory we can proceed according to the general rules regarding the joint distribution of two random variables, as presented in a basic probability course and reviewed in Section 2.4 of this text. We presume that we are given a joint density function of the random variables T_x and T_y, denoted by $f_{x,y}(t_x,t_y)$, for $t_x > 0$ and $t_y > 0$, where T_x and T_y are not necessarily independent.[6] From the joint density function we can then determine all other desired functions.

12.6.1 MARGINAL DISTRIBUTIONS OF T_x AND T_y

We can find the marginal densities of T_x and T_y by integrating the joint density function across the opposite variable. Thus we have

$$f_x(t_x) = \int_{t_y} f_{x,y}(t_x,t_y)\,dt_y \tag{12.65a}$$

and

$$f_y(t_y) = \int_{t_x} f_{x,y}(t_x,t_y)\,dt_x. \tag{12.65b}$$

From the separate marginal distributions we can evaluate any probability or other single-life function as described in earlier chapters.

[6] The case where T_x and T_y *are* independent will be contained within the general analysis as a special case.

12.6.2 THE COVARIANCE OF T_x AND T_y

From the joint PDF of T_x and T_y we can find

$$E[T_x \cdot T_y] \;=\; \int_0^\infty \int_0^\infty t_x t_y \cdot f_{x,y}(t_x,t_y)\, dt_x\, dt_y. \tag{12.66}$$

Then from the separate marginal PDF's of T_x and T_y we find $E[T_x]$ and $E[T_y]$, and therefore

$$Cov(T_x,T_y) \;=\; E[T_x \cdot T_y] - E[T_x]\cdot E[T_y]. \tag{12.67}$$

EXAMPLE 12.13

An electronic device relies on two essential components, denoted (x) and (y), for its operation. The joint density function of the lifetimes of (x) and (y), measured in months, is

$$f_{x,y}(t_x,t_y) \;=\; \frac{t_x+t_y}{27},$$

for $0<t_x<3$ and $0<t_y<3$.

(a) Show that T_x and T_y are not independent.

(b) Find the correlation coefficient of T_x and T_y.

SOLUTION

First we find the marginal density of T_x as

$$\begin{aligned} f_x(t_x) &= \int_0^3 f_{x,y}(t_x,t_y)\, dt_y \\ &= \frac{1}{27}\int_0^3 (t_x+t_y)\, dt_y \;=\; \frac{1}{27}\left(t_xt_y+\frac{1}{2}t_y^2\right)\Bigg|_0^3 \;=\; \frac{1}{27}\left(3t_x+\frac{9}{2}\right) \;=\; \frac{2t_x+3}{18}, \end{aligned}$$

for $0< t_x < 3$. By the symmetry of the joint PDF it follows that

$$f_y(t_y) \;=\; \frac{2t_y+3}{18},$$

for $0< t_y < 3$. Next we find

$$E[T_x] = \int_0^3 t_x \cdot f_x(t_x)\, dt_x \;=\; \frac{1}{18}\int_0^3 (2t_x^2+3t_x)\, dt_x \;=\; \frac{1}{18}\left(\frac{2}{3}t_x^3+\frac{3}{2}t_x^2\right)\Bigg|_0^3 \;=\; 1.75$$

and

$$E[T_x^2] = \int_0^3 t_x^2 \cdot f_x(t_x)\, dt_x \;=\; \frac{1}{18}\int_0^3 (2t_x^3+3t_x^2)\, dt_x \;=\; \frac{1}{18}\left(\frac{1}{2}t_x^4+t_x^3\right)\Bigg|_0^3 \;=\; 3.75,$$

so

$$Var(T_x) \;=\; 3.75-(1.75)^2 \;=\; .6875.$$

Again by symmetry the same values apply to T_y. Directly from the joint PDF we find

$$\begin{aligned} E[T_x \cdot T_y] &= \int_0^3 \int_0^3 t_x t_y \cdot f_{x,y}(t_x, t_y)\, dt_x\, dt_y \\ &= \frac{1}{27}\int_0^3 \int_0^3 (t_x^2 t_y + t_x t_y^2)\, dt_x\, dt_y \\ &= \frac{1}{27}\int_0^3 \left(\frac{1}{3}t_x^3 t_y + \frac{1}{2}t_x^2 t_y^2\right)\Bigg|_0^3 dt_y \\ &= \frac{1}{27}\int_0^3 \left(9t_y + 4.5t_y^2\right) dt_y \\ &= \frac{1}{27}\left(4.5t_y^2 + 1.5t_y^3\right)\Bigg|_0^3 = 3. \end{aligned}$$

(a) We observe that

$$f_x(t_x) \cdot f_y(t_y) \neq f_{x,y}(t_x, t_y),$$

so T_x and T_y are not independent.

(b) From the results developed above we find

$$Cov(T_x, T_y) = 3 - (1.75)(1.75) = -.0625$$

and therefore

$$\rho_{T_x,T_y} = \frac{Cov(T_x, T_y)}{\sqrt{Var(T_x) \cdot Var(T_y)}} = \frac{-.0625}{\sqrt{(.6875)^2}} = -.09091.$$ ❒

12.6.3 OTHER JOINT FUNCTIONS OF T_x AND T_y

If the individual domains of T_x and T_y are both all positive values, then their joint domain will be the entire first quadrant, as illustrated in the following figure.

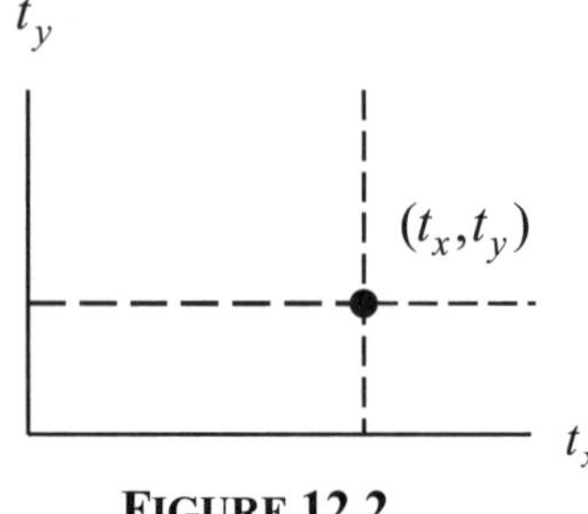

FIGURE 12.2

The joint CDF of T_x and T_y is given by

$$\begin{aligned} F_{x,y}(t_x,t_y) &= Pr(T_x \le t_x \cap T_y \le t_y) \\ &= \int_0^{t_y} \int_0^{t_x} f_{x,y}(r,s)\, dr\, ds \end{aligned} \tag{12.68}$$

for $t_x > 0$ and $t_y > 0$, and $F_{x,y}(t_x,t_y) = 0$ for any other values of t_x and/or t_y. For example, consider the case where $t_x < 0$ and $t_y > 0$, so the point (t_x,t_y) lies in the second quadrant. Since the joint CDF represents $Pr(T_x \le t_x \cap T_y \le t_y)$, it is easy to see that the joint CDF is zero, since the event $T_x \le t_x$ cannot occur. Similar reasoning applies to a point (t_x,t_y) lying in the third or fourth quadrants.

If the joint domain of T_x and T_y does not cover the entire first quadrant, the joint CDF can be non-zero in portions of the first quadrant where the joint PDF is zero. This is illustrated in the following example.

EXAMPLE 12.14

Find the joint CDF for the joint distribution of Example 12.13.

SOLUTION

Consider the following figure:

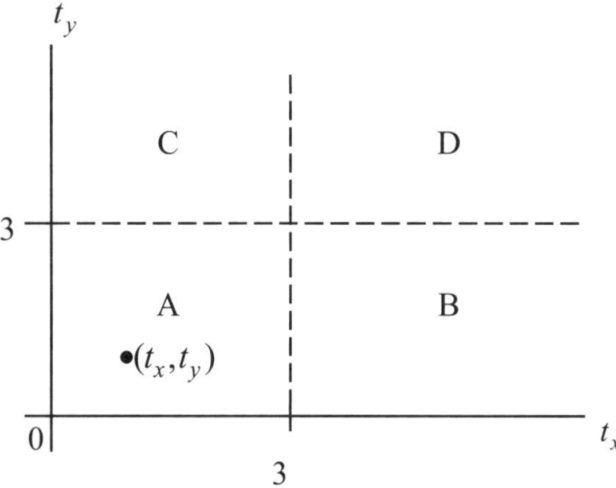

FIGURE 12.3

The joint PDF is non-zero only within Region A of the first quadrant. Within Region A the joint CDF of T_x and T_y is given by

$$\begin{aligned}
F_{x,y}(t_x,t_y) &= \int_0^{t_y}\int_0^{t_x} f_{x,y}(r,s)\,dr\,ds \\
&= \frac{1}{27}\int_0^{t_y}\int_0^{t_x}(r+s)\,dr\,ds \\
&= \frac{1}{27}\int_0^{t_y}\left(\frac{1}{2}r^2+rs\right)\Big|_0^{t_x} ds \\
&= \frac{1}{27}\int_0^{t_y}\left(\frac{1}{2}t_x^2+t_xs\right) ds \\
&= \frac{1}{27}\left(\frac{1}{2}t_x^2s+\frac{1}{2}t_xs^2\right)\Big|_0^{t_y} \;=\; \frac{t_x^2t_y+t_xt_y^2}{54},
\end{aligned}$$

for $0< t_x < 3$ and $0< t_y < 3$. For a point (t_x,t_y) in Region B, the event $T_x \leq t_x$ is certain to occur, since $t_x > 3$ in Region B. Therefore the joint CDF, which is $Pr(T_x \leq t_x \cap T_y \leq t_y)$, is the same as $Pr(T_y \leq t_y)$ since $Pr(T_x \leq t_x)=1$. Then we see that

$$F_{x,y}(t_x,t_y) \equiv F_y(t_y)$$

for $t_x>3$ and $0<t_y<3$. By similar reasoning, for any point in Region C we have

$$F_{x,y}(t_x,t_y) \equiv F_x(t_x)$$

for $0< t_x < 3$ and $t_y > 3$. In Region D both events $T_x \leq t_x$ and $T_y \leq t_y$ are certain to occur so we have

$$F_{x,y}(t_x,t_y) \equiv 1$$

for $t_x > 3$ and $t_y > 3$. ❐

The joint SDF of T_x and T_y is given by

$$S_{x,y}(t_x,t_y) \;=\; Pr\left(T_x > t_x \cap T_y > t_y\right) = \int_{t_y}^{\infty}\int_{t_x}^{\infty} f_{x,y}(r,s)\,dr\,ds, \tag{12.69}$$

for $t_x > 0$ and $t_y > 0$. For a (t_x,t_y) point in the second quadrant, the event $T_x > t_x$ is certain to occur so $Pr(T_x>t_x \cap T_y>t_y)$ is the same as $Pr(T_y>t_y)=S_{T_y}(t_y)$. Similar reasoning for a (t_x,t_y) point in the fourth quadrant shows that $Pr(T_x>t_x \cap T_y>t_y)$ is the same as $Pr(T_x>t_x)= S_{T_x}(t_x)$. In the third quadrant, both events $T_x > t_x$ and $T_y > t_y$ are certain to occur so $S_{x,y}(t_x,t_y)=1$ for $t_x < 0$ and $t_y < 0$.

12.6.4 JOINT AND LAST-SURVIVOR STATUS FUNCTIONS

If the general joint SDF of T_x and T_y is evaluated at a common point, say $t_x = t_y = n$, then we have

$$S_{x,y}(n,n) = Pr\left(T_x > n \cap T_y > n\right) = Pr(T_{xy} > n) = {}_n p_{xy}, \tag{12.70}$$

in actuarial notation. Therefore all joint life functions presented in Section 12.1 can be evaluated from the general joint SDF of T_x and T_y. Note that the relationship ${}_n p_{xy} = {}_n p_x \cdot {}_n p_y$ will generally hold only if T_x and T_y are independent.

EXAMPLE 12.15

Suppose the device described in Example 12.13 fails upon the first failure of its two essential components. Find the probability that the device fails during its first month of operation.

SOLUTION

Since the device fails on the *first* failure of its components, then the two components form a joint status. We seek the probability value given by $q_{xy} = 1 - p_{xy}$. The joint SDF of T_x and T_y in Example 12.13 is given by

$$S_{x,y}(t_x, t_y) = \frac{1}{27}\int_{t_y}^{3}\int_{t_x}^{3}(r+s)\,dr\,ds,$$

so the joint status probability p_{xy} is given by

$$\begin{aligned} p_{xy} &= S_{x,y}(1,1) = \frac{1}{27}\int_1^3\int_1^3 (r+s)\,dr\,ds \\ &= \frac{1}{27}\int_1^3 \left(\frac{1}{2}r^2 + rs\right)\Bigg|_1^3 ds \\ &= \frac{1}{27}\int_1^3 (4+2s)\,ds \\ &= \frac{1}{27}\left(4s+s^2\right)\Big|_1^3 = \frac{16}{27}. \end{aligned}$$

Finally the desired probability is

$$q_{xy} = 1 - p_{xy} = 1 - \frac{16}{27} = \frac{11}{27}.$$

❐

If the general joint CDF of T_x and T_y is evaluated at the common point $t_x = t_y = n$, then we have

$$F_{x,y}(n,n) = Pr\left(T_x \le n \cap T_y \le n\right) = Pr(T_{\overline{xy}} \le n) = {}_n q_{\overline{xy}},$$

in actuarial notation. Thus we see that both the joint and last-survivor distributions can be determined from the general joint distribution of T_x and T_y, where we find the SDF of the joint status from the joint SDF of T_x and T_y and we find the CDF of the last-survivor status from the joint CDF of T_x and T_y.

12.7 COMMON SHOCK – A MODEL FOR LIFETIME DEPENDENCY

A natural example of two lives (x) and (y) having dependent lifetimes might be a married couple or a pair of business partners who travel together, or are otherwise exposed to a common hazard factor, on a regular basis. We refer to this common hazard as a *common shock.*

To analyze the common shock model, we begin by hypothesizing that (x) is subject to a hazard rate, or force of failure, denoted μ^*_{x+t}, that takes into account only failure forces operating at time t that are specific to (x) and not to (y). Similarly, μ^*_{y+t} denotes failure forces operating at time t that are applicable to (y) but not to (x). With regard only to the failure forces represented by μ^*_{x+t} and μ^*_{y+t}, we consider that (x) and (y) have independent survival patterns because of the nature of the hazard factors included in μ^*_{x+t} and μ^*_{y+t}.

Next we assume that the common hazard, or common shock, to which both (x) and (y) are subject can be represented by a constant (over time) hazard function, which we denote by $\mu^c_t = \lambda$. We assume that the hazard forces unique to (x), reflected in μ^*_{x+t}, and the hazard forces reflected in the common shock hazard function μ^c_t are non-overlapping, so the total force of failure to which (x) is subject is given by

$$\mu_{x+t} = \mu^*_{x+t} + \mu^c_t = \mu^*_{x+t} + \lambda. \tag{12.74a}$$

Similarly, the force of failure to which (y) is subject is given by

$$\mu_{y+t} = \mu^*_{y+t} + \mu^c_t = \mu^*_{y+t} + \lambda. \tag{12.74b}$$

The total force of failure operating on the joint-life status (xy) is given by

$$\mu_{x+t:y+t} = \mu^*_{x+t} + \mu^*_{y+t} + \lambda. \tag{12.75}$$

The three forces are additive because each represents hazard factors that are disjoint from each other. Furthermore, the total joint force of failure contains only one λ (not two) since failure of either (x) or (y) due to the common shock constitutes failure of the joint-life status.

The joint-life survival function in the common shock model can then be found from the joint-life force of failure. We have

$$
\begin{aligned}
{}_t p_{xy} &= e^{-\int_0^t \mu_{x+r:y+r}\, dr} \\
&= e^{-\int_0^t (\mu^*_{x+r}+\mu^*_{y+r}+\lambda)\, dr} \\
&= e^{-\int_0^t \mu^*_{x+r}\, dr} \cdot e^{-\int_0^t \mu^*_{y+r}\, dr} \cdot e^{-\int_0^t \lambda\, dr} \\
&= {}_t p^*_x \cdot {}_t p^*_y \cdot e^{-\lambda t}. \qquad (12.76)
\end{aligned}
$$

Note that ${}_t p^*_x$ is not the same as ${}_t p_x$, since the latter survival probability takes into account the common shock hazard factors but the former does not.

There is an alternative, and equivalent, way to develop the common shock model. Let T^*_x and T^*_y denote the future lifetime random variables for (x) and (y), respectively, without regard for the common shock hazard factors. Consistent with the discussion above, we assume that T^*_x and T^*_y are independent. Let S denote the future lifetime of either (x) or (y) with regard to the common shock hazard factors only, where S is independent of both T^*_x and T^*_y. Then it follows that the overall lifetime random variable for (x) is given by

$$T_x = \min(T^*_x, S), \qquad (12.77a)$$

and similarly the overall future lifetime random variable for (y) is given by

$$T_y = \min(T^*_y, S). \qquad (12.77b)$$

Note that whereas T^*_x and T^*_y are independent, T_x and T_y are *not* independent since they both involve the common shock hazard factors and depend on the common future lifetime random variable S.

Since T^*_x and S are independent, however, it follows that the SDF of T_x is the product of the SDF's of T^*_x and S. That is,

$${}_t p_x = S_x(t) = S_{x^*}(t) \cdot S_S(t) = {}_t p^*_x \cdot e^{-\lambda t}, \qquad (12.78a)$$

where $S_S(t) = e^{-\lambda t}$ since the random variable S has a constant hazard rate and therefore an exponential distribution. Similarly, the SDF of T_y is given by

$${}_t p_y = S_y(t) = S_{y^*}(t) \cdot S_S(t) = {}_t p^*_y \cdot e^{-\lambda t}. \qquad (12.78b)$$

We observe that ${}_t p_{xy}$, given by Equation (12.76), is *not* equal to the product of ${}_t p_x$ and ${}_t p_y$, given by Equations (12.78a) and (12.78b), respectively, which shows that T_x and T_y are not independent random variables.

EXAMPLE 12.16

A convenient way to illustrate the common shock model is to assume that both T_x^* and T_y^* have exponential distributions, and therefore constant hazard rates λ_x and λ_y, respectively. Under this assumption, find an expression for the APV of a last-survivor whole life insurance, with benefit paid at the moment of failure of the status.

SOLUTION

The overall force of failure for (x) is then $\mu_{x+t} = \lambda_x + \lambda$, where λ denotes the hazard of the common shock, and the overall force of failure for (y) is $\mu_{y+t} = \lambda_y + \lambda$. The force of failure for the joint-life status (xy) is $\mu_{x+t:y+t} = \lambda_x + \lambda_y + \lambda$. Using results developed in Chapter 7, we then have

$$\bar{A}_x = \frac{\lambda_x + \lambda}{\lambda_x + \lambda + \delta},$$

$$\bar{A}_y = \frac{\lambda_y + \lambda}{\lambda_y + \lambda + \delta},$$

and

$$\bar{A}_{xy} = \frac{\lambda_x + \lambda_y + \lambda}{\lambda_x + \lambda_y + \lambda + \delta},$$

and $\bar{A}_{\overline{xy}}$ then follows as $\bar{A}_x + \bar{A}_y - \bar{A}_{xy}$. ❒

Because of the common hazard factor, such as travel accidents, there is a non-zero probability of simultaneous failure of (x) and (y). When represented as a multi-state model, the earlier Figure 12.1 is modified as shown in Figure 12.4.

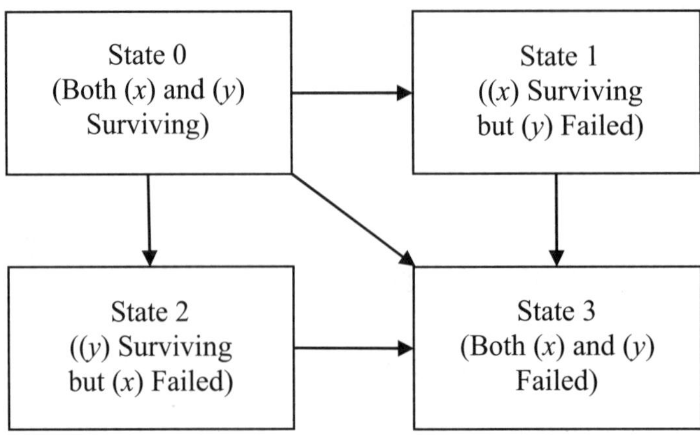

Figure 12.4

The only change in this model from our Figure 12.1 model is that $\mu^{03}_{x+t:y+t}$, the force of transition function for transition directly from State 0 to State 3 is now non-zero. This means that the probability value

$$_t p^{03}_{xy} = Pr[X(t)=3 \mid X(0)=0]$$

can be satisfied by direct transition from State 0 to State 3. In the Figure 12.1 model, $_t p^{03}_{xy}$ could be satisfied only by transition from State 0 to State 1 to State 3 or by transition from State 0 to State 2 to State 3.

12.8 WRITTEN-ANSWER QUESTION EXAMPLES

EXAMPLE 12.17

The symbol $_t p^{01}_{xy}$ denotes the probability that a process in State 0 at time 0 will be in State 1 at time t where State 0 means both (x) and (y) are alive at those ages. To be in State 1 at time t requires that (y) fails in, and (x) survives over, the interval $(0,t]$. (In actuarial notation this is denoted by $_n p_x \cdot {}_n q_y$, assuming that (x) and (y) are independent lives.) Show that the Kolmogorov equation can be solved for this result.

SOLUTION

In Equation (3.14a), $i=0$ and $j=1$ so k takes on the values 0, 2, 3 in the summation. Then we have

$$\begin{aligned}
\frac{d}{dt}\,{}_t p^{01}_{xy} &= {}_t p^{00}_{xy} \cdot \mu^{01}_{x+t:y+t} - {}_t p^{01}_{xy} \cdot \mu^{10} && \text{(at } k=0\text{)} \\
&\quad + {}_t p^{02}_{xy} \cdot \mu^{21} - {}_t p^{01}_{xy} \cdot \mu^{12} && \text{(at } k=2\text{)} \\
&\quad + {}_t p^{03}_{xy} \cdot \mu^{31} - {}_t p^{01}_{xy} \cdot \mu^{13}_{x+t} && \text{(at } k=3\text{)} \\
&= {}_t p^{00}_{xy} \cdot \mu^{01}_{x+t:y+t} - {}_t p^{01}_{xy} \cdot \mu^{13}_{x+t},
\end{aligned}$$

since $\mu^{10} = \mu^{21} = \mu^{12} = \mu^{31} = 0$ for all t. Then integrating from $t=0$ to $t=n$ we have

$$\int_0^n d\,{}_t p^{01}_{xy} = \int_0^n {}_t p^{00}_{xy} \cdot \mu^{01}_{x+t:y+t}\, dt - \int_0^n {}_t p^{01}_{xy} \cdot \mu^{13}_{x+t}\, dt.$$

The left side integrates to $_n p^{01}_{xy}$, as expected, since $_0 p^{01}_{xy} = 0$. The right side is more easily understood when written in actuarial notation. We have

$$\int_0^n {}_t p_{xy} \cdot \mu_{y+t}\, dt - \int_0^n {}_t p_x \cdot {}_t q_y \cdot \mu_{x+t}\, dt,$$

since $\mu^{01}_{x+t:y+t}$ is the force of failure for (y) at age $y+t$ and μ^{13}_{x+t} is the force of failure for (x) at age $x+t$. We can represent both integrals in contingent probability notation, from Section 12.3, obtaining the result

$$ {}_np^{01}_{xy} = {}_nq^{\;1}_{xy} - {}_nq^{\;2}_{xy}. $$

But ${}_nq^{\;2}_{xy} = {}_nq_x - {}_nq^{1}_{xy}$, so we can write our result as

$$ \begin{aligned} {}_np^{01}_{xy} &= {}_nq^{\;1}_{xy} - ({}_nq_x - {}_nq^{1}_{xy}) \\ &= {}_nq_{xy} - {}_nq_x \\ &= 1 - {}_np_x \cdot {}_np_y - 1 + {}_np_x = {}_np_x - {}_np_x \cdot {}_np_y = {}_np_x(1 - {}_np_y) = {}_np_x \cdot {}_nq_y, \end{aligned} $$

as requested. ❐

EXAMPLE 12.18

Consider the two-life model shown in Figure 12.1. Assume a fully-continuous insurance of face amount B. For each of the following insurances, state Thiele's net premium differential equation in multi-state model notation for a process in State 0, and explain the logic of the subtractive term(s).

(a) An insurance whose APV is given by $\bar{A}^{\;1}_{xy}$.

(b) An insurance whose APV is given by $\bar{A}_{xy}$.

(c) An insurance whose APV is given by $\bar{A}^{\;2}_{xy}$.

(d) An insurance whose APV is given by $\bar{A}_{\overline{xy}}$.

SOLUTION

Let $\bar{P}$ denote the continuous net premium rate and ${}_t\bar{V}^{(0)}$ denote the continuous net premium reserve at time t, for a contract (process) in State 0.

(a) The benefit is paid upon transition from State 0 to State 2, which indicates (x) dying before (y). If the process transitions from State 0 to State 1, which indicates (y) dying before (x) then the reserve is released but no benefit is paid. Therefore we have

$$ \begin{aligned} \frac{d}{dt}\,{}_t\bar{V}^{(0)} &= \bar{P} + \delta \cdot {}_t\bar{V}^{(0)} - \mu^{02}_{x+t:y+t}\left(B - {}_t\bar{V}^{(0)}\right) - \mu^{01}_{x+t:y+t}\left(0 - {}_t\bar{V}^{(0)}\right) \\ &= \bar{P} + {}_t\bar{V}^{(0)} \cdot \left(\delta + \mu^{01}_{x+t:y+t} + \mu^{02}_{x+t:y+t}\right) - B \cdot \mu^{02}_{x+t:y+t}. \end{aligned} $$

(b) For this joint-life insurance, the benefit is paid upon transition from State 0 to either State 1 or State 2, so we have

$$ \frac{d}{dt}\,{}_t\bar{V}^{(0)} = \bar{P} + \delta \cdot {}_t\bar{V}^{(0)} - \left(B - {}_t\bar{V}^{(0)}\right)\left(\mu^{01}_{x+t:y+t} + \mu^{02}_{x+t:y+t}\right). $$

(c) Here the benefit is paid upon transition from State 1 to State 3, since it is paid upon the death of (x) provided it comes after the death of (y). If the process transitions from State 0 to State 2, meaning that (x) has died first, no benefit is paid and the reserve is released. If the process transitions from State 0 to State 1, the benefit will eventually be paid when (x) dies. The State 0 reserve is released, and the State 1 reserve is established, upon transition from State 0 to State 1. Therefore we have

$$\begin{aligned}\frac{d}{dt}\,{}_t\overline{V}^{(0)} &= \overline{P}+\delta\cdot{}_t\overline{V}^{(0)}-\mu^{02}_{x+t:y+t}\left(0-{}_t\overline{V}^{(0)}\right)-\mu^{01}_{x+t:y+t}\left({}_t\overline{V}^{(1)}-{}_t\overline{V}^{(0)}\right)\\ &= \overline{P}+{}_t\overline{V}^{(0)}\cdot\left(\delta+\mu^{01}_{x+t:y+t}+\mu^{02}_{x+t:y+t}\right)-{}_t\overline{V}^{(1)}\cdot\mu^{01}_{x+t:y+t}.\end{aligned}$$

(d) For this last-survivor insurance, the benefit is paid upon transition from State 1 to State 3 (as in part (c)) or upon transition from State 2 to State 3. This means that ${}_t\overline{V}^{(0)}$ is released upon transition to either State 1 or State 2, and the appropriate replacement reserve is established. Therefore we have

$$\begin{aligned}\frac{d}{dt}\,{}_t\overline{V}^{(0)} &= \overline{P}+\delta\cdot{}_t\overline{V}^{(0)}-\mu^{01}_{x+t:y+t}\left({}_t\overline{V}^{(1)}-{}_t\overline{V}^{(0)}\right)-\mu^{02}_{x+t:y+t}\left({}_t\overline{V}^{(2)}-{}_t\overline{V}^{(0)}\right)\\ &= \overline{P}+{}_t\overline{V}^{(0)}\cdot\left(\delta+\mu^{01}_{x+t:y+t}+\mu^{02}_{x+t:y+t}\right)-{}_t\overline{V}^{(1)}\cdot\mu^{01}_{x+t:y+t}-{}_t\overline{V}^{(2)}\cdot\mu^{02}_{x+t:y+t}.\end{aligned}$$ ❐

EXAMPLE 12.19

Consider a fully-continuous insurance paying a unit benefit on the death of (x), provided it occurs after the death of (y), with APV denoted by $\overline{A}^{\,2}_{xy}$. Assume that (x) and (y) have independent future lifetimes.

(a) Write an integral expression for $\overline{A}^{\,2}_{xy}$, in standard actuarial notation, where the variable represents the time of death of (x).

(b) Write an integral expression for $\overline{A}^{\,2}_{xy}$, in standard actuarial notation, where the variable represents the time of death of (y).

(c) Show that the integral of part (b) can be evolved into the integral of part (a).

(d) Suppose the force of mortality for (x) after the death of (y) is different than it is while (y) is still alive, as discussed in Section 12.5.2. Which of the two approaches for calculating $\overline{A}^{\,2}_{xy}$, as described in parts (a) and (b), should be used in this case? Why?

(e) Write the part (b) approach in multi-state model notation.

SOLUTION

(a) If t denotes the time of death of (x), we have

$$\bar{A}_{xy}^{2} = \int_0^\infty v^t \cdot {}_tp_x\mu_{x+t} \cdot \left(1 - {}_tp_y\right) dt,$$

since (y) must have already died at the time (x) dies.

(b) If t denotes the time of death of (y), we have

$$\bar{A}_{xy}^{2} = \int_0^\infty v^t \cdot {}_tp_y\mu_{y+t} \cdot {}_tp_x \cdot \bar{A}_{x+t}\, dt.$$

The benefit is not paid at time t, but the APV of the eventual benefit, which is $\bar{A}_{x+t}$, is established at that time.

(c) The $\bar{A}_{x+t}$ term in part (b) can itself be written as an integral, leading to the double integral expression

$$\begin{aligned}\bar{A}_{xy}^{2} &= \int_0^\infty v^t \cdot {}_tp_y\mu_{y+t} \cdot {}_tp_x \cdot \left(\int_0^\infty v^r \cdot {}_rp_{x+t}\mu_{x+t+r}\, dr\right) dt \\ &= \int_0^\infty {}_tp_y\mu_{y+t} \cdot \left(\int_0^\infty v^{t+r} \cdot {}_{t+r}p_x\mu_{x+t+r}\, dr\right) dt.\end{aligned}$$

Making the variable change $s = t+r$ leads to

$$\bar{A}_{xy}^{2} = \int_0^\infty {}_tp_y\mu_{y+t} \cdot \left(\int_t^\infty v^s \cdot {}_sp_x\mu_{x+s}\, ds\right) dt.$$

Reversing the order of integration leads to

$$\begin{aligned}\bar{A}_{xy}^{2} &= \int_0^\infty v^s \cdot {}_sp_x\mu_{x+s} \cdot \left(\int_0^s {}_tp_y\mu_{y+t}\, dt\right) ds \\ &= \int_0^\infty v^s \cdot {}_sp_x\mu_{x+s} \cdot \left(1 - {}_sp_y\right) ds,\end{aligned}$$

which is the integral in part (a), as required.

(d) The part (b) approach should be used, because it separates the functions relating to the mortality of (x) into that applying while (y) is still alive, namely the ${}_tp_x$ function, and that applying after the death of (y), namely the $\bar{A}_{x+t}$ function.

(e) The death of (y) moves the process from State 0 to State 1, and the benefit is eventually paid when the process moves from State 1 to State 3. In multi-state model notation we have

$$\bar{A}_{xy}^{2} = \int_0^\infty v^t \cdot {}_tp_{xy}^{00} \cdot \mu_{x+t:y+t}^{01} \cdot \bar{A}_{x+t}^{13}\, dt. \qquad \square$$

EXAMPLE 12.20

Although not discussed in the text of this chapter, it is possible (and common) for multi-life annuities to be paid m^{thly}. For joint-life and last-survivor annuities, the APV expressions for m^{thly}-payment annuities are analogous to those for single-life annuities as presented in Section 8.5.

(a) Write the APV expressions for each of the following m^{thly}-payment annuities.

(i) $\ddot{a}_{xy}^{(m)}$ (ii) $a_{\overline{xy}}^{(m)}$ (iii) $a_{xy:\overline{n}|}^{(m)}$ (iv) ${}_{n|}\ddot{a}_{\overline{xy}}^{(m)}$

(b) One way to approximate the APVs of m^{thly}-payment annuities is a method analogous to the UDD approach presented in Section 8.5.4. Recall that

$$\ddot{a}_x^{(m)} \approx \alpha(m)\cdot\ddot{a}_x - \beta(m), \tag{8.78a}$$

where $\alpha(m)$ and $\beta(m)$ are defined in Section 8.5.4. Suppose we define the approximation

$$\ddot{a}_{xy}^{(m)} \approx \alpha(m)\cdot\ddot{a}_{xy} - \beta(m).$$

Explain how the assumption underlying this approximation differs from the assumption underlying Equation (8.78a).

(c) State the Woolhouse three-term approximation for $a_{xy}^{(m)}$.

(d) Show that $a_{x|y}^{(m)} = a_{x|y}$ under the two-term Woolhouse approximation, but not under the UDD approximation.

SOLUTION

(a) (i) Analogous to Equation (8.62) we have

$$\ddot{a}_{xy}^{(m)} = \frac{1}{m}\cdot\sum_{t=0}^{\infty} v^{t/m}\cdot {}_{t/m}p_{xy}.$$

(ii) Analogous to Equation (8.58) we have

$$a_{\overline{xy}}^{(m)} = \frac{1}{m}\cdot\sum_{t=1}^{\infty} v^{t/m}\cdot {}_{t/m}p_{\overline{xy}}.$$

(iii) Analogous to Equation (8.59) we have

$$a^{(m)}_{xy:\overline{n}|} = \frac{1}{m}\cdot\sum_{t=1}^{mn} v^{t/m}\cdot{}_{t/m}p_{xy}.$$

(iv) Analogous to Equation (8.64) we have

$${}_{n|}\ddot{a}^{(m)}_{\overline{xy}} = \frac{1}{m}\cdot\sum_{t=mn}^{\infty} v^{t/m}\cdot{}_{t/m}p_{\overline{xy}}.$$

(b) In Equation (8.78a), we assume a uniform distribution of deaths in the single-life survival model (life table). In the joint-life annuity approximation in this question, we are assuming a uniform distribution of the failure of joint statuses. (The approximation of $\ddot{a}^{(m)}_{xy}$ assuming UDD in the single-life table, along with the assumption of independence for (x) and (y), is a considerably more complex expression.)

(c) Analogous to Equation (8.81c) we have

$$a^{(m)}_{xy} = a_{xy} + \frac{m-1}{2m} - \frac{m^2-1}{12m^2}\left(\mu_{xy}+\delta\right).$$

(d) We know that

$$a_{x|y} = a_y - a_{xy}$$

and, similarly,

$$a^{(m)}_{x|y} = a^{(m)}_y - a^{(m)}_{xy}.$$

Under two-term Woolhouse, we have

$$a^{(m)}_{x|y} = a^{(m)}_y - a^{(m)}_{xy} = \left(a_y + \frac{m-1}{2m}\right) - \left(a_{xy} + \frac{m-1}{2m}\right) = a_y - a_{xy} = a_{x|y},$$

as required. Under UDD, we have

$$\begin{aligned} a^{(m)}_{x|y} &= \left[\alpha(m)\cdot a_y + \gamma(m)\right] - \left[\alpha(m)\cdot a_{xy} + \gamma(m)\right] \\ &= \alpha(m)\cdot\left(a_y - a_{xy}\right) = \alpha(m)\cdot a_{x|y} \neq a_{x|y}, \end{aligned}$$

as required. ❑

12.9 EXERCISES

12.1 The Joint-Life Model

12-1 Show that

$$q_{xy} \;=\; q_x + p_x \cdot q_y,$$

assuming independence of the individual lifetimes T_x and T_y.

12-2 Let T_x and T_y be independent future lifetime random variables. Given $q_x = .080$, $q_y = .004$, ${}_tp_x = 1 - t^2 \cdot q_x$, and ${}_tp_y = 1 - t^2 \cdot q_y$, both for $0 \leq t \leq 1$, evaluate the PDF of T_{xy} at $t = .50$.

12-3 Two microwave models, denoted Type I and Type II, follow survival models defined by $\mu_x^I = \ln 1.25$, for $x > 0$, and $\mu_x^{II} = \frac{1}{9-x}$, for $0 < x < 9$, respectively. Given that both models are currently two years old, and that they have independent lifetimes, find the probability that the first failure will occur between ages 3 and 6.

12-4 At all ages greater than 50, the force of failure for smokers is double that for nonsmokers. Suppose the age-at-failure random variable for nonsmokers has a uniform distribution with $\omega = 75$. If (65) and (55) have independent lifetimes, where (65) is a nonsmoker and (55) is a smoker, find the value of $\mathring{e}_{65:55}$.

12-5 Let T_x and T_y be independent future lifetime random variables, each with an exponential distribution with mean 20. Find the value of $Var(T_{xy})$.

12.2 The Last-Survivor Model

12-6 Let T_{80} and T_{85} be independent random variables with uniform distributions with $\omega = 100$. Find the probability that the second failure occurs within five years.

12-7 Derive each of the following identities. Which of them require an assumption of the independence of T_x and T_y?

(a) ${}_tq_{\overline{xy}} \;=\; {}_tq_x + {}_tq_y - {}_tq_{xy}$

(b) $f_{T_{\overline{xy}}}(t) \;=\; {}_tq_x \cdot {}_tp_y\mu_{y+t} + {}_tq_y \cdot {}_tp_x\mu_{x+t}$

(c) ${}_{n|}q_{\overline{xy}} \;=\; {}_nq_x \cdot {}_{n|}q_y + {}_nq_y \cdot {}_{n|}q_x + {}_{n|}q_x \cdot {}_{n|}q_y$

12-8 If T_x and T_y are independent, and each is uniformly distributed over each year of age separately, show that

$$18({}_{1/3}q_{xy}) - 12({}_{1/2}q_{xy}) = q_{\overline{xy}}.$$

12-9 For independent lives (x) and (y), the force of failure is constant over each year of age. Find the value of ${}_{.75}p_{\overline{x+.25:y+.25}}$, given that $q_x = .08$ and $q_y = .06$.

12-10 For the model of Exercise 12-5, find the value of $Cov(T_{xy}, T_{\overline{xy}})$.

12.3 Contingent Probability Functions

12-11 Coffee Maker I follows a survival model defined by $\mu_x^I = \frac{1.80}{9-x}$, for $0 < x < 9$, and Coffee Maker II follows a survival model defined by $\mu_x^{II} = \frac{1.50}{9-x}$, for $0 < x < 9$. The two coffee makers have independent lifetimes. Find the probability that Coffee Maker I fails before Coffee Maker II.

12.4 Contingent Contracts Involving Multi-Life Statuses

12-12 Let Z denote the present value random variable for a contingent contract that pays a unit benefit at the end of the year of the first failure between (x) and (y), and another unit benefit at the end of the year of the second failure. Find the value of $E[Z]$, given the values $a_x = 9$, $a_y = 13$, and $i = .04$.

12-13 Let Y denote the present value random variable for a contingent annuity-due with unit payment made during the first 15 years if at least one of (x) and (y) survive, but made after the first 15 years only if exactly one of (x) and (y) survive. Find the value of $E[Y]$, given the following values:

$$\ddot{a}_x = 9.80 \qquad \ddot{a}_y = 11.60 \qquad \ddot{a}_{xy} = 7.60 \qquad {}_{15|}\ddot{a}_{xy} = 3.70$$

12-14 Let K_{xy} denote the curtate duration at failure of the joint-life status (xy). Find the value of the discount rate d, given the values $\ddot{a}_{xy} = 10$, ${}^2\ddot{a}_{xy} = 7$, and $Var(\ddot{a}_{\overline{K_{xy}+1|}}) = 27$.

12-15 Two lives (x) and (y) have independent and identically distributed future lifetimes. Given the values $P_x = P_y = .10$, $P_{\overline{xy}} = .06$, and $d = .06$, find the value of P_{xy}.

12-16 A discrete unit benefit contingent contract is issued to the last-survivor status $(\overline{xx})$, where the two future lifetime random variables T_x are independent. The contract is funded by discrete net annual premiums, which are reduced by 25% after the first failure. Find the value of the initial net annual premium, under the equivalence principle, given the values $A_x = .40$, $A_{xx} = .55$, and $\ddot{a}_x = 10.00$.

12-17 A continuous two-life annuity has actuarial present value 1180. The annuity pays at annual rate 100 while both (x) and (y) survive, 70 while (x) survives after the failure of (y), and 50 while (y) survives after the failure of (x). Find the value of $\bar{a}_{\overline{xy}}$, given that $\bar{a}_x = 12$ and $\bar{a}_y = 10$.

12.5 Multi-State Model Representation

12-18 Using the multi-state model notation defined earlier, give formulas for each of the following joint-life functions.

(a) $\bar{a}_{xy:\overline{n}|}$ (b) P_{xy} (c) $A_{xy:\overline{n}|}$ (d) $\bar{P}(\bar{A}^{\;1}_{xy:\overline{n}|})$

12-19 Using the model shown in Figure 12.1, give the formula for $a_{x|y}$ in multi-state model notation.

12-20 Using the multi-state model notation defined earlier, give formulas for each of the following continuous contingent insurance functions.

(a) $\bar{A}^{1}_{xy}$ (b) $\bar{A}_{x\overset{1}{y}}$ (c) $\bar{A}^{2}_{xy}$ (d) $\bar{A}_{x\overset{2}{y}}$

12-21 Using the multi-state model notation defined earlier, give formulas for each of the following last-survival functions.

(a) $\bar{a}_{\overline{xy}}$ (b) $\ddot{a}_{\overline{xy}:\overline{n}|}$ (c) $A^{\;1}_{\overline{xy}:\overline{n}|}$ (d) ${}_{n|}\bar{A}_{\overline{xy}}$

12-22 For two persons alive at ages x and y at time 0, solve the Kolmogorov differential equation for ${}_np^{00}_{xy}$, writing the result in standard actuarial notation.

12-23 For a person alive at age x at reset time 0, with (y) failed, solve the Kolmogorov differential equation for (a) ${}_np_x^{11}$ and (b) ${}_np_x^{13}$, writing the results in standard actuarial notation.

12-24 State Thiele's net premium differential equation for an insurance whose APV is given by $\bar{A}_{xy}^{\;2}$, with continuous premium payable only while both (x) and (y) are alive, when the process is in (a) State 0, (b) State 1, and (c) State 2.

12-25 State Thiele's net premium differential equation for an insurance whose APV is given by $\bar{A}_{\overline{xy}}$, with continuous premium payable only while both (x) and (y) are alive, when the process is in (a) State 1, (b) State 2, and (c) State 3.

12.6 General Random Variable Analysis

12-26 Consider the joint density function of T_x and T_y given by

$$f_{x,y}(t_x,t_y) = \frac{4}{(1+t_x+2t_y)^3},$$

for $t_x > 0$ and $t_y > 0$. Show that T_x and T_y are not independent.

12-27 For the survival model of Exercise 12-26, find $S_x(t)$, the marginal survival function of T_x.

12-28 For the survival model of Exercise 12-26, evaluate $F_{x,y}(1,2)$.

12-29 For the survival model of Exercise 12-26, evaluate $S_{x,y}(1,2)$.

12-30 For the survival model of Exercise 12-26, find an expression for ${}_np_{xy}$.

12-31 For the survival model of Exercise 12-26, find an expression for ${}_nq_{\overline{xy}}$.

12.7 Common Shock – A Model for Lifetime Dependency

12-32 The APV for a last-survivor whole life insurance on $(\overline{xy})$, with unit benefit paid at the instant of failure of the status, was calculated assuming independent future lifetimes for (x) and (y) with constant hazard rate .06 for each. It is now discovered that although the total hazard rate of .06 is correct, the two lifetimes are not independent since each includes a common shock hazard factor with constant force .02. The force of interest used in the calculation is $\delta = .05$. Calculate the increase in the APV that results from recognition of the common shock element.

12-33 Lives (x) and (y) have independent future lifetime exponential random variables T_x^* and T_y^* with respect to risk factors unique to (x) and (y), respectively. As well, both (x) and (y) are subject to a constant common hazard rate $\lambda = .01$. Given that $p_x = .96$ and $p_y = .97$, calculate the value of ${}_5p_{xy}$.

12-34 For two persons alive at ages x and y at time 0, show that the Kolmogorov differential equation for ${}_tp_{xy}^{03}$ solves for

$${}_np_{xy}^{03} = {}_nq_{\overline{xy}} + \lambda \cdot \overset{\circ}{e}_{xy},$$

where λ is the constant common shock hazard described in Section 12.7.

CHAPTER THIRTEEN

MULTIPLE-DECREMENT MODELS (THEORY)

For most of this text we have considered models with payments contingent on the occurrence of a particular concept of failure for a specified entity of interest. In this chapter we consider models in which the entity of interest faces multiple types of failure. Each type of failure is called a *decrement*. In earlier chapters, the entity of interest faced only one type of decrement, such as the death of (x) under a life insurance arrangement. Such models are therefore called *single-decrement models*. In this chapter, with simultaneous exposure to multiple concepts of failure, we refer to the models as *multiple-decrement models*.

For example, consider a group insurance plan provided by an employer. At time $t=0$, some number of employees begin coverage under the plan. Over time the number of covered employees will decrease due to death, retirement, disability, or changing jobs. Each of these reasons for leaving the group is a different cause of failure, or a different decrement. To accurately model the costs of such plans we require models that take into account both the time and cause of decrement.

Throughout this chapter we will refer back to formulas and derivations from the single-decrement models developed earlier.

There are many applications of multiple-decrement theory, and we present several of them in Chapter 14. As we shall see then, the multi-state formulation illustrated earlier with various single-decrement models will be particularly useful.

13.1 DISCRETE MULTIPLE-DECREMENT MODELS

Without losing generality, we will introduce our multiple-decrement models in a life insurance context. Consider a closed group of 1000 insureds with annual premium life insurance policies. Each year thcse insureds can leave the group by one of two decrements, either death or withdrawal, but not both. We will refer to death as Cause 1 and withdrawal as Cause 2. We begin by defining several additional actuarial symbols.[1]

We let $q_x^{(j)}$ denote the probability that (x) fails in the next year of age due to Cause j, for $j=1,2$. Since the causes are mutually exclusive, then the probability that (x) fails in the next year due to *any* cause, denoted by $q_x^{(\tau)}$, is given by

$$q_x^{(\tau)} = q_x^{(1)} + q_x^{(2)}. \tag{13.1a}$$

[1] Note that the deterministic (life table) view of Chapter 6 is being taken here.

In general, if there are m distinct causes of decrement, we have

$$q_x^{(\tau)} = \sum_{j=1}^{m} q_x^{(j)}. \tag{13.1b}$$

The probability that (x) does not fail in the next year at all is given by

$$p_x^{(\tau)} = 1 - q_x^{(\tau)}. \tag{13.2}$$

We let $d_x^{(j)}$ denote the number of people in the group at age x who will fail (i.e., be decremented from the group) before age $x+1$ due to Cause j, and $d_x^{(\tau)}$ denote the total number of failures for all causes combined. Clearly we have

$$d_x^{(\tau)} = \sum_{j=1}^{m} d_x^{(j)}. \tag{13.3}$$

More generally, the number who fail due to Cause j over the n-year interval $(x, x+n]$ is denoted by ${}_n d_x^{(j)}$, the number who fail for all causes combined is denoted ${}_n d_x^{(\tau)}$, the probability of failure due to Cause j over $(x, x+n]$ is denoted ${}_n q_x^{(j)}$, the probability of failure due to any cause over $(x, x+n]$ is denoted ${}_n q_x^{(\tau)}$, and the probability of surviving all causes of failure over $(x, x+n]$ is denoted ${}_n p_x^{(\tau)}$. Note that

$${}_n d_x^{(j)} = \sum_{t=0}^{n-1} d_{x+t}^{(j)} \tag{13.4}$$

and

$${}_n d_x^{(\tau)} = \sum_{j=1}^{m} {}_n d_x^{(j)}. \tag{13.5a}$$

Dividing both sides of Equation (13.5a) by the number of survivors in the group at age x, which we denote by $l_x^{(\tau)}$, gives

$${}_n q_x^{(\tau)} = \sum_{j=1}^{m} {}_n q_x^{(j)}. \tag{13.5b}$$

Finally, we let $l_x^{(j)}$ denote the number in the group at age x who eventually fail due to Cause j at some time after age x. Since each person fails due to only one cause, it follows that the total number in the group at age x, already defined as $l_x^{(\tau)}$, is given by

$$l_x^{(\tau)} = \sum_{j=1}^{m} l_x^{(j)}. \tag{13.6}$$

Several additional relationships follow from these definitions, such as

$$d_x^{(j)} = l_x^{(\tau)} \cdot q_x^{(j)}, \tag{13.7a}$$

$$d_x^{(\tau)} = l_x^{(\tau)} \cdot q_x^{(\tau)}, \tag{13.7b}$$

$${}_n d_x^{(j)} = l_x^{(\tau)} \cdot {}_n q_x^{(j)}, \tag{13.7c}$$

$${}_n d_x^{(\tau)} = l_x^{(\tau)} \cdot {}_n q_x^{(\tau)}, \tag{13.7d}$$

$${}_n p_x^{(\tau)} = 1 - {}_n q_x^{(\tau)}, \tag{13.7e}$$

and

$$l_{x+n}^{(\tau)} = l_x^{(\tau)} \cdot {}_n p_x^{(\tau)}. \tag{13.7f}$$

The reader should clearly understand the logic of each relationship.

13.1.1 THE MULTIPLE-DECREMENT TABLE

The functions involved in a discrete multiple-decrement model are conveniently arranged in a tabular form, analogous to the single-decrement life table presented in Chapter 6, called a *multiple-decrement table*. The construction of a multiple-decrement table from the basic probabilities of failure is illustrated in the following example.

EXAMPLE 13.1

Given the following probabilities of decrement, for each of two decrements at certain ages, construct the full multiple-decrement table. (Note that with two causes of decrement, we would refer to the model as a *double-decrement table*.) Assume an initial group (called the *radix* of the table) of size 1000.

x	$q_x^{(1)}$	$q_x^{(2)}$
45	.011	.100
46	.012	.100
47	.013	.100
48	.014	.100
49	.015	.100
50	.016	.100

SOLUTION

In the completed table below, Columns (1), (2), and (3) contain given values. The entries in Column (4) are found from those in Columns (2) and (3) by Equation (13.1a); those in Column (5) are found from those in Column (4) by Equation (13.2); those in Column (6) are found by Equation (13.7f), along with the radix of $l_{45}^{(\tau)} = 1000$; those in Columns (7) and (8) are found by Equation (13.7a).

(1)	(2)	(3)	(4)	(5)	(6)	(7)	(8)
x	$q_x^{(1)}$	$q_x^{(2)}$	$q_x^{(\tau)}$	$p_x^{(\tau)}$	$l_x^{(\tau)}$	$d_x^{(1)}$	$d_x^{(2)}$
45	.011	.100	.111	.889	1000.00	11.00	100.00
46	.012	.100	.112	.888	889.00	10.67	88.90
47	.013	.100	.113	.887	789.43	10.26	78.94
48	.014	.100	.114	.886	700.23	9.80	70.02
49	.015	.100	.115	.885	620.40	9.31	62.04
50	.016	.100	.116	.884	549.05	8.78	54.91

❐

EXAMPLE 13.2

Using the double-decrement table developed in Example 13.1, calculate each of the following.

(a) ${}_3p_{46}^{(\tau)}$

(b) ${}_2d_{47}^{(2)}$

(c) ${}_2q_{46}^{(1)}$

(d) ${}_{2|2}q_{45}^{(1)}$

(e) The probability that a person in the group at age 46 will leave between ages 48 and 49.

SOLUTION

(a) We have ${}_3p_{46}^{(\tau)} = \frac{l_{49}^{(\tau)}}{l_{46}^{(\tau)}} = \frac{620.40}{889.00} = .6979.$ Note that this could also be obtained as

$$ {}_3p_{46}^{(\tau)} = p_{46}^{(\tau)} \cdot p_{47}^{(\tau)} \cdot p_{48}^{(\tau)} = .6979. $$

(b) ${}_2d_{47}^{(2)} = d_{47}^{(2)} + d_{48}^{(2)} = 78.94 + 70.02 = 148.96$

(c) ${}_2q_{46}^{(1)} = \frac{d_{46}^{(1)}+d_{47}^{(1)}}{l_{46}^{(\tau)}} = \frac{10.67+10.26}{889.00} = .02354,$ which could also be obtained as

$$ {}_2q_{46}^{(1)} = q_{46}^{(1)} + p_{46}^{(\tau)} \cdot q_{47}^{(1)} = .02354. $$

(d) ${}_{2|2}q_{45}^{(1)} = \frac{d_{47}^{(1)} + d_{48}^{(1)}}{l_{45}^{(\tau)}} = \frac{10.26+9.80}{1000.00} = .02006$

(e) ${}_{2|}q_{46}^{(\tau)} = \frac{d_{48}^{(1)}+d_{48}^{(2)}}{l_{46}^{(\tau)}} = \frac{9.80+70.20}{889.00} = .08979,$ which could also be obtained as

$$ {}_{2|}q_{46}^{(\tau)} = p_{46}^{(\tau)} \cdot p_{47}^{(\tau)} \cdot q_{48}^{(\tau)} = .08979. $$

❐

13.1.2 RANDOM VARIABLE ANALYSIS

As we have done in several earlier chapters, we can analyze the multiple-decrement model in a stochastic framework. Recall the discrete random variable K_x denoting the curtate duration at failure for an entity of interest with identifying characteristic (x). (Again, without loss of generality, we might assume a person who is age x as our entity of interest.) We now define a second discrete random variable, denoted J_x, which represents the cause of failure for (x). Then $\{K_x = k-1 \cap J_x = j\}$ denotes the joint event of (x) failing in the kth interval (say, year) due to the jth cause. For example, the joint event $\{K_x = 4 \cap J_x = 1\}$ is that (x) fails between ages $x+4$ and $x+5$ due to Cause 1. The probability of this event is denoted by ${}_{4|}q_x^{(1)}$.

The standard rules of multivariate probability will apply here, and we will be interested in three different probability functions.

The *joint probability function* of K_x and J_x is

$$Pr(K_x = k \cap J_x = j) = {}_{k|}q_x^{(j)} = \frac{d_{x+k}^{(j)}}{l_x^{(\tau)}}, \tag{13.8}$$

giving the probability that (x) survives all decrements for k years and then fails due to Cause *j* in the $(k+1)^{st}$ year.

The *marginal probability function* of K_x is

$$Pr(K_x = k) = \sum_{j=1}^{m} Pr(K_x = k \cap J_x = j) = {}_{k|}q_x^{(\tau)} = \frac{d_{x+k}^{(1)} + \cdots + d_{x+k}^{(m)}}{l_x^{(\tau)}}, \tag{13.9}$$

representing the probability that (x) will fail in the $(k+1)^{st}$ year due to any cause. From Equation (13.9) we can see that $Pr(K_x = k)$ is the sum of the $d^{(j)}$ values in the *row* of the multiple-decrement table corresponding to age $x+k$, all divided by $l_x^{(\tau)}$.

The *marginal probability function* of J_x is

$$Pr(J_x = j) = \sum_{k=0}^{\infty} Pr(K_x = k \cap J_x = j) = \sum_{k=0}^{\infty} \frac{d_{x+k}^{(j)}}{l_x^{(\tau)}}, \tag{13.10}$$

representing the probability that (x) will eventually fail due to Cause *j* without restriction as to time of failure. It is the sum of the $d^{(j)}$ values in the *column* of the multiple-decrement table corresponding to Cause *j*, which might be denoted by $l_x^{(j)}$, divided by $l_x^{(\tau)}$.

EXAMPLE 13.3

Using the double-decrement table developed in Example 13.1, find (a) $Pr(K_x = 2 \cap J_x = 1)$ and (b) $Pr(K_x = 3)$ for a person age 46.

SOLUTION

(a) $Pr(K_x = 2 \cap J_x = 1)$ is the probability of failing in the third year due to Cause 1. It is given by

$$_{2|}q_{46}^{(1)} = \frac{d_{48}^{(1)}}{l_{46}^{(\tau)}} = \frac{9.80}{889.00} = .01102.$$

(b) $Pr(K_x = 3)$ is the probability of failure in the fourth year (*i.e.*, between ages 49 and 50) due to any cause, and is given by

$$_{3|}q_{46}^{(\tau)} = \frac{d_{49}^{(1)} + d_{49}^{(2)}}{l_{46}^{(\tau)}} = \frac{9.31 + 62.04}{889.00} = .08026. \qquad \square$$

13.2 THEORY OF COMPETING RISKS

Before investigating multiple-decrement models in the context of continuous random variables, it is necessary to first discuss the *theory of competing risks*. Suppose we currently have 1000 64-year-old employees. During the next year of age, these employees may leave the company either by death (Cause 1) or retirement (Cause 2). Assume that $q_{64}^{(1)} = .02$ and $q_{64}^{(2)} = .30$.

Assume that employees may retire at any time during the year of age and may die at any time during the year of age. The given probabilities refer to the fractions of employees that we expect to see die and retire during the year, respectively, given that the employees are exposed to the risk of both types of decrement at the same time. If we were to change the retirement rules so that no one could retire before age 65, we would see no retirements during the year and death would be the only decrement possible during the year. That is, there would be no case of *competing risks* during the year.

With death and retirement *both* acting on the employees throughout the year, we expect to observe 20 employees die while employed. The key insight here is to realize that if retirement is removed as a decrement, then we should expect to see *more* than 20 employees die. This is because we have more employees exposed to the risk of dying during the year, since the 300 that otherwise would have retired are staying on the job and thus have a greater chance of dying while employed. In other words, death has more of an opportunity to strike more employees and we will observe more deaths of employees. (We might assume these extra deaths will occur in any case, but after retirement; thus we will not observe those deaths since retirement removes an individual from the group under observation. They have already failed due to Cause 2 by the time death strikes.)

This higher probability of death *in the absence of other decrements* (i.e., in the absence of competing risks) is denoted by $q_x^{\prime(1)}$, and is called the *absolute rate of death*. In general, the *absolute rate of decrement due to Cause j* over the interval $(x,x+n]$ is denoted by ${}_nq_x^{\prime(j)}$. It represents the probability of failing due to Cause j in $(x,x+n]$ *if no other causes of decrement were operating*. In light of this, these absolute rates are also called *independent probabilities*, and the multiple-decrement probabilities are called *dependent probabilities.*[2]

But if no other causes of decrement are operating, then we are dealing with a single-decrement model as described in Chapters 5 and 6. Therefore the probability represented by $q_x^{\prime(j)}$ is really the same as the one represented by the simpler q_x in the earlier chapters. For this reason we refer to $q_x^{\prime(j)}$ as the probability of decrement due to Cause j in the *associated single-decrement table*. Note that it will always be true that

$$ {}_nq_x^{\prime(j)} \geq {}_nq_x^{(j)}. \tag{13.11}$$

13.3 CONTINUOUS MULTIPLE-DECREMENT MODELS

For the continuous multiple-decrement models, the pair of discrete random variables for curtate duration at failure, K_x, and cause of failure, J_x, are replaced by a set of continuous random variables. Let $T_x^{(j)}$ denote the continuous random variable for the length of time until the entity represented by (x) fails due to Cause j in the absence of other decrements. It should be clear that $T_x^{(j)}$ is the same as the T_x time-to-failure random variable defined earlier, but with the single cause of decrement specified as Cause j.

Let ${}_tp_x^{\prime(j)} = 1-{}_tq_x^{\prime(j)}$ denote the probability that (x) will survive for t years (i.e., to age $x+t$) in the absence of other decrements. Since the absence of other decrements creates a single-decrement model, then ${}_tp_x^{\prime(j)}$ has exactly the same meaning as the simpler ${}_tp_x$ from earlier chapters. Also let $\mu_{x+t}^{(j)}$ denote the force of failure due to Cause j. Since the force is an *instantaneous* measure, then it is the same whether operating in a single-decrement or a multiple-decrement environment. Thus we do *not* need the separate symbols $\mu_y^{(j)}$ (for force of decrement at age y if competing forces *are also operating*) and $\mu_y^{\prime(j)}$ (for the same concept if competing forces *are not operating*). $\mu_y^{(j)}$ and $\mu_y^{\prime(j)}$ would be identical, and the convention is to use $\mu_y^{(j)}$ without the prime.

By analogy with Equation (6.20) we have the relationship

[2] Older texts have referred to $q_x^{\prime(j)}$ as the *pure probability* due to Cause j; others use the phrase *absolute probability of decrement* due to Cause j.

$$\mu_{x+t}^{(j)} = \frac{-\frac{d}{dt}\,{}_tp_x^{\prime(j)}}{{}_tp_x^{\prime(j)}}, \tag{13.12a}$$

and the companion relationship

$${}_tp_x^{\prime(j)} = \exp\left(-\int_0^t \mu_{x+s}^{(j)}\,ds\right), \tag{13.12b}$$

which is the same as that developed in Exercise 6-17 with our augmented notation.

Similarly, if ${}_tp_x^{(\tau)} = 1 - {}_tq_x^{(\tau)}$ denotes the probability that (x) will not fail for any cause before age $x+t$ (*i.e.*, that (x) survives against all causes for t years), and $\mu_{x+t}^{(\tau)}$ is the total force of failure at time t,[3] then we have

$$\mu_{x+t}^{(\tau)} = \frac{-\frac{d}{dt}\,{}_tp_x^{(\tau)}}{{}_tp_x^{(\tau)}} \tag{13.13a}$$

by analogy with Equation (6.20) and

$${}_tp_x^{(\tau)} = \exp\left(-\int_0^t \mu_{x+s}^{(\tau)}\,ds\right) \tag{13.13b}$$

by analogy with Exercise 6-17.

Finally, by analogy with Equation (5.46), the PDF for the single-decrement time-to-failure random variable $T_x^{(j)}$ is given by

$$f_{x^{(j)}}(t) = {}_tp_x^{\prime(j)} \cdot \mu_{x+t}^{(j)}, \tag{13.14}$$

and its CDF is given by

$$F_{x^{(j)}}(t) = Pr\left[T_x^{(j)} \le t\right] = \int_0^t f_{x^{(j)}}(s)\,ds = \int_0^t {}_sp_x^{\prime(j)} \cdot \mu_{x+s}^{(j)}\,ds. \tag{13.15}$$

In actuarial notation this is denoted by ${}_tq_x^{\prime(j)}$.

If there are m causes of decrement, then the event of survival for length of time t against all causes is the intersection of the m events of survival against each cause separately. If the m causes are independent, then the probability of the intersection event, denoted ${}_tp_x^{(\tau)}$, is the product of the probabilities of the m separate survival events, each such probability denoted ${}_tp_x^{\prime(j)}$, for $j = 1, 2, \ldots, m$. Thus we have the important relationship

[3] The total force of failure is sometimes denoted by $\mu_x^{(\tau)}(t)$; this notation might be used on Exam MLC.

$$ {}_tp_x^{(\tau)} = \prod_{j=1}^{m} {}_tp_x'^{(j)}. \tag{13.16} $$

(See Exercise 13-7 for an alternate derivation of this relationship that does not require the assumption of independence.) From Equations (13.16) and (13.13a) together we can derive another very important result. Starting with Equation (13.13a) we have

$$ \begin{aligned} \mu_{x+t}^{(\tau)} &= \frac{-\frac{d}{dt}\,{}_tp_x^{(\tau)}}{{}_tp_x^{(\tau)}} \\ &= -\frac{d}{dt} \ln {}_tp_x^{(\tau)} \\ &= -\frac{d}{dt} \ln\left[{}_tp_x'^{(1)} \cdot {}_tp_x'^{(2)} \cdot \cdots \cdot {}_tp_x'^{(m)}\right] \\ &= \left(-\frac{d}{dt} \ln {}_tp_x'^{(1)}\right) + \left(-\frac{d}{dt} \ln {}_tp_x'^{(2)}\right) + \cdots + \left(-\frac{d}{dt} \ln {}_tp_x'^{(m)}\right) \\ &= \mu_{x+t}^{(1)} + \mu_{x+t}^{(2)} + \cdots + \mu_{x+t}^{(m)}. \end{aligned} \tag{13.17} $$

This result is intuitive as well as analytical. Since the forces are instantaneous measures, the total force of failure is the sum of the cause-specific forces. This result is analogous to the basic addition rule in probability theory in the case of mutually exclusive events. Since the force is instantaneous, the intersection event of failure by two (or more) causes simultaneously is not possible so the probability of this event is zero. Thus the force of the union event is the sum of the forces of the separate cause events making up the union. (See Exercise 13-7 for an alternate derivation of Equation (13.17).)

We now return to the multiple-decrement probability ${}_tq_x^{(j)}$, defined back in Section 13.1. Recall that the density for (x) failing at time t in the *absence* of other decrements is given by Equation (13.14) as ${}_tp_x'^{(j)} \cdot \mu_{x+t}^{(j)}$. As explained in Chapter 5, this density is the product of the probability of surviving to time t (which is ${}_tp_x'^{(j)}$ in the single-decrement environment) times the force of failure at time t for the single decrement that is operating (which is $\mu_{x+t}^{(j)}$). In the multiple-decrement environment, survival to time t must be accomplished against all decrements, so the survival probability is ${}_tp_x^{(\tau)}$. Then the density for failure at time t due to Cause j in the *presence* of the other decrements is $f_{T,J}(t,j) = {}_tp_x^{(\tau)} \cdot \mu_{x+t}^{(j)}$. From this density it follows that the probability of failure in $(x,x+t]$ due to Cause j in the presence of the other decrements, which we have already denoted by ${}_tq_x^{(j)}$, is given by

$$ {}_tq_x^{(j)} = \int_0^t f_{T,J}(s,j)\,ds = \int_0^t {}_sp_x^{(\tau)} \cdot \mu_{x+s}^{(j)}\,ds. \tag{13.18} $$

Differentiating both sides of Equation (13.18) yields

$$\frac{d}{dt}\,{}_tq_x^{(j)} \;=\; \frac{d}{dt}\int_0^t {}_sp_x^{(\tau)}\cdot\mu_{x+s}^{(j)}\,ds \;=\; {}_tp_x^{(\tau)}\cdot\mu_{x+t}^{(j)},$$

so we have

$$\mu_{x+t}^{(j)} \;=\; \frac{\frac{d}{dt}\,{}_tq_x^{(j)}}{{}_tp_x^{(\tau)}}. \tag{13.19}$$

Then Equations (13.17) and (13.18) together, along with the familiar result

$${}_tq_x^{(\tau)} \;=\; \int_0^t {}_sp_x^{(\tau)}\cdot\mu_{x+s}^{(\tau)}\,ds \tag{13.20}$$

can be used to verify the already-established Equation (13.5b).

EXAMPLE 13.4

If $\mu_{x+t}^{(1)}=.10$ and $\mu_{x+t}^{(2)}=.20$ for all t, find each of (a) ${}_tp_x^{(\tau)}$, (b) ${}_tq_x'^{(1)}$, (c) ${}_tq_x^{(1)}$, and (d) ${}_\infty q_x^{(1)}$.

SOLUTION

(a) We know $\mu_{x+t}^{(\tau)}=\mu_{x+t}^{(1)}+\mu_{x+t}^{(2)}=.30.$ From Equation (13.13b) we have

$${}_tp_x^{(\tau)} \;=\; \exp\left(-\int_0^t .30\,ds\right) \;=\; e^{-.30t}.$$

(b) This is a single-decrement model probability. From Equation (13.12b) we have

$${}_tq_x'^{(1)} \;=\; 1-{}_tp_x'^{(1)} \;=\; 1-\exp\left(-\int_0^t .10\,ds\right) \;=\; 1-e^{-.10t}.$$

(c) Here we use Equation (13.18) and the result from part (a). We have

$$\begin{aligned}{}_tq_x^{(1)} \;&=\; \int_0^t {}_sp_x^{(\tau)}\cdot\mu_{x+s}^{(1)}\,ds\\ &=\; .10\int_0^t e^{-.30s}\,ds \;=\; .10\left(\frac{e^{-.30s}}{-.30}\bigg|_0^t\right) \;=\; \frac{1}{3}(1-e^{-.30t}).\end{aligned}$$

(d) This is the special case of part (c) as $t\to\infty$. We have

$${}_\infty q_x^{(1)} \;=\; .10\int_0^\infty e^{-.30s}\,ds \;=\; .10\left(\frac{e^{-.30s}}{-.30}\bigg|_0^\infty\right) = \frac{1}{3},$$

which is also reached by taking the limit as $t \to \infty$ of the answer in part (c). Note that ${}_{\infty}q_x^{(j)}$ denotes the probability that (x) will eventually fail due to Cause j with no time restriction as to when failure might occur. ❐

13.4 UNIFORM DISTRIBUTION OF DECREMENTS

Recall the discussion in Section 6.6 regarding the various fractional age assumptions used to determine the numerical values of functions not given directly by the life table itself in the single-decrement model. The same issue arises in the multiple-decrement model: given only the multiple-decrement table presented in Section 13.1.1, only values of ${}_nq_x^{(j)}$ and ${}_nq_x^{(\tau)}$ for integral n can be directly determined without making additional assumptions. Furthermore, we cannot establish relationships between the single-decrement probability ${}_tq_x'^{(j)}$ and the multiple-decrement probability ${}_tq_x^{(j)}$ without such additional assumptions.

The reader should recognize that the several forces of decrement, $\mu_{x+t}^{(j)}$ for $j=1,2,\ldots,m$, would together define all other functions in the multiple-decrement models. The several $\mu_{x+t}^{(j)}$ sum to $\mu_{x+t}^{(\tau)}$ (see Equation (13.17)), which leads to ${}_tp_x^{(\tau)}$ and hence ${}_tq_x^{(\tau)}$ (see Equation (13.13b)), which together lead to ${}_tq_x^{(j)}$ (see Equation (13.18)) for any t. Being continuous, the function $\mu_y^{(j)}$ defines the pattern of decrement for all y, so no "additional assumptions" are needed. But if all we have is the discrete model of Section 13.1.1, then the additional assumptions are needed.

The multiple-decrement analogy with the single-decrement model described in Section 6.6 will be clear. Here we consider first the uniform distribution assumption of Section 6.6.1, of which there are two subcases. The exponential distribution assumption of Section 6.6.2 is considered in Section 13.4.3 and Example 13.8.[4]

13.4.1 UNIFORM DISTRIBUTION IN THE MULTIPLE-DECREMENT CONTEXT

We consider first the case where each decrement j is uniformly distributed *in the multiple-decrement context*.[5] That is, each decrement is observed to occur uniformly throughout the year of age when other decrements are also present. In this case we have

$$ {}_tq_x^{(j)} = t \cdot q_x^{(j)}, \tag{13.21}$$

for $0 \leq t \leq 1$. From this we can derive a relationship between the probability of decrement in the multiple-decrement context, ${}_tq_x^{(j)}$, and the corresponding probability of decrement in the associated single-decrement table, ${}_tq_x'^{(j)}$. We begin with

[4] Results based on the hyperbolic assumption of Section 6.6.3 are exceedingly complex at best, and many do not even exist in closed form. They are not considered in this text.

[5] In a bit of whimsy, we might refer to this as the *MUDD assumption*.

$$ {}_tq_x^{(j)} = t \cdot q_x^{(j)} = \int_0^t {}_sp_x^{(\tau)} \cdot \mu_{x+s}^{(j)}\,ds, $$

from Equation (13.18). Differentiating both sides of this equation with respect to t, using the fundamental theorem of calculus for the right side, we obtain

$$ q_x^{(j)} = {}_tp_x^{(\tau)} \cdot \mu_{x+t}^{(j)}. \tag{13.22} $$

If each decrement j is uniformly distributed, then it follows that the total decrement is uniformly distributed as well, so we have

$$ {}_tq_x^{(\tau)} = t \cdot q_x^{(\tau)} \tag{13.23} $$

and hence

$$ {}_tp_x^{(\tau)} = 1 - t \cdot q_x^{(\tau)}. \tag{13.24} $$

Taking Equations (13.22) and (13.24) together we have

$$ \mu_{x+t}^{(j)} = \frac{q_x^{(j)}}{{}_tp_x^{(\tau)}} = \frac{q_x^{(j)}}{1 - t \cdot q_x^{(\tau)}}. \tag{13.25} $$

Next from Equation (13.12b) we have, for $0 \le t \le 1$,

$$ {}_tp_x^{\prime(j)} = \exp\left(-\int_0^t \mu_{x+s}^{(j)}\,ds\right) = \exp\left(-\int_0^t \frac{q_x^{(j)}}{1 - s \cdot q_x^{(\tau)}}\,ds\right), $$

when we substitute for $\mu_{x+s}^{(j)}$ using Equation (13.25). Finally, recognizing that $q_x^{(j)}$ and $q_x^{(\tau)}$ are constants, we can integrate to obtain

$$ {}_tp_x^{\prime(j)} = \exp\left[\frac{q_x^{(j)}}{q_x^{(\tau)}} \cdot \ln\left(1 - t \cdot q_x^{(\tau)}\right)\right] = \left(1 - t \cdot q_x^{(\tau)}\right)^{q_x^{(j)}/q_x^{(\tau)}}. \tag{13.26a} $$

Then given the set of $q_x^{(j)}$, and hence $q_x^{(\tau)}$, Equation (13.26a) allows us to find values of ${}_tp_x^{\prime(j)}$ for all j and for $0 \le t \le 1$. In the special case where $t = 1$, we have

$$ p_x^{\prime(j)} = \exp\left[\frac{q_x^{(j)}}{q_x^{(\tau)}} \cdot \ln p_x^{(\tau)}\right] = \left(p_x^{(\tau)}\right)^{q_x^{(j)}/q_x^{(\tau)}}. \tag{13.26b} $$

It is important to note that Equation (13.26a) results from assuming that the decrements are uniformly distributed in the multiple-decrement context, so that ${}_tq_x^{(j)}$ is a linear function of t. A more common assumption, which we explore in Section 13.4.2, is to assume that the individual decrements are uniformly distributed *in the associated single-decrement tables*. That is, we assume that ${}_tq_x'^{(j)}$ is a linear function of t. This leads to formulas that are generally simpler than those of this section.

EXAMPLE 13.5

If $q_x^{(1)} = .20$ and $q_x^{(2)} = .10$, and both decrements are uniformly distributed over the interval $(x, x+1]$ in the multiple-decrement context, find $q_x'^{(2)}$.

SOLUTION

Using Equation (13.26), with $t = 1$, we have

$$p_x'^{(2)} = \left(1 - q_x^{(\tau)}\right)^{q_x^{(2)}/q_x^{(\tau)}} = (.70)^{1/3} = .88790$$

and therefore

$$q_x'^{(2)} = 1 - .88790 = .11210.$$ ❐

13.4.2 UNIFORM DISTRIBUTION IN THE ASSOCIATED SINGLE-DECREMENT TABLES

This is a more natural assumption than that of uniform distribution in the multiple-decrement context. Here we assume that each decrement would be uniformly distribution *in the absence of other decrements.*[6] Thus we assume

$${}_tq_x'^{(j)} = t \cdot q_x'^{(j)}, \tag{13.27}$$

for $0 \le t \le 1$, which is the same as Equation (6.36) with our augmented notation.

The relationship between probabilities of decrement in the multiple-decrement environment with those in the associated single-decrement tables is simpler under this assumption. Consider first the two-decrement case, where both decrements are uniformly distributed in their associated single-decrement tables. From Equation (6.38) we know that

$${}_tp_x'^{(j)} \cdot \mu_{x+t}^{(j)} = q_x'^{(j)}, \tag{13.28}$$

so, using Equation (13.18), we can write $q_x^{(1)}$ as

$$q_x^{(1)} = \int_0^1 {}_tp_x^{(\tau)} \cdot \mu_{x+t}^{(1)}\, dt = \int_0^1 {}_tp_x'^{(1)} \cdot {}_tp_x'^{(2)} \cdot \mu_{x+t}^{(1)}\, dt.$$

Then using Equations (13.27) and (13.28) we have

$$q_x^{(1)} = \int_0^1 \left(1 - t \cdot q_x'^{(2)}\right) \cdot q_x'^{(1)}\, dt = q_x'^{(1)}\left(1 - \frac{1}{2} \cdot q_x'^{(2)}\right). \tag{13.29a}$$

---

[6] With equal whimsy, we might refer to this as the *SUDD assumption.*

By symmetry it follows that

$$q_x^{(2)} = q_x^{\prime(2)}\left(1-\frac{1}{2}\cdot q_x^{\prime(1)}\right). \tag{13.29b}$$

The reader will be asked to show (see Exercise 13-11) that in the case of three decrements, all of which are uniformly distributed in their associated single-decrement tables, it follows that

$$q_x^{(1)} = q_x^{\prime(1)}\left[1-\frac{1}{2}\left(q_x^{\prime(2)}+q_x^{\prime(3)}\right)+\frac{1}{3}\left(q_x^{\prime(2)}\cdot q_x^{\prime(3)}\right)\right]. \tag{13.30}$$

EXAMPLE 13.6

Repeat Example 13.5, but assume both decrements are uniformly distributed in their associated single-decrement tables.

SOLUTION

From Equations (13.29a) and (13.29b) we have

$$q_x^{(1)} = q_x^{\prime(1)}\left(1-\frac{1}{2}\cdot q_x^{\prime(2)}\right) = .20$$

and

$$q_x^{(2)} = q_x^{\prime(2)}\left(1-\frac{1}{2}\cdot q_x^{\prime(1)}\right) = .10.$$

Solving the first equation for $q_x^{\prime(1)}$ and substituting into the second equation, we obtain

$$q_x^{\prime(2)}\left(1-\frac{.20}{2-q_x^{\prime(2)}}\right) = .10$$

or

$$q_x^{\prime(2)}\left(1.8-q_x^{\prime(2)}\right) = .20-.10q_x^{\prime(2)}.$$

Solving the resulting quadratic produces the result $q_x^{\prime(2)} = .11184$. ❒

EXAMPLE 13.7

At Gallinas Elementary School, students exit their grade by one of only two decrements, either by moving away from the community (Cause 1) or by passing on to the next grade (Cause 2). For any grade (x), the probability values are $q_x^{(1)} = .02$ and $q_x^{(2)} = .96$. (Note there is a probability of remaining in grade (i.e., failing) of $p_x^{(\tau)} = .02$.) Decrement 1 (moving) is uniformly distributed throughout the year in its associated single-decrement table, but Decrement 2 (passing) can occur only at the end of the year.

If circumstances change such that students never move away, then what proportion of the students will pass on to the next grade?

SOLUTION

This example illustrates an important point about the relationship between multiple-decrements probabilities (denoted by $q_x^{(j)}$) and the associated single-decrement rates (denoted by $q_x'^{(j)}$). Generally the two measures differ from each other because other decrements *compete* with Decrement j. In this example all of the Decrement 2 activity (passing to the next grade) occurs at year-end, so it does not compete with the Decrement 1 activity (moving away). Consequently the probability and the rate for Decrement 1 are the same, so we have $q_x^{(1)} = q_x'^{(1)} = .02$. However the Decrement 1 activity *does* compete with the Decrement 2 activity by denying some persons the opportunity to experience Decrement 2 at the end of the year, so $q_x^{(2)} = .96 \neq q_x'^{(2)}$. Out of every 100 students beginning the grade, 2 depart due to Decrement 1 during the year and 96 of the 98 remaining at year-end experience Decrement 2, so the rate of experiencing Decrement 2 is $\frac{96}{98} = .9796$. Then if Decrement 1 were eliminated, so that a single-decrement environment resulted, we would have $q_x^{(2)} = q_x'^{(2)} = .9796$. ❐

13.4.3 CONSTANT FORCES OF DECREMENT

As an alternative to the two uniform distribution assumptions described in this section, we might assume that each decrement has a constant force of decrement over the interval $(x,x+1]$, so that $\mu_{x+t}^{(j)} = \mu^{(j)}$ for all j and for $0 < t \leq 1$. Recall from Section 13.3 that the force of failure due to Cause j is the same whether operating in a single-decrement or a multiple-decrement environment. Therefore we do not have two sub-cases of the constant force assumption as we did for the UDD assumption.

EXAMPLE 13.8

Show that

$$\frac{{}_tq_x^{(j)}}{{}_tq_x^{(\tau)}} = \frac{\mu_{x+t}^{(j)}}{\mu_{x+t}^{(\tau)}},$$

whenever $\mu_{x+t}^{(j)} = \mu^{(j)}$, a constant, for each (j), and where $0 < t \leq 1$.

SOLUTION

From first principles,

$${}_tq_x^{(j)} = \int_0^t {}_sp_x^{(\tau)} \cdot \mu_{x+s}^{(j)}\, ds.$$

If $\mu_{x+s}^{(j)} = \mu^{(j)}$, a constant, for each (j), then it follows that $\mu_{x+s}^{(\tau)} = \mu^{(\tau)}$, a constant, as well, and furthermore ${}_sp_x^{(\tau)} = e^{-s\cdot\mu^{(\tau)}}$. Then we can evaluate the integral to reach

$$
\begin{aligned}
{}_tq_x^{(j)} &= \mu^{(j)} \cdot \int_0^t e^{-s \cdot \mu^{(\tau)}}\, ds \\
&= \mu^{(j)} \cdot \left[\frac{e^{-s \cdot \mu^{(\tau)}}}{-\mu^{(\tau)}} \right]_0^t \\
&= \frac{\mu^{(j)}}{\mu^{(\tau)}} \cdot \left(1 - e^{-t \cdot \mu^{(\tau)}}\right) = \frac{\mu^{(j)}}{\mu^{(\tau)}} \cdot \left(1 - {}_tp_x^{(\tau)}\right),
\end{aligned}
$$

and therefore

$$
\frac{{}_tq_x^{(j)}}{{}_tq_x^{(\tau)}} = \frac{\mu^{(j)}}{\mu^{(\tau)}} = \frac{\mu_{x+t}^{(j)}}{\mu_{x+t}^{(\tau)}}, \tag{13.31a}
$$

as required. Since this relationship holds for all $0 < t \leq 1$, then, as a special case, we also have

$$
\frac{q_x^{(j)}}{q_x^{(\tau)}} = \frac{\mu^{(j)}}{\mu^{(\tau)}}. \tag{13.31b}
$$

❑

Additional results under the constant force assumption are derived in Examples 13.9 and 13.10.

13.5 WRITTEN-ANSWER QUESTION EXAMPLES

EXAMPLE 13.9

Assume that each decrement has a constant force over the interval $(x, x+1]$.

(a) Given a multiple-decrement table of the form shown in Example 13.1, show how to obtain values of ${}_tq_x^{(j)}$, for $0 < t \leq 1$.

(b) Use the result of part (a) to show how to obtain values of ${}_tq_x^{\prime(j)}$, for $0 < t \leq 1$.

(c) How does ${}_tq_x^{\prime(j)}$ under the constant force assumption compare with ${}_tq_x^{\prime(j)}$ under SUDD or MUDD?

SOLUTION

(a) If each force of decrement is constant, then so is the total force. From Equation (13.18) we have

$$
{}_tq_x^{(j)} = \int_0^t {}_sp_x^{(\tau)} \mu_{x+s}^{(j)}\, ds.
$$

With a constant total force, denoted $\mu^{(\tau)}$, we then have ${}_sp_x^{(\tau)} = e^{-s \cdot \mu^{(\tau)}}$. Since $\mu_{x+s}^{(j)} = \mu^{(j)}$ is also constant, we have

$$
\begin{aligned}
{}_tq_x^{(j)} &= \mu^{(j)} \cdot \int_0^t e^{-s \cdot \mu^{(\tau)}}\, ds \\
&= \mu^{(j)} \cdot \left[\frac{e^{-s \cdot \mu^{(\tau)}}}{-\mu^{(\tau)}} \right]_0^t \\
&= \frac{\mu^{(j)}}{\mu^{(\tau)}} \cdot \left[1 - e^{-t \cdot \mu^{(\tau)}} \right] = \frac{\mu^{(j)}}{\mu^{(\tau)}} \cdot \left[1 - {}_tp_x^{(\tau)} \right] = \frac{\mu^{(j)}}{\mu^{(\tau)}} \cdot {}_tq_x^{(\tau)}.
\end{aligned}
$$

(b) The result of part (a) can be written as

$$
{}_tq_x^{(j)} = \frac{t \cdot \mu^{(j)}}{t \cdot \mu^{(\tau)}} \cdot {}_tq_x^{(\tau)} = \frac{-\ln {}_tp_x^{\prime(j)}}{-\ln {}_tp_x^{(\tau)}} \cdot {}_tq_x^{(\tau)}.
$$

This can be rearranged as

$$
\frac{{}_tq_x^{(j)}}{{}_tq_x^{(\tau)}} \cdot \ln {}_tp_x^{(\tau)} = \ln {}_tp_x^{\prime(j)},
$$

so

$$
{}_tp_x^{\prime(j)} = \left({}_tp_x^{(\tau)} \right)^{{}_tq_x^{(j)} / {}_tq_x^{(\tau)}}.
$$

Given the several $q_x^{(j)}$, we directly find $q_x^{(\tau)}$, then $p_x^{(\tau)}$, then ${}_tp_x^{(\tau)} = \left(p_x^{(\tau)}\right)^t$, and finally ${}_tq_x^{(\tau)} = 1 - {}_tp_x^{(\tau)}$. Then ${}_tq_x^{(j)}$ is found from the result in part (a) and values of ${}_tp_x^{\prime(j)}$ and ${}_tq_x^{\prime(j)}$ easily follow.

(c) The result in part (b) gives us

$$
{}_tq_x^{\prime(j)} = 1 - {}_tp_x^{\prime(j)} = 1 - \left({}_tp_x^{(\tau)} \right)^{{}_tq_x^{(j)} / {}_tq_x^{(\tau)}},
$$

which is the same as Equation (13.26a), since $\frac{{}_tq_x^{(j)}}{{}_tq_x^{(\tau)}} = \frac{q_x^{(j)}}{q_x^{(\tau)}}$ by Equation (13.31), so the constant force assumption produces the same result as does the MUDD assumption. ❑

EXAMPLE 13.10

This example builds on Section 13.4 and Example 13.9 to provide a summary of the interrelationships among the independent and dependent probabilities. (We consider here only the case of two decrements, identified as Decrements 1 and 2.) The several relationship sets vary according to what is given, what is sought, and what assumption is made. The several cases are summarized in the following table; the task is to derive the expressions shown in the final column. Explain why Cases E and F, although mathematically possible, are not logical cases to arise in practice.

Case	Given	Sought	Assumption	Results
A1	$q_x'^{(1)}$ and $q_x'^{(2)}$	${}_tq_x^{(1)}$ and ${}_tq_x^{(2)}$	SUDD	${}_tq_x^{(1)} = q_x'^{(1)}\left(t-\frac{t^2}{2}\cdot q_x'^{(2)}\right)$ ${}_tq_x^{(2)} = q_x'^{(2)}\left(t-\frac{t^2}{2}\cdot q_x'^{(1)}\right)$
A2	$q_x'^{(1)}$ and $q_x'^{(2)}$	$q_x^{(1)}$ and $q_x^{(2)}$	SUDD	$q_x^{(1)} = q_x'^{(1)}\left(1-\frac{1}{2}\cdot q_x'^{(2)}\right)$ $q_x^{(2)} = q_x'^{(2)}\left(1-\frac{1}{2}\cdot q_x'^{(1)}\right)$
B1	$q_x'^{(1)}$ and $q_x'^{(2)}$	${}_tq_x^{(1)}$ and ${}_tq_x^{(2)}$	CF	${}_tq_x^{(1)} = \frac{\mu^{(1)}}{\mu^{(\tau)}}\cdot\left(1-{}_tp_x^{(\tau)}\right)$ ${}_tq_x^{(2)} = \frac{\mu^{(2)}}{\mu^{(\tau)}}\cdot\left(1-{}_tp_x^{(\tau)}\right)$
B2	$q_x'^{(1)}$ and $q_x'^{(2)}$	$q_x^{(1)}$ and $q_x^{(2)}$	CF	$q_x^{(1)} = \frac{\mu^{(1)}}{\mu^{(\tau)}}\cdot q_x^{(\tau)}$ $q_x^{(2)} = \frac{\mu^{(2)}}{\mu^{(\tau)}}\cdot q_x^{(\tau)}$
C1	$q_x^{(1)}$ and $q_x^{(2)}$	${}_tq_x'^{(1)}$ and ${}_tq_x'^{(2)}$	MUDD	${}_tq_x'^{(1)} = 1-\left(1-t\cdot q_x^{(\tau)}\right)^{q_x^{(1)}/q_x^{(\tau)}}$ ${}_tq_x'^{(2)} = 1-\left(1-t\cdot q_x^{(\tau)}\right)^{q_x^{(2)}/q_x^{(\tau)}}$
C2	$q_x^{(1)}$ and $q_x^{(2)}$	$q_x'^{(1)}$ and $q_x'^{(2)}$	MUDD	$q_x'^{(1)} = 1-\left(1-q_x^{(\tau)}\right)^{q_x^{(1)}/q_x^{(\tau)}}$ $q_x'^{(2)} = 1-\left(1-q_x^{(\tau)}\right)^{q_x^{(2)}/q_x^{(\tau)}}$
D1	$q_x^{(1)}$ and $q_x^{(2)}$	${}_tq_x'^{(1)}$ and ${}_tq_x'^{(2)}$	CF	${}_tq_x'^{(1)} = 1-\left({}_tp_x^{(\tau)}\right)^{{}_tq_x^{(1)}/{}_tq_x^{(\tau)}}$ ${}_tq_x'^{(2)} = 1-\left({}_tp_x^{(\tau)}\right)^{{}_tq_x^{(2)}/{}_tq_x^{(\tau)}}$
D2	$q_x^{(1)}$ and $q_x^{(2)}$	$q_x'^{(1)}$ and $q_x'^{(2)}$	CF	$q_x'^{(1)} = 1-\left(p_x^{(\tau)}\right)^{q_x^{(1)}/q_x^{(\tau)}}$ $q_x'^{(2)} = 1-\left(p_x^{(\tau)}\right)^{q_x^{(2)}/q_x^{(\tau)}}$
E	$q_x'^{(1)}$ and $q_x'^{(2)}$	$q_x^{(1)}$ and $q_x^{(2)}$	MUDD	$q_x^{(1)} = q_x^{(\tau)}\cdot\left[\frac{\ln p_x'^{(1)}}{\ln p_x^{(\tau)}}\right]$ $q_x^{(2)} = q_x^{(\tau)}\cdot\left[\frac{\ln p_x'^{(2)}}{\ln p_x^{(\tau)}}\right]$
F	$q_x^{(1)}$ and $q_x^{(2)}$	$q_x'^{(1)}$ and $q_x'^{(2)}$	SUDD	See Solution

SOLUTION

Case A1:

From first principles we have

$$ {}_tq_x^{(1)} = \int_0^t {}_sp_x^{(\tau)} \cdot \mu_{x+s}^{(1)}\, ds = \int_0^t {}_sp_x^{\prime(1)} \cdot {}_sp_x^{\prime(2)} \cdot \mu_{x+s}^{(1)}\, ds. $$

Since $0 < s \le t$, and each decrement is UDD, we have

$$ {}_tq_x^{(1)} = q_x^{\prime(1)} \cdot \int_0^t \left(1 - s \cdot q_x^{\prime(2)}\right) ds = q_x^{\prime(1)} \left(t - \frac{t^2}{2} \cdot q_x^{\prime(2)}\right). $$

By symmetry we also have

$$ {}_tq_x^{(2)} = q_x^{\prime(2)} \left(t - \frac{t^2}{2} \cdot q_x^{\prime(1)}\right). $$

Case A2:

These results follow directly from Case A1 by letting $t = 1$ in the general case; they were previously derived as Equations (13.29a) and (13.29b).

Case B1:

We again begin with

$$ {}_tq_x^{(1)} = \int_0^t {}_sp_x^{(\tau)} \cdot \mu_{x+s}^{(1)}\, ds = \int_0^t {}_sp_x^{\prime(1)} \cdot {}_sp_x^{\prime(2)} \cdot \mu_{x+s}^{(1)}\, ds. $$

Each decrement has a constant force over $0 < t \le 1$, denoted by $\mu^{(1)}$ and $\mu^{(2)}$, so we have

$$ \begin{aligned} {}_tq_x^{(1)} &= \int_0^t e^{-s\cdot\mu^{(1)}} \cdot e^{-s\cdot\mu^{(2)}} \cdot \mu^{(1)}\, ds \\ &= \mu^{(1)} \cdot \int_0^t e^{-s\cdot\mu^{(\tau)}}\, ds = \mu^{(1)} \cdot \left[\frac{e^{-s\cdot\mu^{(\tau)}}}{-\mu^{(\tau)}}\right]_0^t = \frac{\mu^{(1)}}{\mu^{(\tau)}}\left(1 - e^{-t\cdot\mu^{(\tau)}}\right) = \frac{\mu^{(1)}}{\mu^{(\tau)}} \cdot \left(1 - {}_tp_x^{(\tau)}\right). \end{aligned} $$

By symmetry we also have

$$ {}_tq_x^{(2)} = \frac{\mu^{(2)}}{\mu^{(\tau)}} \cdot \left(1 - {}_tp_x^{(\tau)}\right). $$

Note that $\mu^{(\tau)}$ is constant because both $\mu^{(1)}$ and $\mu^{(2)}$ are constant. The values of $\mu^{(j)}$ are found as

$$ \mu^{(j)} = -\ln p_x^{\prime(j)}, $$

for $j = 1, 2$.

Case B2:

These follow directly from Case B1 with $t=1$.

Case C1:

These results were derived in Section 13.4.1 (see Equation (13.26a)).

Case C2:

These follow directly with $t=1$.

Case D1:

These results were derived in part (b) of Example 13.9.

Case D2:

These follow directly with $t=1$.

Case E:

In Case C2 we derived expressions for $q_x'^{(1)}$ and $q_x'^{(2)}$, given $q_x^{(1)}$ and $q_x^{(2)}$ and the MUDD assumption. Here we keep that same assumption, but wish to derive expressions for $q_x^{(1)}$ and $q_x^{(2)}$, given $q_x'^{(1)}$ and $q_x'^{(2)}$. To accomplish this, we take the pair of results in Case C2 and solve them for $q_x^{(1)}$ and $q_x^{(2)}$ in terms of $q_x'^{(1)}$ and $q_x'^{(2)}$. We have

$$p_x'^{(1)} = 1-q_x'^{(1)} = \left(p_x^{(\tau)}\right)^{q_x^{(1)}/q_x^{(\tau)}}$$

and

$$p_x'^{(2)} = 1-q_x'^{(2)} = \left(p_x^{(\tau)}\right)^{q_x^{(2)}/q_x^{(\tau)}},$$

so

$$\ln p_x'^{(1)} = \frac{q_x^{(1)}}{q_x^{(\tau)}} \cdot \ln p_x^{(\tau)}$$

and

$$\ln p_x'^{(2)} = \frac{q_x^{(2)}}{q_x^{(\tau)}} \cdot \ln p_x^{(\tau)},$$

from which we easily find

$$q_x^{(1)} = q_x^{(\tau)} \cdot \frac{\ln p_x'^{(1)}}{\ln p_x^{(\tau)}}$$

and similarly

$$q_x^{(2)} = q_x^{(\tau)} \cdot \frac{\ln p_x'^{(2)}}{\ln p_x^{(\tau)}}.$$

(The given values of $q_x^{\prime(1)}$ and $q_x^{\prime(2)}$ imply the values of $p_x^{\prime(1)}$ and $p_x^{\prime(2)}$, hence the value of $p_x^{(\tau)}$ (by multiplication) and hence the value of $q_x^{(\tau)}$.)

Case F:

In Case A2 we derived expressions for $q_x^{(1)}$ and $q_x^{(2)}$, given $q_x^{\prime(1)}$ and $q_x^{\prime(2)}$ and the SUDD assumption. Here we keep that same assumption, but wish to derive expressions for $q_x^{\prime(1)}$ and $q_x^{\prime(2)}$, given $q_x^{(1)}$ and $q_x^{(2)}$. To accomplish this, we take the pair of results in Case A2 and solve them for $q_x^{\prime(1)}$ and $q_x^{\prime(2)}$ in terms of $q_x^{(1)}$ and $q_x^{(2)}$. We have

$$q_x^{(1)} = q_x^{\prime(1)} \cdot \left(1 - \frac{1}{2} \cdot q_x^{\prime(2)}\right)$$

and

$$q_x^{(2)} = q_x^{\prime(2)} \cdot \left(1 - \frac{1}{2} \cdot q_x^{\prime(1)}\right).$$

Then, from the second equation we have

$$q_x^{\prime(2)} = \frac{q_x^{(2)}}{1 - \frac{1}{2} \cdot q_x^{\prime(1)}},$$

which we substitute into the first equation, giving us

$$q_x^{(1)} = q_x^{\prime(1)} \cdot \left(1 - \frac{\frac{1}{2} \cdot q_x^{(2)}}{1 - \frac{1}{2} \cdot q_x^{\prime(1)}}\right),$$

or

$$q_x^{(1)} \cdot \left(1 - \frac{1}{2} \cdot q_x^{\prime(1)}\right) = q_x^{\prime(1)} \left(1 - \frac{1}{2} \cdot q_x^{\prime(1)} - \frac{1}{2} \cdot q_x^{(2)}\right),$$

or

$$q_x^{(1)} = q_x^{\prime(1)} \cdot \left(\frac{1}{2} \cdot q_x^{(1)} - \frac{1}{2} \cdot q_x^{(2)} + 1\right) - \frac{1}{2} \cdot \left(q_x^{\prime(1)}\right)^2$$

or

$$\left(q_x^{\prime(1)}\right)^2 - \left(q_x^{(1)} - q_x^{(2)} + 2\right) \cdot q_x^{\prime(1)} + 2 \cdot q_x^{(1)} = 0,$$

which can be solved for $q_x^{\prime(1)}$ by the quadratic formula. (The resulting symbolic expression is not pretty, but, with $q_x^{(1)}$ and $q_x^{(2)}$ given, a numerical solution is easily obtained.) The value of $q_x^{\prime(2)}$ follows by symmetry.

In general, decrement rates are estimated from sample data, a topic covered on Society of Actuaries Exam C. The raw data are nearly always drawn from experience that includes at least two decrements. The data can be processed in a manner that produces estimates of $q_x^{(1)}$ and $q_x^{(2)}$ (the dependent probabilities), or, alternatively, in a manner that produces estimates of $q_x'^{(1)}$ and $q_x'^{(2)}$ (the independent probabilities). If we then wish to derive independent probabilities from the dependent ones estimated from the multiple-decrement data, the natural assumption to use is MUDD. Conversely, if we first obtain estimates of the independent probabilities, and wish to derive dependent probabilities from them, the natural assumption to use is SUDD. To use the opposite assumption is not only illogical, but, as we see in Case F, involves more complex algebraic manipulation.

13.6 EXERCISES

13.1 Discrete Multiple-Decrement Models

13-1 The following double-decrement table gives probability values for a student at the beginning of each year in a three-year Actuarial Science Graduate School. Some of the entries in the table have been obliterated by tear stains.

Academic Year	Probability of Academic Failure	Probability of Voluntary Withdrawal	Probability of Completing the Year
1	.40	.20	–
2	–	.30	–
3	–	–	.60

It is known that ten times as many students complete Year 2 as fail during Year 3, and the number of students who fail during Year 2 is 40% of the number who complete Year 2. Find the probability that a new student entering the school will voluntarily withdraw before graduation.

13.2 Theory of Competing Risks
13.3 Continuous Multiple-Decrement Models

13-2 Given the following extract from a double-decrement table, find the value of $l_{42}^{(\tau)}$.

x	$l_x^{(\tau)}$	$q_x^{(1)}$	$q_x^{(2)}$	$q_x'^{(1)}$	$q_x'^{(2)}$
40	2000	.24	.10	.25	y
41	--	--	--	.20	$2y$

13-3 The career of a 50-year-old Professor of Actuarial Science is subject to two decrements. Decrement 1 is mortality, which is governed by a uniform survival distribution with $\omega = 100$, and Decrement 2 is leaving academic employment, which is governed by the HRF $\mu_y^{(2)} = .05$, for all $y \geq 50$. Find the probability that this professor remains in academic employment for at least five years but less than ten years.

13-4 Let $f_{J|T}(j \mid t)$ denote the conditional density for Cause j being the cause of decrement, given that t is the time of decrement.

(a) Show that $f_{J|T}(j \mid t) \quad = \quad \dfrac{\mu_{x+t}^{(j)}}{\mu_{x+t}^{(\tau)}}.$

(b) Find an expression for $f_{J|T}(1 \mid t)$ in a triple-decrement model, given $\mu_{x+t}^{(1)} = .03$, $\mu_{x+t}^{(2)} = .03t$, and $\mu_{x+t}^{(3)} = .03t^2$.

13-5 Given the HRF $\mu_{x+t}^{(1)} = \frac{1}{75-t}$, for $0 \leq t < 75$, and $\mu_{x+t}^{(2)} = \frac{2}{50-t}$, for $0 \leq t < 50$, compute each of the following:

(a) ${}_tp_x'^{(1)}$, ${}_tp_x'^{(2)}$, and ${}_tp_x^{(\tau)}$
(b) $f_{T,J}(t,1)$ and $f_{T,J}(t,2)$
(c) $q_x^{(1)}$, $q_x^{(2)}$, and $q_x^{(\tau)}$
(d) $q_x'^{(1)}$ and $q_x'^{(2)}$
(e) $f_J(1)$ and $f_J(2)$
(f) $f_{J|T}(1 \mid 1)$ and $f_{J|T}(2 \mid 1)$

13-6 A double-decrement model with the following properties applies to students entering a certain four-year college:

(i) 1000 students enter college at time $t = 0$.
(ii) Students leave for reasons of failure (Decrement 1) or any other cause (Decrement 2).
(iii) $\mu_t^{(1)} = \mu$, for $0 \leq t \leq 4$, and $\mu_t^{(2)} = .04$, for $0 \leq t \leq 4$.
(iv) 48 students are expected to leave during the first year for all causes combined.

Calculate the expected number of students to leave during the fourth year due to failure.

13-7 Use Equations (13.13a), (13.5b), (13.19), (13.13b), and (13.12b), in that order, to derive Equation (13.17) and then Equation (13.16), without assuming independence of causes.

13.4 Uniform Distribution of Decrements

13-8 Find the value of $q_x^{(1)}$, given $q_x'^{(1)} = .20$, $q_x'^{(2)} = .10$, and decrements are uniformly distributed over $(x, x+1)$ in the multiple-decrement context.

13-9 A company has 1000 employees all age x, who are subject to the decrements death (Decrement 1) and retirement (Decrement 2). Deaths are uniformly distributed over the year of age but retirements can occur only at the midpoint of the year of age. Given that $q_x'^{(1)} = .015$ and $q_x'^{(2)} = .030$, determine the expected number of deaths and retirements during the next year.

13-10 Find the value of $p_x'^{(1)}$, given $q_x^{(1)} = .48$, $q_x^{(2)} = .32$, $q_x^{(3)} = .16$, and each decrement is uniformly distributed over $(x, x+1)$ in the multiple-decrement context.

13-11 Derive Equation (13.30).

13-12 Find the value of $1000q_x'^{(1)}$, given $q_x^{(1)} = .02$, $q_x^{(2)} = .06$, and each decrement is uniformly distributed over $(x, x+1)$ in its associated single-decrement table.

The following information applies to Exercises 13-13, 13-14, and 13-15.

Students can leave a certain three-year school only for reasons of failure (Decrement 1) or voluntary withdrawal (Decrement 2), where each decrement is uniformly distributed over $(x, x+1)$ in its associated single-decrement table. The following values are given:

x	$q_x'^{(1)}$	$q_x'^{(2)}$	$q_x^{(1)}$	$q_x^{(2)}$
0	.10	.25	–	–
1	.20	.20	–	–
2	.20	.10	–	–

13-13 Calculate the six missing probability values for the table.

13-14 (a) Find the marginal probabilities $p_{J_0}(1)$ and $p_{J_0}(2)$.

(b) Find the marginal probabilities $p_{K_0}(1)$, $p_{K_0}(2)$, and $p_{K_0}(3)$.

13-15 (a) Given that a person decrements from school in the third year, find the probability that the decrement was a failure.

(b) Given that a student enters Year 2, find the probability of eventually decrementing due to failure.

13-16 A triple-decrement model allows for mortality (Decrement 1), disability (Decrement 2), and withdrawal (Decrement 3). Mortality and disability are uniformly distributed over each year of age in their associated single-decrement tables, but withdrawals can occur only at the end of a year of age. Given the values $q_x^{\prime(1)} = .01$, $q_x^{\prime(2)} = .05$, and $q_x^{\prime(3)} = .10$, find the value of $q_x^{(3)}$.

13-17 Decrement 1 is uniformly distributed over the year of age in its associated single-decrement table with $q_x^{\prime(1)} = .100$. Decrement 2 always occurs at age $x + .70$ in its associated single-decrement table with $q_x^{\prime(2)} = .125$. Find the value of $q_x^{(2)}$.

CHAPTER FOURTEEN

MULTIPLE-DECREMENT MODELS (APPLICATIONS)

In this chapter we present a number of applications of multiple-decrement theory.

One very important application, which we consider in Section 14.3, arises in connection with regular single-life insurance and annuity contracts, when we consider the right of the insured or annuitant to surrender the contract and receive a benefit of some amount when doing so. Surrender of a contract is also referred to as withdrawal from the contract. Accordingly, we will often view such contracts in a double-decrement context, where the two decrements are failure (or death) and withdrawal.

We first consider, in Section 14.1, the theory of actuarial present value in a multiple-decrement environment. From the relevant APVs we can find premiums and reserves in the same manner as with single-decrement models earlier in the text. A special type of policy value called the asset share is discussed in Section 14.2.

In Section 14.4 we return to the use of multi-state models, introduced earlier, to represent a number of multiple-decrement situations. In Section 14.5 we present a brief overview of defined benefit and defined contribution pension plans.

14.1 ACTUARIAL PRESENT VALUE

In the multiple-decrement environment, the APV of a contingent payment is calculated in much the same way as in the single-decrement case, except that care must be taken if the payment depends on mode of decrement as well as time of decrement. Recall from Equation (7.2) that the APV of a unit payment to a status of interest denoted by (x) paid at the end of the interval of failure is given by

$$A_x = \sum_{k=0}^{\infty} v^{k+1} \cdot Pr(K_x = k). \tag{14.1}$$

In the multiple-decrement environment, the APV of a unit payment made at the end of the interval of failure if (x) fails due to Decrement j is given by

$$A_x^{(j)} = \sum_{k=0}^{\infty} v^{k+1} \cdot Pr(K_x = k \cap J_x = j). \tag{14.2}$$

If the time and cause of decrement are independent, this can be written as

$$A_x^{(j)} = \sum_{k=0}^{\infty} v^{k+1} \cdot Pr(K_x = k) \cdot Pr(J_x = j) \tag{14.3a}$$

or

$$A_x^{(j)} = \sum_{k=0}^{\infty} v^{k+1} \cdot {}_kp_x^{(\tau)} \cdot q_{x+k}^{(j)} \tag{14.3b}$$

in actuarial notation. If the benefit is paid at the instant of failure we have

$$\bar{A}_x^{(j)} = \int_0^{\infty} v^t \cdot {}_tp_x^{(\tau)} \cdot \mu_{x+t}^{(j)}\, dt. \tag{14.4}$$

EXAMPLE 14.1

A five-year bond, issued at time 0, faces the decrements of (1) Default, (2) Call (i.e., prepayment), and (3) Maturity.

The probabilities of decrement by curtate duration and cause are shown in the following table:

Curtate Duration k	**Default** $q_k^{(1)}$	**Call** $q_k^{(2)}$	**Maturity** $q_k^{(3)}$
0	.02	.03	.00
1	.02	.04	.00
2	.02	.05	.00
3	.02	.06	.00
4	.02	.00	.98

A guarantor has contracted to pay 1000 at the end of the year of default if default occurs, and nothing otherwise. Find the APV of this contingent payment contract using an annual interest rate of 6%.

SOLUTION

First we extend the above table to include two additional columns:

k	$q_k^{(1)}$	$q_k^{(2)}$	$q_k^{(3)}$	${}_kp_0^{(\tau)}$	v^{k+1}
0	.02	.03	.00	1.000	.943
1	.02	.04	.00	.950	.890
2	.02	.05	.00	.893	.840
3	.02	.06	.00	.830	.792
4	.02	.00	.98	.764	.747

The APV is given by

$$\begin{aligned} APV &= 1000\sum_{k=0}^{4} v^{k+1}\cdot {}_kp_0^{(\tau)}\cdot q_k^{(1)} \\ &= 1000[(.943)(.02)+(.890)(.950)(.02)+(.840)(.893)(.02) \\ &\qquad +(.792)(.830)(.02)+(.747)(.764)(.02)] \\ &= 75.33. \end{aligned}$$ ❐

EXAMPLE 14.2

A whole life insurance with immediate payment of claims pays 1000 at the instant of death by natural causes (NC) or 2000 at the instant of death by accidental causes (AC). Find the APV of the insurance using a force of interest of .05 and constant hazard rates (forces of mortality) $\mu_y^{NC}=.01$ for natural causes and $\mu_y^{AC}=.002$ for accidental causes, for all y.

SOLUTION

We can think of the insurance either as a combination of two single-decrement contingent contracts with APV given by

$$APV = 2000\bar{A}_x^{(AC)}+1000\bar{A}_x^{(NC)}$$

or as an "all causes" insurance plus an *additional* accidental cause insurance. Using the second approach we have

$$\begin{aligned} APV &= 1000\left(\bar{A}_x+\bar{A}_x^{(AC)}\right) \\ &= 1000\left[\int_0^\infty v^t\cdot {}_tp_x^{(\tau)}\cdot\mu_{x+t}^{(\tau)}\,dt+\int_0^\infty v^t\cdot {}_tp_x^{(\tau)}\mu_{x+t}^{(AC)}\,dt\right] \\ &= 1000\int_0^\infty e^{-.05t}\cdot e^{-.012t}(.014)\,dt \;=\; 225.81. \end{aligned}$$ ❐

Net premium calculations in the multiple-decrement environment are closely related to those in the single-decrement environment. The key concept to keep in mind is that premiums are paid only as long as the contingent contract is in force, which means that the entity of interest has not yet failed for any cause. The following example illustrates the development of premiums and reserves in a multiple-decrement environment that also includes consideration of expenses. (See Sections 9.6 and 11.4 for the incorporation of expenses in the single-decrement environment.)

EXAMPLE 14.3

Consider a five-year endowment insurance, with gross annual premiums and annual expenses paid at the beginning of each year and benefits paid at the end of the year. The contingent benefit is 1000 for death (Decrement 1) within the five-year period, or at time $t=5$ if death has not previously occurred. A withdrawal benefit (Decrement 2) will be paid in the event of withdrawal from the plan at the end of any of the first four years. All parameter values for the insurance are shown in the following table:

Curtate Duration k	0	1	2	3	4
Percent-of-Premium Expense	.05	.05	.05	.05	.05
Constant Contract Expense	30	30	30	30	30
Failure Benefit Amount	1000	1000	1000	1000	1000
Withdrawal Benefit Amount	50	100	300	600	0
Endowment Benefit Amount	0	0	0	0	1000
$q_{x+k}^{(1)}$	.02	.03	.04	.05	.06
$q_{x+k}^{(2)}$	.30	.20	.20	.10	.00
$q_{x+k}^{(\tau)}$	.32	.23	.24	.15	.06
$p_{x+k}^{(\tau)}$	.68	.77	.76	.85	.94

All cash flows are discounted at annual interest rate 6%.

(a) Find the gross annual premium using the equivalence principle.

(b) Find the gross premium reserve ${}_tV^G$ for $t = 1,2,3,4,5$.

SOLUTION

The APV of the failure benefit is

$$\begin{aligned}
APV^{(1)} &= \sum_{k=0}^{4} b_{k+1}^{(1)} \cdot v^{k+1} \cdot {}_kp_x^{(\tau)} \cdot q_{x+k}^{(1)} \\
&= 1000\left[\frac{.02}{1.06} + \frac{(.68)(.03)}{(1.06)^2} + \frac{(.68)(.77)(.04)}{(1.06)^3}\right. \\
&\qquad \left. + \frac{(.68)(.77)(.76)(.05)}{(1.06)^4} + \frac{(.68)(.77)(.76)(.85)(.06)}{(1.06)^5}\right] \\
&= 1000[.01887 + .01816 + .01758 + .01576 + .01517] = 85.538.
\end{aligned}$$

The APV of the withdrawal benefit is

$$\begin{aligned}
APV^{(2)} &= \sum_{k=0}^{4} b_{k+1}^{(2)} \cdot v^{k+1} \cdot {}_kp_x^{(\tau)} \cdot q_{x+k}^{(2)} \\
&= \frac{(50)(.30)}{1.06} + \frac{(100)(.68)(.20)}{(1.06)^2} \\
&\qquad + \frac{(300)(.68)(.77)(.20)}{(1.06)^3} + \frac{(600)(.68)(.77)(.76)(.10)}{(1.06)^4} \\
&= 14.151 + 12.104 + 26.377 + 18.912 = 71.544.
\end{aligned}$$

The APV of the endowment benefit is

$$\begin{aligned} APV^{(3)} &= 1000v^5 \cdot {}_5p_x^{(\tau)} \\ &= \frac{(1000)(.68)(.77)(.76)(.85)(.94)}{(1.06)^5} = 237.591. \end{aligned}$$

The APV of the expenses is

$$\begin{aligned} (30+.05G)\cdot \ddot{a}_{x:\overline{5}|}^{(\tau)} &= (30+.05G)\left[1+\frac{.68}{1.06}+\frac{(.68)(.77)}{(1.06)^2}\right. \\ &\qquad \left. +\frac{(.68)(.77)(.76)}{(1.06)^3}+\frac{(.68)(.77)(.76)(.85)}{(1.06)^4}\right] \\ &= 81.286+.13547G. \end{aligned}$$

Finally, the APV of the premium stream itself is

$$G\cdot \ddot{a}_{x:\overline{5}|}^{(\tau)} = 2.70955G.$$

(a) The gross annual premium by the equivalence principle is then found from

$$2.70955G = 85.538+71.544+237.591+81.286+.13547G,$$

leading to

$$G = \frac{475.959}{2.57408} = 184.90.$$

(b) The gross premium reserves are found prospectively by subtracting the APV of future gross premiums from the APV of future benefits and expenses. The results are shown in the following table, and the calculations are left as an additional exercise for the reader.[1]

t	${}_tV^G$
1	175.60
2	377.30
3	597.80
4	797.80
5	0.00

❐

14.2 ASSET SHARES

In Example 14.3 we combined the multiple-decrement theory developed in Chapter 13 with the expense and gross premium material developed in Section 9.6. We now take this combination even further to develop *projections of the expected accumulation of assets* under

[1] The complete solution can be found on the ACTEX Publications website.

a single contingent contract (such as an insurance policy) or for a block of such contracts. The results are known as *projected asset shares*.

Suppose we have a contingent payment contract funded by a level annual contract premium G. The contract pays in the event of the failure (such as death) of a specified entity of interest or in the event of withdrawal from the contingent contract. The payment due in the event of failure in Year k is denoted $b_k^{(1)}$ and the payment due in the event of withdrawal is denoted $b_k^{(2)}$; in either case the benefit is paid at the end of the year. As in Example 14.3, expenses are paid at the beginning of each year and are of both the percent-of-premium and contract constant types.

The projected asset share at duration k, which is the actuarial accumulated value of premiums minus expected benefits and expenses, is denoted by ${}_kAS$. All notation used in this section is summarized in the following table.

Symbol	**Concept**
G	Annual contract premium
$b_k^{(1)}$	Benefit paid at end of Year k for failure during Year k
$b_k^{(2)}$	Benefit paid at end of Year k for withdrawal during Year k
r_k	Percent-of-premium expense factor paid at beginning of Year k
e_k	Fixed contract expense paid at beginning of Year k
i	Effective annual rate of interest (presumed constant)
$q_{x+k-1}^{(1)}$	Conditional probability of failure during Year k, given that the contract is still in force at time $k-1$
$q_{x+k-1}^{(2)}$	Conditional probability of withdrawal during Year k, given that the contract is still in force at time $k-1$
$p_{x+k-1}^{(\tau)}$	Conditional probability of the contract staying in force through Year k, given that it is still in force at time $k-1$
${}_kAS$	The projected asset share associated with the contract at the end of Year k

We denote the initial asset share at time 0 by ${}_0AS$, and note that ${}_0AS$ may or may not equal zero. Successive values of ${}_kAS$ are then found recursively by expanding the discussion in Sections 10.2 and 11.4 to now include multiple decrements. For $k=1$ we have

$$\left[{}_0AS+G(1-r_1)-e_1\right](1+i) = b_1^{(1)}\cdot q_x^{(1)}+b_1^{(2)}\cdot q_x^{(2)}+{}_1AS\cdot p_x^{(\tau)}, \tag{14.5a}$$

so

$$ {}_1AS = \frac{\left[{}_0AS+G(1-r_1)-e_1\right](1+i)-b_1^{(1)}\cdot q_x^{(1)}-b_1^{(2)}\cdot q_x^{(2)}}{p_x^{(\tau)}}. \tag{14.5b}$$

For k in general we have

$$\left[{}_{k-1}AS+G(1-r_k)-e_k\right](1+i) = b_k^{(1)}\cdot q_{x+k-1}^{(1)}+b_k^{(2)}\cdot q_{x+k-1}^{(2)}+{}_kAS\cdot p_{x+k-1}^{(\tau)} \tag{14.6a}$$

so

$$_{k}AS = \frac{\left[{}_{k-1}AS + G(1-r_k) - e_k\right](1+i) - b_k^{(1)} \cdot q_{x+k-1}^{(1)} - b_k^{(2)} \cdot q_{x+k-1}^{(2)}}{p_{x+k-1}^{(\tau)}}. \qquad (14.6b)$$

EXAMPLE 14.4

Consider the five-year endowment insurance described in Example 14.3. If the contract premium is $G = 200.00$[2] and the initial asset share is $_{0}AS = 50$, find $_{k}AS$ for $k = 1,2,3,4,5.$

SOLUTION

Using the recursive relationship given by Equation (14.6b), the following values are obtained. (The details of the calculations are left to the reader as an exercise.[3])

k	$_{k}AS$
1	275.90
2	535.10
3	837.90
4	1115.03
5	373.90

The projected asset share is calculated using the actual contract premium and projected, or expected, experience regarding interest, mortality, withdrawal, and expenses. As the experience actually unfolds, asset shares can also be calculated using the actual contract premium and actual experience. Asset shares calculated in this way are often called *historical asset shares.* ❐

14.3 NON-FORFEITURE OPTIONS

As we have seen, a long-term insurance contract, such as a whole life or endowment contract, builds up a reserve because the premiums in the early years of the contract exceed the cost of insurance in those years. In the early days of insurance, if the policyholder discontinued the premiums on such a contract the excess premium payment was forfeited to the insurer. The contract reserve was being held for the eventual payment of the face amount in the case of death, but no payment was required to be made in the case of premium cessation. In most modern contracts, however, the policyholder's equity in the contract is not forfeited upon premium default, but instead various *non-forfeiture options* are available to the policyholder. We discuss several of these options in this section.

14.3.1 CASH VALUES

Discontinuation of regular premium payments by the policyholder is referred to as *surrendering* the insurance contract. The amount of the cash value available at each duration of the contract is generally predetermined and printed in the policy. The insurer is required to

---

[2] The premium might exceed the value calculated in Example 14.3 to reflect considerations of competition and profit.

[3] The complete solution can be found on the ACTEX Publications website.

provide a cash value no less than the legal minimum cash value defined in the U.S. insurance regulation known as the Standard Non-Forfeiture Law.[4] The cash value is likely to be less than the policy reserve in the early years of the contract to compensate for acquisition expenses, but could equal the policy reserve in later years.

Most policies that provide a cash value also permit policyholders to borrow against the equity they have in their policies at a stated interest rate. Then if failure occurs under a contract with an outstanding loan balance, the amount of the indebtedness is deducted from the face amount otherwise payable.

Note that term insurance contracts, which build up very small amounts of policyholder equity, often do not provide cash values.

14.3.2 REDUCED PAID-UP INSURANCE

In lieu of taking the cash value upon surrender of the contract, the policyholder can generally elect to keep the contract in force at a reduced benefit amount with no future premium requirement. Suppose a whole life policy issued at age x is surrendered at duration t, with a cash value of amount ${}_tCV_x$ available at that time. If the reduced paid-up option is elected, the amount of paid-up whole life insurance available would be

$$RPU = \frac{{}_tCV_x}{A_{x+t}}, \tag{14.8}$$

since the cash value acts as the APV of the future whole life coverage.

In the special case where the cash value equals the NLP reserve, the amount of paid-up insurance is denoted by ${}_tW_x$ and would be

$${}_tW_x = \frac{{}_tV_x}{A_{x+t}}, \tag{14.9}$$

per unit of coverage under the surrendered policy.

If a policy loan of amount L is outstanding at the time of contract surrender, the APV of the reduced paid-up insurance would be ${}_tCV_x - L$.

14.3.3 EXTENDED TERM INSURANCE

Another option in lieu of taking the cash value is to use it to provide term insurance, of the same face amount as under the surrendered policy, for as long a term as the cash value will provide. Again presuming a whole life policy of unit amount, issued at age x and surrendered at duration t, the length of extended term insurance is the value of n satisfying

$${}_tCV_x = A^{\,1}_{x+t:\overline{n}|}, \tag{14.10}$$

where n would need to be approximated by interpolation in the life table upon which the calculation is based.

---

[4] The definition of legal minimum cash values by the Standard Non-Forfeiture Law is beyond the scope of this text. It is usually based on model legislation promulgated by the National Association of Insurance Commissioners (NAIC).

An interesting special case arises if an endowment contract is surrendered late in its term with cash value given by ${}_tCV_{x:\overline{n}|}$, where $t<n$. It is quite possible that the cash value could provide extended term insurance beyond the original maturity date of the endowment, which the insurer might wish not to do. In this case the insurance is extended to the original maturity date, and a reduced pure endowment benefit is paid if survival to that date occurs. The equation of value at duration t would be

$$ {}_tCV_{x:\overline{n}|} = A^{\,1}_{x+t:\overline{n-t}|} + PE \cdot {}_{n-t}E_{x+t}, \tag{14.11} $$

from which PE can be determined.

14.4 MULTI-STATE MODEL REPRESENTATION, WITH ILLUSTRATIONS

Recall that a recurring feature of the multi-state model representations presented earlier in the text was that death was the *only* cause of decrement, so that any state, once left, could never be reentered. In this section we consider several types of multiple-decrement models, some of which will continue to have that property and some will not.

14.4.1 THE GENERAL MULTIPLE-DECREMENT MODEL

As already defined in Chapter 13, the multiple-decrement model considers a group of entities (generally persons), and addresses the activity of persons being decremented from that group due to one of m possible causes. Once decremented from the original group due to Cause j, the decremented person cannot thereafter be decremented by any other cause. That is, if failure due to Cause j is represented as transition from the initial state to State j, then State j would be an absorbing state.[5] This notion is represented in the following diagram:

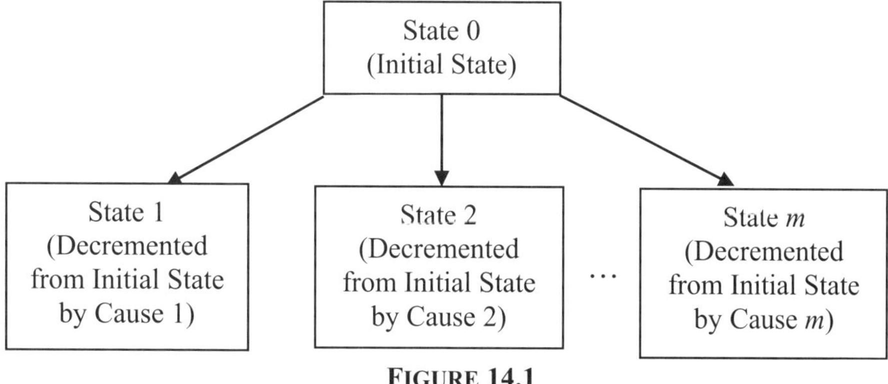

FIGURE 14.1

[5] In this context we say that there are no *secondary decrements*. In Section 14.4.2 we consider a model with one secondary decrement, in Section 14.4.3 we consider a model with two secondary decrements, and in Section 14.4.4 we consider a model with three secondary decrements.

EXAMPLE 14.6

Analyze Example 14.2 in the multi-state model context.

SOLUTION

The model for this insurance is the general multiple-decrement model with $m = 2$, as shown in Figure 14.2.

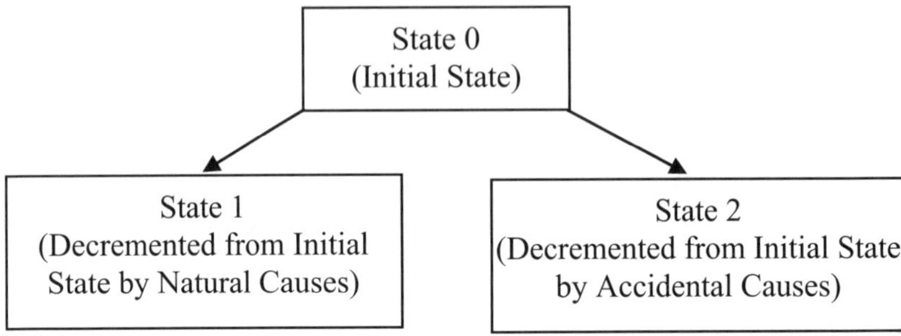

FIGURE 14.2

The insurance pays 1000 at the instant of transition to State 1, or 2000 at the instant of transition to State 2, for a person alive in the initial state at age x at time 0. The APV is calculated exactly as in Example 14.2, except using different notation. ❐

EXAMPLE 14.7

Analyze Example 14.3 in the multi-state model context.

SOLUTION

The model for this insurance is the general multiple-decrement model with $m=3$, as shown in Figure 14.3. The insurance pays 1000 at the end of the year of transition to State 1, or 1000 at the time of transition to State 3 (which can occur only at time $t=5$), or a variable amount at the end of the year of transition to State 2. The gross premium and gross premium reserves are calculated exactly as in Example 14.3, except for using different notation. ❐

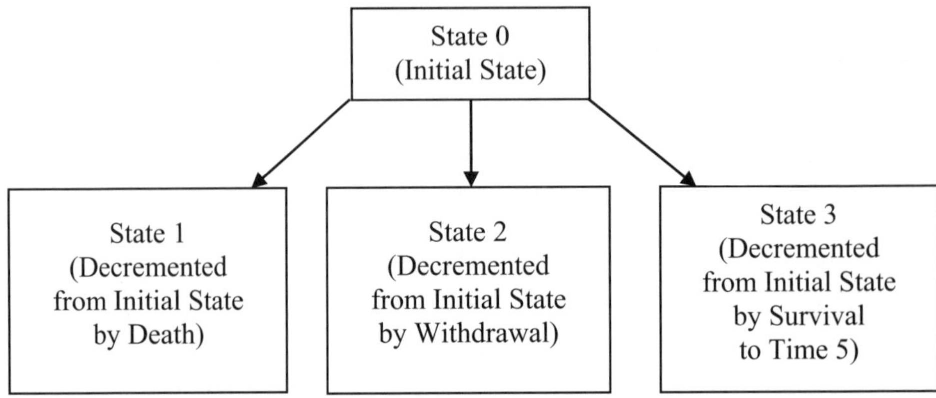

FIGURE 14.3

We can combine the ideas of multiple decrements and multiple lives in the multi-state model context. This is pursued in the following example.

EXAMPLE 14.8

Consider two business partners, denoted by (x) and (y), operating a partnership together. They have an agreement whereby a trust will make a payment to either partner upon retirement from the business, and also make a payment to a named beneficiary upon the death of either partner. This creates a nine-state model. Define the nine states and, just for fun, draw the multi-state model diagram.

SOLUTION

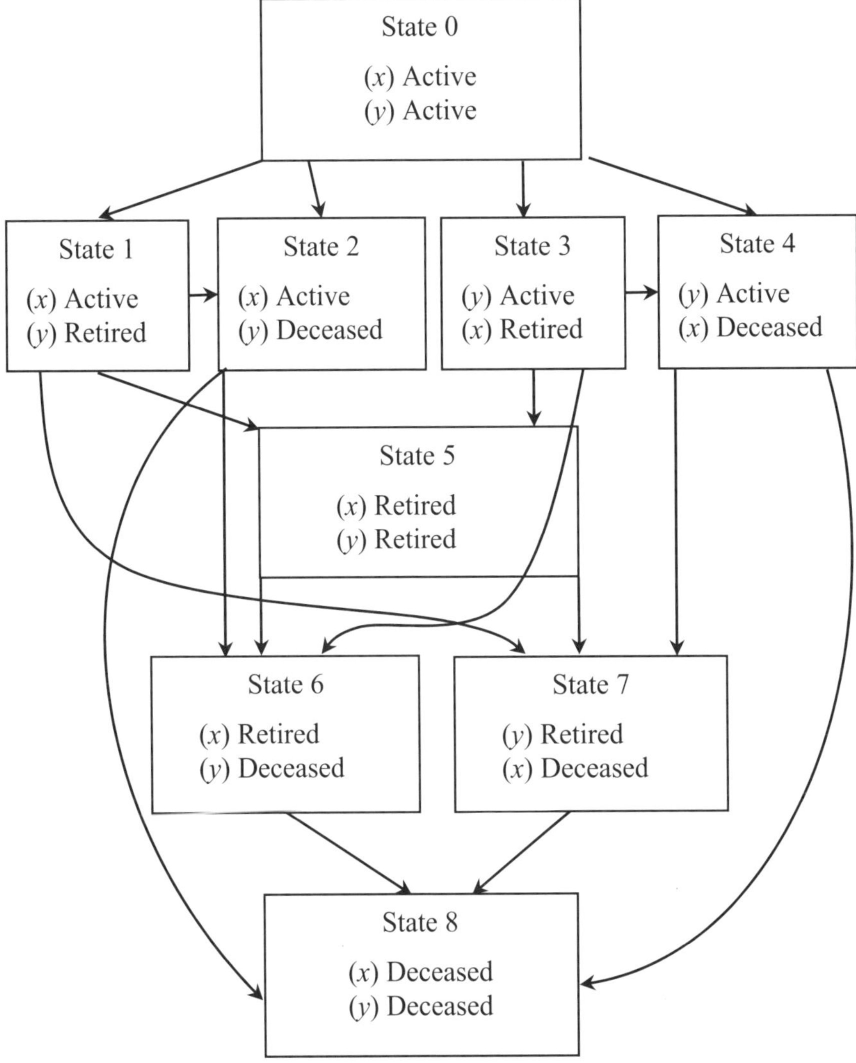

FIGURE 14.4

The initial state (State 0) finds both partners alive and active in the business. Then State i is defined as shown in the following table.

i	Definition of State i
1	(x) still active; (y) retired
2	(x) still active; (y) deceased
3	(y) still active; (x) retired
4	(y) still active; (x) deceased
5	(x) and (y) both retired
6	(x) retired; (y) deceased
7	(y) retired; (x) deceased
8	(x) and (y) both deceased

This nine-state model is represented in Figure 14.4, where the arrows indicate possible transitions between states. (Note that retirement is deemed to be non-reversible, and simultaneous deaths or retirements cannot occur.) Observe how complicated the model becomes with only two lives and two decrements. (See also Exercise 14-9.) ❐

14.4.2 THE TOTAL AND PERMANENT DISABILITY MODEL

In this case we have an insurance contract issued to a healthy person that provides for periodic income if the insured becomes totally and permanently disabled during the term of the contract. As the word "permanent" implies, once insureds have become disabled they remain disabled until death. In the multi-state model context, the coverage is described in Figure 14.5.

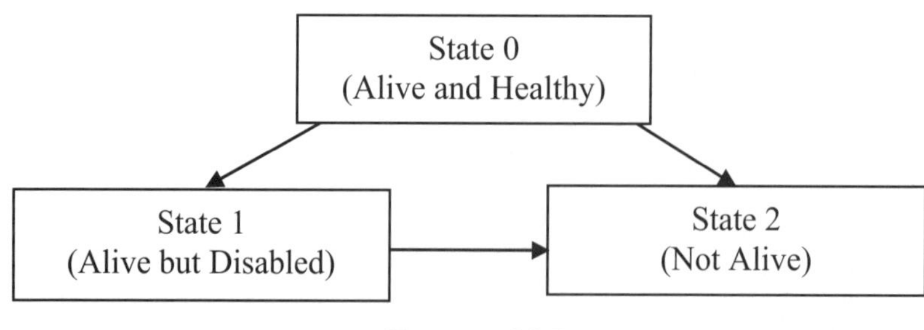

FIGURE 14.5

The contract may provide (a) a lump sum failure benefit (death benefit) for failure while healthy (i.e., upon transition from State 0 to State 2), and/or (b) a similar failure (death) benefit for failure while disabled (i.e., upon transition from State 1 to State 2, as implied by the horizontal arrow in Figure 14.5. (In this case we have an example of a secondary decrement.) Such contracts do not normally pay lump sum benefits upon becoming disabled (i.e., upon transition from State 0 to State 1). Rather, they pay (c) a periodic income to the insured while disabled (i.e., while in State 1). (Note that being decremented from State 1 due to recovery from the disability is not assumed to be possible in this model.)

Consider a healthy person age x being issued such a contract at time 0. The APV for Benefit (a) is a familiar concept, namely

$$ {}^{h}\bar{A}_{x}^{(f)} = \int_{0}^{\infty} v^{t} \cdot {}_{t}p_{x}^{(\tau)} \cdot \mu_{x+t}^{(f)} \, dt \tag{14.12a} $$

in actuarial notation, where $\mu_{x+t}^{(f)}$ denotes the force of failure (or force of mortality) for a healthy person.[6] In multi-state model notation we would write

$$ \bar{A}_{x}^{02} = \int_{0}^{\infty} v^{t} \cdot {}_{t}p_{x}^{00} \cdot \mu_{x+t}^{02} \, dt, \tag{14.12b} $$

since the unit benefit for death while healthy would be payable at the instant of transition from State 0 to State 2.

For Benefit (b), the insured must become disabled first and then die. (Since recovery is not possible, then death while disabled is inevitable once disability has occurred.) To develop the APV for a unit death benefit in this case, suppose disability occurs at time t, which happens with density ${}_{t}p_{x}^{(\tau)} \cdot \mu_{x+t}^{(d)}$, where $\mu_{x+t}^{(d)}$ denotes the force of disability for a healthy person. Conditional on this event occurring, we then have a person in the disabled state at age $x+t$, facing the single decrement of death. The APV of a unit death benefit for a person alive but disabled at time t (age $x+t$) is ${}^{d}\bar{A}_{x+t}$, where the superscript d implies that ${}^{d}\bar{A}_{x+t}$ is to be calculated using a single-decrement survival model appropriate for a disabled person. We know that

$$ {}^{d}\bar{A}_{x+t} = \int_{0}^{\infty} v^{s} \cdot {}_{s}p_{x+t}^{d} \cdot \mu_{x+t+s}^{d} \, ds \tag{14.13a} $$

in actuarial notation, or

$$ \bar{A}_{x+t}^{12} = \int_{0}^{\infty} v^{s} \cdot {}_{s}p_{x+t}^{11} \cdot \mu_{x+t+s}^{12} \, ds \tag{14.13b} $$

in multi-state model notation, since the benefit is paid at the instant of transition from State 1 to State 2. Then the APV at issue of the contract to a healthy person age x at time 0 is

$$ \begin{aligned} {}^{h}\bar{A}_{x}^{d} &= \int_{0}^{\infty} v^{t} \cdot {}_{t}p_{x}^{(\tau)} \cdot \mu_{x+t}^{(d)} \cdot {}^{d}\bar{A}_{x+t} \, dt \\ &= \int_{0}^{\infty} v^{t} \cdot {}_{t}p_{x}^{(\tau)} \cdot \mu_{x+t}^{(d)} \cdot \left(\int_{0}^{\infty} v^{s} \cdot {}_{s}p_{x+t}^{d} \cdot \mu_{x+t+s}^{d} \, ds \right) dt, \end{aligned} \tag{14.14a} $$

in actuarial notation, or

$$ {}^{h}\bar{A}_{x}^{d} = \int_{0}^{\infty} v^{t} \cdot {}_{t}p_{x}^{00} \cdot \mu_{x+t}^{01} \cdot \left(\int_{0}^{\infty} v^{s} \cdot {}_{s}p_{x+t}^{11} \cdot \mu_{x+t+s}^{12} \, ds \right) dt, \tag{14.14b} $$

[6] Throughout this section, we define actuarial notation as needed, hopefully in a logical and consistent way. The multi-state model notation, on the other hand, has already been defined.

in multi-state model notation. (Note that there is no special multi-state model notation for the time 0 APV.)

For Benefit (c), we again consider that disability occurs at time t, which happens with density ${}_tp_x^{(\tau)} \cdot \mu_{x+t}^{(d)}$. At that time the APV of a continuous unit income benefit for a disabled person is ${}^d\bar{a}_{x+t}$, where again the superscript d implies that ${}^d\bar{a}_{x+t}$ is calculated using a survival model appropriate for a disabled person. Then it follows that the APV at issue of the contract for the disability income stream is

$$\begin{aligned} {}^h\bar{a}_x^d &= \int_0^\infty v^t \cdot {}_tp_x^{(\tau)} \cdot \mu_{x+t}^{(d)} \cdot {}^d\bar{a}_{x+t}\ dt \\ &= \int_0^\infty v^t \cdot {}_tp_x^{(\tau)} \cdot \mu_{x+t}^{(d)} \cdot \left(\int_0^\infty v^s \cdot {}_sp_{x+t}^d\ ds \right) dt \qquad (14.15a) \end{aligned}$$

in actuarial notation, or

$$\bar{a}_x^{01} = \int_0^\infty v^t \cdot {}_tp_x^{00} \cdot \mu_{x+t}^{01} \cdot \left(\int_0^\infty v^s \cdot {}_sp_{x+t}^{11}\ ds \right) dt \qquad (14.15b)$$

in multi-state model notation.

Note that two models are required in order to determine the several APVs for this contract. The primary model is a double-decrement model for the decrements of failure and disability. The secondary model is a single-decrement model for failure only, but appropriate for a disabled person. The total APV for the contract is the sum of the APVs for Benefits (a), (b), and (c).

EXAMPLE 14.9

Referring to Figure 14.5, consider a healthy person age x at time 0, which means the process is in State 0. We wish to consider the probability of this person being alive but disabled at age $x+n$ (time n), which means the process would be in State 1 at time n. The multi-state model notation for this probability is ${}_np_x^{01}$. (There is no standard actuarial symbol for this probability value; other texts[7] have adopted the symbol ${}_np_x^{ai}$.) Using multi-state model notation, this probability would be given by

$${}_np_x^{01} = \int_0^n {}_tp_x^{00} \cdot \mu_{x+t}^{01} \cdot {}_{n-t}p_{x+t}^{11}\ dt,$$

where μ_{x+t}^{01} denotes the force of disability for a healthy person age $x+t$, subject to a double-decrement model, and ${}_{n-t}p_{x+t}^{11}$ denotes the probability of survival from age $x+t$ to age $x+n$ for a disabled person, subject to a single-decrement survival model. Solve the Kolmogorov differential equation to show that

$${}_np_x^{01} = \int_0^n {}_tp_x^{00} \cdot \mu_{x+t}^{01} \cdot {}_{n-t}p_{x+t}^{11}\ dt.$$

[7] See, for example, Section 12.2 of Jordan [14].

SOLUTION

In Equation (3.14a), $i=0$ and $j=1$ so k takes on the values 0 and 2 in the summation. Then we have

$$\begin{aligned} \frac{d}{dt}\,{}_tp_x^{01} &= {}_tp_x^{00}\cdot\mu_{x+t}^{01} - {}_tp_x^{01}\cdot\mu^{10} && (\text{at } k=0) \\ &\quad + {}_tp_x^{02}\cdot\mu^{21} - {}_tp_x^{01}\cdot\mu_{x+t}^{12} && (\text{at } k=2) \\ &= {}_tp_x^{00}\cdot\mu_{x+t}^{01} - {}_tp_x^{01}\cdot\mu_{x+t}^{12}, \end{aligned}$$

since $\mu^{10}=\mu^{21}=0$ for all t. Then integrating from $t=0$ to $t=n$ we have

$$\int_0^n d\,{}_tp_x^{01} = \int_0^n {}_tp_x^{00}\cdot\mu_{x+t}^{01}\,dt - \int_0^n {}_tp_x^{01}\cdot\mu_{x+t}^{12}\,dt.$$

As expected, the left side integrates to ${}_np_x^{01}$, since ${}_0p_x^{01}=0$. On the right side, μ_{x+t}^{01} is the force of disability for a healthy person at age $x+t$, subject to a double-decrement model. μ_{x+t}^{12} is the force of mortality for a disabled person at age $x+t$, subject to a single-decrement survival model. Then substituting the integral expression given in the example for ${}_tp_x^{01}$, we have

$${}_np_x^{01} = \int_0^n {}_tp_x^{00}\cdot\mu_{x+t}^{01}\,dt - \int_0^n \mu_{x+t}^{12}\cdot\left(\int_0^t {}_sp_x^{00}\cdot\mu_{x+s}^{01}\cdot{}_{t-s}p_{x+s}^{11}\,ds\right)dt.$$

Reversing the order of integration in the subtractive term we obtain

$$\int_0^n {}_sp_x^{00}\cdot\mu_{x+s}^{01}\cdot\left(\int_s^n {}_{t-s}p_{x+s}^{11}\cdot\mu_{x+t}^{12}\,dt\right)ds = \int_0^n {}_sp_x^{00}\cdot\mu_{x+s}^{01}\cdot{}_{n-s}p_{x+s}^{12}\,ds.$$

Then we finally have

$$\begin{aligned} {}_np_x^{01} &= \int_0^n {}_tp_x^{00}\cdot\mu_{x+t}^{01}\,dt - \int_0^n {}_sp_x^{00}\cdot\mu_{x+s}^{01}\cdot{}_{n-s}p_{x+s}^{12}\,ds \\ &= \int_0^n \left({}_tp_x^{00}\cdot\mu_{x+t}^{01} - {}_tp_x^{00}\cdot\mu_{x+t}^{01}\cdot{}_{n-t}p_{x+t}^{12}\right)dt, \end{aligned}$$

upon changing s to t in the second integral, and finally

$$\begin{aligned} {}_np_x^{01} &= \int_0^n {}_tp_x^{00}\cdot\mu_{x+t}^{01}\left(1-{}_{n-t}p_{x+t}^{12}\right)dt \\ &= \int_0^n {}_tp_x^{00}\cdot\mu_{x+t}^{01}\cdot{}_{n-t}p_{x+t}^{11}\,dt, \end{aligned}$$

as required. ❐

14.4.3 DISABILITY MODEL ALLOWING FOR RECOVERY

In this section we consider the same insurance contract as in Section 14.4.2, except that disability is not presumed to be permanent. Premiums are paid while the insured is healthy, but not while disabled. If the insured becomes disabled, whether by accident or illness, periodic income payments are made. The income payments cease upon either death or recovery from the disability. In the case of recovery, the insured returns to the active state and resumes premium payments. As a multi-state model, the coverage is described by Figure 14.6 in which the possibility of recovery is indicated by the arrow showing possible transition from State 1 back to State 0.

As we shall see, the possibility of recovery complicates our analysis considerably. We resolve this complication by numerically approximating a solution to the Kolmogorov differential equation rather than solving it analytically.

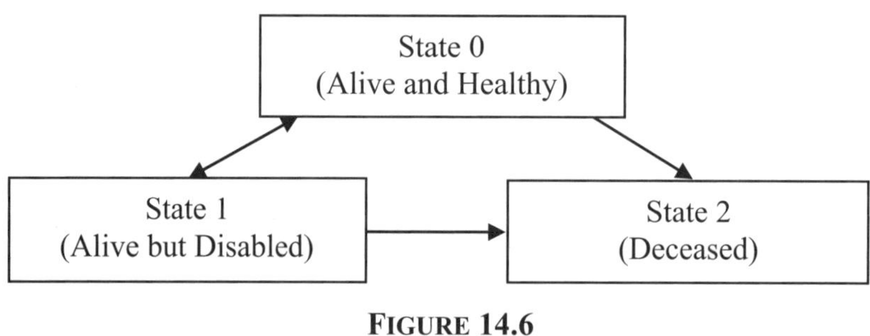

FIGURE 14.6

Whereas the secondary model in Section 14.4.2 was a single-decrement model for mortality only, the secondary model in this case is a double-decrement model for the decrements of death and recovery. In this section we use this new model to value the same three benefits described in Section 14.4.2.

We should first note that Equation (14.12b) is still a correct expression for the APV of Benefit (a). However, when the model allows for reentry to the healthy state, as our new model does, the probability value denoted by ${}_tp_x^{00}$ cannot be determined analytically. Recall that ${}_tp_x^{00}$ is the probability that a person in State 0 at time 0 will be in State 0 at time t. This event can occur (1) if the person never left State 0 before time t, or (2) if the person had transitioned to State 1 but returned to State 0 before time t, or (3) if the person had moved from State 0 to State 1, and back again, several times before time t. Due to the possibility of unlimited transitions to State 1, and back again to State 0, the probability value ${}_tp_x^{00}$ does not have a closed form expression, except in degenerate cases. To remedy this problem, we will make use of Euler's Method, first introduced in Example 10.11.

We now consider the Kolmogorov differential equation given by Equation (3.14a). To solve for ${}_tp_x^{00}$, we have $i=0$ and $j=0$ so k takes on the values 1 and 2 in the summation. Then we have

$$\begin{aligned}
\frac{d}{dt}\,{}_tp_x^{00} &= {}_tp_x^{01}\cdot\mu_{x+t}^{10} - {}_tp_x^{00}\cdot\mu_{x+t}^{01} && \text{(at } k{=}1)\\
&+ {}_tp_x^{02}\cdot\mu_{x+t}^{20} - {}_tp_x^{00}\cdot\mu_{x+t}^{02} && \text{(at } k{=}2)\\
&= {}_tp_x^{01}\cdot\mu_{x+t}^{10} - {}_tp_x^{00}\cdot\left[\mu_{x+t}^{01}+\mu_{x+t}^{02}\right], && (14.17)
\end{aligned}$$

since only $\mu_{x+t}^{20}=0$ in this case. To solve for ${}_tp_x^{01}$, we have $i=0$ and $j=1$ so k takes on the values 0 and 2 in the summation. We have

$$\begin{aligned}
\frac{d}{dt}\,{}_tp_x^{01} &= {}_tp_x^{00}\cdot\mu_{x+t}^{01} - {}_tp_x^{01}\cdot\mu_{x+t}^{10} && \text{(at } k{=}0)\\
&+ {}_tp_x^{02}\cdot\mu_{x+t}^{21} - {}_tp_x^{01}\cdot\mu_{x+t}^{12} && \text{(at } k{=}2)\\
&= {}_tp_x^{00}\cdot\mu_{x+t}^{01} - {}_tp_x^{01}\cdot\left[\mu_{x+t}^{10}+\mu_{x+t}^{12}\right], && (14.18)
\end{aligned}$$

since only $\mu_{x+t}^{21}=0$ in this case. Since both of Equations (14.17) and (14.18) include both ${}_tp_x^{00}$ and ${}_tp_x^{01}$, we apply Euler's Method to both equations simultaneously and produce approximate values for both functions.

Consider a healthy person being issued this type of disability coverage at time 0 at age x. The process necessarily begins in State 0 at time 0 so, necessarily, ${}_0p_x^{00}=1$ and ${}_0p_x^{01}=0$. These are the initial conditions for use in our recursive calculation of values of ${}_tp_x^{00}$ and ${}_tp_x^{01}$.

Adapting Euler's Method from Example 10.11 to this problem, where $f(x)$ is represented by ${}_tp_x^{ij}$, we have

$$_{t+h}p_x^{ij} \approx {}_tp_x^{ij} + \frac{d}{dt}\,{}_tp_x^{ij}\cdot h. \tag{14.19}$$

Then for $i=j=0$, we substitute the right side of Equation (14.17) for the derivative term in Equation (14.19), obtaining

$$_{t+h}p_x^{00} \approx {}_tp_x^{00} + h\left\{{}_tp_x^{01}\cdot\mu_{x+t}^{10} - {}_tp_x^{00}\cdot\left[\mu_{x+t}^{01}+\mu_{x+t}^{02}\right]\right\}. \tag{14.20}$$

Similarly, for $i=0$ and $j=1$, we substitute the right side of Equation (14.18) for the derivative term in Equation (14.19), obtaining

$$_{t+h}p_x^{01} \approx {}_tp_x^{01} + h\left\{{}_tp_x^{00}\cdot\mu_{x+t}^{01} - {}_tp_x^{01}\cdot\left[\mu_{x+t}^{10}+\mu_{x+t}^{12}\right]\right\}. \tag{14.21}$$

Then by selecting a value for h, along with initial values ${}_0p_x^{00}=1$ and ${}_0p_x^{01}=0$, we can recursively calculate values of ${}_tp_x^{00}$ and ${}_tp_x^{01}$ for $t=h, 2h, 3h, \ldots$.

EXAMPLE 14.10

Suppose the forces of transition are $\mu_{x+t}^{01} = .10t + .20$, $\mu_{x+t}^{02} = .20$, $\mu_{x+t}^{10} = .50$, and $\mu_{x+t}^{12} = .125t + .20$, for $0 \le t \le 2$ in all cases. Using the value $h = .10$, calculate the approximate values of ${}_tp_x^{00}$ and ${}_tp_x^{01}$ for $t = .10, .20, \ldots, 2.00$.

SOLUTION

Starting at $t = 0$, and using $h = .10$, we find

$$\begin{aligned} {}_{.10}p_x^{00} &\approx {}_0p_x^{00} + .10\left\{ {}_0p_x^{01} \cdot \mu_x^{10} - {}_0p_x^{00} \cdot \left[\mu_x^{01} + \mu_x^{02} \right] \right\} \\ &= 1 + .10\left[0 - (1)(.20 + .20) \right] = .96 \end{aligned}$$

from Equation (14.20), and

$$\begin{aligned} {}_{.10}p_x^{01} &\approx {}_0p_x^{01} + .10\left\{ {}_0p_x^{00} \cdot \mu_x^{01} - {}_0p_x^{01} \cdot \left[\mu_x^{10} + \mu_x^{12} \right] \right\} \\ &= 0 + .10\left[(1)(.20 - 0) \right] = .02 \end{aligned}$$

from Equation (14.21). Continuing in this recursive manner we obtain the values shown in the following table:

t	${}_tp_x^{00}$	${}_tp_x^{01}$
0.00	1	0
0.10	.960	.020
0.20	.922	.039
0.30	.885	.056
0.40	.850	.072
0.50	.816	.087
0.60	.784	.101
0.70	.753	.114
0.80	.723	.125
0.90	.694	.135
1.00	.667	.144
1.10	.641	.152
1.20	.616	.160
1.30	.592	.166
1.40	.569	.171
1.50	.547	.175
1.60	.525	.179
1.70	.505	.182
1.80	.485	.184
1.90	.466	.185
2.00	.448	.186

Once the values of ${}_tp_x^{00}$ and ${}_tp_x^{01}$ have been determined, a number of financial values can be calculated from these ${}_tp_x^{ij}$ values. This is illustrated in the following example.

EXAMPLE 14.11

A healthy person age x is issued a contract that pays 10,000 at the end of the tenth of the year of death for death while healthy, and 1,000 at the end of each tenth of the year if disabled at that time. Premiums are payable at the beginning of each tenth of the year while healthy.[8] The coverage is for a two-year period only. Assuming a nominal interest rate of $i^{(10)} = .05$, and the transition forces of Example 14.10, find each of the following.

(a) The APV at issue of the death benefit.

(b) The APV at issue of the disability benefit.

(c) The net benefit premium payable each tenth of the year, using the equivalence principle.

SOLUTION

(a) The effective interest rate each tenth of a year is $\frac{i^{(10)}}{10} = .005$. The force of mortality for a healthy person, which is given by μ_{x+t}^{02} in this case, is constant at .20, so the probability of death in any tenth of a year is also constant at

$$q = 1-e^{-\int_0^{.10} .20\, dt} = .01980.$$

Then the APV of the death benefit is

$$\begin{aligned} APV(a) &= 10{,}000(v \cdot q + v^2 \cdot {}_{.10}p_x^{00} \cdot q + \cdots + v^{20} \cdot {}_{1.90}p_x^{00} \cdot q) \\ &= 198\left[\frac{1}{1.005} + \frac{{}_{.10}p_x^{00}}{(1.005)^2} + \cdots + \frac{{}_{1.90}p_x^{00}}{(1.005)^{20}}\right]. \end{aligned}$$

Substituting the ${}_tp_x^{00}$ values calculated in Example 14.10, we obtain the result $APV(a) = 2649.03$, which the reader can verify.

(b) The disability benefit is paid at the end of each tenth of the year if disabled at that time, which means the process is in State 1. The APV of the benefit is

$$APV(b) = 1{,}000\left[\frac{{}_{.10}p_x^{01}}{1.005} + \frac{{}_{.20}p_x^{01}}{(1.005)^2} + \cdots + \frac{{}_{2.00}p_x^{01}}{(1.005)^{20}}\right].$$

Substituting the ${}_tp_x^{01}$ values calculated in Example 14.10, we obtain the result $APV(b) = 2472.12$, which the reader can verify.

---

[8] In practice, it would be more natural to pay premiums and disability benefits monthly. The calculations in Example 14.10 would have used $h = 1/12$ instead of $h = 1/10$.

(c) If the net periodic premium, payable at the beginning of each tenth of the year while healthy, is denoted by P, then the APV of the premium stream is

$$APV(c) = P\left[1 + \frac{{}_{.10}p_x^{00}}{1.005} + \frac{{}_{.20}p_x^{00}}{(1.005)^2} + \cdots + \frac{{}_{1.90}p_x^{00}}{(1.005)^{19}}\right].$$

Again using the ${}_tp_x^{00}$ values from Example 14.10, we find the APV of the premium stream to be $13.44582P$. Then the net premium is

$$P = \frac{APV(a) + APV(b)}{13.44582} = 380.87.$$ ❑

Note that the availability of ${}_tp_x^{ij}$ values at discrete values of t allows us to calculate discrete APVs directly. If APVs for continuous functions were desired, we would resort to approximate numerical integration, such as the trapezoidal rule or Simpson's rule, using the available discrete values.

The calculation of several other results from the Figure 14.6 model is pursued in the exercises.

The Figure 14.6 model assumes that a person who has recovered from a disability, thereby returning to State 0 from State 1, is then subject to the same forces of transition as other persons in State 0 who have never been disabled. An alternative view is to define a separate state for those who have recovered from a disability. This model is illustrated in Figure 14.7.

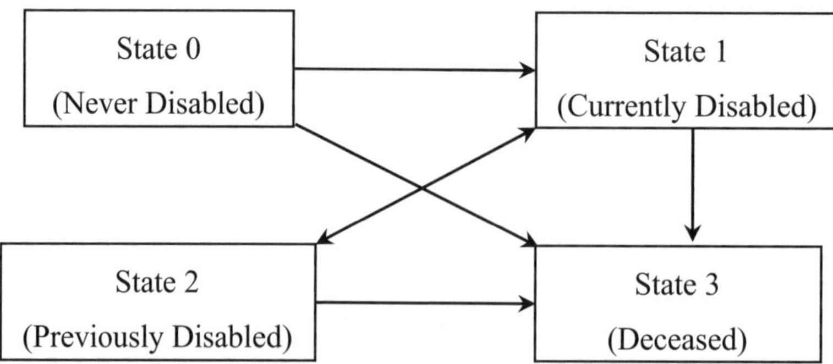

FIGURE 14.7

In this model, transition from State 1 or State 2 back to State 0 is not possible, nor is transition from State 0 to State 2, so $\mu_{x+t}^{02} = \mu_{x+t}^{10} = \mu_{x+t}^{20} = 0$. As always, State 3 is an absorbing state, so $\mu_{x+t}^{30} = \mu_{x+t}^{31} = \mu_{x+t}^{32} = 0$ as well. Note that a previously disabled person could become disabled again, so transition from State 2 to State 1 is possible (i.e., $\mu_{x+t}^{21} \neq 0$).

The added complexity of this model makes it even more difficult to obtain analytical results, even approximately. In practice, simulation techniques would be used. (Simulation techniques are not covered in this text.)

14.4.4 CONTINUING CARE RETIREMENT COMMUNITIES

Another model that lends itself to convenient analysis in the multi-state model context is that of a *continuing care retirement community* (CCRC). The CCRC model we consider in this section was proposed by Jones [14].[9] It consists of a set of *individual living units* (ILU) along with two skilled nursing facilities. One healthy retiree lives in each ILU. One nursing facility houses retirees with temporary nursing needs and is referred to as the *temporary nursing facility* (TNF); the other, the *permanent nursing facility* (PNF), houses retirees on a permanent basis. When an individual dies or moves to the PNF, his or her ILU is made available for a new member and we assume it is occupied as soon as it becomes available. While a member is in the TNF, his or her ILU is held vacant. We will predict future occupancy rates at our CCRC by treating it as a homogeneous discrete-time Markov Chain. This is illustrated in Figure 14.8.

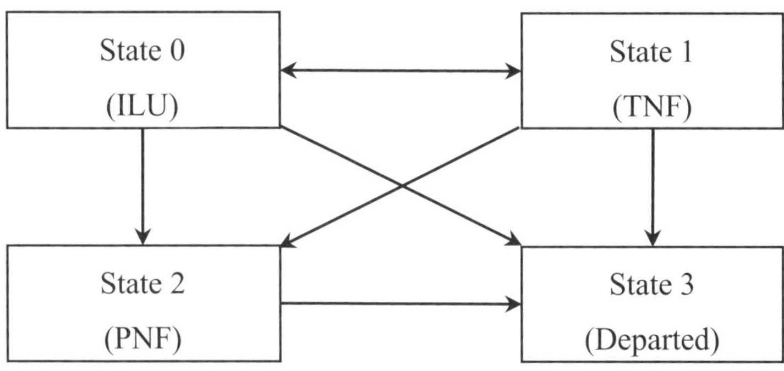

FIGURE 14.8

Residents in State 2 (the PNF) cannot return to either State 0 or State 1, so $\mu_{x+t}^{20} = \mu_{x+t}^{21} = 0$ for all t. As usual, $\mu_{x+t}^{30} = \mu_{x+t}^{31} = \mu_{x+t}^{32} = 0$ as well. Transitions among states are governed by a monthly transition probability matrix given by

$$P = \begin{vmatrix} .94 & .03 & .02 & .01 \\ .50 & .30 & .18 & .02 \\ 0 & 0 & .93 & .07 \\ 0 & 0 & 0 & 1 \end{vmatrix}.$$

Note that the number of possible transitions is greater than under any of the models previously considered. The complexity of the model suggests that analysis of it might best be done by simulation, although several elementary calculations from the model are pursued in Exercises 14-19 and 14-20.

14.4.5 THIELE'S DIFFERENTIAL EQUATION IN THE MULTIPLE-DECREMENT CASE

In this section we illustrate the calculation of reserves in several multiple-decrement situations.

---

[9] Interested readers should consult this reference for a more complete analysis of the model.

We begin with the simpler disability model of Section 14.4.2, and illustrated in Figure 14.5, where disability is presumed permanent so that return from the disabled to the healthy state is not possible. In Section 14.4.2 we developed the APVs at issue of the contract at age x for each of (a) a unit benefit for death while healthy, (b) a unit benefit for death while disabled, and (c) a unit of continuous income while disabled. These APVs are given by Equations (14.12a), (14.14a), and (14.15a), respectively.

The continuous annuity factor for a healthy life is the familiar

$$\bar{a}_x^{00} = \int_0^\infty v^t \cdot {}_tp_x^{00}\, dt. \tag{14.22}$$

Then the continuous annual premium rate for this contract, payable while healthy, is

$$\bar{P} = \frac{APVB}{\bar{a}_x^{00}}, \tag{14.23}$$

where *APVB* denotes the sum of the APVs for Benefits (a), (b), and (c).

Expressions for the reserves follow from the APVs and premium rate. There are two different reserves to consider.

If the insured is still healthy at duration t (i.e., still in State 0), which is age $x+t$, we determine the *healthy life reserve* at that time, which we denote by ${}_t\bar{V}^{(0)}$, in multi-state model notation. Prospectively the reserve is the total APV of the three benefits, given by the three equations mentioned above with x replaced by $x+t$, minus the APV of future premiums, which is $\bar{P}\cdot\bar{a}_{x+t}^{00}$.

If the insured is disabled at duration t (i.e., in State 1), we determine the *disabled life reserve* at that time, which we denote by ${}_t\bar{V}^{(1)}$. Since there are no future premiums after disability occurs, the disabled life reserve is simply the APV of the future benefits. The APV of the future unit disability benefit is

$$\bar{a}_{x+t}^{11} = \int_0^\infty v^s \cdot {}_sp_{x+t}^{11}\, ds, \tag{14.24}$$

where $\bar{a}_{x+t}^{11}$ is calculated using a survival model appropriate for a disabled person. The APV of the future death-while-disabled benefit is given by Equation (14.13b), in multi-state model notation.

Since we have precise expressions for both types of reserve under the Section 14.4.2 disability model, they can be calculated without resorting to approximations, provided we are given a parametric double-decrement model for death and disability while healthy, and a parametric single-decrement model for death while disabled.

The disability model of Section 14.4.3, and illustrated in Figure 14.6, is more complicated than the Section 14.4.2 model due to the possibility of recovery from disability back to the healthy state. We saw in Example 14.10 how we might approximate the probabilities of being either healthy or disabled at sequential discrete intervals, and then used these probabilities to calculate APVs in Example 14.11. The APVs and the premium then allow us to calculate both healthy life and disabled life reserves at duration t of the contract, given whichever state applies.

In the case of a fully-continuous model, the reserves can be approximated at sequential discrete durations by using Thiele's differential equation adapted to the multiple-decrement case. Again we consider the disability income model of Section 14.4.3, with death benefit B, paid at death while either healthy or disabled, and income paid continuously at rate R while disabled. As mentioned above, we must consider both the fully-continuous healthy life reserve, denoted ${}_t\bar{V}^{(0)}$, and the fully-continuous disabled life reserve, denoted ${}_t\bar{V}^{(1)}$.

As we did in Chapters 10 and 11, we analyze the derivative of the reserve function as its rate of change, which is made up of its components of change. For the healthy life reserve, the reserve is increasing due to premium payment and interest earnings, and decreasing due to the decrements of death and disability. Then we have

$$\frac{d}{dt}\,{}_t\bar{V}^{(0)} = \bar{P}+\delta\cdot{}_t\bar{V}^{(0)}-\mu_{x+t}^{02}\left(B-{}_t\bar{V}^{(0)}\right)-\mu_{x+t}^{01}\left({}_t\bar{V}^{(1)}-{}_t\bar{V}^{(0)}\right). \tag{14.25}$$

The first three terms in Equation (14.25) are the same as shown in Exercise 10-24, where μ_{x+t}^{02} denotes the force of mortality while healthy. The benefit of B is paid at death and the healthy life reserve is released. If disability occurs at age $x+t$, again the healthy life reserve is released. Instead of paying out a fixed amount at disability, however, the insurer must establish the APV at that time of future benefits paid while disabled. This APV is the disabled life reserve at that time, ${}_t\bar{V}^{(1)}$.

The rate of change in the disabled life reserve, given by its derivative, will not contain the premium income term. It will have three decremental terms, one for the income paid at rate R while disabled, one for death while disabled, and one for recovery. We have

$$\frac{d}{dt}\,{}_t\bar{V}^{(1)} = \delta\cdot{}_t\bar{V}^{(1)}-R-\mu_{x+t}^{12}\left(B-{}_t\bar{V}^{(1)}\right)-\mu_{x+t}^{10}\left({}_t\bar{V}^{(0)}-{}_t\bar{V}^{(1)}\right), \tag{14.26}$$

where μ_{x+t}^{12} and μ_{x+t}^{10} denote the forces of mortality and recovery, respectively, for a disabled life. In the case of either decrement, the disabled life reserve ${}_t\bar{V}^{(1)}$ is released. The death benefit B is paid if failure occurs, and the healthy life reserve is established if recovery occurs.

Since each differential equation contains both reserve functions, no closed form solution for them exists. Instead we use Euler's Method just as we did earlier to approximate a solution to Kolmogorov's differential equation, with one important difference. In the Kolmogorov problem, the starting values for the recursion were available at time 0, so the recursion moved *forward* in steps of size h. In our current problem, the starting values for the recursion are at the end of the term of coverage, so the recursion moves *backward* in steps of size h. The end of the term is time $t=n$ for coverage of a fixed term or time $t=\omega-x$ for whole life coverage. (Without loss of generality we can use n in both cases.)

In the Kolmogorov problem, we approximated $f'(x)$ as

$$f'(x) \approx \frac{f(x+h)-f(x)}{h}.$$

It is equally reasonable to approximate $f'(x)$ as

$$f'(x) \approx \frac{f(x)-f(x-h)}{h}.$$

We use this version to accommodate the backward recursion. Then we can rewrite Equation (14.25) as

$$\frac{{}_t\bar{V}^{(0)} - {}_{t-h}\bar{V}^{(0)}}{h} \approx \bar{P}+\delta\cdot {}_t\bar{V}^{(0)} - \mu_{x+t}^{02}\left(B-{}_t\bar{V}^{(0)}\right) - \mu_{x+t}^{01}\left({}_t\bar{V}^{(1)} - {}_t\bar{V}^{(0)}\right),$$

or

$${}_{t-h}\bar{V}^{(0)} \approx {}_t\bar{V}^{(0)} - h\left\{\bar{P}+\delta\cdot {}_t\bar{V}^{(0)} - \mu_{x+t}^{02}\left(B-{}_t\bar{V}^{(0)}\right) - \mu_{x+t}^{01}\left({}_t\bar{V}^{(1)} - {}_t\bar{V}^{(0)}\right)\right\}. \quad (14.27)$$

By similar reasoning we also rewrite Equation (14.26) as

$${}_{t-h}\bar{V}^{(1)} \approx {}_t\bar{V}^{(1)} - h\left\{\delta\cdot {}_t\bar{V}^{(1)} - R - \mu_{x+t}^{12}\left(B-{}_t\bar{V}^{(1)}\right) - \mu_{x+t}^{10}\left({}_t\bar{V}^{(0)} - {}_t\bar{V}^{(1)}\right)\right\}. \quad (14.28)$$

Then using the starting values ${}_n\bar{V}^{(0)} = {}_n\bar{V}^{(1)} = 0$, the force of interest δ, the premium rate $\bar{P}$, the interval size h, and the four force functions, we can recursively calculate values of ${}_t\bar{V}^{(0)}$ and ${}_t\bar{V}^{(1)}$ at all desired values of t.

EXAMPLE 14.12

Using the force functions of Example 14.10, along with $B=R=1000$, $h=.10$, $\delta=.04$, and $\bar{P}=446.95$, calculate all values of ${}_t\bar{V}^{(0)}$ and ${}_t\bar{V}^{(1)}$ for a two-year term contract.

SOLUTION

We start at $t=2.00$. Using the given information we have

$$\begin{aligned}{}_{1.90}\bar{V}^{(0)} &= {}_{2.00}\bar{V}^{(0)} - h\left\{\bar{P}+\delta\cdot {}_{2.00}\bar{V}^{(0)} - \mu_{x+2}^{02}\left[B-{}_{2.00}\bar{V}^{(0)}\right] - \mu_{x+2}^{01}\cdot\left[{}_{2.00}\bar{V}^{(1)} - {}_{2.00}\bar{V}^{(0)}\right]\right\} \\ &= 0-.10[446.95+(.04)(0)-(.20)(1000-0)-(.40)(0-0)] = -24.70,\end{aligned}$$

from Equation (14.27), and

$$ {}_{1.90}\overline{V}^{(1)} = {}_{2.00}\overline{V}^{(1)} - h\left\{\delta \cdot {}_{2.00}\overline{V}^{(1)} - R - \mu_{x+2}^{12} \cdot \left[B - {}_{2.00}\overline{V}^{(1)}\right] - \mu_{x+2}^{10} \cdot \left[{}_{2.00}\overline{V}^{(0)} - {}_{2.00}\overline{V}^{(1)}\right]\right\} $$

$$ = 0 - .10[(.04)(0) - 1000 - (.45)(1000-0) - (.50)(0-0)] = 145.00, $$

from Equation (14.28). Continuing in this recursive manner we obtain the values shown in the table below. Since $\overline{P} = 446.95$ is approximately the equivalence principle premium, it follows that ${}_0\overline{V}^{(0)} \approx 0$.

t	${}_t\overline{V}^{(0)}$	${}_t\overline{V}^{(1)}$
2.00	0.00	0.00
1.90	−24.70	145.00
1.80	−42.18	273.34
1.70	−53.87	387.36
1.60	−60.95	489.02
1.50	−64.38	580.00
1.40	−64.98	661.74
1.30	−63.41	735.44
1.20	−60.22	802.15
1.10	−55.87	862.74
1.00	−50.75	917.99
0.90	−45.16	968.55
0.80	−39.38	1014.97
0.70	−33.60	1057.75
0.60	−28.03	1097.29
0.50	−22.79	1133.96
0.40	18.02	1168.07
0.30	−13.82	1199.89
0.20	−10.26	1229.66
0.10	−7.44	1257.58
0.00	−5.39	1283.82

In theory, the backward recursion should result in ${}_0\overline{V}^{(0)} = 0$ and ${}_0\overline{V}^{(1)} = 0$ as well, since disability contracts are not sold to already-disabled people. The value ${}_0\overline{V}^{(0)} = -5.39$ reflects the approximate nature of the process. The values of ${}_t\overline{V}^{(1)}$ should be interpreted as the disabled life reserve at time t if the policyholder is known to be disabled at that time.

We can generalize the process described in this section by allowing the benefit amounts, the premium and/or the force of interest to vary with time. We can also introduce expenses and gross premium, provided the expenses are paid continuously. (See Exercise 14-21.) We can also generalize the process to more than three states (see Exercise 14-22).

14.5 DEFINED BENEFIT PENSION PLANS

Another major application of multiple decrements is the *defined benefit pension plan* (DB plan), which is a legal promise created by an employer to provide its employees with a defined amount of pension income during retirement.[10]

Although the retirement benefit is the basic benefit provided by a DB plan, it is not uncommon for a plan to also provide some level of benefit upon the death or disability of an employee, as well as upon withdrawal from the plan due to termination of employment before normal (or early) retirement age. Accordingly, a four-decrement table, of the type described in Section 14.1.1, is often used for DB plan calculations.[11] In this section we adopt the letters r, d, i, and w to denote the decrements of retirement, death, disability, and withdrawal, respectively.

As an application of the general multiple-decrement model, the DB plan can be represented as a multi-state model (see Figure 14.1) with $m = 4$, as shown in Figure 14.9.

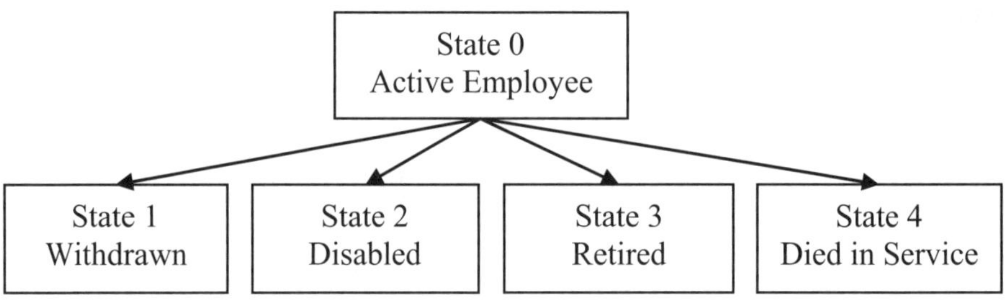

FIGURE 14.9

Note that the arrows are in one direction only. Although it is possible for terminated, disabled, or even retired employees to return to active service, actuarial valuations generally do not anticipate this. If and when a decremented employee does return to active service, the next valuation will reflect the new information.[12]

In the remainder of this section, we focus primarily on the retirement benefit, including the case of retirement earlier than the normal retirement age, and the withdrawal benefit.

---

[10] An alternative approach, called a *defined contribution plan* (DC plan), obligates the employer only to contribute a defined amount to the plan, rather than guaranteeing a defined benefit. In a DC plan, the employees would project their future salaries, contributions, investment returns, and annuity prices at retirement, in order to determine the size of the lifetime annuity they could purchase at that time. If the projected benefit is deemed insufficient, they will decide how much more to contribute, or they could plan to work longer.

[11] A multiple-decrement table prepared specifically for use with DB plans is traditionally called a *service table*.

[12] When the pension plan is represented as a multi-state model, we can apply any of the techniques presented for such models earlier in this chapter, including applications of Kolmogorov's differential equation solved either exactly or approximately via Euler's method.

14.5.1 NORMAL RETIREMENT BENEFITS

The primary benefit of a DB plan is the *lifetime retirement benefit*, payable starting at the plan's *normal retirement age* (NRA), commonly age 65. The targeted amount of the retirement benefit might be defined as p percent of the employee's projected salary at the time of retirement, and is generally a function of years of service as well. Often the projected average salary over the final, say, three years of employment is used. Then the projected annual benefit (PAB), to begin at normal retirement age z, for an employee hired at attained age x, would be

$$PAB_z = .01p \cdot YOS_z \cdot FAS_z, \tag{14.29}$$

where YOS_z denotes the years of service and FAS_z denotes the final average salary at retirement.

The final average salary is estimated by projecting the salary at attained age x to later years by using a set of *salary scale factors*, denoted here by s_k, for $k = x, x+1, \ldots, z-1$. Then if the average is taken over the final three years of employment, the projected final average salary would be

$$FAS_z = \frac{1}{3}\left(\frac{s_{z-3}+s_{z-2}+s_{z-1}}{s_x}\right) \cdot CAS_x, \tag{14.30}$$

where CAS_x denotes the current annual salary at attained age x.

A salary scale could be as simple as a constant percentage increase; for example, setting $s_{20} = 1$ and $s_k = (1.04)^{k-20}$, for $k = 21, 22, \ldots, z-1$, defines a salary scale allowing for a constant annual salary increase of 4%. A more sophisticated salary scale could be derived from a study of salary data.

In theory, but never in practice, the discrete salary scale factors could be replaced by a continuous *salary rate function*, denoted by $\bar{s}_y$, suggesting that an employee's salary is changing (hopefully increasing) continuously. The relationship between this $\bar{s}_y$ and the discrete s_y is given by

$$s_y = \int_y^{y+1} \bar{s}_r \, dr \approx \frac{1}{2}\left(\bar{s}_y + \bar{s}_{y+1}\right) \approx \bar{s}_{y+\frac{1}{2}} \tag{14.31a}$$

or, equivalently,

$$\bar{s}_y \approx s_{y-\frac{1}{2}}. \tag{14.31b}$$

EXAMPLE 14.13

Consider an employee entering a DB pension plan at age 35, with a current salary of 60,000. The plan guarantees an annual retirement benefit of 2% of final three-year average salary at normal retirement age 65 for each year of service, and uses the 4% constant salary scale model described above. What is the projected annual retirement benefit?

SOLUTION

From Equation (14.30) we find the projected final average salary at age 65 to be

$$\begin{aligned} FAS_{65} &= \frac{1}{3}\left(\frac{s_{62}+s_{63}+s_{64}}{s_{35}}\right)\cdot CAS_{35} \\ &= \frac{1}{3}\left(\frac{(1.04)^{42}+(1.04)^{43}+(1.04)^{44}}{(1.04)^{15}}\right)\cdot(60,000) = 180,014.43. \end{aligned}$$

Then the projected annual retirement benefit is

$$PAB_{65} = (.02)(30)(180,014.43) = 108,008.66,$$

since we are projecting 30 years of service for the employee. □

Note, in Example 14.13, that the employee's projected final annual salary (between ages 64 and 65) is $60,000(1.04)^{29} = 187,119.09$. The projected annual retirement benefit of 108,008.66 is $\frac{108,008.66}{180,014.43} = .60$, or 60%, of the final three-year average salary, and it is $\frac{108,008.66}{187,119.09} = .577$, or 57.7%, of the final year's salary. Upon retirement, the employee's final salary is replaced by a retirement benefit that is 57.7% of the final salary. In pension terminology, this value is called the *replacement ratio*.

As an alternative to the final average salary method described above, the retirement benefit amount is sometimes based on the employee's projected aggregate career salary. Then for an employee entering a plan at age x, the projected aggregate salary at retirement age z would be

$$PAS_z = \frac{1}{s_x}\cdot\sum_{k=x}^{z-1} s_k \cdot CAS_x, \tag{14.32a}$$

and the projected annual retirement benefit would be defined as

$$PAB_z = .01p\cdot PAS_z. \tag{14.32b}$$

Note that years of service are reflected in the aggregate salary, so multiplication by YOS_z is not necessary.

The examples presented thus far refer to an employee at the time of hire. For employees hired in the past, their actual past salaries and service are used to determine their projected benefits. For example, if the final average salary method is used, years of expected future service are added to the actual years of past service to determine the YOS_z term, and FAS_z is then determined from the now-current salary. If the career average salary method is used, the actual total past salaries would be added to the projected future aggregate salary figure before multiplying by $.01p$ to determine the projected annual benefit.

Finally we should note that some plans for hourly workers use a simpler projected annual benefit formula that does not depend on salary, such as one that promises a PAB_z of, say, 600 for each year of service.

With the projected annual benefit to begin at age z now established, we can find the actuarial present value (APV) of the projected benefit, as of attained age x, as

$$APV_x^{NR} = PAB_z \cdot v^{z-x} \cdot {}_{z-x}p_x^{(\tau)} \cdot {}^r\ddot{a}_z^{(12)}. \tag{14.33}$$

In Equation (14.33), ${}_{z-x}p_x^{(\tau)}$ is the survival probability taken from the applicable service table, and ${}^r\ddot{a}_z^{(12)}$ is the APV of the retirement benefits, presumed to be paid monthly, as of age z. The pre-superscript r is used to remind us that the annuity APV is based on survival rates appropriate for retired lives, which might be different from those in the service table.

The annuity factor ${}^r\ddot{a}_z^{(12)}$ in Equation (14.33) suggests that the retirement benefit is paid as a monthly whole life annuity to (z).[13] Alternatively, the form of payment might be life with n years certain (see Example 8.13), often with a ten-year certain period, or as a last-survivor annuity (see Section 12.2) involving both the retiree and the retiree's spouse.[14] In the latter case, the benefit amount often decreases to one-half or two-thirds of the original amount if the retiree dies first, but not if the spouse dies first.

If the plan presumes a whole life annuity for the retiree, but permits the election of a life with term certain annuity or a joint-and-contingent annuity instead, the options must be actuarially equivalent. For example, if the whole life monthly benefit is X, then the ten-year certain and life monthly benefit would be Y, where

$$12X \cdot {}^r\ddot{a}_z^{(12)} = 12Y \cdot \left[\ddot{a}_{\overline{10}|}^{(12)} + {}_{10|}{}^r\ddot{a}_z^{(12)} \right].$$

It should be clear that $Y < X$. We can write $Y = f \cdot X$, where $f < 1$ is called the *benefit reduction factor* or *benefit conversion factor*.

If the employee has contributed to the cost of the plan,[15] it is generally provided that if the retiree dies before receiving retirement benefits at least equal to his or her accumulated contributions, then the excess of the accumulated contributions over the retirement benefits paid would be paid to a designated beneficiary. The excess could be paid either in a lump sum (called a *cash refund* arrangement) or by continuing the retirement benefits (called an *installment refund* arrangement).[16]

---

[13] Any of the approximate methods described in Section 8.5.4 could be used to determine the monthly annuity factors. Historically pension actuaries have used the two-term Woolhouse approximation, but others might be more accurate, especially when interest rates are high.

[14] Pension actuaries refer to the last-survivor annuity as a *joint-and-contingent* (J&C) annuity.

[15] *Contributory plans* are not very common with private employer DB pension plans today, although they remain popular in plans sponsored by state and local governments.

[16] Neither cash refund nor installment refund annuities are discussed in this text. The interested reader is referred to Section 17.2 of Bowers, et al. [4].

14.5.2 EARLY RETIREMENT BENEFITS

It is also customary to provide a retirement benefit to employees who retire earlier than the normal retirement age. A typical rule would allow early retirement at age 55 or after 10 years of service, whichever is later. Note that we distinguish between early retirement and withdrawal, because the benefits associated with the two types of decrement are different.

Suppose an employee is hired at age 25 and terminates employment at age 35. Such employee may be eligible for a withdrawal benefit (see Section 14.5.3), but not a retirement benefit. Conversely, if this person remains in employment to age 55 and terminates then, he or she would qualify for retirement benefits and a withdrawal benefit would not apply. This suggests that retirement decrements should be a function of both age and service, and when $q_k^{(r)} > 0$ (i.e., age and service combination for which retirement is possible), then $q_k^{(w)} = 0$. If the service table is a function of age alone, then $q_k^{(w)} = 0$ at the age when retirement is first possible (age 55 in the above example), and a gain will occur when an employee with fewer than ten years of service leaves with the smaller withdrawal benefit.

When an early retirement occurs, the retirement benefit payments might begin immediately, or might be deferred until the NRA. Only salaries and years of service up to the early retirement age (ERA), which we denote by y, would be counted in determining the benefit amount.

EXAMPLE 14.14

Suppose the employee of Example 14.13 would be eligible for an early retirement benefit if retirement occurs at age 60 or later. Find (a) the projected benefit at early retirement age y, (b) the benefit amount if paid immediately, and (c) the APV of the early retirement benefit.

SOLUTION

(a) Employees tend to retire throughout the year of age, so it is typical to assume retirements in the middle of the year on average. If early retirement is between age y and age $y+1$, the projected final average salary would be determined at age $y+\frac{1}{2}$ as

$$FAS_{y+1/2} = \frac{1}{3}\left(\frac{\frac{1}{2}s_{y-3}+s_{y-2}+s_{y-1}+\frac{1}{2}s_y}{s_{35}}\right)\cdot CAS_{35},$$

and the projected benefit, payable starting at age $z=65$, would be

$$PAB_{y+1/2} = (.02)\left(y+\frac{1}{2}-35\right)\cdot FAS_{y+1/2},$$

for $y=60,61,62,63,64,$ since there would have been $y+\frac{1}{2}-35$ years of service.

(b) DB plans generally allow retirement benefits to begin immediately. If the employee elects to receive it early, the benefit amount $PAB_{y+1/2}$ is reduced to reflect that benefits begin earlier and would be expected to continue for more years. Plans often use a simple formula for reducing the benefit, such as a reduction of 5% for each year that retirement precedes the NRA $(z=65$ in this example), which approximates the actuarial value of the deferred benefit payable at NRA.[17]

The projected annual retirement benefit payable immediately at age $y+\frac{1}{2}$ will now be $PAB_{y+1/2}\cdot\left[1-.05\left(65-y-\frac{1}{2}\right)\right]$, since it is reduced by 5% for each of $65-y-\frac{1}{2}$ years.

(c) Then the APV would be

$$APV_{35}^{ER} = \sum_{y=60}^{64} PAB_{y+1/2}\cdot\left[1-.05\left(65-y-\frac{1}{2}\right)\right]\cdot v^{y+1/2-35}\cdot {}_{y-35}p_{35}^{(\tau)}\cdot q_y^{(r)}\cdot {}^{r}\ddot{a}_{y+1/2}^{(12)}, \quad (14.34)$$

since payments begin at age $y+\frac{1}{2}$ rather than at age 65. Note that the survival factor for surviving to age y is taken from the plan's service table, but the annuity factor is taken from a table appropriate for retired persons. Pension actuaries often approximate the value of ${}^{r}\ddot{a}_{y+1/2}^{(12)}$ as $\frac{1}{2}\left({}^{r}\ddot{a}_{y}^{(12)}+{}^{r}\ddot{a}_{y+1}^{(12)}\right)$. ❐

14.5.3 WITHDRAWAL AND OTHER BENEFITS

In the past, employees who quit before NRA or ERA could forfeit all of their pension benefit, but employers today generally pay 100% of the *accrued benefit* if an employee has at least five years of service. The concept of earning a withdrawal benefit is called *vesting*, and the portion of the accrued benefit taken into account is called the *vesting percentage*. The accrued benefit, denoted AB_y, is the benefit determined by using service and average salary as of the current date only.

Some pension plans provide immediate benefits to employees who become disabled while working. Five years of service are often required for this benefit. It is valued similar to early retirement benefits, except that the annuity factor would be based on a life table appropriate for disabled persons. At the very least, a disabled person must receive the vested benefit available to a withdrawing employee (or retiring employee, if eligible).

Pension plans must provide an immediate survivor annuity upon the death of a married employee, equal to at least the benefit the spouse would have received if the employee had retired immediately before death occurred, under the J&C benefit form (assuming the employee was eligible to retire at that time), if death occurs after the earliest retirement age. The APV formula would be similar to the early retirement APV above, except for the benefit amount, and the annuity factor would be based on a single life table appropriate for the spouse.

---

[17] If the reduction is less than 5% per year, to encourage early retirement or to meet union demands, we say that the early retirement benefit has been *subsidized* by the employer. An actuarially equivalent "early retirement reduction factor" would be the ratio of the APV of a deferred annuity starting at the NRA to the APV of an annuity starting immediately at the early retirement date.

EXAMPLE 14.15

Again consider the DB plan and the employee of Examples 14.13 and 14.14. Find the APV of the withdrawal benefit, assuming the five-year vesting rule.

SOLUTION

Assuming employees take their withdrawal benefit at NRA, the APV at age 35 is

$$APV_{35}^{W} = \sum_{y=40}^{59} PAB_{y+1/2} \cdot v^{30} \cdot {}_{y-35}p_{35}^{(\tau)} \cdot q_{y}^{(w)} \cdot {}_{65-y-1/2}^{\;\;w}p_{y+1/2} \cdot {}^{r}\ddot{a}_{65}^{(12)}, \tag{14.35}$$

where the survival factor ${}_{65-y-1/2}^{\;\;w}p_{y+1/2}$ reflects the mortality of persons who have withdrawn from the plan. The limits on the summation show there is no benefit for withdrawal at any age $y < 40$, nor at any age $y \geq 60$, since termination at those ages is considered early retirement rather than withdrawal. ❐

As an alternative to deferred payments starting at NRA, some DB plans allow a reduced benefit starting at ERA. They may also allow the value of the withdrawal benefit at NRA to be taken as a lump sum.

14.5.4 FUNDING AND RESERVING

The APV of a benefit under a DB pension plan can be interpreted as the net single benefit premium required to fund the eventual benefit. For the plan we have been considering in Examples 14.13 through 14.15, the total APV for our employee hired at age 35 would be the sum of the APVs for each of the decrements.

It is not likely that the benefits would be funded by paying the entire APV_{35}^{T} at the time of hire. Rather the benefits could be funded over the employee's working lifetime. For example, the contributions could be determined by the equivalence principle first encountered in Chapter 9. In pension terminology, the net annual funding payment is called the *normal cost* of the DB plan. Using the equivalence principle, we have

$$NC_{x}^{EAN} = \frac{APV_{x}^{T}}{\ddot{a}_{x:\overline{z-x}|}^{(\tau)}}, \tag{14.36}$$

where x is the employee's age at entry into the DB plan and z is the normal retirement age. Note that the annuity factor in the denominator is calculated from the plan's service table, so NC_{x} is payable only while the employee is active in the plan. When the normal cost is determined in this way we say that the *Entry Age Normal cost method* (EAN) is being used.

For an employee still active at duration t, the status of the funding plan (which we called the net benefit reserve in Chapter 10),[18] can be determined prospectively as

[18] The term "reserve" is not generally used in pension terminology.

$$_tV_x^T = APV_{x+t}^T - NC_x^{EAN} \cdot \ddot{a}_{x+t:\overline{z-x-t}|}^{(\tau)} \tag{14.37a}$$

or retrospectively as

$$_tV_x^T = NC_x^{EAN} \cdot \ddot{s}_{x:\overline{t}|}^{(\tau)}, \tag{14.37b}$$

if there have been no past benefits as of duration t. (If there could have been past benefits, their actuarial accumulated value would need to be subtracted.)

The reader should recognize that the level normal costs described above are analogous to level net benefit premiums as described in Chapter 9. An alternative to level normal costs would be to fund each year the portion of the eventual benefit that accrues each year. This approach, which is called the *Unit Credit cost method* (UC), can be seen to be analogous to funding a traditional insurance benefit with a series of one-year term insurance net premiums.

For our sample career average salary plan with a normal retirement benefit of 2% of career average salary for each year of service, the benefit that accrues in the upcoming year is $.02CAS_x$. For the sample final average salary plan, it is $AB_{x+1} - AB_x$, which is larger since it must update the past accruals to the current salary level.[19] This accrual replaces the PAB term in each of Equations (14.33) through (14.35) to determine the unit credit normal cost. (The normal cost is just the APV of the current year's accrual.) For example, at any attained age x, the APV of the benefit that accrued between ages x and $x+1$ would be

$$APV_x^{NR} = (AB_{x+1} - AB_x) \cdot v^{z-x} \cdot {}_{z-x}p_x^{(\tau)} \cdot {}^r\ddot{a}_z^{(12)}.^{20} \tag{14.38}$$

The total Unit Credit normal cost, which we denote by NC_x^{UC}, is the sum of the APVs for the several decrements. If it is contributed each year, then the plan is being funded by the Unit Credit cost method.

Under the Unit Credit cost method, if experience is the same as forecasted by the assumptions, then the plan is *fully funded*, which means the plan holds assets equal to the total APV of benefits accrued at the current date. That amount is called the *accrued liability*; it can be determined by calculating the total APV using the accrued benefit instead of using the accrual in the same formulas.[21]

If the benefit formula uses salaries, then pension and accounting rules may require use of the Projected Unit Cost (PUC) method for determining the normal cost and accrued liability. It is similar to the UC cost method, except that each employee's current year accrual is generally changed to the projected benefit divided by the total years of service. This accrues the benefit linearly over each employee's total service, which is a faster accrual than the UC

---

[19] See Exercise 14-27 for a numerical illustration of this.

[20] The reader should carefully note the difference between APV_x^{NR} as defined by Equation (14.38) and the one defined by Equation (14.33). The earlier one is the APV at age x of *all future projected benefits*, whereas the one defined by Equation (14.38) is for the benefit accrued in the current year only.

[21] The Unit Credit accrued liability is less than the entry age liability (or reserve), because the level Entry Age Normal cost needs to build up a margin for when the increasing cost of benefit accruals exceeds the level normal cost.

cost method. The PUC accrued liability for each employee is then calculated using that employee's projected benefit times the ratio of the past service to the total service.

It is unlikely that experience will be exactly as assumed, so assets may be more or less than the accrued liability. If assets are less than the accrued liability, the plan is *underfunded.* The plan can also become underfunded if assumptions change, such as lowering the interest rate, which would increase the liability. The employer can make additional contributions to amortize the underfunding over n years, according to funding rules specified in the regulations addressing DB plans.[22]

14.6 GAIN AND LOSS ANALYSIS

We consider, for the third time, the notion of gain or loss by source, this time in a multiple-decrement and gross premium environment. For the $(t+1)^{st}$ contract year, Expression (11.30a) is expanded to include, say, two decrements, producing

$$[{}_tV^G+G_{t+1}(1-r_{t+1})-e_{t+1}](1+i_{t+1})-[(b_{t+1}^{(1)}+s_{t+1}^{(1)})\cdot q_{x+t}^{(1)}+(b_{t+1}^{(2)}+s_{t+1}^{(2)})\cdot q_{x+t}^{(2)}+p_{x+t}^{(\tau)}\cdot {}_{t+1}V^G], \tag{14.39a}$$

where we assume an expense of $s_{t+1}^{(1)}$ to settle a benefit claim due to Cause 1 and an expense of $s_{t+1}^{(2)}$ to settle a benefit claim due to Cause 2 in the $(t+1)^{st}$ year.

The reader should by now understand the ensuing calculations. If all factors actually experienced in the $(t+1)^{st}$ contract year are the same as those assumed in the gross premium and gross premium reserve calculations, there would be neither gain nor loss in that year. That is,

$$[{}_tV^G+G_{t+1}(1-r_{t+1})-e_{t+1}](1+i_{t+1})-[(b_{t+1}^{(1)}+s_{t+1}^{(1)})\cdot q_{x+t}^{(1)}+(b_{t+1}^{(2)}+s_{t+1}^{(2)})\cdot q_{x+t}^{(2)}+p_{x+t}^{(\tau)}\cdot {}_{t+1}V^G] = 0. \tag{14.39b}$$

Then, just as described in Section 11.5, and illustrated in Examples 11.9 and 11.10, an order for calculating the gains by source must be chosen. The process is the same as in Section 11.5, except that here we have four sources (interest, expenses, Cause 1, and Cause 2), rather than three.

Under a life insurance policy, it is often the case that Cause 1 is death and Cause 2 is surrender of (or withdrawal from) the contract. Expression (14.39a) presumes that both death and withdrawal can occur at any time throughout the contract year. Alternatively, we might assume that death can occur throughout the year, but withdrawal can occur only at year end. In this case, Expression (14.39a) is modified to

[22] Readers specializing in pension plans at a later point in their actuarial education will study these pension regulations in considerable detail.

$$[{}_tV^G + G_{t+1}(1-r_{t+1}) - e_{t+1}](1+i_{t+1})$$
$$-[(b_{t+1}^{(1)} + s_{t+1}^{(1)}) \cdot q_{x+t}^{\prime(1)} + (b_{t+1}^{(2)} + s_{t+1}^{(2)})(1-q_{x+t}^{\prime(1)}) \cdot q_{x+t}^{\prime(2)} + p_{x+t}^{(\tau)} \cdot {}_{t+1}V^G], \qquad (14.40)$$

since, with withdrawal not possible within the contract year, mortality is operating in a single-decrement environment and the policyholder must survive death throughout the year in order for the Cause 2 (i.e., withdrawal) benefit to be paid.)

The concepts presented in this section are reviewed in Exercises 14-28 and 14-29.

14.7 WRITTEN-ANSWER QUESTION EXAMPLES

EXAMPLE 14.16

A 20-pay discrete whole life policy for unit face amount is issued to (30). At duration $t=10$ the insured wishes to discontinue the annual premium payments, but to keep the policy in force as paid-up insurance. Assume that the cash value equals the NLP reserve and there is no outstanding loan on the policy. Ignore expenses.

(a) Show that the amount of reduced paid-up whole life insurance that can be provided is

$$ {}_{10}^{20}W_{30} = 1 - \frac{A_{30}}{A_{40}} \cdot \frac{\ddot{a}_{40:\overline{10}|}}{\ddot{a}_{30:\overline{20}|}}.$$

(b) The insured offers to make a one-time payment at time $t=10$ to restore the amount of paid-up whole life insurance to the original unit amount.

(i) Actuary A suggests the payment should be

$$ {}_{20}P_{30} \cdot \ddot{a}_{40:\overline{10}|}.$$

(ii) Actuary B suggests the payment should be

$$\left(1 - {}_{10}^{20}W_{30}\right) \cdot A_{40}.$$

(iii) Actuary C suggests the payment should be

$$A_{40} - {}_{10}^{20}V_{30}.$$

Explain the logic employed by each actuary.

(c) In fact, all three actuaries are correct. Show that the three expressions for the one-time payment are all equal.

SOLUTION

(a) At duration $t=10$ the reserve, and therefore the cash value, is

$${}^{20}_{10}V_{30} = A_{40} - {}_{20}P_{30} \cdot \ddot{a}_{40:\overline{10}|},$$

which acts as the APV for the reduced paid-up whole life coverage. Then the amount of the paid-up coverage is

$${}^{20}_{10}W_{30} = \frac{{}^{20}_{10}V_{30}}{A_{40}} = 1 - \frac{{}_{20}P_{30} \cdot \ddot{a}_{40:\overline{10}|}}{A_{40}} = 1 - \frac{A_{30}}{A_{40}} \cdot \frac{\ddot{a}_{40:\overline{10}|}}{\ddot{a}_{30:\overline{20}|}},$$

as required.

(b) (i) The policy would become fully paid-up at age 40 if the original premium were continued to be paid. Therefore it can be fully paid-up at age 30 by paying the then-APV of the remaining premiums, which is

$${}_{20}P_{30} \cdot \ddot{a}_{40:\overline{10}|}.$$

(ii) The current cash value (reserve) will provide the amount ${}^{20}_{10}W_{30}$ of paid-up insurance, so the one-time payment at age 40 must provide the amount $(1-{}^{20}_{10}W_{30})$. To do this with a single payment, the payment must be the APV of the amount of paid-up coverage purchased, which is

$$(1-{}^{20}_{10}W_{30}) \cdot A_{40}.$$

(iii) If the unit coverage were fully paid-up at age 40, the reserve would then be A_{40} since there would be no future premiums. The reserve is currently ${}^{20}_{10}V_{30}$, so the one-time payment would have to be

$$A_{40} - {}^{20}_{10}V_{30}.$$

(c) The duration 10 reserve is, prospectively,

$${}^{20}_{10}V_{30} = A_{40} - {}_{20}P_{30} \cdot \ddot{a}_{40:\overline{10}|},$$

so

$$A_{40} - {}^{20}_{10}V_{30} = {}_{20}P_{30} \cdot \ddot{a}_{40:\overline{10}|},$$

which shows the equality of (i) and (iii). Recall that

$$ {}_{10}^{20}W_{30} = \frac{{}_{10}^{20}V_{30}}{A_{40}}, $$

so

$$ (1 - {}_{10}^{20}W_{30}) \cdot A_{40} = A_{40} - {}_{10}^{20}V_{30}, . $$

which shows the equality of (ii) and (iii).

EXAMPLE 14.17

Consider the Section 14.4.2 total and permanent disability model, with constant forces of transition $\mu_{x+t}^{02} = .02$, $\mu_{x+t}^{01} = .005$, and $\mu_{x+t}^{12} = .10$.

(a) For a healthy insured age x, calculate the probability of ever becoming disabled.

(b) For a healthy insured age x, calculate the expected length of time of being disabled.

(c) For a healthy insured age x, calculate the APV of an insurance that pays a death benefit of 100,000 for death while healthy or a one-time payment of 500,000 at the time of disability, but not both. Assume $\delta = .05$.

SOLUTION

(a) To become disabled, the insured must transition from State 0 to State 1 before transitioning to State 2. The probability of this is

$$ {}_{\infty}p_x^{01} = \int_0^{\infty} {}_tp_x^{00} \cdot \mu_{x+t}^{01}\, dt. $$

The total force of leaving State 0 is $\mu_{x+t}^{01} + \mu_{x+t}^{02} = .025$, so the probability of remaining in State 0 to time t is ${}_tp_x^{00} = e^{-.025t}$. Then

$$ {}_{\infty}p_x^{01} = .005\int_0^{\infty} e^{-.025t}\, dt = .005\left(\frac{e^{-.025t}}{-.025}\right)_0^{\infty} = .005\left(\frac{1}{.025}\right) = .20. $$

(b) The force of leaving State 1, due to death while disabled, is constant, so the length of time spent in State 1 is exponential with expected value $\frac{1}{\mu_{x+t}^{12}} = 10$, given transition to State 1. From part (a), the probability of transition to State 1 is .20, so the unconditional expected time spent in State 1 is

$$ E[T_1] = E[T_1 \mid State0 \rightarrow State1] \cdot \Pr(State0 \rightarrow State1) = (10)(.20) = 2. $$

(c) The APV is

$$APV_x = 100{,}000\int_0^\infty e^{-\delta t}\cdot {}_tp_x^{00}\cdot \mu_{x+t}^{02}\,dt + 500{,}000\int_0^\infty e^{-\delta t}\cdot {}_tp_x^{00}\cdot \mu_{x+t}^{01}\,dt$$

$$= (100{,}000)(.02)\int_0^\infty e^{-.05t}\cdot e^{-.025t}\,dt + (500{,}000)(.005)\int_0^\infty e^{-.05t}\cdot e^{-.025t}\,dt$$

$$= (2000+2500)\int_0^\infty e^{-.075t}\,dt = 4500\left(\frac{e^{-.075t}}{-.075}\right)_0^\infty = \frac{4500}{.075} = 60{,}000.$$

EXAMPLE 14.18

Consider the Section 14.4.3 disability model allowing for recovery, with forces of transition as given in Example 14.10. A two-year term contract is issued to (x), paying a death benefit of 1000 at the moment of death while either healthy or disabled, and continuous disability income at annual rate 1000 while disabled. Premium is paid continuously while healthy, including the case of a return to the healthy state after a period of disability, at annual rate $\overline{P}$. The continuously-compounded interest rate is $\delta = .04$. There are no expenses.

(a) Give an integral expression, in multi-state model notation, for the annual continuous premium rate $\overline{P}$.

(b) Explain why the integrals in part (a) cannot be evaluated analytically. How could we approximate the value of $\overline{P}$?

(c) Use the forces of transition and the approximate values of ${}_tp_x^{00}$ and ${}_tp_x^{01}$ developed in Example 14.10, and the trapezoidal rule for numerical integration with width $h = 1$, to approximate the value of $\overline{P}$.

(d) Use Microsoft Excel, or similar software, to repeat the calculation of $\overline{P}$ using $h = .10$.

(e) Explain the process for obtaining the correct value of $\overline{P}$, within two decimal places of accuracy.

SOLUTION

(a) There are three benefits under the contract, namely (a) death while healthy, (b) death while disabled, and (c) continuous income while disabled. The insured person (x) is in State 0 when the contract is issued. Using multi-state model notation, the annual continuous premium rate is given by

$$\bar{P} = \frac{1000\left[\int_0^2 v^t \cdot \left({}_tp_x^{00}\mu_{x+t}^{02} + {}_tp_x^{01}\mu_{x+t}^{12} + {}_tp_x^{01}\right)dt\right]}{\int_0^2 v^t \cdot {}_tp_x^{00}\,dt}.$$

(b) In the expression for $\bar{P}$, the probability functions ${}_tp_x^{00}$ and ${}_tp_x^{01}$ do not have functional forms, since the model allows for multiple transitions between States 0 and 1. We could approximate the value of $\bar{P}$ by approximating the values of the integrals using numerical integration.

(c) With width $h=1$, the integral $\int_0^2 f(t)\,dt$ is approximated by

$$\frac{1}{2}\cdot f(0) + f(1) + \frac{1}{2}\cdot f(2).$$

Then the integral in the numerator of $\bar{P}$ is approximated by

$$\frac{1}{2}\left[v^0 \cdot \left({}_0p_x^{00}\mu_x^{02} + {}_0p_x^{01}\mu_x^{12} + {}_0p_x^{01}\right)\right]$$

$$+\left[v^1 \cdot \left({}_1p_x^{00}\mu_{x+1}^{02} + {}_1p_x^{01}\mu_{x+1}^{12} + {}_1p_x^{01}\right)\right]$$

$$+\frac{1}{2}\left[v^2 \cdot \left({}_2p_x^{00}\mu_{x+2}^{02} + {}_2p_x^{01}\mu_{x+2}^{12} + {}_2p_x^{01}\right)\right].$$

The required force of transition values are $\mu_x^{02} = \mu_{x+1}^{02} = \mu_{x+2}^{02} = .200$, $\mu_x^{12} = .20$, $\mu_{x+1}^{12} = .325$, and $\mu_{x+2}^{12} = .450$. The required probability values are ${}_0p_x^{00} = 1$, ${}_1p_x^{00} = .667$, ${}_2p_x^{00} = .448$, ${}_0p_x^{01} = 0$, ${}_1p_x^{01} = .144$, and ${}_2p_x^{01} = .186$. The required discount factors are $v^0 = 1$, $v^1 = e^{-.04} = .96079$, and $v^2 = e^{-.08} = .92312$. Then the integral is approximated by

$$(.50)[(1)(.20)] + (.96079)[(.667)(.20) + (.144)(.325) + .144]$$

$$+(.50)(.92312)[(.448)(.20) + (.186)(.450) + .186]$$

$$= .10000 + .31149 + .16584 = .57733.$$

The integral in the denominator is approximated by

$$\frac{1}{2}\left(v^0 \cdot {}_0p_x^{00}\right) + v^1 \cdot {}_1p_x^{00} + \frac{1}{2}\left(v^2 \cdot {}_2p_x^{00}\right)$$

$$= (.50)(1) + (.96079)(.667) + (.50)(.92312)(.448) = 1.34763.$$

Then we have

$$\overline{P} = \frac{(1000)(.57733)}{1.34763} = 428.40.$$

(d) This time, with $h = .10$, an integral of the form $\int_0^2 f(t)\,dt$ is approximated by

$$.10\left[\frac{1}{2}\cdot f(0) + f(.10) + f(.20) + \cdots + f(1.90) + \frac{1}{2}\cdot f(2.00)\right].$$

Using the force of transition functions and the approximate values of ${}_tp_x^{00}$ and ${}_tp_x^{01}$ from Example 14.10, we approximate the numerator integral as .59256 and the denominator integral as 1.32580, leading to

$$\overline{P} = \frac{(1000)(.59256)}{1.32580} = 446.95.$$

(e) Repeat the entire process with smaller and smaller values of h, until successive values of $\overline{P}$ converge within two decimal places. (Note that for $h < .10$, additional values of ${}_tp_x^{00}$ and ${}_tp_x^{01}$ will have to be generated as in Example 14.10.)

14.8 EXERCISES

14.1 Actuarial Present Value

14-1 A company hires all new employees at age 25. An employee can leave the company via death while employed (Decrement 1), resignation prior to age 65 (Decrement 2), or retirement at age 65. The company provides the following benefits for its employees:

(a) Employees who retire at age 65 receive continuous retirement income at an annual rate of 500 for each year of employment with the company.

(b) Employees who die while employed receive a one-time death benefit of 200,000 at the precise time of death.

(c) Employees who resign prior to age 65, but survive on to age 65, receive continuous retirement income at an annual rate of 400 for each year of employment with the company (including partial years).

Write expressions involving continuous annuities and/or integrals for the APV at time of hire for each of the three benefits.

14.2 Asset Shares

14-2 Show that

$$_kAS = \left[{}_{k-1}AS + G(1-r_k) - e_k\right](1+i) - q_{x+k-1}^{(1)} \cdot (b_k^{(1)} - {}_kAS) - q_{x+k-1}^{(2)} \cdot (b_k^{(2)} - {}_kAS).$$

(This relationship shows that the difference between the withdrawal value and the asset share is important to the progression of the asset share values. If the asset share were paid as a withdrawal value, then the asset share values would progress independently of the withdrawal risk.)

14.3 Non-Forfeiture Options

14-3 A whole life contract of face amount 100,000 is issued to (30). The 20th year cash value is 90% of the NLP reserve. The insured has previously borrowed 5,000 against the policy. Using the life table in Appendix A with 6% interest, find the cash value payable for surrender of the contract at the end of its 20th year.

14-4 If the policyholder in Exercise 14-3 elects the reduced paid-up insurance option at the time of surrender instead of taking the cash value, how much reduced paid-up insurance could be purchased?

14-5 Show that

$$_tW_x = 1 - \frac{P_x}{P_{x+t}}.$$

14-6 For a fully continuous whole life policy, the analogous formula to Equation (14.9) for the fully discrete case is

$$_t\bar{W}(\bar{A}_x) = \frac{_t\bar{V}(\bar{A}_x)}{\bar{A}_{x+t}}.$$

Show that

$$\frac{d}{dt}\,{}_t\bar{W}(\bar{A}_x) = \frac{\bar{P}(\bar{A}_x) - \mu_{x+t}\left[1 - {}_t\bar{W}(\bar{A}_x)\right]}{\bar{A}_{x+t}}.$$

14-7 A 20-year endowment contract of face amount 100,000 is issued to (40) and surrendered at age 55. The cash value at that time is 60,000. If the extended term insurance option is selected, find the amount of pure endowment payable at age 60 using the life table in Appendix A with 6% interest.

14.4 Multi-State Model Representation, with Illustrations

14-8 (a) Referring to the model in Example 14.7, solve the Kolmogorov differential equation for ${}_np_x^{02}$, the probability that a person issued this insurance at age x at time 0 will have withdrawn from the contract by time n, and translate the result into standard actuarial notation.

(b) Use the data given in Example 14.3 to evaluate this probability at $n=3$.

14-9 Suppose the model of Example 14.8 involved three partners instead of two. When represented in multi-state form, how many states are in the model (a) if death and retirement continue to be the only decrements, or (b) if disability is also a decrement? (In both cases, let State 0 denote the status of all partners being alive, healthy, and active (not retired).)

14-10 For the model of Figure 14.5, (a) solve the Kolmogorov differential equation for ${}_np_x^{00}$, the probability that a person alive and healthy at time 0 will still be alive and healthy at time n, and (b) translate the result into standard actuarial notation.

14-11 Repeat Exercise 14-10 to (a) solve for ${}_np_x^{02}$, the probability that a person alive and healthy at time 0 will be not alive at time n, and (b) translate the result into standard actuarial notation.

14-12 Repeat Exercise 14-10 to (a) solve for ${}_np_x^{12}$, the probability that a person alive but disabled at reset time 0 will be not alive at reset time n, and (b) translate the result into standard actuarial notation.

14-13 The model of Figure 14.6 can arise in many other applications other than disability allowing for recovery. For example, a magazine publisher models all persons who ever subscribed to its magazine as those still subscribing (State 0), those no longer subscribing (State 1), and those former subscribers who are now deceased (State 2). Former subscribers who wish to become active subscribers again are encouraged to do so. The model is viewed as a homogeneous discrete-time Markov Chain, with matrix of annual transition probabilities given by

$$\mathbf{P} = \begin{vmatrix} .65 & .32 & .03 \\ .25 & .72 & .03 \\ 0 & 0 & 1 \end{vmatrix}.$$

Find the probability that a new subscriber at time 0 will be alive but a non-subscriber just after time 3.

14-14 A person is currently employed at age x at time 0, which we call State 0. Let State 1 denote unemployment and State 2 denote deceased. The transition forces between states are as follows:

(i) $\mu_{x+t}^{01} = .20 + .0002t^2$

(ii) $\mu_{x+t}^{02} = \mu_{x+t}^{12} = .05$

(iii) $\mu_{x+t}^{10} = .80 - .04t$

(iv) $\mu^{20} = \mu^{21} = 0$

(a) Draw the transition state diagram for this model.

(b) Using one-year time-steps ($h = 1$) to approximate the solutions to the Kolmogorov differential equation, estimate ${}_tp_x^{00}$ and ${}_tp_x^{01}$ for $t = 1, 2, \ldots, 20$.

(c) Use half-year time-steps to estimate the same functions for $t = 0.5, 1.0, \ldots, 10.0$, and compare the results for ${}_{10}p_x^{00}$ and ${}_{10}p_x^{01}$ to those obtained in part (b). Which result should be closer to the true solution?

(d) Use tenth-year time-steps to estimate the same functions for $t = 0.1, 0.2, \ldots, 10.0$, and compare the results for ${}_{10}p_x^{00}$ and ${}_{10}p_x^{01}$ to those obtained in parts (b) and (c).

14-15 Referring to Exercise 14-14, a 20-year insurance contract is issued that pays 1400 at the end of each month that the person is unemployed.

(a) For this contract, what is the natural time-step to use to approximate a solution to the Kolmogorov differential equation?

(b) Assuming a nominal interest rate of $i^{(12)} = .04$, find the APV at issue of the unemployment benefit.

14-16 Immediately after the contract of Exercise 14-15 is issued, the person becomes disabled, so the company issuing the contract must adjust its reserve to reflect the changed APV of the contract. Find the APV of the unemployment insurance for a person who is currently unemployed at time 0.

14-17 For the insurance of Exercise 14-15, suppose the insured is required to pay a level premium at the beginning of each month that she is employed. Find the net benefit premium P.

14-18 Suppose the insurance of Exercise 14-15 also pays 50,000 at the end of the month of death if the insured is unemployed at time of death. Find the APV for this contract.

14-19 For the model of Section 14.4.4, as illustrated in Figure 14.8, find the probability that a person in State 0 (ILU) at time 0 will be in State 0 at the end of the third month.

14-20 Repeat Exercise 14-19, this time for the probability that a person in State 0 at time 0 will be in State 2 at the end of the third month.

14-21 Generalize the Thiele differential equations, given by Equations (14.25) and (14.26), to allow the benefits, premiums, and force of interest to vary with time, and to allow for percent-of-premium and continuous fixed expenses.

14-22 The most general case considers that we have m distinct states, with premium paid continuously at rate $\bar{G}_t^{(i)}$ while in State i (with $\bar{G}_t^{(i)}=0$ for some values of i), percent-of-premium expense rate $r_t^{(i)}$ at time t if in State i, fixed expense payable continuously at rate $\bar{e}_t^{(i)}$ at time t if in State i, benefit paid continuously at rate $\bar{b}_t^{(i)}$ if in State i at time t, single-sum benefit of amount $b_t^{(ij)}$ paid for transition from State i to State j at time t, and interest credited to the reserves at force of interest δ_t at time t regardless of state. Let ${}_t\bar{V}^{(i)}$ denote the reserve at time t if the process is in State i. State the general form of Thiele's differential equation in this general case.

14-23 A health insurer divides its insured population into the three risk classes of low, moderate, and high. The following table shows the percentage of insureds in each risk class in Year Z, and the reallocation of them among the three risk classes in Year $Z+1$.

Risk Class	**Year Z Distribution**	**Year $Z+1$ Distribution**		
		Low	**Moderate**	**High**
Low	69.5%	57.4%	11.7%	0.4%
Moderate	28.7%	9.9%	17.7%	1.1%
High	1.8%	0.2%	0.9%	0.7%
Totals	100%	67.5%	30.3%	2.2%

(a) From the data in the table, develop a matrix of transition probabilities for transition among risk classes.

(b) The average claim costs in Year Z for the three risk classes are 500 for low, 10,000 for moderate, and 50,000 for high. Find the average claim cost in Year Z for the entire insured population.

(c) Assuming a homogeneous discrete time Markov process, find the percentage distribution of the insured population in Year $Z+2$ and in Year $Z+3$.

(d) Assume that claim costs increase by 5% each year in all risk classes. Find the average claim cost in Year $Z+3$ for the entire population.

14.5 Defined Benefit Pension Plans

14-24 Consider a newly hired employee age 30, earning 100,000 in the first year of employment. Regular salary increases are assumed to be 4% per year; in addition, employees are assumed to receive merit increases of 6% at each of their first three employment anniversaries. The pension benefit formula is 1% of the final five-year average salary per year of service.

(a) Find the final five-year average salary.

(b) Find the projected pension benefit at age 65.

(c) Find the employee's replacement ratio, defined as the pension benefit divided by the final year's salary.

(d) What would a 1% career average benefit be as a percentage of this final five-year average benefit?

14-25 Consider a worker taking early retirement at age 55 under a plan where the NRA is 65, and the early retirement benefit is the actuarial equivalent of the benefit at NRA. The equivalence is determined at interest rate 6% and the life table shown in Appendix A.

(a) Find the age 55 early retirement reduction factor.

(b) What is the informal "5% per year early" factor described in Example 14.15(b)?

14-26 Consider a newly hired employee age 51. The salary at hire is 100,000 and is projected to increase by 4% per year. Vesting occurs after five years of service, and no benefits will be paid before that time. The normal retirement age is 65, and is mandatory at that time so $q_{65}^{(r)}=1$; the retirement benefit is 1% of final three-year average salary per year of service. The employee is eligible for early retirement at age 61, with a 3% reduction per year early. The withdrawal benefit is the then accrued benefit otherwise payable at NRA. The disability benefit is the then accrued benefit payable immediately, without reduction, if the employee has at least five years of service. The death benefit requires ten years of service, and is set at 50% of the then accrued benefit, reduced as for early retirement. Assume the surviving beneficiary is three years younger than the employee.

Write the APV formulas for each of (a) normal retirement, (b) early retirement, (c) withdrawal, (d) disability, and (e) death. Assume early retirement, withdrawal, disability, or death occur half way through the year of age, on average.

14-27 Assume the employee of Exercise 14-25 is now exact age 56, with a salary of 150,000 in the year from age 55 to age 56 and a salary of 156,000 in the year from age 56 to age 57. Determine each of the following:

(a) The benefit accrual for the year from age 56 to age 57.
(b) The unit credit normal cost.
(c) The accrued liability under the unit credit cost method.

14.6 Gain and Loss Analysis

14-28 Consider the general double-decrement model given by Expression (14.39a). Let the actual earned interest rate in the $(t+1)^{st}$ year be denoted by i^*_{t+1}, and the actual Cause 2 decrement probability be denoted by $q^{*(2)}_{x+t}$. If the gain from interest is calculated first and the gain from the Cause 2 decrement is calculated second, show that the gain from the Cause 2 decrement is

$$G^{(2)} = \left(b^{(2)}_{t+1} + s^{(2)}_{t+1} - {}_{t+1}V^G\right)\left(q^{(2)}_{x+t} - q^{*(2)}_{x+t}\right).$$

14-29 A block of 1000 fully discrete insurances, issued at age 70, are in force at age 79. The gross premium is $G=16$, the ninth gross premium reserve is 115.00, the tenth gross premium reserve is 128.83, the tenth year death benefit is 1000, the tenth year withdrawal benefit is 110, and the assumed interest rate is .06. Expenses are 3 per policy, incurred at the beginning of the year, and there are no claim settlement expenses. Withdrawals can occur only at the end of the contract year. The assumed decrement rates are $q'^{(d)}_{79} = .01$ and $q'^{(w)}_{79} = .10$. During the tenth contract year there are 15 deaths and 100 withdrawals. Calculate, in order, (a) the gain from mortality and (b) the gain from withdrawal on this block of policies.

Part Three

Specialized Topics

For all of the values calculated thus far in the text, we have assumed a fixed interest rate to apply. In Chapter 15, we relax that assumption and consider the effect of variable interest rates.

When an insurer makes a contractual promise to pay certain benefits, and calculates a premium rate to fund those benefits, it assumes that the reserve funds it holds will earn a certain rate of investment return. If they fail to earn the assumed rate, this works to the insurer's financial disadvantage. In this case we say that the insurer assumes the *interest rate risk*, or the *investment risk*. This is a characteristic of the traditional insurance and annuity contracts considered in Part Two of the text.

In Chapter 16 we present a class of modern insurance contracts, known as *Universal Life Insurance*. In some cases the applicable interest rates might be allowed to vary according to certain external conditions. Due to the influence of the external conditions, these insurance products are often referred to as *interest-sensitive* products. We will also see that, in certain cases, the interest rate risk can be transferred, in whole or in part, from the insurer to the insured or annuitant.

In Chapter 17 we return to the notion of gain or loss under insurance or annuity contracts, considered at various points earlier in the text, and expand on the earlier work for a more complete *profit analysis* of these products.

CHAPTER FIFTEEN

MODELS WITH VARIABLE INTEREST RATES

Thus far in the text, when calculating the actuarial present value (APV) for contingent payment models, including insurance products, we have treated time until failure and mode of failure as random variables. But we have always assumed that a single interest rate was valid throughout the life of the model, however long that might be. It can be risky to assume that interest rates will remain constant at today's rates. Indeed some insurance companies around the world have experienced severe losses as a result of pricing products at interest rates that proved to be too optimistic.

In this chapter we address contingent payment models using interest rates that vary with time. Sections 15.1 and 15.2 address models with deterministic contingent payment amounts evaluated using non-deterministic interest rates. The term structure of interest rates and implied forward rates of interest are introduced in Sections 15.3 and 15.4.

The treatment of topics in Chapter 15 follows a heuristic approach. To simplify the discussion in Sections 15.1 and 15.2, we make the assumption that the market consists only of *one-period securities*. For our discussion of interest rates, the only securities available for investment are one-period bonds that pay a single coupon plus principal at the end of the period. This assumption enables us to introduce features of interest rate variability without having to deal with issues such as a term structure or partial-period payments. In addition, there is no distinction (in the absence of default) between the interest rate of a bond and the rate of return on that bond. In Sections 15.3 and 15.4 we broaden the discussion to include multi-period bonds, including those with partial-period payments (coupons). This will enable us to develop the term structure of spot interest rates along with implied forward rates of interest.

15.1 ACTUARIAL PRESENT VALUES USING VARIABLE INTEREST RATES

Interest rates in the United States have varied substantially over time. Table 15.1 shows sample one-year U.S. Treasury interest rates between 1962 and 2009.[1] This table gives a good indication of just how variable interest rates can be over time. In this section, we discuss one method for incorporating this variability into calculating the actuarial present value for contingent payment models. This method involves the construction of *interest rate scenarios* for the future. An interest rate scenario is a possible future path for interest rates. For example, Table 15.2 shows three illustrative interest rate scenarios for one-year interest rates in the first five years of a contingent contract. Each row represents a different scenario for the one-year interest rate in each year over the next five years. The pre-subscript j on the interest rate symbol

[1] Source: www.ustreas.gov.

indicates the scenario from which that rate was taken. For example, ${}_3i_3 = .04$ means that the interest rate in the third interest rate scenario in the third year is 4%.

TABLE 15.1

Year	Rate	Year	Rate	Year	Rate
1962	3.10%	1978	8.34%	1994	5.32%
1963	3.36	1979	10.65	1995	5.94
1964	3.85	1980	12.00	1996	5.52
1965	4.15	1981	14.80	1997	5.63
1966	5.20	1982	12.27	1998	5.05
1967	4.88	1983	9.58	1999	5.08
1968	5.69	1984	10.91	2000	6.11
1969	7.12	1985	8.42	2001	3.49
1970	6.90	1986	6.45	2002	2.00
1971	4.89	1987	6.77	2003	1.24
1972	4.95	1988	7.65	2004	1.31
1973	7.32	1989	8.53	2005	2.79
1974	8.20	1990	7.89	2006	4.38
1975	6.78	1991	5.86	2007	5.00
1976	5.88	1992	3.89	2008	3.17
1977	6.08	1993	3.43	2009	0.40

TABLE 15.2

Scenario j	${}_ji_1$	${}_ji_2$	${}_ji_3$	${}_ji_4$	${}_ji_5$
1	6%	7%	8%	9%	10%
2	6	6	6	6	6
3	6	5	4	3	2

EXAMPLE 15.1

For each of the three interest rate scenarios in Table 15.2, find the actuarial present value of a five-year pure endowment issued at age $x = 65$ for amount \$1000. The mortality rates for each year of age are $q_{65} = .03$, $q_{66} = .04$, $q_{67} = .05$, $q_{68} = .06$, and $q_{69} = .07$.

SOLUTION

In each scenario, the APV is

$$1000\,{}_5E_{65} = 1000({}_jv^5 \cdot {}_5p_{65}),$$

where ${}_j v^5$ represents five years of discounting at interest rates given by Scenario j. Regardless of the chosen scenario,

$$ {}_5p_{65} = (.97)(.96)(.95)(.94)(.93) = .7734. $$

We can find ${}_1 v^5$, for example, as

$$ {}_1 v^5 = \left(\frac{1}{1.06}\right)\left(\frac{1}{1.07}\right)\left(\frac{1}{1.08}\right)\left(\frac{1}{1.09}\right)\left(\frac{1}{1.10}\right) = .6809, $$

so the APV under Scenario 1 is $(1000)(.7734)(.6809) = 526.61$. Under Scenarios 2 and 3 the APV's are 577.93 and 635.97, respectively. (The reader is asked to verify these results in Exercise 15-1.) ❒

We can imagine that an insurer who has priced a pure endowment contract assuming level interest rates of 6% (Scenario 2) will be unhappy if it chooses to invest the net single premium in one-year bonds, and the interest rates then emerge similarly to Scenario 3.[2]

EXAMPLE 15.2

Using the same mortality and interest assumptions as in Example 15.1, find the actuarial present value for a five-year term insurance of unit amount issued at age $x = 65$, with benefit paid at the end of the year of failure. Find a separate APV for each of the three scenarios.

SOLUTION

We adapt Equation (7.8) to find the actuarial present value for the five-year term insurance under Scenario j, and we denote this APV by ${}_j A^{1}_{65:\overline{5}|}$.

TABLE 15.3

t	Year t Rate	${}_1 v^t$	${}_{t-1|}q_{65}$	${}_1 v^t \cdot {}_{t-1|}q_{65}$
1	.06	.9434	.0300	.0283
2	.07	.8817	.0388	.0342
3	.08	.8164	.0466	.0380
4	.09	.7490	.0531	.0398
5	.10	.6809	.0582	.0396
		${}_1 A^{1}_{65:\overline{5}|}$		**.1799**

[2] In practice, the situation is more complicated than that presented here, because the insurer will generally try to invest in securities with a maturity similar to that of the product from which the net single premium arose. In this case the insurer will only have to worry about current interest rates for bond cash flows requiring reinvestment. However, for some very long-term contracts such as whole life contingent annuities, whole life insurance, or long term care insurance, this problem can be serious.

The results of the calculation for Scenario 1 are shown in Table 15.3 in spreadsheet form. Note how the term v^k in Equation (7.8), which assumes a constant interest rate, is generalized to $_jv^k = \prod_{t=1}^{k}(1+{}_ji_t)^{-1}$ in the case of the jth variable interest rate scenario. The APV under Scenario 1 is $_1A^{\;1}_{65:\overline{5}|} = .1799$. (The reader should repeat the steps depicted in Table 15.3 under Scenarios 2 and 3 to verify that $_2A^{\;1}_{65:\overline{5}|} = .1875$ and $_3A^{\;1}_{65:\overline{5}|} = .1958$.) Note that the APV is higher for the lower interest rate scenarios. ❐

15.2 DETERMINISTIC INTEREST RATE SCENARIOS

Interest rate scenarios used in actuarial analysis are of two distinct types. *Deterministic scenarios*, described in this section, are determined *a priori* and are often used to "stress" a product's profitability in the event future interest rates are unfavorable. Scenarios of this type are sometimes prescribed by regulatory agencies to provide a test of sensitivity to interest rates that is common across products and companies. *Stochastic scenarios* are scenarios that are created using a stochastic interest rate simulator based on an assumed probability distribution for future interest rates.

We address the deterministic scenarios in this section by studying a sample regulatory policy designed to test the interest sensitivity of insurance products. If a product "fails" the interest sensitivity test, the company selling the product must hold additional capital as contingent funds for adverse changes in interest rates. Although the example here is fictional, similar deterministic scenarios are performed in some jurisdictions as part of cash flow testing of products for interest sensitivity.

EXAMPLE 15.3

An annuity company sells the following two products:

(a) A five-year annual payment temporary immediate annuity

(b) A five-year pure endowment

The national regulatory authority requires the following two-step interest rate test in order to determine if the annuity company must hold additional capital:

(1) The net single premium (NSP) for each product is calculated under three deterministic interest rate scenarios:

 (i) Rates remain level at the current rate.
 (ii) Rates rise 1% per year until they reach twice the current rate, and then remain level in succeeding years.
 (iii) Rates fall 1% per year until they reach one-half the current rate, and then remain level in succeeding years.

(2) If the NSP under the falling interest rate scenario is 5% or more above the NSP in the level rate case, the company must hold additional capital.

If the probability of death in any given year remains constant at $q_x = .02$ and the current interest rate is 6%, determine whether this annuity company must hold additional capital for either product.

SOLUTION

(a) For the five-year temporary immediate annuity, we first calculate the NSP (or APV) in the level rate case, using Equation (8.21). We obtain

$$_l a_{x:\overline{5}|} = \sum_{t=1}^{5} {}_l v^t \cdot {}_t p_x = \sum_{t=1}^{5} \left(\frac{1}{1.06}\right)^t \cdot (.98)^t = 3.9756,$$

where the pre-subscript l denotes the level interest rate case. For the falling interest rate case, denoted by the pre-subscript f, the NSP is given by

$$_f a_{x:\overline{5}|} = \sum_{t=1}^{5} {}_f v^t \cdot {}_t p_x = \sum_{t=1}^{5} {}_f v^t \cdot (.98)^t.$$

The calculation is summarized in Table 15.4 below. The reader should repeat the steps depicted in Table 15.4 to calculate the APV under the rising interest rate scenario, obtaining the value $_r a_{x:\overline{5}|} = 3.8461$ (see Exercise 15-3(a)). Since the falling interest rate scenario does not produce an APV more than 5% greater than under the level rate case, the annuity company does not need to hold additional reserves for its five-year temporary immediate annuity product.

TABLE 15.4

t	Year t Rate	$_f v^t$	$_t p_x$	$_f v^t \cdot {}_t p_x$
1	.06	.9434	.9800	.9245
2	.05	.8985	.9604	.8629
3	.04	.8639	.9412	.8131
4	.03	.8388	.9224	.7737
5	.03	.8143	.9039	.7360
		$_f a_{x:\overline{5}|}$		**4.1102**

(b) For the five-year pure endowment, we again calculate first the APV in the level interest case, obtaining

$$_l A_{x:\overline{5}|}^{\;\;1} = {}_l v^5 \cdot {}_5 p_x = \left(\frac{1}{1.06}\right)^5 \cdot (.98)^5 = .6755.$$

Under the falling interest rate scenario, we have ${}_f v^5 = .8143$ (from Table 15.4) along with the value ${}_5 p_x = (.98)^5 = .9039$, so the APV for the five-year pure endowment is $(.8143)(.9039) = .7361$. The ratio of the falling rate APV to the level rate APV is $\frac{.7361}{.6755} = 1.0897$.

Since the falling rate APV is more that 5% above the level rate APV, the annuity company is required to hold additional capital for each five-year pure endowment product that it sells. ❒

15.3 SPOT INTEREST RATES AND THE TERM STRUCTURE OF INTEREST RATES

We now drop the assumption made in Sections 15.1 and 15.2 that the market consists only of one-period securities, and move to a more realistic set of investment products. We assume that it is possible to buy interest-bearing securities of varying maturities. Also, we assume that some of these interest-bearing securities make periodic interest payments every six months and make an interest and principal payment at maturity. For the sake of simplicity, we assume that all of these securities are risk-free (i.e., they are certain to pay interest and principal with no chance of default), and we refer to all of them as *bonds*. Bonds with periodic interest payments are called *coupon bonds* whereas bonds with no periodic payments and a single payment at maturity are called *zero-coupon bonds*. There is a large market in United States Treasury securities fitting these descriptions.

Table 15.5 shows available interest rates for coupon-bearing treasury securities of varying maturities on a particular date.[3]

TABLE 15.5

Maturity (in years)	Nominal Annual Yield for Coupon-bearing Bonds ($i^{(2)}$)
0.5	2.44%
1.0	2.60
1.5	2.76
2.0	2.93

This table suggests that on the day in question, we could expect to purchase a treasury security with a maturity of six months at a yield of 2.44%.[4] In other words, for an investment of \$1000, we would expect to receive \$1012.20 in six months. Note that the coupon payment, made in addition to the principal, is half the stated yield. A one-year bond purchased the same day would pay \$13 in six months and \$1013 at the end of one year.

[3] Source: Daily Treasury Yield Curve Rates at www.ustreas.gov; 1.5 year yield is interpolated.

[4] In reality, such a security with exact yield and maturity dates may not be available on that day.

Similarly, a two-year bond would entitle the purchaser to three semi-annual payments of \$14.65 and a final payment of \$1014.65.

The first important feature of this table is that bonds with differing maturities offer differing rates of interest. The extra yield for longer-term bonds reflects the loss of liquidity that investors suffer by committing their money for a longer period of time, and can be thought of as a type of *liquidity premium*. Differences in yield also reflect market expectations for what the future short-term rates of interest will be. On occasion, expectations for lower short-term rates in the future will offset the liquidity premium and longer maturities will have lower yields than shorter maturities.

A second important feature of the table is that there is an implied set of zero-coupon bond interest rates for each maturity listed in the table, which can be derived from the coupon-bearing bond yields using a method called *bootstrapping*. First, the zero-coupon bond yield for a maturity of six-months must equal that of the coupon-bearing bond, since both consists of only a single payment at that maturity. Therefore the nominal annual yield, convertible semiannually, for a six-month zero-coupon bond, denoted $z_{0.5}$, is $z_{0.5} = 2.440\%$, or 1.220% as an effective semiannual rate.

To calculate the yield for a zero-coupon bond which matures in one year, we use the six-month zero-coupon rate to value the six-month coupon payment and the original price of the bond to determine the implied one-year zero-coupon rate. For example, the one-year bond described above pays \$13 in six months and \$1013 in one year for the price of \$1000. Therefore the implied one-year zero-coupon yield, denoted $z_{1.0}$, must satisfy

$$1000 = \frac{13}{1.01220} + \frac{1013}{\left(1+\frac{z_{1.0}}{2}\right)^2},$$

where .01220 is effective semiannual and $z_{1.0}$ is nominal annual, convertible semiannually. From this we obtain $z_{1.0} = 2.601\%$. Similarly, $z_{1.5}$ must satisfy

$$1000 = \frac{13.80}{1.01220} + \frac{13.80}{\left(1+\frac{.02601}{2}\right)^2} + \frac{1013.80}{\left(1+\frac{z_{1.5}}{2}\right)^3}.$$

(The reader should note that the one-year zero-coupon rate was used for that maturity, rather than the one-year coupon-bearing rate.) From this we obtain $z_{1.5} = 2.763\%$. Finally, using

$$1000 = \frac{14.65}{1.01220} + \frac{14.65}{\left(1+\frac{.02601}{2}\right)^2} + \frac{14.65}{\left(1+\frac{.02763}{2}\right)^3} + \frac{1014.65}{\left(1+\frac{z_{2.0}}{2}\right)^4},$$

we determine that $z_{2.0} = 2.936\%$. In summary, the bootstrap method produces the results shown in Table 15.6.

TABLE 15.6

Maturity (in years)	Nominal Annual Yield for Coupon-bearing Bonds	Nominal Annual Yield for Zero-coupon Bonds
0.5	2.44%	2.440%
1.0	2.60	2.601
1.5	2.76	2.763
2.0	2.93	2.936

Regarding Table 15.6, the dependence of available yields on years to maturity is referred to as the *term structure of interest rates.* The associated zero-coupon bond rates are often referred to as *spot rates*. Once a set of spot rates has been obtained, it is easy to value any set of cash flows, whether or not those cash flows are uniform.

EXAMPLE 15.4

To finance the construction of an auditorium, a college has agreed to make the following payments at the following maturity times:

Payment	$200,000	$50,000	$50,000	$100,000
Maturity	Today	6 months	12 months	24 months

Using the term structure of interest rates in Table 15.6, calculate the net present value of these payments.

SOLUTION

We directly find

$$NPV \;=\; 200{,}000+\frac{50{,}000}{1.01220}+\frac{50{,}000}{\left(1+\frac{.02601}{2}\right)^2}+\frac{100{,}000}{\left(1+\frac{.02936}{2}\right)^4} \;=\; 392{,}459.12. \qquad \square$$

EXAMPLE 15.5

A client age 60 purchases a five-year term life insurance policy that will pay $1,000,000 at the end of the year of death. The client will fund the policy with level annual premiums, and the insurance company has the ability to lock in appropriate forward rates of interest on those premiums. Using the information in Table 15.7, calculate the net level annual premium for the policy.

TABLE 15.7

Maturity (in years)	Annual Yield for Zero-coupon Bonds	x	q_x
1.0	3.0%	60	.02
2.0	4.0	61	.03
3.0	5.0	62	.04
4.0	6.0	63	.05
5.0	7.0	64	.06

SOLUTION

The most straightforward solution to this problem is to calculate the APV of the premium payments and set it equal to the APV of the insurance death benefit, using the equivalence principle. For a level annual premium, P, the APV of premium is

$$P \cdot \ddot{a}_{60:\overline{5}|} = P(1+vp_{60} + v^2 \;{}_2p_{60} + v^3 \;{}_3p_{60} + v^4 \;{}_4p_{60}),$$

where each v^t value is calculated using the t-year spot rate. Using this and the mortality rates shown above, we have

$$P \cdot \ddot{a}_{60:\overline{5}|} = P\left[1+\frac{.98}{1.03}+\frac{(.98)(.97)}{(1.04)^2}+\frac{(.98)(.97)(.96)}{(1.05)^3}+\frac{(.98)(.97)(.96)(.95)}{(1.06)^4}\right].$$

From this we find the APV of the premiums to be $4.3054P$. The APV of the death benefit is

$$A^{1}_{60:\overline{5}|} = vq_{60} + v^2 p_{60} \cdot q_{61} + v^3 \;{}_2p_{60} \cdot q_{62} + v^4 \;{}_3p_{60} \cdot q_{63} + v^5 \;{}_4p_{60} \cdot q_{64},$$

where, again, spot interest rates are used. (As an exercise, the reader should verify that $A^{1}_{60:\overline{5}|} = .1527$.) Then the net level premium is

$$P = \frac{(1{,}000{,}000)(.1527)}{4.3054} = 35{,}467.09.$$

❒

15.4 FORWARD INTEREST RATES

For this section, we assume a financial environment in which investors can buy and sell zero-coupon bonds that pay interest at current spot rates in any dollar amount and with no transaction costs. In such an environment, current spot rates imply another set of interest rates that can be locked in today for future deposits. For example, suppose an investor simultaneously undertakes the following pair of transactions:

Transaction A: Buy a \$1000 par value two-year zero-coupon bond paying 2.96% interest.

Transaction B: Sell a \$1000 par value one-year zero-coupon bond paying 2.62% interest.

With this pair of transactions, the investor has a net cash flow of zero today. In one year he must pay principal and interest on the one-year bond, and in two years he will receive principal and interest on the two-year bond. The resulting net cash flows experienced by the investor are shown in Table 15.8.

TABLE 15.8

Time (in years)	Net Cash Flow
0	$ 0.00
1	−1026.20
2	1060.08

These are the same cash flows that would be experienced by an investor who agrees one year in advance to invest $1026.20 in a zero-coupon bond at 3.30% interest (except for some small round-off error). Therefore by purchasing and selling securities of differing maturities today, an investor can "lock in" a return on an investment one or more periods from now. In the current example, we say that the 3.30% interest rate obtained for an investment one year from now is the *one-year forward one-year rate*, since the interest rate obtained is for an investment one year from now (i.e., one year forward) and is obtained for a one-year security. When a similar set of transactions is implemented to lock in a rate n years from now on a k-year zero coupon bond, the resulting rate is called the *n-year forward k-year rate*. We denote this rate by $f_{n,k}$.

EXAMPLE 15.6

Using the yields in Table 15.9, find all possible forward rates for forward securities with maturities of one, two, three, and four years.

TABLE 15.9

Maturity (in years)	Annual Yield for Zero-coupon Bonds
1.0	3.0%
2.0	4.0
3.0	5.0
4.0	6.0
5.0	7.0

SOLUTION

We show here the calculations for $f_{1,4}$ and $f_{2,2}$. (Calculations for other forward rates are similar, and are left to the reader as Exercise 15-12.) $f_{1,4}$ is the only forward four-year rate that can be calculated from the rates in the table. This rate is most easily calculated using the logic that an investor obtains the same total return *either* by buying a five-year zero-coupon bond, *or* by investing in a one-year bond and then investing the proceeds for four years at the one-year forward four-year rate. That is,

$$(1+z_5)^5 = (1+z_1)^1 \cdot (1+f_{1,4})^4. \qquad (15.1)$$

In this case we have

$$(1.07)^5 = (1.03)^1 \cdot (1+f_{1,4})^4,$$

from which we find $f_{1,4} = 8.024\%$. Similarly, $f_{2,2}$ must satisfy

$$(1+z_4)^4 = (1+z_2)^2 \cdot (1+f_{2,2})^2, \tag{15.2}$$

from which we find $f_{2,2} = 8.038\%$. All of the forward rates, rounded to four decimal places, are shown in Table 15.10. ❐

TABLE 15.10

n	$f_{n,1}$	$f_{n,2}$	$f_{n,3}$	$f_{n,4}$
1.0	5.01%	6.01%	7.02%	8.02%
2.0	7.03	8.04	9.05	–
3.0	9.06	10.07	–	–
4.0	11.10	–	–	–

EXAMPLE 15.7

A five-year pure endowment contract issued to a person age 60 is funded with level annual premiums and has a maturity benefit of $10,000. Premiums are payable at the beginning of each year, and the benefit is payable at the end of the fifth year. Table 15.11 shows mortality rates for a 60-year-old and forward rates that are currently available. Use this information to calculate the net level annual premium for the pure endowment. Note that $f_{0,5} = z_5$.

TABLE 15.11

y	$f_{y,5-y}$	x	q_x
0	4.0%	60	.02
1	5.0	61	.03
2	6.0	62	.04
3	7.0	63	.05
4	8.0	64	.06

SOLUTION

Since we are given forward rates, it will be easiest to determine the level annual premium retrospectively. The premiums must accumulate with interest and survivorship to total $10,000 at the end of the fifth year. That is,

$$10{,}000 = P \cdot \ddot{s}_{60:\overline{5}|} = P\left(\frac{1}{{}_5E_{60}} + \frac{1}{{}_4E_{61}} + \frac{1}{{}_3E_{62}} + \frac{1}{{}_2E_{63}} + \frac{1}{{}_1E_{64}}\right),$$

where, for example,

$$_3E_{62} = \frac{_3p_{62}}{(1+f_{2,3})^3} = \frac{(.96)(.95)(.94)}{(1.06)^3} = .7198.$$

Similar calculations produce

$$10{,}000 = P \cdot \ddot{s}_{60:\overline{5}|} = P\left(\frac{1}{.6698}+\frac{1}{.6841}+\frac{1}{.7198}+\frac{1}{.7800}+\frac{1}{.8704}\right),$$

from which we find $P = 1476.02$.

Note that we could also have found the net level annual premium prospectively by first converting the forward rates to current spot rates. We first note that $z_5 = f_{0,5} = 4.0\%$. Then to calculate z_n for $n < 5$, we use the relationship

$$(1+z_n)^n \cdot (1+f_{n,5-n})^{5-n} = (1+z_5)^5. \tag{15.3}$$

The resulting spot rates, rounded to four decimal places, are shown in Table 15.12. (The reader should verify that they are correct.)

TABLE 15.12

n	z_n
1	0.094%
2	1.071
3	2.049
4	3.023
5	4.000

Then prospectively we have

$$10{,}000\,_5E_{60} = P \cdot \ddot{a}_{60:\overline{5}|} = P(1+v \cdot {_1p_{60}} + v^2 \cdot {_2p_{60}} + v^3 \cdot {_3p_{60}} + v^4 \cdot {_4p_{60}}).$$

The left side of this equation evaluates to

$$10{,}000v^5 \cdot {_5p_{60}} = \frac{(10{,}000)(.98)(.97)(.96)(.95)(.94)}{(1.04)^5} = 6698.13,$$

where the five-year spot rate has been used. For the right side of the equation, each v^n is calculated using the corresponding spot rate z_n. From this we find $\ddot{a}_{60:\overline{5}|} = 4.53795$, from which we again find

$$P = \frac{6698.13}{4.53795} = 1476.02.$$

❐

15.5 TRANSFERRING THE INTEREST RATE RISK

The overriding theme of this text is that persons facing financial risks can be relieved of those risks by paying an insurer to assume them. From the insurer's perspective, there are three primary risks associated with a contract of life insurance, namely those of expenses, mortality, and interest.

The insurer charges for the expenses of doing business by increasing the net premiums to reach the contract premiums (or gross premiums), actually paid. If operational expenses turn out to be less than assumed in setting the contract premiums, the insurer makes a profit on the expense element. If the opposite turns out to be the case, then the insurer loses money on the expense element. Generally insurers are fairly good at charging for their expenses, so the *expense risk* is not very great.

For many years the view was held that the major risk to the insurer was the *mortality risk*. If failures occurred earlier than, or at greater rates than, as predicted by the underlying survival model, the insurer suffered losses on the mortality element under life insurance contracts. Under annuities, the opposite would be true; the insurer would suffer a loss if mortality was lighter (i.e., if annuitants lived longer) than as predicted by the survival model.

By assuming that the lifetimes of different policyholders are independent, the insurer can *diversify* the mortality risk over the collection of policyholders. Some will fail earlier and some later, so that the aggregate risk can be better predicted. In light of this, we refer to the mortality risk as a *diversifiable risk*. (This concept was illustrated in Section 9.3.)[5]

When the insurer selects an interest rate for the premium calculation, it is assuming that it will be able to earn that rate on its invested assets backing the insurance or annuity contracts. If it earns interest on its assets at a greater rate than that assumed, it makes a profit on the interest element. On the other hand, the insurer faces an *interest rate risk* that earned rates will fall below assumed rates and it will therefore suffer a loss on the interest element. This has been a problem for many insurers in recent years.

If an interest loss occurs, due to falling interest rates in the investment marketplace, it will occur on all contracts alike. For this reason we refer to the interest rate risk as a *non-diversifiable risk*.

Although the insurer cannot diversify the interest rate risk across the collection of policyholders, it is possible for the insurer to *transfer* part or all of that risk back to the insured. When this is done under a life insurance or annuity contract, we say that the policyholder is participating in the interest rate risk.[6]

In this text we explore how this is accomplished under variable or indexed universal life insurance contracts. (See Sections 16.2.1 and 16.2.3.) For annuity contracts, transferring all or part of the interest rate risk to the annuitant occurs under *variable annuity contracts*. Such contracts are not discussed in this text.

---

[5] See Appendix C for a mathematical analysis of risk diversification.

[6] Another strategy available to an insurer to reduce interest rate risk is *hedging*.

15.6 EXERCISES

15.1 Actuarial Present Values Using Variable Interest Rates

15-1 Complete Example 15.1 for Scenarios 2 and 3.

15-2 Complete Example 15.2 for Scenarios 2 and 3.

15.2 Deterministic Interest Rate Scenarios

15-3 (a) Complete part (a) of Example 15.3 for the rising interest rate scenario.

(b) Complete part (b) of Example 15.3 for the rising interest rate scenario.

15-4 A company sells insurance in a country where only one-year bonds are available as investments to back its business. Our task is to compare the interest sensitivity of the following three products in this environment.

(i) A 5-year immediate annuity-certain, where payments are made regardless of survival status.
(ii) A 5-year immediate life annuity.
(iii) A single premium 5-year term insurance contract.

The applicable failure rates are $q_x = .10, q_{x+1} = .15, q_{x+2} = .20, q_{x+3} = .25,$ and $q_{x+4} = .30.$

(a) Assuming today's interest rate is 7%, calculate the actuarial present value for each of the three products using each of the following two interest rate scenarios:

(1) Increasing: rates rise by 1% each year, but do not exceed 11% in any year.
(2) Decreasing: rates fall by 1% each year, but do not fall below 3% in any year.

(b) Which of the products is least interest sensitive in this environment? Explain.

15-5 For the same country and interest scenarios as in Exercise 15-4, we wish to evaluate the following two similar products:

(1) Single premium 10-year term insurance of face amount \$1000, with benefit paid at the end of the year of failure.
(2) Annual premium 10-year term insurance of face amount \$1000, with benefit paid at the end of the year of failure. The level annual premiums are paid at the beginning of each year.

(a) For both products, assume $q_x = .05$ for all years. Calculate the benefit premium for each product, assuming rates remain level over the life of the product.

(b) Calculate the actuarial present value of the gain for each product under the increasing and decreasing scenarios. (Note that the premium was chosen so that the actuarial present value in each case is zero in the event of level rates.)

(c) In terms of interest risk, which payment scheme appears less risky for the insurance company? Explain.

15.3 Spot Interest Rates and the Term Structure of Interest Rates

15-6 Verify that $A^{\,1}_{60:\overline{5}|} = .1527$ in Example 15.5.

15-7 Use the nominal annual coupon yields in the table below to calculate the corresponding zero-coupon yields of the same maturities. (In both cases the nominal annual yield rates are convertible semiannually.)

Maturity (in years)	Nominal Annual Yield for Coupon-bearing Bonds	Nominal Annual Yield for Zero-coupon Bonds
0.5	2.0%	
1.0	4.0	
1.5	6.0	
2.0	8.0	

15-8 Use the annual coupon yields in the table below to calculate the corresponding zero-coupon yields of the same maturities. (For this exercise, we assume annual-payment coupon bonds rather than semiannual-payment coupon bonds.) How does the solution compare to that of Exercise 15-7?

Maturity (in years)	Annual Yield for Coupon-bearing Bonds	Annual Yield for Zero-coupon Bonds
1	2.0%	
2	4.0	
3	6.0	
4	8.0	

15-9 Use the annual zero-coupon yields in the table below to calculate the corresponding yields for annual-payment coupon bonds of the same maturities. (We assume here that coupon bonds pay coupons annually rather than semiannually.)

Maturity (in years)	Annual Yield for Coupon-bearing Bonds	Annual Yield for Zero-coupon Bonds
1		2.0%
2		4.0
3		6.0
4		8.0

15-10 Assume the following zero-coupon rates and calculate the implied yields for coupon bonds with equivalent maturities. (In both cases the nominal annual yield rates are convertible semiannually.)

Maturity (in years)	Nominal Annual Yield for Coupon-bearing Bonds	Nominal Annual Yield for Zero-coupon Bonds
0.5		2.0%
1.0		4.0
1.5		6.0
2.0		8.0

15-11 The regents of Fantastic University provide a four-year scholarship for one incoming freshman who plans to major in actuarial science. Current tuition at Fantastic is \$26,000 per year and tuition is expected to increase 8% per year over the next four years. The first annual tuition payment is due today. Each year we assume a 25% chance that the scholarship recipient will change majors or drop out of school; either event cancels future scholarship payments. Using the table of yields from Exercise 15-9, calculate the actuarial present value of this scholarship.

15.4 Forward Interest Rates

15-12 Complete Example 15.6 by verifying the $f_{n,k}$ values shown in Table 15.10.

15-13 Verify the spot rate values shown in Table 15.12.

15-14 Using the n-year forward one-year rates in the following table, find all determinable spot rates.

n	$f_{n,1}$
0	4.0%
1	5.0
2	6.0
3	7.0
4	8.0

15-15 Using the n-year forward one-year rates from Exercise 15-14, find all available forward rates.

15-16 In connection with taking over a client's retirement account, the client agrees to invest \$300,000 of that account with your firm for three years, starting two years from now.

(a) According to the interest rates in Exercise 15-15, what rate of interest can be locked in for the investment period?

(b) What spot-rate transactions should be entered into today in order to lock in the yield found in part (a)? Include the term and principal amount of the two transactions.

15-17 Due to the demise of a distant relative, you will receive $25,000 in one year that you would like to invest at that time for two years.

(a) According to the rates in Exercise 15-15, what rate can be locked in for the investment period?

(b) What transactions should be entered into today in order to lock in the rate from part (a)? Include the terms and principal amounts of the two transactions.

15-18 Calculate all forward rates that can be inferred from the annual coupon-bearing bond yield rates in the following table.

Maturity (in years)	Annual Yield Rates for Coupon-bearing Bonds
1	2.0%
2	4.0
3	6.0
4	8.0

15.5 Transferring the Interest Rate Risk

15-19 Give examples of mortality risk that is not diversifiable.

15-20 Explain the differences in interest rate risk for whole life insurance versus term life insurance.

15-21 Why is interest rate risk considered a non-diversifiable risk? Give an example of the effects of interest rate risk.

CHAPTER SIXTEEN

UNIVERSAL LIFE INSURANCE

The *universal life* (UL) insurance product entered the life insurance market in the early 1980s. The intent of the new product was to provide a great degree of flexibility for individual insureds. It allows for a combination of insurance protection and investment growth, and permits the insured to place relative emphasis on one or the other, within limits. Many variations on the basic universal life idea exist, and several of these are discussed throughout this chapter.

16.1 DEFINITIONS AND BASIC MECHANICS

There are two basic types of UL contracts, distinguished from each other by the definition of the death benefit amount. If the death benefit is a *fixed* specified amount, the contract is called *Type A Universal Life*. If the death benefit is defined to be a specified amount plus the account value at the end of the time interval of death, which in total produces a *variable* death benefit, the contract is called *Type B Universal Life*. The mechanics of each type of contract are presented in Sections 16.1.1 and 16.1.2.

A basic characteristic of UL insurance is that a great degree of flexibility is available to the policyholder. An important example of this flexibility is that the premiums paid by the policyholder need not be fixed at any one amount, and can be stopped and restarted at the policyholder's option, subject to some limits.[1]

The policyholder has a degree of choice regarding the balance between death benefit coverage and savings accumulation, with the caveat that a minimum amount of insurance coverage may be required by the tax laws to prevent the contract from becoming one of investment only, which would have a less favorable tax status. This minimum insurance amount, or minimum death benefit, is defined in the contract by provisions called *corridor factors*; these provisions are discussed in Section 16.1.3.

Surrender benefits provided by the contract are discussed in Section 16.1.4 and policy loan provisions are discussed in Section 16.1.5.

[1] Because the premium is not fixed, it is customary to refer to the payments made by the policyholder as "contributions" rather than "premiums." Notwithstanding this custom, the Society of Actuaries has announced that the term "premium" will be used on Exam MLC.

16.1.1 UNIVERSAL LIFE WITH VARIABLE DEATH BENEFIT (TYPE B)

In this version, a contract of insurance, either term or whole life, is issued with a *fixed face amount* of death benefit, which we denote by B. At the beginning of the tth year,[2] the policyholder pays a premium of amount G_t.[3] The insurer deducts the contractual expense charges from the premium. Here we assume a percent-of-premium expense factor r_t and fixed expense amount e_t for the tth year. Then the net premium invested in the contract is $G_t(1-r_t)-e_t$ at the beginning of the tth year.

The fixed death benefit of amount B is funded as one-year term insurance. Then for a contract issued at age x, or at select age $[x]$, the first year's cost of insurance (COI) is

$$COI_1 = \frac{B \cdot q_x}{1+i^q}, \tag{16.1}$$

at the beginning of the year. The remainder of the net contribution, after deducting COI_1, then earns interest at rate i^c to the end of the first year.[4] The accumulated value at that time is called the *account value* at time 1, which we denote by AV_1. Then we have

$$AV_1 = \left[G_1(1-r_1)-e_1-COI_1\right](1+i^c), \tag{16.2}$$

where COI_1 is defined by Equation (16.1). Note that AV_1 will be positive as long as the net contribution exceeds the cost of insurance.

If death occurs in the first year, the face amount benefit of B is provided by the one-year term insurance coverage. The account value AV_1 is released to the insured, since the contract is completed, so the total death benefit is $B+AV_1$. (This explains why the death benefit is variable although the face amount of the contract is fixed.)

If death does not occur in the first year, the process is repeated, producing an account value at the end of the second year of

$$AV_2 = \left[AV_1+G_2(1-r_2)-e_2-COI_2\right](1+i^c). \tag{16.3}$$

In general, for the tth year we have

---

[2] Time could be measured in years, quarters, months, or even shorter intervals. For convenience here we assume the annual case, with extension to shorter intervals easy to see.

[3] We denote the premium by G_t to reflect the fact that premiums need not be, and often are not, level.

[4] Note that, for maximum generality, we allow for the interest rate used in the COI calculation, which we denote by i^q, to be different from the rate used to accumulate the account value, which we denote by i^c. In practice, these two rates will often be the same, and denoted by simply i.

$$AV_t = \left[AV_{t-1} + G_t(1-r_t) - e_t - COI_t\right](1+i^c), \tag{16.4}$$

where

$$COI_t = \frac{B \cdot q_{x+t-1}}{1+i^q}, \tag{16.5a}$$

so the total death benefit would be $B + AV_t$ for death in the tth year. The process of updating the account value is called *account value roll forward*. Note that if the process is carried out on a, say, monthly basis, with monthly premiums, the mortality rate q_{x+t-1} must be available at monthly ages. (See Exercise 16-1.)

Recall from earlier mention that the *net amount at risk* (NAR) is defined to be the excess of the death benefit over the year-end reserve, or the year-end account value in this case. For a Type B Universal Life contract, the death benefit in the tth year is $B + AV_t$, so the NAR is

$$NAR_t = B + AV_t - AV_t = B. \tag{16.5b}$$

Then, in general, the tth year cost of insurance, which is based on the NAR, is

$$COI_t = \frac{NAR_t \cdot q_{x+t-1}}{1+i^q}, \tag{16.5c}$$

which becomes Equation (16.5a) in this case.

Another term used for the net amount at risk is the *additional death benefit* (ADB), meaning the amount of death benefit *in addition to* the year-end account value, which is amount B in this case.

Note that no terminal reserve need be held for the face amount death benefit B, since it is provided by a sequence of one-year (or one-period) term insurances. Since the account value is also paid at death, it, or a function of it, would be held as a financial liability by the insurer.

EXAMPLE 16.1

Consider a Type B Universal Life contract issued to (30), with face amount 100,000. The percent-of-premium expense factors are $r_1 = .75$ in the first year and $r_t = .10$ in all subsequent years; the fixed expense amount is $e_1 = 100$ in the first year and $e_t = 20$ in all subsequent years. The interest rates are $i^q = i^c = .03$, the mortality rates are given in Appendix A, and the insured pays an annual premium of $G_t = 5{,}000$. Calculate the account value at the end of each of the first five years.

SOLUTION

The calculations are shown in Table 16.1 on the following page.

TABLE 16.1

Year t	Prior Year Account Value Plus Net Contribution $AV_{t-1}+G_t(1-r_t)-e_t$	Cost of Insurance $100{,}000v\cdot q_{x+t-1}$	End-of-Year Account Value
1	$5{,}000(.25)-100$ $=1{,}150.00$	$\frac{(100{,}000)(.00076)}{1.03}=73.79$	$(1{,}150.00-73.79)(1.03)$ $=1{,}108.50$
2	$1{,}108.50+5{,}000(.90)-20$ $=5{,}588.50$	$\frac{(100{,}000)(.00081)}{1.03}=78.64$	$(5{,}588.50-78.64)(1.03)$ $=5{,}675.16$
3	$5{,}675.16+5{,}000(.90)-20$ $=10{,}155.16$	$\frac{(100{,}000)(.00085)}{1.03}=82.52$	$(10{,}155.16-82.52)(1.03)$ $=10{,}374.82$
4	$10{,}374.82+5{,}000(.90)-20$ $=14{,}854.82$	$\frac{(100{,}000)(.00090)}{1.03}=87.38$	$(14{,}854.82-87.38)(1.03)$ $=15{,}210.46$
5	$15{,}210.46+5{,}000(.90)-20$ $=19{,}690.46$	$\frac{(100{,}000)(.00095)}{1.03}=92.23$	$(19{,}690.46-92.23)(1.03)$ $=20{,}186.18$

❐

Because the annual premium in Example 16.1 is considerably in excess of the annual expenses plus cost of insurance, the account value continues to increase. Note that it would be possible to pay reduced premiums, or even to pay no premium at all, in certain years without impairing the contract as long as the account value remains sufficient to provide the annual cost of insurance. Of course the account value, and hence the total death benefit, would decline if no premiums are paid.

16.1.2 UNIVERSAL LIFE WITH FIXED DEATH BENEFIT (TYPE A)

If the total death benefit is to be fixed at face amount B, then the amount of one-year term insurance to be purchased each year is the excess of B over the year-end account value. Then when death occurs, the one-year term insurance benefit plus the released year-end account value together provide a total death benefit of B. Once again, the amount of one-year term insurance is called the *net amount at risk* (NAR),[5] and is equal to $B-AV_t$. In this case Equation (16.4) still applies, but now the COI charge is defined as

$$COI_t=\frac{\left(B-AV_t\right)\cdot q_{x+t-1}}{1+i^q}. \tag{16.6}$$

Then we have

$$AV_t=\left[AV_{t-1}+G_t\left(1-r_t\right)-e_t-\frac{\left(B-AV_t\right)\cdot q_{x+t-1}}{1+i^q}\right]\left(1+i^c\right), \tag{16.7}$$

[5] Note the similarity with ordinary life insurance, as presented in Chapters 10 and 11. There the net amount at risk was the excess of the face amount over the terminal reserve; here it is the excess of the fixed face amount over the year-end account value.

as the general account value roll forward equation. Note that AV_t appears on the right side of Equation (16.7). Solving explicitly for AV_t we have

$$AV_t = \frac{\left[AV_{t-1} + G_t(1-r_t) - e_t - \frac{B \cdot q_{x+t-1}}{1+i^q}\right](1+i^c)}{1 - q_{x+t-1} \cdot \frac{1+i^c}{1+i^q}}. \tag{16.8}$$

In the special case where $i^q = i^c = i,$ which is quite common, Equation (16.8) simplifies to

$$AV_t = \frac{\left[AV_{t-1} + G_t(1-r_t) - e_t\right](1+i) - B \cdot q_{x+t-1}}{p_{x+t-1}}. \tag{16.9}$$

In practice, the COI for a Type A Universal Life insurance is sometimes calculated in a way that is slightly different from the theoretically correct way shown in Equation (16.6), with the goal of not having AV_t appear on both sides of the account value roll forward equation. That is, the COI is defined without involving the AV_t value. This is explored in Exercise 16-2.

EXAMPLE 16.2

Repeat Example 16.1, except that the total death benefit is to remain fixed at 100,000.

SOLUTION

From Equation (16.9) we have

$$AV_1 = \frac{[5{,}000(.25) - 100](1.03) - (.00076)(100{,}000)}{.99924} = 1{,}109.34,$$

$$AV_2 = \frac{[1{,}109.34 + 5{,}000(.90) - 20](1.03) - (.00081)(100{,}000)}{.99919} = 5{,}680.62,$$

$$AV_3 = \frac{[5{,}680.62 + 5{,}000(.90) - 20](1.03) - (.00085)(100{,}000)}{.99915} = 10{,}389.27,$$

$$AV_4 = \frac{[10{,}389.27 + 5{,}000(.90) - 20](1.03) - (.00090)(100{,}000)}{.99910} = 15{,}239.06,$$

and

$$AV_5 = \frac{[15{,}239.06 + 5{,}000(.90) - 20](1.03) - (.00095)(100{,}000)}{.99905} = 20{,}234.86.$$ ❒

We observe that the account values are larger here than in Example 16.1, which is to be expected since a smaller total death benefit is being provided by the same level of premium. Again no terminal reserve is required for the one-year term insurance, but the insurer must hold the account value, or a function of it, as a financial liability.

As with the Type B contract of Section 16.1.1, several variations of the Type A contract described in this section exist in practice. We will pursue this later in the chapter.

16.1.3 CORRIDOR FACTORS

At the end of the term of the UL contract, the policyholder receives the final account value. In light of this, if death does not occur UL insurance functions like an endowment insurance policy; a level of death benefit protection has been provided, and the contract has acted as an investment vehicle. Even without waiting until the end of the term of the contract, the policyholder can surrender the contract for its cash value, with the same result. If the death benefit feature did not exist, or if the death benefit were inappropriately small, the contract would be one of investment only and its accumulation would be taxed in a manner less favorable to the policyholder. Accordingly, UL contracts define a minimum death benefit in relationship to the account value.

To illustrate this idea, consider our Type A contract of Example 16.2, with face amount 100,000. The contract might contain a provision stating that the minimum allowable death benefit in Year t is some multiple, such as 2.0 or 2.5, of the year-end account value AV_t. This multiple is called the *corridor factor*. When the contract is in its early years, with low account values, the face amount of 100,000 will exceed the defined minimum death benefit coverage. But if the corridor factor is 2.5, then whenever the account value exceeds 40,000 the minimum death benefit will exceed 100,000. In this case, the value of $2.5 \times AV_t$ becomes the death benefit under the contract. In other words, the death benefit in the tth year is defined to be

$$DB_t = max\left[B \text{ or } f \cdot AV_t\right], \tag{16.10a}$$

where B is the face amount of the contract and f is the corridor factor.

In the case of a Type B contract, where the normal death benefit would be the face amount plus the year-end account value, the concept of a minimum death benefit also applies. In this case the tth year death benefit is defined to be

$$DB_t = max\left[\left(B + AV_t\right) \text{ or } f \cdot AV_t\right]. \tag{16.10b}$$

To illustrate, consider our Type B contract of Example 16.1, with face amount 100,000 and a corridor factor of 2.0, so that the minimum death benefit is $2 \cdot AV_t$. The normal death benefit of $100{,}000 + AV_t$ will apply as long as the year-end account value is less than 100,000. The minimum death benefit of $2 \cdot AV_t$ kicks in whenever $AV_t > 100{,}000$.

If the corridor factor applies, so the death benefit is $f \cdot AV_t$, then the net amount at risk is

$$NAR_t = DB_t - AV_t = f \cdot AV_t - AV_t = (f-1) \cdot AV_t, \tag{16.11a}$$

and the cost of insurance is

$$COI_t^{CF} = \frac{NAR_t \cdot q_{x+t-1}}{1+i^q} = \frac{(f-1) \cdot AV_t \cdot q_{x+t-1}}{1+i^q}, \tag{16.11b}$$

where we use COI_t^{CF} to denote the cost of insurance when the corridor factor applies. Note that Equations (16.11a) and (16.11b) apply equally to Type A and Type B contracts.

Note that both Equation (16.6) and Equation (16.11b) include AV_t in their definitions of COI_t and COI_t^{CF}, respectively, and, in turn, AV_t involves the cost of insurance term. In Exercise 16-3(a), the reader is asked to derive explicit formulas for COI_t for Type A and the common COI_t^{CF} for both Type A and Type B.

If the corridor factor applies, then the death benefit is larger than if it does not apply, and the cost of insurance will be larger as well. This suggests a convenient way to calculate AV_t from AV_{t-1} whenever it is not obvious whether or not the corridor factor applies. Given the parameters of the contract, we calculate both COI_t and COI_t^{CF}, pick the larger of the two, and use that value for the cost of insurance term in Equation (16.4). This is illustrated in Exercise 16-3(b).

16.1.4 SURRENDER BENEFITS

If the contract is surrendered by the policyholder, the account value is released by the insurer. If the contract has been in force for a sufficiently long time, the entire account value might be paid as the cash value upon surrender of the contract. If the contract is still in its early years, however, it is customary to deduct a surrender charge from the account value to determine the cash value payable to the policyholder.

Premium cessation can occur without contract surrender. The account value, along with interest on it, continues to provide the death benefit in the standard format of successive one-year term insurance purchases. Once the account value is no longer sufficient to pay the COI, the contract would lapse without value unless there is a special provision, called a *no-lapse guarantee*, to keep it in force. This is an example of a secondary guarantee, and is discussed further in Section 16.2.2.

16.1.5 POLICY LOAN PROVISIONS

Universal Life contracts normally permit the policyholder to borrow up to the amount of the account value, at interest rates specified in the contract. If the contract is then surrendered, with a policy loan outstanding, the cash value otherwise payable upon surrender is reduced by the amount of the outstanding loan plus accrued interest.

16.2 VARIATIONS ON THE BASIC FORM[6]

The Type A and Type B Universal Life contracts discussed in Section 16.1 can be viewed as the most basic forms of this type of insurance contract. In this section we present several variations on those basic forms.

16.2.1 VARIABLE UNIVERSAL LIFE (VUL) INSURANCE

If the interest rate credited on the account value is guaranteed by the insurer, then the insurer bears the risk that the associated assets might not earn that guaranteed rate. If marketplace rates were to fall below the guaranteed credited rate, policyholders could take advantage of the premium flexibility allowed in these contracts, make relatively large premium payments, earn the higher guaranteed rate, and then surrender their contracts when market rates increase, all to the insurer's disadvantage.

A common feature of modern universal life contracts is that the net premiums are invested in *separate investment accounts*, and the rates earned on these accounts are used to accumulate the contract account values. Then if market rates fall, the interest earned on the account values falls as well. The interest rate risk has been transferred to the insured from the insurer. Contracts with this feature are referred to as *variable universal life insurance* (VUL). The death benefit continues to be provided by sequential one-period term insurances. The other features of cash and loan values are also available as long as the account value remains positive.

A separate investment account is not established for each individual VUL contract, of course. Rather the net premiums paid under a collection of similar contracts would be pooled and invested in the various separate accounts, which would likely have different investment philosophies. Each individual contract would own a number of units, or shares, in the various separate accounts, and the account value would then be the product of the unit value and the number of units owned, similar to the mechanics of a mutual fund.

EXAMPLE 16.3

A VUL contract has 100 units invested in Fund A, with unit value 20, and 200 units invested in Fund B, with unit value 10. A premium of 1000 is paid.

(a) How many units are purchased if the entire premium is allocated to Fund A?

(b) If the market value of Fund A increases by 20%, what is the account value of the contract?

SOLUTION

(a) The Fund A unit value is 20, so a premium of 1000 will purchase 50 units.

---

[6] The variations presented in this section are likely not included in the curriculum for Exam MLC.

(b) The new unit value in Fund A is $(20)(1.20) = 24$, and the contract now owns 150 units in Fund A and 200 units in Fund B. Then the account value is

$$(150)(24)+(200)(10) = 5600.00.$$ ❐

A special version of investment in a separate account is investment in a mutual fund directly tied to some published stock index, such as the S&P 500. Then interest is credited to the universal life contract at rates being earned by the index fund. This version is discussed further in Section 16.2.3.

16.2.2 SECONDARY GUARANTEES

Strictly speaking, under VUL the account values grow according to actually earned interest rates, with the policyholder bearing the interest rate risk. Furthermore, whether the contract is basic UL or VUL, a depleted account value might result in having the contract provide little or no death or surrender benefit. In practice, however, UL contracts may contain *secondary guarantees*, which provide for a minimum guaranteed cash value, death benefit, and/or maturity value regardless of the performance of the underlying investments. An example would be a guarantee that the contract will stay in force at the original schedule of benefits, as long as a specified premium is paid, even if such premium would have been insufficient in the absence of the guarantee.

Another example is the case where the insurer guarantees a minimum credited interest rate, if it is higher than the actually earned rate under a VUL contract. In this case there is a sharing of the interest rate risk between the insured and the insurer.

Secondary guarantees naturally embody a cost to the insurer and must therefore be funded and reserved. These topics are more advanced than the basic features we have considered thus far, and are further pursued in Sections 16.3 (for pricing) and 16.4 (for reserving).[7]

16.2.3 INDEXED UNIVERSAL LIFE INSURANCE

Also known as *equity-indexed universal life* (EIUL), interest is credited to this contract at a rate that depends on some published stock index, such as the S&P 500 (currently the most popular), the Dow Jones Industrial Average, or the Europe, Australia and Far East (EAFE) Index. (In some cases an average or other combination of several indices might be used, such as 75% of the highest, 25% of the second highest, and 0% of the lowest.) The appeal of such contracts is the potential for strong growth in value from growth in the equity market without direct participation in equity trading. The contract guarantees a minimum credited rate, providing some protection against loss of funds.

Once the underlying index and the length of the indexing period are chosen, an indexing method is selected. The *annual point-to-point indexing method* defines the index growth rate as

[7] These advanced topics are also not likely to be included in the curriculum for Exam MLC.

$$i_P = \frac{Final\ Index\ Closing\ Value}{Initial\ Index\ Closing\ Value} - 1, \tag{16.12}$$

and the *monthly average indexing method* defines the index growth rate as

$$i_{MA} = \frac{\frac{1}{12}\sum Monthly\ Index\ Closing\ Values}{Initial\ Index\ Closing\ Value} - 1. \tag{16.13}$$

The monthly method would ease some of the volatility that might be produced by the point-to-point method.

Once the indexing method is chosen, there are several other factors that are considered in setting the index-based credited interest rate.

(1) The *participation rate* is the percentage of the raw index growth rate that enters the calculation of the credited rate.

(2) The *index floor* is the minimum rate to be credited. It is usually set at 0%, but could be set higher.

(3) The *index margin* is a fixed reduction in the index growth rate. It can be applied either before or after the participation rate, but cannot reduce the credited rate below the index floor.

(4) The *index cap* is the maximum credited rate that can apply in any period. As with the index margin, it can serve to set the credited rate lower than the actual index growth rate.

The mechanics of the process of setting the credited rate, given the index growth rate, are illustrated in the following two examples.

EXAMPLE 16.4

Consider an EIUL contract using the annual point-to-point indexing method, with a 10% index cap, a 1% index floor, and a 110% participation rate. Given the index values shown in Column (2) of Table 16.2 on the following page, calculate the credited interest rates shown in Column (5).

SOLUTION

The index growth rate (before participation) in Column (3) for Year t is the ratio of the index value for Year t to the index value for Year $t-1$. The adjusted rates in Column (4) are those in Column (3) times 1.10. The final credited rates in Column (5) are the Column (4) rates adjusted for the 10% cap or the 1% floor.

TABLE 16.2

Year (1)	Index Closing Value (2)	Index Growth Rate (Before Participation) (3)	Index Growth Rate (After Participation) (4)	Credited Interest Rate (5)
0	1000			
1	1050	5.00%	5.50%	5.50%
2	1200	14.29	15.72	10.00
3	1100	– 8.33	– 9.16	1.00
4	950	– 13.64	– 15.00	1.00
5	1060	11.58	12.74	10.00
6	1150	8.49	9.34	9.34

❒

EXAMPLE 16.5

Suppose the EIUL contract of Example 16.4 used the monthly average indexing method instead. Given the monthly index closing values shown in Table 16.3, calculate the credited interest rate.

TABLE 16.3

Month	Index Closing Value
0	1000
1	1020
2	1100
3	1150
4	1080
5	1040
6	960
7	1030
8	1000
9	1070
10	1150
11	1200
12	1150

SOLUTION

The index growth rate is

$$i_{MA} = \frac{\frac{1}{12}(1020+1100+\cdots+1150)}{1000} - 1 = .07917.$$

Neither the 10% cap nor the 1% floor will apply, so the credited interest rate is 7.92%. ❒

16.3 PRICING CONSIDERATIONS

In this section we discuss the important assumptions involved in pricing universal life insurance products. These considerations apply to all three of basic universal life, variable universal life, and indexed universal life contracts.

16.3.1 MORTALITY

The *mortality rates* used to determine the cost of insurance are generally in select and ultimate form (see Section 6.7), with a select period of at least 15 years. They are estimated from the insurer's own past experience, or possibly from the experience of several similar insurers combined.

The rates based on past experience are generally then adjusted upward to reflect the effects of any *anti-selection* anticipated to be more severe than that contained in past experience. Anti-selection occurs when a portion of a group of insured lives elects to lapse their policies for various reasons. Those who lapse tend to be healthier than those who persist, so the level of mortality to be expected from the remaining insured lives is greater than that expected from the original total group.

16.3.2 LAPSE

The *lapse rates* assumed in pricing universal life contracts generally vary only by duration since issue, but could also vary by issue age as well (i.e., select and ultimate). They could also vary by such factors as contribution frequency, policy size, product type, or amount of insurance coverage.

Surrender charges may be deducted from the account value when the contract is totally surrendered or possibly also when only a part of the account value is withdrawn. An exception to the latter case occurs if the contract specifically allows a portion of its value to be withdrawn without penalty.

Considering mortality and withdrawal together, we see that our universal life insurance products are priced according to a double-decrement model (see Chapter 13). Letting $q_x^{(d)}$ and $q_x^{(w)}$ denote the probabilities of death and withdrawal, respectively, we recall that the probability of not being decremented from the group of lives between ages x and $x+1$ is

$$p_x^{(\tau)} = 1-q_x^{(\tau)} = 1-q_x^{(d)}-q_x^{(w)}. \tag{16.14}$$

For simplicity, an insurer's pricing actuary might assume that lapse can occur only at the end of the policy year. In that case, mortality is the only decrement during the year, so the probability of surviving to the end of the year is $1-q_x^{(d)}$.[8] Given survival to the end of the year, the probability of withdrawing is then $q_x^{(w)}$ so the probability of surviving into the next year in this case is

$$p_x^{(\tau)} = (1-q_x^{(d)})(1-q_x^{(w)}). \tag{16.15}$$

[8] In the notation and terminology of Chapter 13, we say that $q_x^{(d)} = q_x'^{(d)}$; the probability and rate of mortality are the same when withdrawal does not operate.

EXAMPLE 16.6

Consider a UL contract with face amount 100,000 issued at age x. The contributions, mortality rates, and withdrawal rates are shown in Table 16.4 for the first five years.

TABLE 16.4

Year t	Contribution	$q_{[x]+t-1}^{(d)}$	$q_{[x]+t-1}^{(w)}$
1	20,000	.001	.02
2	25,000	.002	.02
3	25,000	.003	.03
4	30,000	.004	.04
5	20,000	.005	.05

Assume that withdrawals occur only at the end of the year. Calculate each of the following:

(a) The persistency rate for policy year t.

(b) The survival rate to the end of policy year t.

SOLUTION

(a) From Equation (16.15), the persistency rate for policy year t is

$$p_{[x]+t-1}^{(\tau)} = \left(1-q_{[x]+t-1}^{(d)}\right)\left(1-q_{[x]+t-1}^{(w)}\right).$$

Then for $t=1,2,3,4,5,$ we have the following results:

$$p_{[x]}^{(\tau)} = (.999)(.98) = .97902$$

$$p_{[x]+1}^{(\tau)} = (.998)(.98) = .97804$$

$$p_{[x]+2}^{(\tau)} = (.997)(.97) = .96709$$

$$p_{[x]+3}^{(\tau)} = (.996)(.96) = .95616$$

$$p_{[x]+4}^{(\tau)} = (.995)(.95) = .94525$$

(b) The survival rate to the end of year t is

$${}_tp_{[x]}^{(\tau)} = p_{[x]}^{(\tau)} \cdot p_{[x]+1}^{(\tau)} \cdot \cdots \cdot p_{[x]+t-1}^{(\tau)},$$

so we directly have $p_{[x]}^{(\tau)} = .97902$, ${}_2p_{[x]}^{(\tau)} = .95752$, ${}_3p_{[x]}^{(\tau)} = .92601$, ${}_4p_{[x]}^{(\tau)} = .88541$, and ${}_5p_{[x]}^{(\tau)} = .83694$ ❐

16.3.3 EXPENSES

For the purpose of pricing these contracts, the *expense assumptions* are derived from an analysis of the insurer's incurred expenses.[9] These include the following:

(1) *Acquisition expenses*, which are those related to acquiring new business. They can be expressed as percent of contribution or face amount, or as a fixed amount per policy, and are usually incurred in the first year only.

(2) *Commission expenses*, which are those paid to sales agents plus other sales expenses. The first year expense is higher and renewal year expenses are lower.

(3) *Maintenance expenses*, which are those of contribution billing and collecting, contribution tax payment, policy record maintenance, accounting, valuation, pricing, and other policyholder services. They can be expressed as any of percent of contribution, percent of face amount, or a fixed amount per policy.

16.3.4 INVESTMENT INCOME

The insurer earns *investment income* on the assets backing the policy account value that are already invested at the start of a contract year, as well as the net cash flow during the year.

An alternative approach is to base investment income on the *cumulative cash flow*, which ignores capital contributions and distributions. Negative cumulative cash flows accumulate negative interest in the early policy years. The method is often used by mutual insurers who have no shareholders and therefore no outside source of capital. It is also used to calculate asset shares (see Section 14.2).

16.3.5 PRICING FOR SECONDARY GUARANTEES

There are two methods in use to provide the secondary guarantees.

The *stipulated premium method* provides that a defined premium, if paid on a regular basis, will guarantee the death benefit for the duration of the contract. Furthermore, if the policyholder pays less than that required to maintain the guarantee for a temporary period, a *premium catch-up provision* gives the policyholder the right to make up past premium deficiencies, in which case the guarantee is reinstated.

EXAMPLE 16.7

A UL contract is issued with a cumulative premium catch-up provision in which the lifetime coverage is guaranteed as long as the stipulated premium of 10,000 is paid each year. Assume the policy is in force at the end of ten years, with cumulative contributions paid of 90,000. What must the policyholder do at this time to maintain the lifetime guarantee?

---

[9] See Section 9.6.

SOLUTION

The cumulative paid contribution is 10,000 short of the amount required to maintain the guarantee, but the shortfall can be rectified under the catch-up provision. The policyholder must pay 20,000 at this time, representing a 10,000 catch-up premium plus the 10,000 stipulated premium required for the next year. ❒

The *shadow fund method* has become the more popular design in recent years. Under it a "shadow" account value is maintained based on credited interest rates higher than the contract's guaranteed minimum, and cost of insurance (COI) rates lower than the contract's guaranteed maximum. As long as the shadow fund remains positive, the death benefit secondary guarantee remains in place. Note that the shadow account value is not available to the policyholder; its only purpose is to maintain the death benefit.

EXAMPLE 16.8

Consider a UL contract exhibiting the values shown in Table 16.5.

TABLE 16.5

Contract Year	Contract Account Value	Surrender Charge	Cash Value	Shadow Account Value
1	1000	900	100	1100
2	800	800	0	900
3	400	600	0	700
4	100	400	0	500
5	0	200	0	200
6	0	100	0	0

At what point does the contract lapse (a) if there were no secondary guarantee, or (b) under the shadow fund method of providing a secondary guarantee?

SOLUTION

(a) With no secondary guarantee, the contract would lapse by the end of the fifth year where the account value becomes zero.

(b) Under the shadow fund secondary guarantee, the contract remains in force until the end of the sixth year where the shadow fund becomes zero. (Note that the shadow account exceeds the contract account, as expected, since it is based on higher interest and lower mortality and expense charges.) ❒

If the shadow account value falls negative, it can be reestablished to a positive position by making additional contributions. This is a similar catch-up provision to that mentioned under the stipulated premium method above. If the shadow fund becomes too deeply negative, however, the amount required to bring it back to a positive position might become prohibitively large.

16.4 RESERVING CONSIDERATIONS

In light of their special contract features, the valuation approaches used for universal life insurance contracts differ considerably from those used for traditional life insurance (see Chapters 10 and 11). In this section we describe the reserving approaches, separately for basic UL, VUL, IUL, and secondary guarantees.

16.4.1 BASIC UNIVERSAL LIFE

In addition to the flexibility in both the amount and timing of future contributions, future death benefits are also unknown if they depend on the contributions made or the underlying account value. Therefore the prospective reserve method discussed in Chapters 10 and 11 cannot be used here.

In 1983 the NAIC promulgated a model regulation to define a *minimum reserving standard* for UL products, which presumes a hypothetical premium and incorporates the actual policy performance. The process is summarized in the following steps:

(1) At policy issue, a *guaranteed maturity premium* (GMP) is calculated as the level gross premium sufficient to endow the policy at its maturity date. The GMP is based on the policy guarantees of premium loads, interest rates, and expense and mortality charges.

(2) Also at policy issue, a sequence of *guaranteed maturity funds* (GMF) is calculated based on the roll forward of the GMP and the policy guarantees.

(3) At the valuation date, the actual account value is determined by the account value roll forward process.

(4) At the valuation date, the ratio of the actual account value to the GMF is calculated as

$$r_t = \frac{AV_t}{GMF_t}, \tag{16.16}$$

subject to a maximum value of 1.00.

(5) At the valuation date, the greater of the account value or the GMF is projected forward based on the GMP and the policy guarantees, producing a sequence of guaranteed death benefits (GDB) and a sequence of guaranteed maturity benefits (GMB).

(6) At the valuation date, the present value of the projected future benefits $(PVFB)_t$ and the present value of the future GMP stream $(PVFP)_t$ are calculated using valuation assumptions. Then the *pre-floor CRVM reserve* is defined as

$$_tV^{\text{pre-floor CRVM}} = r_t \cdot \left[(PVFB)_t - (PVFP)_t\right], \tag{16.17}$$

where r_t is defined in Step (4) above.

(7) The *CRVM reserve floor* is defined as the greater of (a) the half-month term reserve based on minimum valuation mortality and interest, or (b) the cash surrender value at time t (CSV_t).

(8) Then the final CRVM reserve is the greater of the pre-floor CRVM reserve defined in Step (6) or the CRVM reserve floor defined in Step (7).[10]

EXAMPLE 16.9

Consider a UL contract of 100,000 face amount, with a 4% of contribution expense rate, a 3% guaranteed interest rate, a 5% current interest rate, and a GMP of 14.49 per 1000 of face amount. At the end of the ninth policy year, the account value is 57.60 per 1000 of face amount and the GMF is 140.40 per 1000 of face amount. At the beginning of the tenth policy year, the guaranteed policy charge is 11.80 per 1000 of face amount and the current policy charge is 10.76 per 1000 of face amount. No contribution is received for the tenth policy year, there is no outstanding loan on the contract, and there is no surrender charge for surrender in the tenth policy year. Calculate each of the following at the end of the tenth year:

(a) The cash value.

(b) The GMF.

(c) The value of r_{10}.

(d) The pre-floor CRVM reserve, given that $(PVFB)_{10} - (PFVP)_{10}$ is 70 per 1000 of face amount.

SOLUTION

(a) At the end of the tenth year, the account value per 1000 of face amount is

$$AV_{10} = (57.60 - 10.76)(1.05) = 49.182,$$

since there is no tenth year premium. Then the total account value would be $(49.182)(100) = 4918.20$. There is no surrender charge, so the cash value is also 4918.20.

(b) The GMF accumulates using the GMP and the guaranteed charges and interest rate. Then per 1000 of face amount we have

$$GMF_{10} = [140.40 + 14.49(1-.04) - 11.80] \cdot (1.03) = 146.7857.$$

The total value of GMF_{10} is $(146.7857)(100) = 14,678.57$.

10 The regulation also defines *alternative minimum reserves* (AMR). First the valuation net premium is calculated at policy issue based on the GMP and the policy guarantees. Then if the GMP is less than the valuation net premium, the reserve held should be the greater of (a) the reserve calculated using the actual method and assumptions of the policy and the valuation net premium, or (b) the reserve calculated using the actual method but with minimum valuation assumptions and the GMP.

(c) From Equation (16.16) we have

$$r_{10} = \frac{AV_{10}}{GMF_{10}} = \frac{4,918.20}{14,678.57} = .33506.$$

(d) From Equation (16.17) we have

$$\begin{aligned} {}_{10}V^{\text{pre-floor CRVM}} &= r_{10} \cdot [(PVFB)_{10} - (PVFP)_{10}] \\ &= (.33506)(70) = 23.4542 \end{aligned}$$

per 1000 of face amount, or 2345.42 in total. ❐

16.4.2 VARIABLE UNIVERSAL LIFE

The NAIC regulation mentioned above specifically exempts VUL products, since its prospective techniques would be inappropriate because the future investment performance is not guaranteed. The model regulation simply states that the reserves should be established using actuarial procedures that recognize the variable nature of the provided benefits. However, if a VUL product offers a general account investment option, with its more predictable interest rates, then the reserve is determined in the same manner as for a basic UL product.

In the case of flexible premium VUL, we distinguish between front-end loaded and back-end loaded products. For fully front-end loaded VUL products, the policy's cash value can serve as a sufficient reserve in the absence of future guarantees. For back-end loaded products, the reserve is typically the type defined by the UL regulation, with the interest rate used to project future benefits taken as one of (a) the long-term guaranteed rate in the fixed account, (b) the net valuation rate, (c) the rate used to calculate guideline level premiums, or (d) the policy loan rate. The reserve for a back-end loaded product should be no less than the cash value.

Under the *New York Life Design*, the death benefit at any time is the original face amount times the ratio of the actual account value to the tabular account value which has been calculated using the assumed interest rate (AIR). Then the reserves are identical to those of a non-variable policy with the same current death benefit, issue age, and duration.

Under the *Equitable Design*, any net investment earnings over the AIR are used to purchase variable paid-up additions at net rates using the AIR. If net investment earnings are less than the AIR, *negative* paid-up additions are purchased. Then the reserves are equal to tabular reserves calculated for a non-variable policy of the same face amount, issue age, and duration. Reserves for the paid-up additions are equal to those for similar non-variable paid-up additions.

16.4.3 INDEXED UNIVERSAL LIFE

The valuation standards for IUL contracts are specified in NAIC Actuarial Guideline 36 (AG 36), which is available from the NAIC or from the American Academy of Actuaries, with the intent of showing that the computational methods comply with the Standard Valuation Law and the UL regulation mentioned earlier. There are three types of computational methods, as follows:

(1) The *implied guaranteed rate* (IGR) *method*, which requires insurers to satisfy the *hedged-as-required* criteria.[11] These criteria set forth a strenuous constraint requiring exact, or nearly exact, hedging, as well as an indexed interest-crediting term of not more than one year.

(2) The *CRVM with updated market value* (CRVM/UMV) *method* must be used if the contract has an indexed interest-crediting term of more than one year, or if the renewal participation rate guarantee gives an implied guaranteed rate greater than the maximum valuation rate. This method can be volatile when market conditions change.

(3) The *CRVM with updated average market value* (CRVM/UAMV) *method* is a hybrid of the other two, designed for an insurer who qualifies for the first method above but does not wish to satisfy the hedged-as-required criteria.

In this text we consider further only the CRVM/UMV method, described below. It applies the UL regulation to IUL contracts by requiring a number of calculations at issue of the contract and at the valuation date.

The issue date calculations are as follows:

(1) An *implied guaranteed interest rate* for the duration of the initial term, which is the guaranteed rate plus the *accumulated option cost* expressed as a percentage of the policy value to which the indexed benefit is applied.[12] In turn, the accumulated option cost is the amount needed to provide the index-based benefit in excess of any other interest rate guarantee, accumulated to the end of the initial term at the appropriate maximum valuation rate.

(2) An implied guaranteed rate for the period after the initial term.

(3) The GMP, GMF, and valuation net premium based on the implied guaranteed rate.

The valuation date calculations are as follows:

(1) The implied guaranteed rate for the remainder of the current period, using the option cost based on the market conditions at the valuation date.

(2) The implied guaranteed rate for the period following the current period, based on the option cost on the valuation date.

---

[11] This refers to the option replication strategy to offset the liability positions. (The reader will study hedging strategies elsewhere in his or her actuarial education process.)

[12] The option cost for the underlying liability guarantee can be valued by an option valuation tool such as the Black-Scholes projection method.

(3) A re-projection of future guaranteed benefits based on the implied guaranteed rate on the valuation date.

(4) The present value of the re-projected future guaranteed benefits.

Note that the GMP, GMF, and valuation net premium remain the same as calculated at issue.

EXAMPLE 16.10

Consider an IUL contract using the annual point-to-point indexing method, with a 10% current index cap, a 3% minimum guaranteed index cap, a 0% guaranteed index floor, and a 100% participation rate. The option cost at issue, expressed as a percent of the policy value to which the index benefit is applied, is 5% for a 10% index cap and 2% for a 3% index cap. The valuation rate is 4%. Find the implied guaranteed interest rate for (a) the initial term and (b) the period beyond the initial term.

SOLUTION

(a) For the initial term, the implied guaranteed interest rate is the guaranteed floor rate plus the option cost accumulated for one year at the valuation rate, producing

$$.00+.05(1.04) = .052,$$

or 5.2%.

(b) For the period beyond the initial term, the option cost percentage is 2%, rather than 5%, because the 3% index cap applies, producing

$$.00+.02(1.04) = .0208,$$

or 2.08%. ❐

16.4.4 CONTRACTS WITH SECONDARY GUARANTEES

UL products with secondary guarantees have gained in popularity compared with traditional whole life insurance. The UL products offer the same guarantees of premium level and death benefit as do traditional products, but at much lower cost. The trade-off is that the guaranteed cash value may likely be lower under secondary guarantee UL, but many consumers are content to accept a lower cash value in exchange for a lower premium that is permanently guaranteed. In light of the lower cash value, regulators and many industry people have expressed concern regarding the adequacy of the reserves for the secondary guarantees under UL policies. In response, the NAIC promulgated Actuarial Guideline 38 (AG 38) to address the calculation of such reserves.

AG 38 reserves are calculated in nine steps:

(1) The *minimum gross premium* required to satisfy the secondary guarantees is derived at issue of the contract; the value of this premium will depend on whether the stipulated premium method or the shadow fund method (see Section 16.3.5) is in use. Its calculation uses the policy charges and credited interest rate guaranteed in the contract.

(2) The basic and deficiency reserves for the secondary guarantees are calculated using the minimum gross premium described in Step (1).

(3) The amount of actual contributions made in excess of the minimum gross premiums is determined, again with the process depending on whether the stipulated premium method or the shadow fund method is used.

(4) At the valuation date, a determination is made regarding amounts needed to fully fund the secondary guarantee.

   (a) Under the shadow fund method, this would be the amount of the shadow fund account needed to fully fund the guarantee.

   (b) Under contracts not using the shadow fund method, this would be the amount of cumulative premiums paid in excess of the required level such that no future premiums are required to fully fund the guarantee.

Special rules apply to policies for which the secondary guarantee cannot be fully funded in advance. Here a *prefunding ratio*, r, which cannot exceed 1.00, is calculated that measures the level of prefunding for the secondary guarantee, and is eventually used in the calculation of reserves. It is defined as

$$r = \frac{\textit{Excess Payment}}{\textit{Net Single Premium Required to Fully Fund the Guarantee}}. \tag{16.18}$$

(5) At the valuation date, the net single premium for the secondary guarantee coverage for the remainder of the secondary guarantee period is computed.

(6) A *net amount of additional premiums* is determined by multiplying the prefunding ratio described in Step (4) times the difference between the net single premium of Step (5) and the basic plus deficiency (if any) reserve of Step (2).

(7) A *reduced deficiency reserve* is determined by multiplying the deficiency reserve (if any) by the complement of the prefunding ratio from Step (4).

(8) Then the actual reserve is the lesser of (a) the net single premium of Step (5), or (b) the amount in Step (6) plus the basic and deficiency (if any) reserve from Step (2). This result might be reduced by applicable policy surrender charges.

(9) An *increased basic reserve* is computed by subtracting the reduced deficiency reserve of Step (7) from the reserve computed in Step (8), which then becomes the basic reserve.

EXAMPLE 16.11

Consider a UL contract with secondary guarantee provided by the shadow fund method. As of time t the shadow fund balance is 60,000, the net single premium required to fully fund the guarantee is 100,000, the valuation net premium is 150,000, the applicable surrender charge is 5,000, and the basic reserve is 10,000. There is no deficiency reserve. Calculate the AG38 reserve for this contract.

SOLUTION

The excess premium paid is the shadow fund balance of 60,000. From Equation (16.7) we find the prefunding ratio to be

$$r = \frac{60{,}000}{100{,}000} = .60.$$

The net amount of additional premium, as defined in Step (6) above, is

$$r \cdot (\textit{Valuation NSP} - \textit{Basic and Deficiency Reserve}) = .60(150{,}000\text{–}10{,}000) = 84{,}000.$$

Since there is no deficiency reserve, there is also no reduced deficiency reserve. Then the actual reserve, as defined in Step (8) above, is found by adding the basic and deficiency reserve of 10,000 to the *smaller* of the valuation net premium of 150,000 or the net amount of additional premium from Step (6), minus the applicable surrender charge. In this case we have

$$10{,}000 + 84{,}000 - 5{,}000 = 89{,}000.$$

Since the reduced deficiency reserve is zero, then the final AG38 reserve is the amount calculated in Step (8), which is 89,000. ❐

16.5 EXERCISES

16.1 Definitions and Basic Mechanics

16-1 The account value roll forward process under a universal life contract is often done on a monthly basis. Suppose the contract in Example 16.1 receives *annual* premiums of 5000, earns interest at $i^{(12)} = .03$, assesses expense charges at 50% of premium plus 10 per month, and estimates monthly mortality rates at 1/12 the corresponding annual rate. Calculate the account values at the ends of each of the first three months.

16-2 In practice, the net amount at risk under a Type A universal life contract paying a failure benefit fixed at amount B is often defined as the excess of B over the prior period ending account value plus the current period net premium, before deducting fixed expenses. The cost of insurance is then defined as the mortality rate times the net amount at risk, without the discount factor. Rework Example 16.2 under these definitions of NAR and COI.

16-3 (a) Derive the cost of insurance expressions shown in the table on the following page:

Type of Contract	Formula for Cost of Insurance
Type A, with Corridor Factor	$COI_t^{CF} = \dfrac{\frac{q_{x+t-1}}{1+i^q}\left[AV_{t-1}+G_t(1-r_t)-e_t\right](1+i^c)(f-1)}{1+\left(\frac{q_{x+t-1}}{1+i^q}\right)(1+i^c)(f-1)}$
Type B, with Corridor Factor	$COI_t^{CF} = \dfrac{\frac{q_{x+t-1}}{1+i^q}\left[AV_{t-1}+G_t(1-r_t)-e_t\right](1+i^c)(f-1)}{1+\left(\frac{q_{x+t-1}}{1+i^q}\right)(1+i^c)(f-1)}$
Type A, without Corridor Factor	$COI_t = \dfrac{\frac{q_{x+t-1}}{1+i^q}\left[B-\left(AV_{t-1}+G_t(1-r_t)-e_t\right)(1+i^c)\right]}{1-\left(\frac{q_{x+t-1}}{1+i^q}\right)(1+i^c)}$
Type B, Without Corridor Factor	$COI_t = \dfrac{B\cdot q_{x+t-1}}{1+i^q}$

(b) Consider a Type A contract with $B=100{,}000$ face amount, $G_t=1500$, $r_t=.025$, $e_t=50$, $q_{x+t-1}=.00278$, $i^q=.06$, $i^c=.07$, $f=2.50$, and $AV_{t-1}=40{,}000$. Calculate the value of AV_t.

16-4 A Type A universal life insurance contract with fixed death benefit of 100,000 has an account value of 4000 on April 30. A premium of 1000 is paid on May 1. The annual credited interest rate is 4.5%, the percent of premium expense rate is 4.0%, the monthly administrative expense charge is 40, and the monthly mortality rate is .0001. The surrender charge at this duration of the contract is 10 per 1000 of face amount. There is no outstanding loan balance. Calculate, as of May 31, each of (a) the account value, (b) the cash value, and (c) the cash surrender value. (Use the simplified definition of NAR given in Exercise 16-2.)

16-5 A universal life insurance contract of face amount 100,000 has an account value of 4000 on April 30. A premium payment of 1000 is made on May 1 and another of 500 is made on May 15. The annual credited interest rate is 5.0%, the percent of premium expense rate is 4.0%, the monthly administrative charge is 40, and the monthly mortality rate is .0001. The surrender charge at this duration of the contract is 10 per 1000 of face amount. There is an outstanding loan balance of 700. Policy charges are taken at the beginning of the month, and interest is credited at the end of the month. Calculate each of the following as of May 31.

(a) The account value

(b) The cash value

(c) The cash surrender value

16-6 In Section 11.5 we analyzed the total gain, and the gain by source, for a regular life insurance policy. The same analysis can be applied to a universal life policy, with the account values replacing the gross premium reserves. Consider a Type B universal life policy with face amount 10,000.00, annual premium 3,000.00, account values $AV_t = 9{,}015.81$ and $AV_{t+1} = 12{,}365.10$, no death benefit settlement expense, and no corridor factor. The following parameters apply to the $(t+1)^{st}$ contract year:

	Interest Rates	**Mortality Rates**	**Premium Expenses**	**Per-Policy Expenses**
Assumed	$i_{t+1} = .05$	$q_{x+t} = .022$	$r_{t+1} = .01$	$e_{t+1} = 0$
Actual	$i'_{t+1} = .06$	$q'_{x+t} = .020$	$r'_{t+1} = 0$	$e'_{t+1} = 50$

(a) Show that Expression (11.30a), modified to apply to this policy, is

$$[9{,}015.81 + 3{,}000(1 - r_{t+1}) - e_{t+1}](1 + i_{t+1}) - 10{,}000q_{x+t} - 12{,}365.10.$$

(b) Show that the expression in part (a) evaluates to zero under the assumed parameters.

(c) Calculate the total gain in the $(t+1)^{st}$ contract year.

(d) Calculate the gain from interest first, the gain from expenses second, and the gain from mortality third, and show that they sum to the total gain.

16.2 Variations on the Basic Form

16-7 At time t a variable UL contract has 100 units invested in Fund A, with unit value 20, and 200 units invested in Fund B, with unit value 10. The market value of Fund A is 10,000,000 and that of Fund B is 5,000,000. From time t to time $t+1$ Fund A increases by 20% and Fund B decreases by 10%.

(a) Find the unit value of Fund A and Fund B at time $t+1$.

(b) Find the market value of Fund A and Fund B at time $t+1$.

(c) A premium payment of 2000 is made at time t, allocated equally to Fund A and Fund B. Find the account value of the contract at time $t+1$.

16-8 An equity-indexed UL contract of face amount 100,000 uses the annual point-to-point indexing method, with a 10% index cap, a 1% index floor, a 100% participation rate, a 4% premium expense rate, and an annual administrative charge of 50. A premium of 1000 is paid at the beginning of each year, policy charges are deducted at the beginning of each year, and interest is credited at the end of each year. The following values apply over the next three years:

Year	**Index Closing Value**	**Cost of Insurance per 1000 of Amount at Risk**	**Surrender Charge per 1000 of Face Amount**
0	1000		
1	1080	2.0	5.00
2	1200	3.0	4.00
3	1100	4.0	3.00

(a) Find the credited interest rate for the contract at the end of each of the next three years.

(b) Find the cash value of the contract at the end of each of the next three years.

16.3 Pricing Considerations

16-9 Consider the UL contract of face amount 100,000 issued to (x) with premiums, mortality rates, and withdrawal rates as described in Example 16.6.

(a) Assuming 5% annual interest rate, calculate the actuarial present value of the premiums.

(b) Suppose the contract pays the face amount as a pure endowment benefit upon survival to the end of five years. Find the actuarial present value of the pure endowment benefit.

16-10 Suppose the contract described in Example 16.6 and Exercise 16-9 incurs the following expenses:

(i) Commissions of 80% in first year and 5% in renewal years.
(ii) Sales expense of 110% of first year commission.
(iii) Acquisition expense of 50% of first year premium plus 100 per policy.
(iv) Annual maintenance expense of .20% of face amount plus 50 per policy.
(v) Claim settlement expense of 100 per policy.

Calculate the actuarial present value of expenses at policy issue.

16.4 Reserving Considerations

16-11 Consider the UL contract described in Example 16.9, and assume a premium of 1000 at the beginning of the tenth policy year. (All other details of the contract remain the same.) Calculate each of (a) the cash value, (b) the GMF, and (c) the value of r_{10} at the end of the tenth year.

16-12 An equity-linked UL contract uses the annual point-to-point indexing method, with a 70% current participation rate, a 50% guaranteed participation rate, no index cap, and a 0% guaranteed index floor. The option cost at issue, as a percent of the policy value to which the index benefit is applied, is 7% for a 100% participation rate. The valuation interest rate is 4%. Calculate (a) the implied guaranteed interest rate for the initial term, and (b) the implied guaranteed interest rate for the guarantees beyond the current term.

16-13 Refer to Example 16.11, and recalculate the AG38 reserve assuming a deficiency reserve of 5000.

CHAPTER SEVENTEEN

PROFIT ANALYSIS

Recall our discussion of gain and loss presented in Section 10.6 (in a net premium context where only interest and mortality could be sources of gain), Section 11.5 (in a gross premium context where expenses could also be a source of gain), and Section 14.6 (where a second decrement, usually lapse or surrender, could also be a source of gain).

The *profit analysis*[1] that we do in this chapter expands considerably on the presentation contained in the three earlier sections. The process described here is equally applicable to ordinary life insurance, universal life insurance, annuities, and contracts issued in a multi-state model environment.

17.1 DEFINITIONS OF BASIC CONCEPTS

We begin with Expression (14.39a), found in Section 14.6, as the general form of what we now call our expression for *expected profit* in the $(t+1)^{st}$ contract year. As has been stated several times, if the same set of interest, expense, and decrement assumptions used to calculate the gross premium and gross premium reserves are used in Expression (14.39a), then its value will be zero. On the other hand, if the gross premium has been increased beyond the value calculated from the interest, mortality, and decrement assumptions, then the value of Expression (14.39a) will exceed zero. In that case, "expected profit in the $(t+1)^{st}$ contract year" is a logical way to describe this value.[2] We repeat Expression (14.39a) here for convenience of reference. Using its new name we have

$$Pr_{t+1} = \left[\,{}_tV^G + G_{t+1}(1-r_{t+1}) - e_{t+1}\right](1+i_{t+1}) \\ -\left[\left(b_{t+1}^{(1)} + s_{t+1}^{(1)}\right)\cdot q_{x+t}^{(1)} + \left(b_{t+1}^{(2)} + s_{t+1}^{(2)}\right)\cdot q_{x+t}^{(2)} + {}_{t+1}V^G \cdot p_{x+t}^{(\tau)}\right]. \tag{17.1}$$

Note that the expected profit is measured at the end of the contract year.[3]

[1] In some texts, the term *profit testing* is preferred to the term profit analysis.

[2] In Section 9.6 we referred to the premium calculated to cover benefits and expenses, but not profit, as the *expense-augmented premium*, and the premium calculated to provide an element of profit as well as the *gross premium*. For many applications throughout the text, we have assumed them to be equal; in this chapter that assumption will no longer hold.

[3] Including the reserve factors in the calculation of expected profit means the profit is being determined on an accrual accounting basis. The alternative of omitting the reserve factors would determine the profit of a cash accounting basis. The former way of determining profit is far preferable to the latter, and is the accepted industry standard.

17.1.1 PRE-CONTRACT EXPENSES

An insurer will generally incur expenses associated with a new insurance contract before the contract is actually issued and the first gross premium is collected, which we refer to as *pre-contract expenses*.[4] In light of this, we consider that the contract has already lost money for the insurer as of time 0, the issue date of the contract. We denote the pre-contract expenses as Pr_0, and observe that, necessarily, $Pr_0 < 0$.

17.1.2 THE PROFIT VECTOR

The values of Pr_{t+1}, for $t = 0,1,2,\cdots$, generated by Equation (17.1), constitute the set of expected profits in sequential contract years. We express these values, along with the special Pr_0 value resulting from pre-contract expenses, in the row vector

$$\mathbf{Pr} = (Pr_0, Pr_1, Pr_2, \cdots, Pr_n), \tag{17.2}$$

which is called, appropriately, the *profit vector*. Note that the nth contract year is the latest one for which the expected profit is determined, but the profit vector contains $n+1$ elements.

EXAMPLE 17.1

Consider a discrete three-year term insurance of face amount 50,000 issued to (40). The interest rate is $i = .06$, mortality is given by the table in Appendix A, expenses are 5% of gross premium plus 10 per contract, and there are no lapses. The gross annual premium is $G = 95.00$, the reserves are ${}_1V = 5.66$ and ${}_2V = 6.17$, and the pre-contract expense is 15.00. Determine the profit vector for this contract.

SOLUTION

For this contract, Equation (17.1) reduces to

$$Pr_{t+1} = \left[{}_tV + (.95)(95.00) - 10\right](1.06) - \left[50{,}000 \cdot q_{40+t} + {}_{t+1}V \cdot p_{40+t}\right].$$

With ${}_0V = 0$, we find

$$Pr_1 = (80.25)(1.06) - (50{,}000)(.00142) - (5.66)(.99858)$$

$$= 85.07 - 71.00 - 5.65 = 8.42,$$

$$Pr_2 = (5.66 + 80.25)(1.06) - (50{,}000)(.00153) - (6.17)(.99847)$$

$$= 91.06 - 76.50 - 6.16 = 8.40,$$

[4] Examples of pre-contract expenses would be underwriting expenses, the expenses of printing the contract, and other costs associated with policy issue. Pre-contract expenses are also referred to as *acquisition expenses*.

and

$$Pr_3 = (6.17+80.25)(1.06)-(50,000)(.00166) = 91.61-83.00 = 8.61,$$

since no reserve is established for survival to age 43. Then the profit vector is

$$\mathbf{Pr} = (Pr_0, Pr_1, Pr_2, Pr_3) = (-15.00, 8.42, 8.40, 8.61.)$$ ❐

Note that each value of expected profit is calculated assuming that the contract is still in force at the beginning of the $(t+1)^{st}$ contract year.

17.1.3 THE PROFIT SIGNATURE

Since the profit vector assumes the contract is in force at the beginning of the year for which the expected profit is being calculated, we can interpret each value as being the expected profit *per policy in force at the start of the year.* An alternative would be to measure the expected profit in each year *per policy issued.* We denote this concept of expected profit in the $(t+1)^{st}$ contract year by Π_{t+1}. The relationship of Π_{t+1} to Pr_{t+1} is that the value of Pr_{t+1} must be "discounted" for the probability of being in force at time t to reach the value of Π_{t+1}. That is,

$$\Pi_{t+1} = Pr_{t+1} \cdot {}_tp_x. \tag{17.3}$$

Note that, necessarily, $\Pi_0 = Pr_0$ and $\Pi_1 = Pr_1$, since an issued policy is certainly in force at time $t=0$. The values of Π_{t+1} are similarly represented as the vector

$$\mathbf{\Pi} = (\Pi_0, \Pi_1, \Pi_2, \cdots, \Pi_n), \tag{17.4}$$

which is called the *profit signature.*[5]

EXAMPLE 17.2

Determine the profit signature for the contract of Example 17.1.

SOLUTION

From Equation (17.3) we have

$$\Pi_2 = Pr_2 \cdot p_{40} = (8.40)\,(.99858) = 8.39$$

and

$$\Pi_3 = Pr_3 \cdot {}_2p_{40} = (8.61)(.99858)(.99847) = 8.58.$$

Along with $\Pi_0 = Pr_0$ and $\Pi_1 = Pr_1$, the profit signature is

$$\mathbf{\Pi} = (\Pi_0, \Pi_1, \Pi_2, \Pi_3) = (-15.00,\ 8.42,\ 8.39, 8.58).$$ ❐

---

[5] We might refer to the profit vector elements as *conditional* expected profits, and the elements in the profit signature as *unconditional* expected profits.

17.1.4 NET PRESENT VALUE

The *net present value* of the expected profits is found by discounting the expected profits per policy issued back to time $t=0$ at a specified interest rate. (The interest rate for discounting the values of Π_{t+1} need not be the same as the interest rate used for accumulating beginning-of-year values in the expected profit calculation.) That is,

$$NPV = \Pi_0 + \frac{\Pi_1}{1+r} + \frac{\Pi_2}{(1+r)^2} + \cdots + \frac{\Pi_n}{(1+r)^n}. \tag{17.5}$$

Note that this gives the APV of the expected profits, without using probability terms in Equation (17.5), since the values of Π_{t+1} have already been appropriately "discounted" for the probability of contract survival.

EXAMPLE 17.3

Calculate the net present value of the expected profits for the contract of Example 17.1, discounting at rate $r=.10$.

SOLUTION

Using the values in the profit signature, we have

$$NPV = -15.00 + \frac{8.42}{1.10} + \frac{8.39}{(1.10)^2} + \frac{8.58}{(1.10)^3} = -15.00 + 7.65 + 6.93 + 6.45 = 6.03.$$

(Note that $\Pi_0 = -15.00$ is measured at time $t=0$, so no discounting is used for this term.) ❐

The rate of interest r used to discount the expected profit values is sometimes called the *risk discount rate* or the *hurdle rate*.

17.1.5 INTERNAL RATE OF RETURN

The risk discount rate that makes the net present value of the expected profits equal to zero is called the *internal rate of return*.

EXAMPLE 17.4

Show that the internal rate of return for the contract of Example 17.1 is $r=31.635\%$.

SOLUTION

At this rate the net present value is

$$NPV = -15.00 + 6.40 + 4.84 + 3.76 = 0,$$

as required. ❐

17.1.6 PROFIT MARGIN

The *profit margin* is defined to be the ratio of the net present value (see Section 17.1.4) to the APV of the gross premiums, using the same risk discount rate as is used to determine the NPV.

EXAMPLE 17.5

Calculate the profit margin for the contract of Example 17.1.

SOLUTION

In our example, the gross premium is $G = 95.00$, the risk discount rate is $r = .10$, and the relevant probability values are $p_{40} = .99858$ and $p_{41} = .99847$. The APV of the gross premiums is

$$APV_{GP} = 95.00\left[1+\frac{.99858}{1.10}+\frac{(.99858)(.99847)}{(1.10)^2}\right] = 259.52.$$

From Example 17.3, the NPV is 6.03, so the profit margin is $\frac{6.03}{259.52} = .02324$. ❐

A measure similar to the profit margin is the ratio of the net present value to the pre-contract expenses. In our example, this ratio would be $\frac{6.03}{15.00} = .40200$.

17.1.7 DISCOUNTED PAYBACK PERIOD

We can calculate the net present value over a number of years less than the full term of the contract, which we refer to as a *partial net present value*. We denote the partial net present value calculated over t years by $NPV(t)$, for $t = 0,1,\cdots,n-1$. (Note that $NPV(n)$ would mean the regular net present value defined in Section 17.1.4.)

EXAMPLE 17.6

For the contract of Example 17.1, calculate $NPV(t)$, for $t = 0,1,2$.

SOLUTION

From the profit signature elements given in Example 17.2, and the NPV calculation shown in Example 17.3, we easily find

$$NPV(0) = -15.00,$$

$$NPV(1) = -15.00+\frac{8.42}{1.10} = -7.35,$$

and

$$NPV(2) = -15.00 + \frac{8.42}{1.10} + \frac{8.39}{(1.10)^2} = -.42.$$

Note that $NPV(3) = NPV(2) + \frac{8.58}{(1.10)^3} = 6.03$, which is NPV as already known. ❒

Since Π_0 is necessarily negative, and $NPV(0) = \Pi_0$, then the sequence of partial net present values will be negative at first and (hopefully) eventually turn positive. The duration at which the partial net present value first becomes positive (or zero) is called the *discounted payback period*, or the *breakeven term*. In our example, this does not occur until duration 3, which is the terminal duration of the contract. In most cases the discounted payback period will be less than the full term of the contract.

17.1.8 A COMPREHENSIVE EXAMPLE

In this section we illustrate anew most of the concepts defined thus far, and comment on the results. For these examples, we assume a fully discrete five-year term insurance of 1,000,000 face amount, gross annual premium of 19,250.00, pre-contract expenses of 5,000.00, annual per policy expenses of 240.00 (payable at the beginning of the year), an interest rate of $i = .06$ on invested assets, and a risk discount rate of $r = .10$. Table 17.1 gives values of the terminal reserves and the mortality factors. There are no surrenders.

TABLE 17.1

Policy Year t	q_{x+t-1}	p_{x+t-1}	${}_tp_x$	${}_tV^G$
1	.015	.985	.98500	2,500.00
2	.017	.983	.96826	4,000.00
3	.019	.981	.94986	5,000.00
4	.021	.979	.92991	4,000.00
5	.024	.976	.90759	0.00

EXAMPLE 17.7

For the policy described above, calculate the profit vector and the total expected profit.

SOLUTION

The profit each year is calculated by assuming the policy to be in force at the beginning of that year. The calculation details are shown in Table 17.2.

TABLE 17.2

Policy Year t	Prior Reserve, Plus Premium Minus Expenses	End-of-Year Accumulation at $i=.06$	Expected Death Benefit	Expected Year-End Reserve	Year-End Expected Profit (Pr_t)
1	0 +19,010.00 =19,010.00	(19,010.00)(1.06) =20,150.60	$1{,}000{,}000\,q_x$ =15,000.00	${}_1V^G \cdot p_x$ =2,462.50	20,150.60 −17,462.50 =2,688.10
2	2,500.00 +19,010.00 =21,510.00	(21,510.00)(1.06) =22,800.60	$1{,}000{,}000\,q_{x+1}$ =17,000.00	${}_2V^G \cdot p_{x+1}$ =3,932.00	22,800.60 −20,932.00 =1,868.60
3	4,000.00 +19,010.00 =23,010.00	(23,010.00)(1.06) =24,390.60	$1{,}000{,}000\,q_{x+2}$ =19,000.00	${}_3V^G \cdot p_{x+2}$ =4,905.00	24,390.60 −23,905.00 =485.60
4	5,000.00 +19,010.00 =24,010.00	(24,010.00)(1.06) =25,450.60	$1{,}000{,}000\,q_{x+3}$ =21,000.00	${}_4V^G \cdot p_{x+3}$ =3,916.00	25,450.60 −24,916.00 =534.60
5	4,000.00 +19,010.00 =23,010.00	(23,010.00)(1.06) =24,390.60	$1{,}000{,}000\,q_{x+4}$ =24,000.00	${}_5V^G \cdot p_{x+4}$ =0.00	24,390.60 −24,000.00 =390.60

Along with the special term $Pr_0 = -5{,}000.00$, the profit vector values are given in the last column of Table 17.2. The total expected profit is the sum, without discounting, of the elements in the profit vector, which is

$$-5{,}000.00 + 2{,}688.10 + 1{,}868.60 + 485.60 + 534.60 + 390.60 = 967.50.$$ ❐

EXAMPLE 17.8

Using the information in Example 17.7, calculate (a) the profit signature, (b) the net present value, and (c) the profit margin.

SOLUTION

(a) The first two elements are $\Pi_0 = Pr_0 = -5{,}000.00$ and $\Pi_1 = Pr_1 = 2{,}688.10$. Then we also find

$$\Pi_2 = Pr_2 \cdot p_x = (1{,}868.60)(.98500) = 1{,}840.57,$$

$$\Pi_3 = Pr_3 \cdot {}_2p_x = (485.60)(.96826) = 470.19,$$

$$\Pi_4 = Pr_4 \cdot {}_3p_x = (534.60)(.94986) = 507.80,$$

and

$$\Pi_5 = Pr_5 \cdot {}_4p_x = (390.60)(.92991) = 363.22.$$

These are the six elements of the profit signature.

(b) The net present value of the expected profits is

$$NPV = -5{,}000.00 + \frac{2{,}688.10}{1.10} + \frac{1{,}840.57}{(1.10)^2} + \frac{470.19}{(1.10)^3} + \frac{507.80}{(1.10)^4} + \frac{363.22}{(1.10)^5}$$

$$= -5{,}000.00 + 2{,}443.73 + 1{,}521.13 + 353.26 + 346.83 + 225.53$$

$$= -109.52.$$

(c) The APV of the gross premiums is

$$APV_{GP} = 19{,}250.00\left(1 + \frac{.98500}{1.10} + \frac{.96826}{(1.10)^2} + \frac{.94986}{(1.10)^3} + \frac{.92991}{(1.10)^4}\right)$$

$$= 19{,}250.00(1 + .89545 + .80021 + .71364 + .63514)$$

$$= 77{,}855.49,$$

so the profit margin is

$$\frac{-109.52}{77{,}855.49} = -.00141.$$

❒

17.1.9 COMMENTARY ON THE COMPREHENSIVE EXAMPLE

Note that the example presumes no cash surrender values, which is appropriate for a five-year term insurance.

We calculated the profit signature elements by multiplying the profit vector elements by the probability of survival to the start of each year. We could, of course, modify each entry in Table 17.2 by the appropriate survival probability and reach the same profit signature values, but it is easier to simply adjust the profit vector values.

The net present value is the most frequently used measure of overall contract profitability, and we need to have a good understanding of the meaning of the interest rate used to calculate it. We assumed in Examples 17.7 and 17.8 that the insurer could earn 6% on its invested assets. However, to compensate the insurer for the risk assumed in an insurance enterprise, a higher rate of return on its invested funds is required. This higher rate, which we have already called the risk discount rate or hurdle rate, is also called the *rate of return on equity*, or the ROE rate.[6] In our example, the additional 4% in the ROE rate represents the additional return to compensate for the additional risk.

---

[6] Here "equity" refers to the shareholder equity in a stock insurance company or the policyholder equity in a mutual company.

Since the NPV in our example is negative, we conclude that the given premium, reserve requirements, and interest, mortality and expense assumptions in combination do not meet the insurer's 10% profitability standard. One solution to this problem would be to increase the gross premium (see Section 17.2.1), if we believe that a larger gross premium will be acceptable in this marketplace.

With all other assumptions remaining the same, we find that a gross premium of 19,279 is the smallest integral value that will generate a positive net present value at $r = .10$. We also find that a gross premium of 19,500 produces a net present value, at $r = .10$, of 864.88, and an internal rate of return of 19.39% (within rounding). (These results are left to the reader as Exercises 17-4 and 17-5.) The insurer should be quite happy with an ROE rate of 19.39%, when only 10% was initially required. An option for the insurer would be to reduce the 19,500 gross premium somewhat (but not below 19,279) in order to sell more of this product.

We observe that the net present value calculations considered thus far have ignored the effects of taxation. In practice, profits are subject to taxation, which is therefore a component in the calculation of after-tax profits. Clearly the after-tax NPV will be smaller than the pre-tax NPV using the same ROE rate. When a particular internal rate of return is sought, it must be made clear whether the desired rate is on a pre-tax or post-tax basis.

17.2 USES OF PROFIT ANALYSIS

Now that we have a good understanding of the mechanics of profit analysis, we consider the uses of this analysis within an insurance enterprise.

17.2.1 PREMIUM DETERMINATION

Earlier in the text we discussed the calculation of the premium by the equivalence principle (see Section 9.6) and also by the percentile premium principle (see Section 9.3). Now we have a third method, which is to select the premium that will produce a specified internal rate of return. As mentioned in Section 17.1.9, the premium must be at least 19,279 to produce a 10% rate of return for our example.

Another possible pricing method would be to establish a minimum required profit margin, such as 5%. We found in Example 17.8 that our premium of 19,250 implied a profit margin of −1.41%, another indication that a premium of that amount is inadequate. Holding all other assumptions constant, we find that the premium needs to be 20,335 in order to produce a 5% profit margin (see Exercise 17-6).

17.2.2 RESERVE DETERMINATION

In Chapter 10 we presented an extensive discussion of net level premium reserves, and expanded this to a consideration of gross premium reserves in Chapter 11. As has been stated, the insurance regulators establish a legal minimum level for the reserves. Insurers assess their financial positions and set their reserves accordingly, now often considering the cash flow analysis discussed in this chapter. (We discuss the relationship of reserves to profit analysis more completely in Section 17.3.)

17.2.3 CASH MANAGEMENT

It is possible for an insurer to be solvent and profitable on a long-term basis, but lack the funds necessary to meet immediate cash flow needs such as those created by acquisition expenses. Because profit analysis projects cash flows into the future, it is a good method for assessing the adequacy of available cash *vis-à-vis* cash needs.

17.2.4 PROFIT EMERGENCE

Although we might conclude that the profit on a block of insurance contracts is adequate in the aggregate, we might find that the pattern of profit emergence is not what we would prefer. The type of profit analysis discussed in this chapter produces useful information on the profit emergence pattern. This is particularly useful when considering the issue of profit distribution back to policyholders under participating insurance contracts (see Section 17.4).

17.2.5 COMPLETE FINANCIAL EVALUATION

Adequate reserving is the basic method for establishing that policyholders can feel secure in the promises made under their insurance contracts. But the policyholders are only one group with an interest in the financial wellbeing of the company. The interests of the owners of the company must also be considered, and these interests are accommodated in the models we can construct under modern profit analysis.[7]

17.3 USING PROFIT ANALYSIS TO DETERMINE RESERVES

To explore the significance of the reserve values, we first consider our profit analysis outcomes if we hold no reserves at all.[8] This is illustrated in the following example.

EXAMPLE 17.9

Using the minimum profitable gross premium of 19,279 and no reserves, along with all other assumptions from our comprehensive example, develop (a) the profit vector, (b) the profit signature, and (c) the net present value (at $r = .10$) of the expected profits.

SOLUTION

Table 17.3 shows the calculations under these assumptions.

[7] In general, any party with a financial interest in an enterprise is referred to as a *stakeholder*. A model that addresses all financial interests is sometimes called a *model office*.

[8] This case is totally hypothetical, since insurers would not consider, and regulators would not permit, such a situation.

TABLE 17.3

Policy Year t	Prior Reserve, Plus Premium Minus Expenses	End-of-Year Accumulation at $i=.06$	Expected Death Benefit	Expected Year-End Reserve	Year-End Expected Profit
1	0 $+19{,}039.00$ $=19{,}039.00$	$(19{,}039.00)(1.06)$ $=20{,}181.34$	$1{,}000{,}000\,q_x$ $=15{,}000.00$	${}_1V^G \cdot p_x$ $=0.00$	$20{,}181.34$ $-15{,}000.00$ $=5{,}181.34$
2	0 $+19{,}039.00$ $=19{,}039.00$	$(19{,}039.00)(1.06)$ $=20{,}181.34$	$1{,}000{,}000q_{x+1}$ $=17{,}000.00$	${}_2V^G \cdot p_{x+1}$ $=0.00$	$20{,}181.34$ $-17{,}000.00$ $=3{,}181.34$
3	0 $+19{,}039.00$ $=19{,}039.00$	$(19{,}039.00)(1.06)$ $=20{,}181.34$	$1{,}000{,}000q_{x+2}$ $=19{,}000.00$	${}_3V^G \cdot p_{x+2}$ $=0.00$	$20{,}181.34$ $-19{,}000.00$ $=1{,}181.34$
4	0 $+19{,}039.00$ $=19{,}039.00$	$(19{,}039.00)(1.06)$ $=20{,}181.34$	$1{,}000{,}000q_{x+3}$ $=21{,}000.00$	${}_4V^G \cdot p_{x+3}$ $=0.00$	$20{,}181.34$ $-21{,}000.00$ $=-818.66$
5	0 $+19{,}039.00$ $=19{,}039.00$	$(19{,}039.00)(1.06)$ $=20{,}181.34$	$1{,}000{,}000q_{x+4}$ $=24{,}000.00$	${}_5V^G \cdot p_{x+4}$ $=0.00$	$20{,}181.34$ $-24{,}000.00$ $=-3{,}818.66$

(a) Along with the special term $Pr_0 = -5{,}000.00$, the profit vector values are in the last column of Table 17.3.

(b) The profit signature values are

$$\Pi_0 = Pr_0 = -5{,}000.00,$$

$$\Pi_1 = Pr_1 = 5{,}181.34,$$

$$\Pi_2 = Pr_2 \cdot p_x = (3{,}181.34)(.98500) = 3{,}133.62,$$

$$\Pi_3 = Pr_3 \cdot {}_2p_x = (1{,}181.34)(.96826) = 1{,}143.84,$$

$$\Pi_4 = Pr_4 \cdot {}_3p_x = (-818.66)(.94986) = -777.61,$$

and

$$\Pi_5 = Pr_5 \cdot {}_4p_x = (-3{,}818.66)(.92991) = -3{,}551.01.$$

These are the six elements of the profit signature.

(c) The net present value of the expected profits is

$$NPV = -5{,}000.00 + \frac{5{,}181.34}{1.10} + \frac{3{,}133.62}{(1.10)^2} + \frac{1{,}143.84}{(1.10)^3} - \frac{777.61}{(1.10)^4} - \frac{3{,}551.01}{(1.10)^5}$$

$$= -5{,}000.00 + 4{,}710.31 + 2{,}589.77 + 859.38 - 531.12 - 2{,}204.90$$

$$= 423.44.$$

We observe that the net present value is positive under these assumptions. However, the negative expected cash flows in the last two policy years would be a concern to both the insurer and the regulators. ❐

We now consider a process referred to as *zeroized reserves*, whereby the reserves are determined so as to produce profit vector elements of zero in all policy years, except that reserves calculated to be negative are reset to zero.[9] The reserves are calculated recursively, starting with the boundary condition ${}_5V^G = 0.00$, in our example, and working backward. Again using the assumptions of our example with $G = 19{,}279.00$, we find

$$Pr_5 = ({}_4V^Z + 19{,}039.00)(1.06) - 24{,}000 = 0,$$

which solves for

$${}_4V^Z = \frac{24{,}000}{1.06} - 19{,}039.00 = 3{,}602.51.$$

Then

$$Pr_4 = ({}_3V^Z + 19{,}039.00)(1.06) - 21{,}000.00 - (3{,}602.51)(.979) = 0,$$

which solves for

$${}_3V^Z = \frac{21{,}000.00 + (3{,}602.51)(.979)}{1.06} - 19{,}039.00 = 4{,}099.54.$$

Continuing in this way we find

$$Pr_3 = ({}_2V^Z + 19{,}039.00)(1.06) - 19{,}000.00 - (4{,}099.54)(.981) = 0$$

so

$${}_2V^Z = \frac{19{,}000.00 + (4{,}099.54)(.981)}{1.06} - 19{,}039.00 = 2{,}679.54,$$

[9] Again we are ignoring the possibility that the regulators will deem such reserves to be less than the legal minimum values.

and

$$Pr_2 = ({}_1V^Z + 19{,}039.00)(1.06) - 17{,}000.00 - (2{,}679.54)(.983) = 0$$

so

$${}_1V^Z = \frac{17{,}000.00 + (2{,}679.54)(.983)}{1.06} - 19{,}039.00 = -516.37,$$

which we reset to ${}_1V^Z = 0$. Then

$$Pr_1 = ({}_0V^Z + 19{,}039.00)(1.06) - 15{,}000.00 - (0.00)(.985) = 0$$

so

$${}_0V^Z = \frac{15{,}000}{1.06} - 19{,}039.00 = -4{,}888.06,$$

which is also reset to ${}_0V^Z = 0$. With the calculated values of ${}_0V^Z$ and ${}_1V^Z$ reset to zero, the profit vector values Pr_1 and Pr_2 will no longer be equal to zero. We have

$$Pr_1 = (19{,}039.00)(1.06) - 15{,}000.00 = 5{,}181.34$$

and

$$Pr_2 = (9{,}039.00)(1.06) - 17{,}000 - (2{,}679.54)(.983) = 547.35.$$

Since ${}_2V^Z$, ${}_3V^Z$ and ${}_4V^Z$ retain their positive calculated values, we will still have

$$Pr_3 = Pr_4 = Pr_5 = 0.$$

Then the profit vector is

$$\mathbf{Pr} = (-5{,}000.00,\ 5{,}181.34,\ 547.35,\ 0.00,\ 0.00,\ 0.00),$$

the profit signature is

$$\mathbf{\Pi} = (-5{,}000.00,\ 5{,}181.34,\ 539.14,\ 0.00,\ 0.00,\ 0.00),$$

and the net present value is

$$NPV = -5{,}000.00 + \frac{5{,}181.34}{1.10} + \frac{539.14}{(1.10)^2} = 155.88.$$

We have seen that a gross premium of 19,279.00 will generate a positive net present value under the original set of reserves (see Exercise 17-4), under the assumption of no reserves (see Example 17.9), and now under the method of zeroized reserves, but with different patterns of profit emergence. (The zeroized reserve method "front-loads" the profit into the early contract years.) Given this premium and the interest, mortality and expense assumptions, the contract is profitable. Different sets of reserves will allocate the profit differently among policy years, resulting in different net present values.

17.4 PROFIT DISTRIBUTION

In this section we consider the issue of returning a portion of the profit actually generated by an insurance contract back to a policyholder insured under a participating policy.[10] The amount of profit returned to the insured is called a *policyholder dividend*.[11]

17.4.1 PARTICIPATING INSURANCE

The concept of *participating insurance* was defined in Section 4.2.1. It was, at one time, the most popular form of insurance sold, but its share of the market has declined in recent years. Under participating insurance (often shortened to *par insurance*), a share of the profits earned over a time interval is distributed back to the "participating" policyholders. (The significance of the term is that these policyholders get to "participate" in the insurer's profit.)[12]

17.4.2 ACTUAL VS. EXPECTED PROFIT

Throughout this chapter we have discussed the concept of *expected profit*, which arises because the gross premium has been explicitly increased to generate a profit or because it was calculated from assumptions (interest, mortality and expenses) that were more conservative than those really expected.

Similarly, we can calculate the *actual profit* over a contract year by using the contract's gross premium and gross premium reserves, along with the interest, mortality and expenses actually experienced in that contract year.

17.4.3 GAIN AND LOSS

At this point we return to our presentation of gain and loss described in Sections 10.6, 11.5, and 14.6. We now define the *gain* over a time interval as the excess of the actual profit over the expected profit.[13] In some cases, the expected profit could be zero (as we have seen); in such cases the gain and the actual profit would be identical.

---

[10] Viewing the terms "profit" and "surplus" as nearly synonymous, we observe that this issue has traditionally been referred to as *distribution of surplus*. In the past, when mutual insurance companies and participating insurance were more common, entire textbooks were written on this subject.

[11] In some texts, particularly those written from a British or European perspective, policyholder dividends are referred to as *reversionary bonuses*.

[12] In some texts, particularly those written from a British or European perspective, participating insurance is called *with profit* insurance.

[13] Our definition of gain is consistent with the definition given by the Society of Actuaries in the document "Notation and Terminology Used on Exam MLC."

To illustrate, we consider first a life insurance contract with no cash surrender (or withdrawal) benefit, and with percent-of-premium expenses only. For this contract, Equation (17.1) for expected profit in the $(t+1)^{st}$ contract year reduces to

$$Pr_{t+1} = \left[{}_tV^G + G_{t+1}(1-r_{t+1}) \right](1+i_{t+1}) - B \cdot q_{x+t} - {}_{t+1}V^G \cdot p_{x+t}, \tag{17.6a}$$

since $e_{t+1} = b_{t+1}^{(2)} = s_{t+1}^{(1)} = s_{t+1}^{(2)} = 0$. Then using primed symbols for actual experience, we have

$$Pr'_{t+1} = \left[{}_tV^G + G_{t+1}(1-r'_{t+1}) \right](1+i'_{t+1}) - B \cdot q'_{x+t} - {}_{t+1}V^G \cdot p'_{x+t}. \tag{17.6b}$$

Note that the gross premium, gross premium reserves, and face amount of insurance are fixed quantities. The total gain in the $(t+1)^{st}$ contract year is then

$$\begin{aligned} G^T &= Pr'_{t+1} - Pr_{t+1} \\ &= \left\{ \left[{}_tV^G + G_{t+1}(1-r_{t+1}) \right](1+i_{t+1}) - B \cdot q_{x+t} - {}_{t+1}V^G \cdot p_{x+t} \right\} \\ &\quad - \left\{ \left[{}_tV^G + G_{t+1}(1-r'_{t+1}) \right](1+i'_{t+1}) - B \cdot q'_{x+t} - {}_{t+1}V^G \cdot p'_{x+t} \right\}. \end{aligned}$$

EXAMPLE 17.10

Consider a life insurance contract issued to (45) with face amount 100,000. The gross annual premium is $G_{t+1} = 2{,}264.12$ (in all years), the assumed interest rate is $i_{t+1} = .04$ (in all years), and the assumed percent-of-premium expense factor is $r_{t+1} = .06$ (in all years). The gross premium terminal reserves for policy years 9 and 10 are ${}_9V^G = 6{,}559.89$ and ${}_{10}V^G = 7{,}460.99$. The assumed mortality rate in the 10th policy year is $q_{54} = .00812$. The rates actually experienced in the 10th policy year are $i'_{10} = .06$, $q'_{54} = .00700$, and $r'_{10} = .08$. Calculate the total gain in the 10th policy year.

SOLUTION

From Equation (17.6a) we find the expected profit to be

$$\begin{aligned} Pr_{10} &= [6{,}559.89 + (.94)(2{,}264.12)](1.04) - (100{,}000)(.00812) - (7{,}460.99)(.99188) \\ &= (8{,}688.16)(1.04) - 812.00 - 7{,}400.41 = 823.28. \end{aligned}$$

From Equation (17.6b) we find the actual profit to be

$$\begin{aligned} Pr'_{10} &= [6{,}559.89 + (.92)(2{,}264.12)](1.06) - (100{,}000)(.00700) - (7{,}460.99)(.99300) \\ &= (8{,}642.88)(1.06) - 700.00 - 7{,}408.76 = 1{,}052.69. \end{aligned}$$

Then the gain is

$$G^T = 1{,}052.69 - 823.28 = 229.41$$ ❐

As we did in earlier chapters, we can analyze the total gain by source. First we use the identity $p_{x+t} = 1 - q_{x+t}$ to rewrite Equation (17.6a) as

$$Pr_{t+1} = \left[\,{}_tV^G + G(1-r)\right](1+i) - q_{x+t}(B - {}_{t+1}V^G) - {}_{t+1}V^G, \tag{17.7a}$$

and to rewrite Equation (17.6b) as

$$Pr'_{t+1} = \left[\,{}_tV^G + G(1-r')\right](1+i') - q'_{x+t}(B - {}_{t+1}V^G) - {}_{t+1}V^G, \tag{17.7b}$$

dropping the subscripts on all symbols that are constant. Then we can write

$$\begin{aligned} G^T &= Pr'_{t+1} - Pr_{t+1} \\ &= \left\{\left[\,{}_tV^G + G(1-r')\right](1+i') - q'_{x+t}(B - {}_{t+1}V^G)\right\} \\ &\quad - \left\{\left[\,{}_tV^G + G(1-r)\right](1+i) - q_{x+t}(B - {}_{t+1}V^G)\right\}, \end{aligned}$$

where the ${}_{t+1}V^G$ terms cancel. This can be rearranged as

$$G^T = ({}_tV^G + G)(i' - i) + (B - {}_{t+1}V^G)(q_{x+t} - q'_{x+t}) + G\left[r(1+i) - r'(1+i')\right]. \tag{17.8}$$

We can interpret the first term in Equation (17.8) as a *gain from interest* (which is positive if $i' > i$), and the second term as the *gain from mortality* (which is positive if $q'_{x+t} < q_{x+t}$). The third term represents a mixture of gain from both interest and expenses. To calculate a true gain from interest and a true gain from expenses, we have to choose an order for calculating the gains, as we have seen earlier in the text. Before we do this, however, we want to verify that the three elements of gain in Equation (17.8) sum to the total gain.

EXAMPLE 17.11

Evaluate the three elements of gain, for the policy described in Example 17.10, and show that they sum to the total gain.

SOLUTION

We have

$$G^I = (6{,}559.89 + 2{,}264.12)(.06 - .04) = 176.48,$$

$$G^M = (100{,}000 - 7{,}460.99)(.00812 - .00700) = 103.65,$$

and

$$G^{I\&E} = 2{,}264.12\big[(.06)(1.04) - (.08)(1.06)\big] = -50.72,$$

which is actually a loss because the higher actual expense more than offsets the higher actual interest rate. The total gain is

$$G^T = 176.48 + 103.65 - 50.72 = 229.41,$$

as expected. ❐

If we agree to calculate the gain from interest first, we evaluate the right side of Equation (17.7a) but with $i' = .06$ in place of $i = .04$. This gives us

$$\big[6{,}559.89 + (.94)(2{,}264.12)\big](1.06) - .00812(100{,}000 - 7{,}460.99) - 7{,}460.99$$

$$= (8{,}688.16)(1.06) - (.00812)(92{,}539.01) - 7{,}460.99 = 997.04.$$

From this quantity we subtract the expected profit value of 823.28, calculated earlier, to reach

$$G^I = 997.04 - 823.28 = 173.76$$

as our gain from interest. (This could also be calculated as $\left[{}_tV^G + G(1-r)\right](i'-i)$; see Exercise 17-8.) The mortality terms in our profit expressions do not overlap with either interest or expense items (since $s_{t+1} = 0$), so the gain from mortality is still $G^M = 103.65$. The gain from expenses becomes the balancing item, which is

$$G^E = G^T - G^I - G^M = 229.41 - 173.76 - 103.65 = -48.00.$$

(The gain from expenses could also be calculated as $(e-e')(1+i') = G(r-r')(1+i')$; see Exercise 17-9.)

17.4.4 DISTRIBUTABLE SURPLUS (PROFIT)

Thus far we have focused on determining the amount of total gain, and an analysis of the gain by source. How much of the gain should be distributed to the participating policyholders?

Note first that we would not distribute the entire actual profit to the policyholders, since it includes the expected profit within it. The expected profit is anticipated by the insurer as a return on its invested capital. At most, only the gain, or the excess of actual profit over expected profit, would be considered as available for policyholder dividends. In practice, not all of the gain would be distributed. The insurer would normally retain a portion of the gain, perhaps 10-25%, and distribute the remainder to the participating policyholders.

17.5 FORMS OF DISTRIBUTION

Once the amount of profit to return to the policyholders has been decided, we consider the question of optional forms of the actual distribution.

17.5.1 CASH

An obvious option is to simply pay the dividend to the policyholder in cash. In certain circumstances (see Section 17.5.2), a cash dividend might be taxable income to the policyholder.

17.5.2 PREMIUM REDUCTION

For a policy in a premium-paying status, the dividend declared at the end of policy year t could be used to reduce the premium due at the beginning of policy year $(t+1)$. The amount of premium reduction is not taxable to the insured. If the dividend is paid to the policyholder in cash, and the full amount of the next premium is paid to the insurer, the net effect is the same so the cash dividend is likewise not taxable to the insured.

If the policy has a limited premium paying period, such as a 20-pay whole life policy, dividends paid in cash at durations beyond the premium paying period would be taxable income to the insured.

17.5.3 TERMINAL BONUSES

Some contracts allow the option of having the insurer retain the dividends and accumulate them at interest. This would be similar to having the insured receive the dividends in cash and invest them in a savings account at a bank. The accumulated fund is released to the beneficiary upon the insured's death, or released to the insured upon surrender or maturity of the contract. Under this option, the interest portion of the accumulated dividends would be taxable income.[14]

17.5.4 PURCHASE OF ADDITIONAL INSURANCE

A popular option is to use the policyholder dividends to purchase additional paid-up insurance coverage of the same type as the policy producing the dividend. For example, if a whole life policy of face amount B issued at age x pays a dividend of amount Div_t at the end of the tth policy year, which is at age $x+t$, the dividend can act as a net single premium to purchase additional paid-up whole life insurance of amount

[14] Naturally the insurer must hold a reserve for these savings accounts. One insurer that failed to properly reserve for terminal bonuses became insolvent when its contractual obligations to pay them came due.

$$X_t = \frac{Div_t}{A_{x+t}}. \tag{17.9}$$

The cumulative paid-up additions are added to the face amount to reach the total death benefit paid. The reserve for the cumulative paid-up additions is separate from the reserve for the basic policy, since the paid-up additions reserve is simply the APV of the future benefit.

If the amount of paid-up addition is viewed as a multiple of the basic policy face amount, in the form

$$X_t = p \cdot B, \tag{17.10}$$

the parameter p is called the *simple reversionary bonus rate*. Generally the cumulative paid-up additions themselves generate more paid-up additions. For example, suppose a whole life policy issued at age x has paid a dividend at the end of each of its first $(t-1)$ years, and each dividend has been used to purchase paid-up additions. Then the cumulative amount of paid-up additions entering the tth policy year is

$$\sum_{r=1}^{t-1} X_r = \sum_{r=1}^{t-1} \frac{Div_r}{A_{x+r}}. \tag{17.11}$$

If the amount of paid-up addition purchased by the dividend at the end of the tth policy year is viewed as a multiple of the basic policy face amount *plus* the cumulative paid-up additions, in the form

$$X_t = p' \cdot \left(B + \sum_{r=1}^{t-1} X_r \right), \tag{17.12}$$

the parameter p' is called the *compound reversionary bonus rate*.[15] This concept is illustrated in the following example.

EXAMPLE 17.12

Consider a participating discrete whole life policy of face amount 50,000 issued to (30). The gross premium is 280.00, the annual expense is 50.00 (payable at the beginning of the year), the earned interest rate is $i = .07$, and the 21st year mortality rate is $q_{50} = .00356$. At the beginning of the 21st year, the policy had accumulated 10,000 face amount of paid-up additions. Calculate each of the following:

(a) The NLP reserve for both the basic policy and the cumulative paid-up additions at both $t = 20$ and $t = 21$, using the life table in Appendix A.

(b) The profit generated in the 21st policy year.

(c) The amount of paid-up addition purchased at $t = 21$, if the dividend is declared to be 85% of the profit, using the table in Appendix A.

(d) The compound reversionary bonus rate for the 21st policy year.

---

[15] There is also a concept of super compound reversionary bonus; see Exercise 17-12.

SOLUTION

(a) The basic policy NLP reserves are

$$50{,}000\,{}_{20}V_{30} = 50{,}000\left(\frac{A_{50}-A_{30}}{1-A_{30}}\right) = 50{,}000\left(\frac{.19908-.07570}{1-.07570}\right) = 6{,}674.24$$

and

$$50{,}000\,{}_{21}V_{30} = 50{,}000\left(\frac{A_{51}-A_{30}}{1-A_{30}}\right) = 50{,}000\left(\frac{.20820-.07570}{1-.07570}\right) = 7{,}167.59.$$

The NLP reserves for the cumulative paid-up additions are

$${}_{20}V = 10{,}000A_{50} = 1{,}990.80$$

and

$${}_{21}V = 10{,}000A_{51} = 2{,}082.00.$$

(b) The profit is

$$Pr_{21} = (6{,}674.24+1{,}990.80+280.00-50.00)(1.07)$$

$$-(.00356)(60{,}000.00)-(.99644)(7{,}167.59+2{,}082.00)$$

$$= (8{,}895.04)(1.07)-178.00-9{,}216.66 = 123.03.$$

(c) The dividend is $Div_{21} = (.85)(123.03) = 104.58$, so the amount of paid-up additions purchased at $t = 21$ is

$$X_{21} = \frac{Div_{21}}{A_{51}} = \frac{104.58}{.20820} = 502.30.$$

(d) The compound reversionary bonus rate, from Equation (17.12), is

$$p' = \frac{502.30}{60{,}000.00} = .00837.$$ ❐

Note, in Example 17.12, that we first determined the amount of paid-up addition purchased at $t = 21$, and then solved for the compound reversionary bonus rate from it. In practice, an insurer might declare the compound reversionary bonus rate from other analysis, and then calculate the amount of paid-up addition for each policy by multiplying the declared rate times the total in-force death benefit $\left(\text{i.e., } B+\sum X_t\right)$ at that time.

As an alternative to purchasing whole life paid-up additions, the contract might give the insured the option of purchasing paid-up term insurance instead. In this case, the amount of paid-up n-year term insurance would found as

$$Y_t = \frac{Div_t}{A^{\;1}_{x+t:\overline{n}|}}. \tag{17.12}$$

This might be elected by a policyholder in poor health wishing to maximize the amount of additional death benefit over the near-range future.

17.5.5 DISTRIBUTION TO TERMINATING POLICYHOLDERS

The question arises as to whether policyholders terminating their contracts in the tth policy year, either by death or by surrender, should receive the same dividend as a policyholder continuing the contract into the $(t+1)^{st}$ year. Since the policy is terminated, the only option for distributing the dividend would be in cash. Especially in the case of termination early in the policy year, an argument could be made for paying less than the full dividend to terminating policyholders. The industry practice seems to favor paying the full dividend amount in the case of death, but may pay a reduced dividend amount in the case of surrender.

17.6 EXERCISES

17.1 Definitions of Basic Concepts

17-1 A policy with a gross premium of 1000 and a survival model given by

$$q_{x+t} = .05 + .01t,$$

for $t = 0,1,2,3,$ produces the profit signature

$$\mathbf{\Pi} = (-300,100,90,80,70).$$

The hurdle rate is $r = .10.$

(a) Calculate the net present value of the profits at issue.

(b) Show that the internal rate of return is 5.54%.

(c) Find the discounted payback period.

(d) Calculate the profit margin.

17-2 A discrete three-year term policy of 1,000,000 face amount has annual gross premium of 17,500.00, pre-contract expenses of 3,000.00, per policy expenses after issue of 100.00, reserves of ${}_1V^G = {}_2V^G = 800.00$, and no settlement expenses. Assume mortality rates of $q_x = .015$, $q_{x+1} = .017$, and $q_{x+2} = .019$, a cash flow accumulation rate of $i = .05$, and a risk discount rate of $r = .10$.

(a) Develop a spreadsheet similar to Table 17.2 to determine the profit vector.

(b) Determine the profit signature.

(c) Calculate the net present value.

(d) Determine the internal rate of return.

(e) What is the policy's breakeven term?

(f) What is the policy's profit margin?

17-3 Consider a two-year discrete term policy issued to (40), with gross annual premium of 100.00, profit margin of −10%, and profit vector $Pr = (-300, 75, 250)$. Given that $q_{40} = .00278$, find the value of the risk discount rate.

17-4 Write a program in Excel (or otherwise) to perform the profit vector calculations as shown in Table 17.2. Show that a gross premium of 19,279.00 generates a profit vector which has a positive net present value, but a gross premium of 19,278.00 generates a negative net present value.

17-5 Repeat Exercise 17-4 using a gross premium of 19,500.00.

(a) Show that the net present value, at $r = .10$, is 864.88.

(b) Use a financial calculator (or otherwise) to show that the internal rate of return is 19.39%.

17.2 Uses of Profit Analysis

17-6 Repeat Exercise 17-4 using a gross premium of 20,335.00. Show that this gross premium produces a profit margin of 5%.

17.3 Using Profit Analysis to Determine Reserves

17-7 A discrete five-year term policy is issued to (x). The mortality assumption is

$$q_{x+t} = .013 + .001t,$$

for $t = 0,1,2,3,4$, and the interest assumption is $i = .05$. Ignoring reserves, the profit vector is

$$\mathbf{Pr} = (-300,\ 450,\ 230,\ 100,\ -50,\ -220).$$

The insurer wishes to set reserves by zeroization.

(a) Calculate the sequence of zeroized reserves.

(b) Calculate the profit vector using the zeroized reserves.

17.4 Profit Distribution

17-8 Using the model of Section 17.4.3, show that the gain from interest, if calculated first, can be found as

$$G^I = \left[{}_tV^G + G(1-r) \right](i' - i),$$

and verify the Example 17.11 value of $G^I = 173.76$.

17-9 Using the model of Section 17.4.3, show that the gain from expenses, if calculated second after the gain from interest, can be found as

$$G^E = G(r - r')(1 + i'),$$

and verify the Example 17.11 value of $G^E = -48.00$.

17.5 Forms of Distribution

17-10 Suppose the paid-up additions for the policy in Example 17.12 are themselves non-participating. Determine the simple reversionary bonus rate for the 21st policy year.

17-11 Calculate the amount of paid-up five-year term insurance that can be purchased by the 21st policy dividend in Example 17.12. (Use the table in Appendix A.)

17-12 As in Section 17.5.4 and Example 17.12, let $B=50,000$ be the face amount of a whole life policy issued to (x), and let $PA_{20}=\sum_{r=1}^{20}X_r=10,000$ be the cumulative paid-up additions at the end of the 20th policy year. Suppose the policy face amount generates paid-up additions at reversionary bonus rate $p_1=.010$, and the cumulative paid-up additions generate further paid-up additions at reversionary bonus rate $p_2=.008$. (This model of different rates for the face amount and the cumulative paid-up additions is called *super compound reversionary bonus* in some texts.)

(a) Find the total amount of paid-up additions purchased at $t=21$.

(b) What is the amount of the cash dividend, Div_{21}, that is actuarially equivalent to this amount of paid-up additions?

17.6 Written-Answer Question Exercises

17-13 Consider a two-year term policy of face amount 100,000 issued to (60). Semi-annual gross premiums of 185 are paid every six months, and death benefits are paid at the moment of death. The policy reserves are ${}_1V^G=14.40$, ${}_2V^G=19.70$, ${}_3V^G=15.20$, and ${}_4V^G=0.00$, where time is measured in semiannual periods. To perform profit analysis (or profit testing), we assume expenses to be 10% of the first semiannual premium and 5% of renewal premiums, an annual interest rate of $i=.07$, a survival model defined by $\mu_x=.0002+B(1.125)^x$, and deaths occurring in the middle of each semiannual period. We assume no pre-contract expenses. We are also given the value $Pr_4=4.30744$, where time is measured in semiannual periods.

(a) Find the value of the Makeham parameter B.

(b) Calculate the profit vector.

(c) Calculate the profit signature.

(d) Calculate the net present value at $r=.10$.

(e) Calculate the profit margin.

17-14 All of the examples and exercises considered thus far in this chapter have been based on a single-decrement (death) model, ignoring surrender probabilities and cash values.[16] Now consider a whole life contract of face amount 100,000 issued to (45), with either death benefit or surrender benefit paid at the end of the year of decrement. The gross annual premium is 2264.12, the pre-contract expense is 5,000.00, the interest rate is $i=.04$, and the percent-of-premium expense rates are 6% in the first year and 3% in all renewal years.

[16] All of the prior examples and exercises have been based on short-term term insurance contracts, which generally do not offer cash surrender values.

The following table gives the decrement factors, gross premium reserves, and cash surrender values for each of the first ten contract years:

Policy Year t	$q_{45+t-1}^{(d)}$	$q_{45+t-1}^{(w)}$	$p_{45+t-1}^{(\tau)}$	${}_tp_{45}^{(\tau)}$	${}_tV_{45}^G$	${}_tCV_{45}$
1	.00390	.04990	.94620	.94620	0.00	0.00
2	.00420	.04989	.94591	.89502	0.00	0.00
3	.00454	.04988	.94558	.84631	0.00	0.00
4	.00491	.04987	.94522	.79995	1,415.00	0.00
5	.00532	.04986	.94482	.75581	3,035.00	5,708.00
6	.00583	.02991	.96426	.72880	4,738.00	7,310.40
7	.00632	.02990	.96378	.70240	6,476.00	8,912.80
8	.00687	.02990	.96323	.67657	8,251.00	10,515.2
9	.00747	.02989	.96264	.65130	10,062.00	12,117.6
10	.00812	.02988	.96200	.62655	11,908.00	13,720.00

(a) Adapt Equation (17.1) to this contract.

(b) Using an Excel spreadsheet, or otherwise, calculate the profit vector values for the first ten contract years.

(c) Calculate the profit signature values for the first ten years.

(d) Calculate the net present value of the expected profits using $r = .10$.

(e) Calculate the profit margin.

17-15 All of the examples and exercises considered thus far in this chapter have involved a single insured person, with an insurance contract that terminated at death or surrender. Now we consider insurance contracts involving multiple lives or multiple decrements, where the first death or the first decrement does not necessarily terminate the contract. Our familiar multi-state model notation will be convenient to use in these cases, with minor exceptions. The mechanics of determining profit vector, profit signature, net present value, and profit margin are the same as with the earlier cases. Only the form of the expected profit expression, analogous to Equation (17.1), will be different.

(a) Consider the multi-state model described by Figure 12.1, and a discrete insurance of face amount B payable at the end of the year of death of (x), provided it occurs after the death of (y). The level gross annual premium is payable only while both (x) and (y) are alive. Assume no common shock, no cash values, no settlement expense, and constant rates of interest, fixed expense, and percent-of-premium expense. If both (x) and (y) are alive at time t, verify that the expected profit in the $(t+1)^{st}$ contract year is

$$Pr_{t+1} = \left[{}_tV^{(0)} + G(1-r) - e \right](1+i)$$

$$-B \cdot q^{\,2}_{x+t:y+t} - {}_{t+1}V^{(1)} \cdot p^{01}_{x+t:y+t} - {}_{t+1}V^{(0)} \cdot p^{00}_{x+t:y+t},$$

explaining the meaning and logic of each term. (Why can we not use $p^{03}_{x+t:y+t}$ for the probability that the face amount is paid at the end of the $(t+1)^{st}$ year?)

b) For the contract described in part (a), suppose the process is in State 1 at time t. Verify that the expected profit in the $(t+1)^{st}$ contract year is

$$Pr_{t+1} = \left[{}_tV^{(1)} - e \right](1+i) - B \cdot p^{13}_{x+t} - {}_{t+1}V^{(1)} \cdot p^{11}_{x+t},$$

explaining the meaning of each term.

(c) Consider the total and permanent disability model described by Figure 14.5, and a discrete insurance contract issued to (x) paying B at the end of the year of death or R at the end of each year of disability. Assume (x) is alive and healthy at time t. Verify that the expected profit in the $(t+1)^{st}$ contract year is

$$Pr_{t+1} = \left[{}_tV^{(0)} + G(1-r) - e \right](1+i)$$

$$-B \cdot p^{02}_{x+t} - \left(R + {}_{t+1}V^{(1)}\right) \cdot p^{01}_{x+t} - {}_{t+1}V^{(0)} \cdot p^{00}_{x+t},$$

explaining the meaning of each term.

(d) For the contract described in part (c), suppose (x) is alive but disabled at time t. Verify that the expected profit in the $(t+1)^{st}$ contract year is

$$Pr_{t+1} = \left[{}_tV^{(1)} - e \right](1+i) - B \cdot p^{12}_{x+t} - \left(R + {}_{t+1}V^{(1)}\right) \cdot p^{11}_{x+t},$$

explaining the meaning of each term.

APPENDIX A

USING MICROSOFT EXCEL AND VISUAL BASIC MACROS TO COMPUTE ACTUARIAL FUNCTIONS

As mentioned in Chapter 6, the basic representation of the tabular survival model is in terms of the values of ℓ_x. All other functions, such as d_x, p_x, q_x, A_x, ${}_nE_x$, and so on, can be derived from ℓ_x. In this appendix, we present some examples that use Microsoft Excel and Visual Basic macros to make the computations easier and more efficient.

A.1 DOWNLOADING THE BASIC LIFE TABLE FROM THE ACTEX WEBSITE

On the ACTEX website, the 1989-91 U.S. Life Table (for female lives) is posted to serve as an example for these calculations. The table is in Microsoft Excel files. You can download the table directly to your own computer to work on the calculations.

There are two ways to access the life table:

1. Go to actexmadriver.com/client/client_pages/actex_downlods2.cfm.

   There you will see the Illustrative Life Table Microsoft Excel (.xls) under *Models for Quantifying Risk* in the Free Downloads section.

2. Alternatively, you can go to the main page of our website at actexmadriver.com.

   Click on Free Downloads under Services on the left side. Then click on the link for ACTEX Textbooks, and you will find the same Illustrative Life Table.

A.2 USING EXCEL SPREADSHEETS TO CALCULATE d_x, p_x, AND q_x

A.2.1 REVIEW OF FORMULAS

Consider first the simple formula $d_x = \ell_x - \ell_{x+1}$. Since ℓ_x represents the size of the cohort group at age x, and ℓ_{x+1} represents the number of them still surviving at age $x+1$, then clearly d_x gives the number who fail (or die) between ages x and $x+1$.

EXAMPLE A.1

From the Illustrative Life Table on the ACTEX website, find the number who fails between ages 5 and 6.

SOLUTION

At age 5,

$$\begin{aligned} d_5 &= \ell_5 - \ell_6 \\ &= 99{,}006 - 98{,}983 = 23. \end{aligned}$$ ❒

Next consider the survival probability $p_x = \frac{\ell_{x+1}}{\ell_x}$, where p_x denotes the conditional probability of surviving to age $x+1$, given alive at age x.

EXAMPLE A.2

From the Illustrative Life Table on the ACTEX website, find the probability of surviving to age 6, given alive at age 5.

SOLUTION

We have

$$p_5 = \frac{\ell_6}{\ell_5} = \frac{98{,}983}{99{,}006} = .99977.$$ ❒

Next consider $q_x = \frac{d_x}{\ell_x} = \frac{\ell_x - \ell_{x+1}}{\ell_x} = 1 - p_x$, where q_x gives the conditional probability of failure before age $x+1$, given alive at age x.

EXAMPLE A.3

From the Illustrative Life Table, find the probability of failure before age 6, given alive at age 5.

SOLUTION

This time

$$q_5 = \frac{d_5}{\ell_5} = \frac{23}{99{,}006} = .00023 = 1 - p_5.$$ ❒

A.2.2 USING MICROSOFT EXCEL TO DO THE ABOVE CALCULATIONS

The above calculations can be made very easily and efficiently by using the formulas and functions in Microsoft Excel. Consider the calculation of d_0 shown in the following spreadsheet.

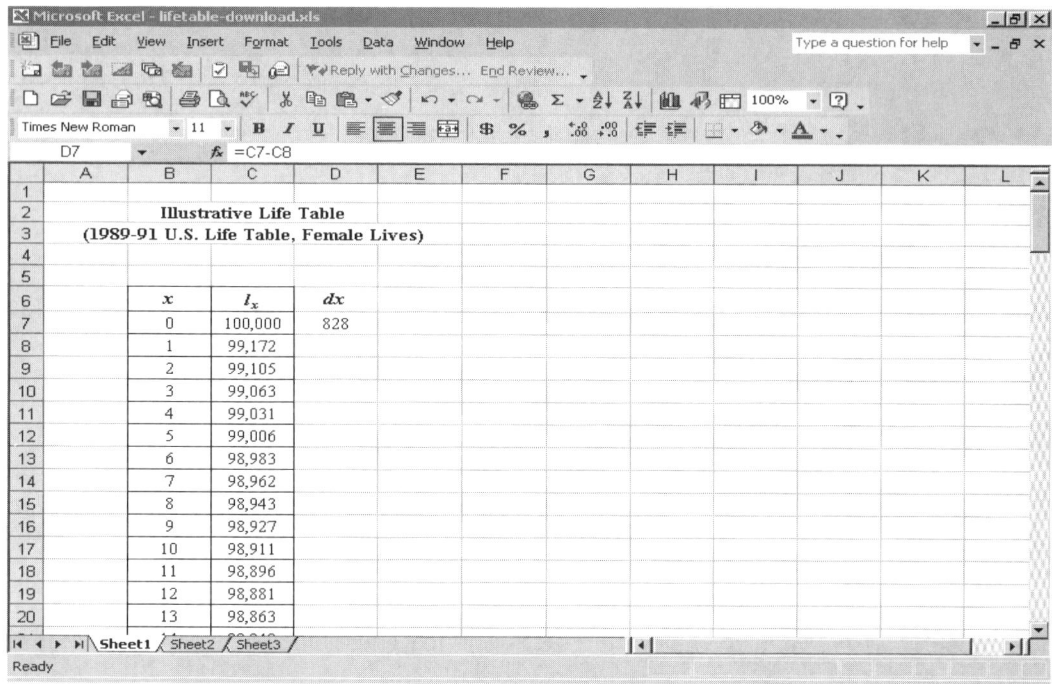

FIGURE A.1

To calculate

$$\begin{aligned} d_0 &= \ell_0 - \ell_1 \\ &= 100{,}000 - 99{,}172 = 828, \end{aligned}$$

we take the following steps:

1. Click on the cell (D7) where you want to enter a formula.
2. Type an equal sign $(=)$ to begin the formula.
3. Type the formula $(= \text{C7} - \text{C8})$, and then press the **Enter** key.
4. The result of the calculation appears in the cell $(d_0 = 828)$.

For the calculation of $d_1, d_2, \ldots,$ we need the same formula, in relationship to the location into which it is to be typed. There are a number of ways to perform this operation. One way is to use the short cut **Fill Down**.

1. Select the cell that has the original formula (D7).
2. Hold the **Shift** key down and click on the last cell in the series that needs the formula, which is D117 for the Illustrative Life Table.
3. Under the **Edit** menu, go down to **Fill** and over to **Down**.

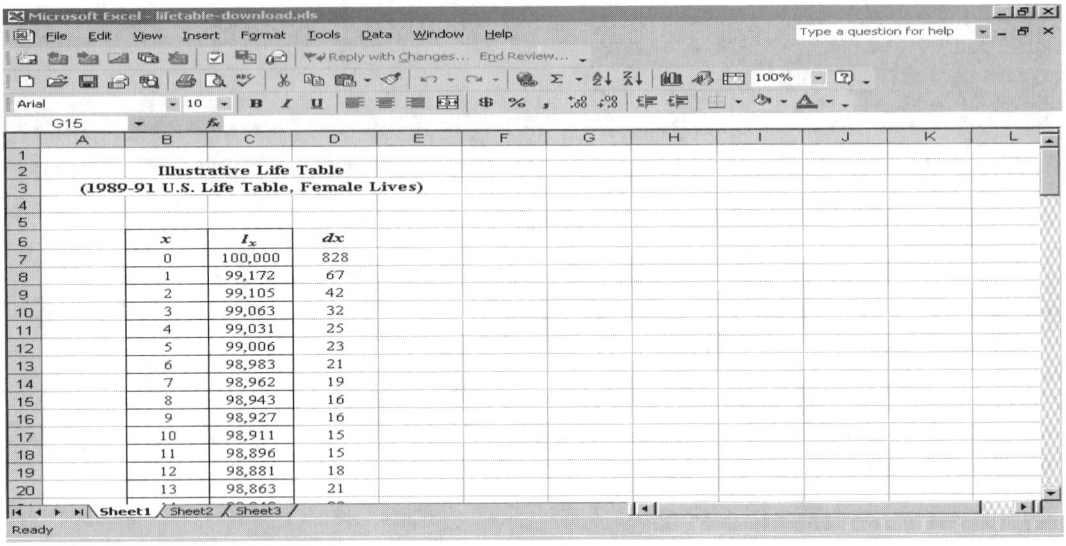
Microsoft Excel - lifetable-download.xls
File Edit View Insert Format Tools Data Window Help
Type a question for help
Reply with Changes... End Review...
Arial
G15
Illustrative Life Table
(1989-91 U.S. Life Table, Female Lives)
x | l_x | dx
0 | 100,000 | 828
1 | 99,172 | 67
2 | 99,105 | 42
3 | 99,063 | 32
4 | 99,031 | 25
5 | 99,006 | 23
6 | 98,983 | 21
7 | 98,962 | 19
8 | 98,943 | 16
9 | 98,927 | 16
10 | 98,911 | 15
11 | 98,896 | 15
12 | 98,881 | 18
13 | 98,863 | 21
Sheet1 Sheet2 Sheet3
Ready

FIGURE A.2

The equation pasted into D8 would be $(C8-C9)$, the equation pasted into D9 would be $(C9-C10)$, and so on.

Alternatively, we can use the **Auto Fill Options** button to do the copying of formulas.

1. Position the mouse over the bottom right corner of the cell (mouse changes to **+)**.
2. Drag the mouse + over the cells you want to include in the series.

The calculations of p_x and q_x can be done in a similar way using Microsoft Excel, and are left to the reader as exercises.

A.3 CALCULATING A_x USING VISUAL BASIC MACROS

Although most simple computations can be made using formulas and built-in functions in Excel, Visual Basic macros can make the complicated computations easier and more efficient. For example, consider the discrete whole life insurance APV, denoted by A_x, and given by

$$A_x = \sum_{k=0}^{w-x-1} v^{k+1} \cdot {}_{k|}q_x = \sum_{k=0}^{w-x-1} v^{k+1} \cdot \frac{d_{x+k}}{\ell_x}. \tag{A.1}$$

We can still use the Excel spreadsheet to calculate A_x, but we will find that using Visual Basic macros will simplify the computations. We use the following Visual Basic code to calculate A_x:

```
Private Sub CalculateAx()
    Dim r As Double, v As Double
    Dim I As Integer, K As Integer
    Dim OffsetV As Integer
    Dim Ax As Double
```

```
'We assume that the interest rate is 6%. (This can be changed.)[1]

r = .06

'v is the discount rate corresponding to the given interest rate r.

v = 1 / (1 + r)

'Offset V defines the vertical position of the starting cell A0 within the Excel spreadsheet.
OffsetV = 7
Sheet1.Cells(OffsetV - 1, 7) = "Ax"
For I = 0 To 110
Ax = 0
    For K = 0 To 111 - I - 1
    Ax = Ax + v ^ (K+1) * Sheet1.Cells(I + K + OffsetV, 4) / Sheet1.Cells(I+OffsetV, 3)
    Next K
    Sheet1.Cells(I + OffsetV, 7) = Ax
Next I
End Sub
```

(Note that to make the Visual Basic code more understandable, we followed the formulas in a straightforward manner. However, the computation can be made more efficient, and the interested reader might try other ways to write the program.)

The result of the computation of A_x is depicted in the following spreadsheet.

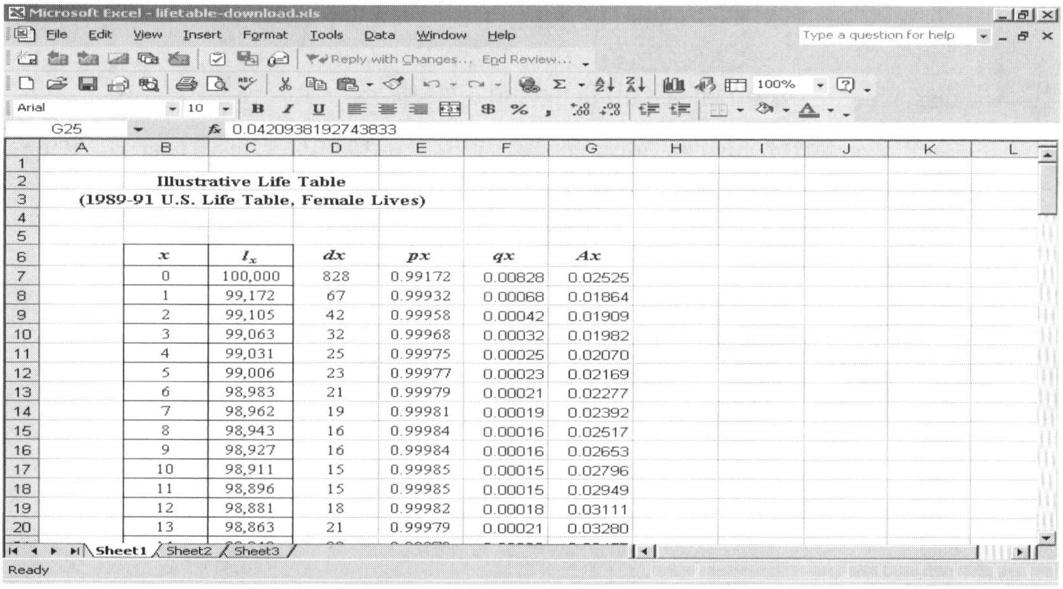

Microsoft Excel - lifetable-download.xls

G25 0.0420938192743833

Illustrative Life Table
(1989-91 U.S. Life Table, Female Lives)

x	l_x	dx	px	qx	Ax
0	100,000	828	0.99172	0.00828	0.02525
1	99,172	67	0.99932	0.00068	0.01864
2	99,105	42	0.99958	0.00042	0.01909
3	99,063	32	0.99968	0.00032	0.01982
4	99,031	25	0.99975	0.00025	0.02070
5	99,006	23	0.99977	0.00023	0.02169
6	98,983	21	0.99979	0.00021	0.02277
7	98,962	19	0.99981	0.00019	0.02392
8	98,943	16	0.99984	0.00016	0.02517
9	98,927	16	0.99984	0.00016	0.02653
10	98,911	15	0.99985	0.00015	0.02796
11	98,896	15	0.99985	0.00015	0.02949
12	98,881	18	0.99982	0.00018	0.03111
13	98,863	21	0.99979	0.00021	0.03280

Sheet1 Sheet2 Sheet3

Ready

FIGURE A.3

[1] Lines that begin with the symbol (') are comments, but not commands in the program.

A.4 CALCULATING $_nE_x$ USING MICROSOFT EXCEL

Throughout the text we have seen that the n-year pure endowment function $_nE_x = v^n \cdot {_np_x}$ is very important in the calculation of other functions, such as

$$A^{\,1}_{x:\overline{n}|} = A_x - {_nE_x} \cdot A_{x+n}. \tag{A.2}$$

Given the age (x) and the number of years n, $_nE_x$ can easily be computed using ℓ_x, ℓ_{x+n}, and the discount rate v.

EXAMPLE A.4

Given the Illustrative Life Table and the interest rate $i = .06$, find $_5E_{45}$.

SOLUTION

Since $i = .06$, then $v = \frac{1}{1+i} = .9434$. Then

$$_5E_{45} = v^5 \cdot {_5p_{45}} = v^5 \cdot \frac{\ell_{50}}{\ell_{45}} = .73724.$$ ❐

To compute $_5E_{45}$ in Microsoft Excel, we can do the following:

1. Type interest rate $i = .06$ as input in the cell (I3).

2. The discount rate v is calculated using the formula $v = \frac{1}{1+i}$.
   Click on the cell (I4), type the formula (=1/(1+$I$3)), and press the **Enter** key; the result 94.34% then appears in the cell (I4).

3. To calculate $_5E_{45}$, click on the cell (I47) where we want to enter the formula, type the formula (=$I$4^5*C57/C52), and press the **Enter** key, to get the value of $_5E_{45}$ (=.73724) in the cell (I47).

The computation of $_5E_{45}$ is depicted in the following spreadsheet:

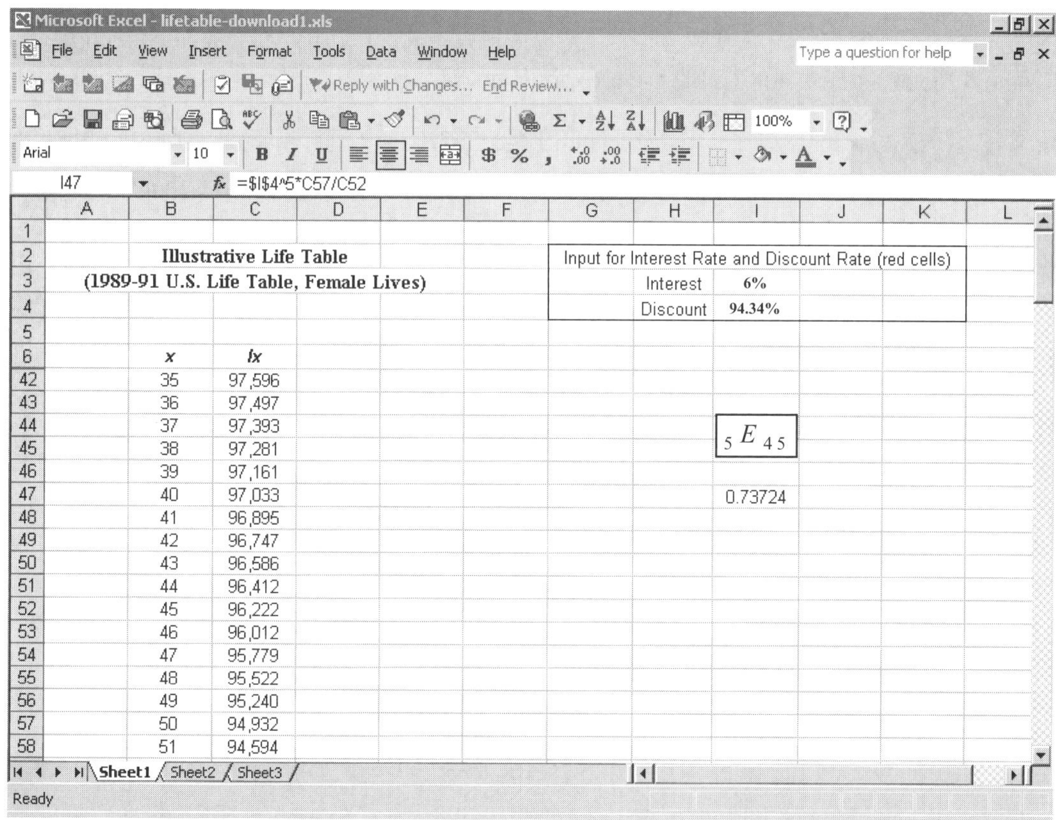

FIGURE A.4

Using an interest rate of 6%, the following table illustrates selected values of ${}_nE_x$.

TABLE A.1

x	n=5	n=10	n=15	n=20	n=25
5	.747	.557	.416	.310	.231
25	.745	.554	.412	.305	.225
45	.737	.539	.389	.276	.190
65	.690	.455	.279	.151	.065
85	.430	.127	.023	.002	.000

The reader should choose several combinations of n and x and practice the calculation of ${}_nE_x$.

A.5 CALCULATING SECOND MOMENTS AND VARIANCES

Recall from Chapter 7 that ${}^2A_x$ is the same kind of function as A_x, except that it is calculated at a force of interest that is double the force of interest used to calculate A_x. That is, if interest rate i is used to calculate A_x, then ${}^2A_x$ is calculated at rate $i' = (1+i)^2 - 1$, not $i' = 2i$. For example, if $i = .06$, then $i' = .1236$. It is important to remember that ${}^2A_x$ is calculated at double the force of interest, not double the effective rate of interest.

In Section A.3, we showed how to calculate A_x using Visual Basic macros. After doubling the force of interest, we can use the same method to compute ${}^2A_x$, being careful to put the values in the right positions. Then the variance of the present value random variable Z_x is given by

$$Var(Z_x) = {}^2A_x - A_x^{\,2}. \tag{A.3}$$

EXAMPLE A.5

Given the 1989-91 U.S. Life Table on the ACTEX website, and interest rate $i = .06$, find the variance of Z_{30} from the values shown in Table A.2.

SOLUTION

From Table A.2 we find $A_{30} = .07570$ and ${}^2A_{30} = .01489$. Then

$$Var(Z_{30}) = {}^2A_{30} - A_{30}^{\,2} = .01489 - (.07570)^2 = .00916. \quad \square$$

Table A.2, shown on pages 591-593, depicts the 1989-91 U.S Life Table (for female lives), with the completed calculations of d_x, p_x, q_x, A_x, and ${}^2A_x$, where A_x and ${}^2A_x$ are calculated at interest rate 6%. The reader could practice his or her programming skills by reproducing the entire table.

A.6 CALCULATING JOINT-LIFE STATUS FUNCTIONS

For a joint-life status assuming independence of the individual lifetimes, the survival distribution function is

$${}_tp_{xy} = {}_tp_x \cdot {}_tp_y. \tag{A.4}$$

EXAMPLE A.6

Given the Illustrative Life Table, calculate the value of ${}_5p_{40:50}$.

SOLUTION

We have

$${}_5p_{40:50} = {}_5p_{40} \cdot {}_5p_{50} = \frac{\ell_{45}}{\ell_{40}} \cdot \frac{\ell_{55}}{\ell_{50}} = \frac{96{,}222}{97{,}033} \cdot \frac{92{,}881}{94{,}932} = .9702. \quad \square$$

For the calculation of A_{xy}, we can use the formula connecting insurance and annuity functions, which is

$$A_{xy} = 1 - d \cdot \ddot{a}_{xy}, \tag{A.5}$$

since the calculation of $\ddot{a}_{xy}$ is easier to make than is the calculation of A_{xy}. Recall that

$$\ddot{a}_{xy} = \sum_{t=0}^{\infty} v^t \cdot {}_tp_x \cdot {}_tp_y, \tag{A.6}$$

which can be done using either Microsoft Excel or Visual Basic macros.

EXAMPLE A.7

Given the Illustrative Life Table and interest rate $i = .06$, calculate the value of $A_{80:85}$.

SOLUTION

First we find

$$\ddot{a}_{80:85} = \sum_{t=0}^{\infty} v^t \cdot {}_tp_{80} \cdot {}_tp_{85} = 4.450419$$

and then

$$A_{80:85} = 1 - d \cdot \ddot{a}_{80:85} = 1 - \frac{.06}{1.06} \times 4.450419 = .74809.$$ ❐

The above computation can be carried out using Microsoft Excel or Visual Basic macros. Here we give the Visual Basic code as an example. The reader is encouraged to do the calculation himself or herself using the Excel spreadsheet.

```
Private Sub Calculate_Axy()
    Dim r As Double, v As Double, d As Double
    Dim J As Integer
    Dim x As Integer, y As Integer
    Dim axy As Double, A_xy As Double
    Dim tpx As Double, tpy As Double
    Dim OffsetV As Integer

    'The interest rate is assumed to be 6%. (This can be changed.)
    r = .06
    'The discount factor v and the effective discount rate d can be calculated.
    v = 1 / (1 + r)
    d = r * v
    'x and y define the ages for a two-life joint status.
    x = 80
    y = 85
    'OffsetV defines the vertical position of the starting cell of ℓ0 in the spreadsheet.
    OffsetV = 7
    axy = 0
    For J = 0 To 111 - y
```

```
    tpx = Sheet2.Cells(J + OffsetV + x, 3) / Sheet2.Cells(OffsetV + x, 3)
    tpy = Sheet2.Cells(J + OffsetV + y, 3) / Sheet2.Cells(OffsetV + y, 3)
    axy = axy + v ^ J * tpx * tpy
    Next J
    Sheet2.Cells(11, 6) = axy
    A_xy = 1 - d * axy
    Sheet2.Cells(16, 6) = A_xy
End Sub
```

The results of the above program are depicted in the following spreadsheet:

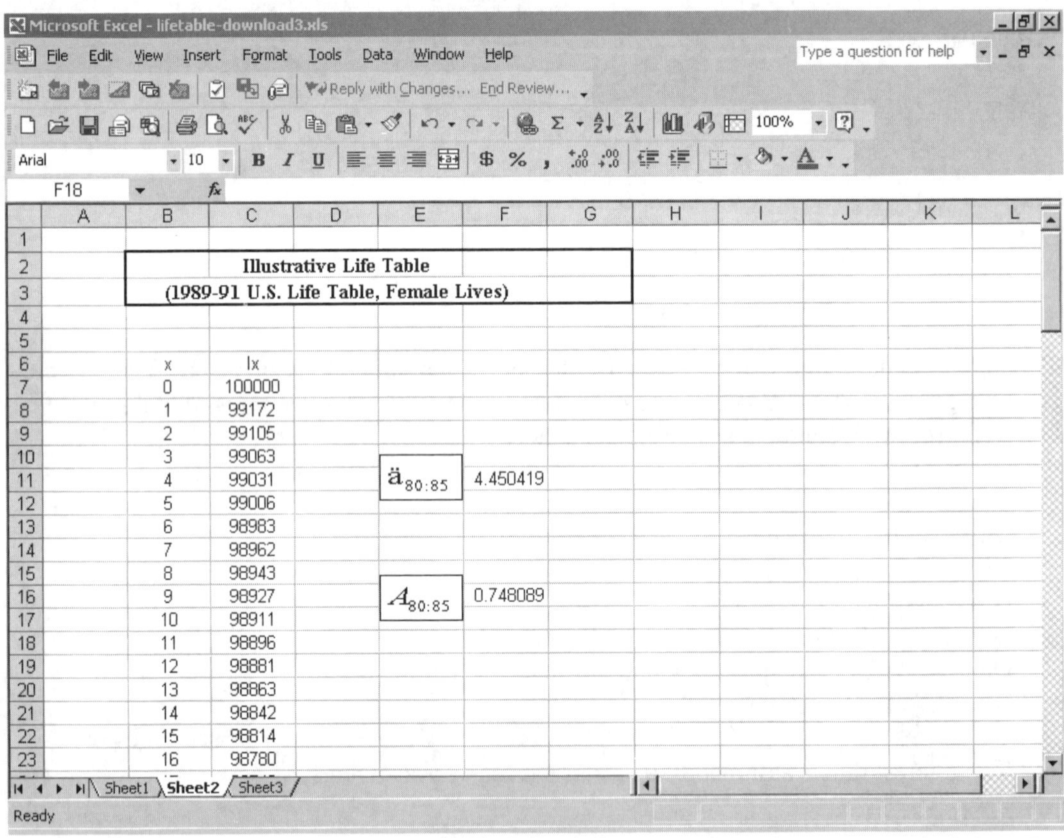

FIGURE A.5

We emphasize that A_x and ${}_nE_x$ are the basic functions to be understood. Then all the other functions, such as term insurance, annuities, reserves, and so on, can be derived from A_x and ${}_nE_x$.

TABLE A.2

1989-91 U.S. Life Table (for female lives)

x	ℓ_x	d_x	p_x	q_x	A_x	${}^2A_x$
0	100,000	828	.99172	.00828	.02525	.01015
1	99,172	67	.99932	.00068	.01864	.00315
2	99,105	42	.99958	.00042	.01909	.00286
3	99,063	32	.99968	.00032	.01982	.00279
4	99,031	25	.99975	.00025	.02070	.00282
5	99,006	23	.99977	.00023	.02169	.00291
6	98,983	21	.99979	.00021	.02277	.00304
7	98,962	19	.99981	.00019	.02392	.00321
8	98,943	16	.99984	.00016	.02517	.00341
9	98,927	16	.99984	.00016	.02653	.00367
10	98,911	15	.99985	.00015	.02796	.00396
11	98,896	15	.99985	.00015	.02949	.00430
12	98,881	18	.99982	.00018	.03111	.00468
13	98,863	21	.99979	.00021	.03280	.00508
14	98,842	28	.99972	.00028	.03457	.00550
15	98,814	34	.99966	.00034	.03637	.00590
16	98,780	40	.99960	.00040	.03822	.00628
17	98,740	45	.99954	.00046	.04012	.00666
18	98,695	48	.99951	.00049	.04209	.00703
19	98,647	50	.99949	.00051	.04416	.00741
20	98,597	51	.99948	.00052	.04632	.00783
21	98,546	54	.99945	.00055	.04861	.00828
22	98,492	54	.99945	.00055	.05100	.00876
23	98,438	56	.99943	.00057	.05355	.00930
24	98,382	57	.99942	.00058	.05622	.00989
25	98,325	58	.99941	.00059	.05905	.01053
26	98,267	59	.99940	.00060	.06204	.01125
27	98,208	61	.99938	.00062	.06520	.01205
28	98,147	65	.99934	.00066	.06853	.01293
29	98,082	69	.99930	.00070	.07203	.01387
30	98,013	74	.99924	.00076	.07570	.01489
31	97,939	79	.99919	.00081	.07955	.01599
32	97,860	83	.99915	.00085	.08359	.01717
33	97,777	88	.99910	.00090	.08783	.01846
34	97,689	93	.99905	.00095	.09228	.01986
35	97,596	99	.99899	.00101	.09696	.02139
36	97,497	104	.99893	.00107	.10186	.02304
37	97,393	112	.99885	.00115	.10702	.02485
38	97,281	120	.99877	.00123	.11242	.02680
39	97,161	128	.99868	.00132	.11808	.02891
40	97,033	138	.99858	.00142	.12401	.03121

1989-91 U.S. Life Table (for female lives)						
x	ℓ_x	d_x	p_x	q_x	A_x	${}^2A_x$
41	96,895	148	.99847	.00153	.13021	.03370
42	96,747	161	.99834	.00166	.13671	.03639
43	96,586	174	.99820	.00180	.14349	.03929
44	96,412	190	.99803	.00197	.15056	.04242
45	96,222	210	.99782	.00218	.15794	.04578
46	96,012	233	.99757	.00243	.16559	.04936
47	95,779	257	.99732	.00268	.17352	.05317
48	95,522	282	.99705	.00295	.18174	.05721
49	95,240	308	.99677	.00323	.19025	.06151
50	94,932	338	.99644	.00356	.19908	.06609
51	94,594	372	.99607	.00393	.20820	.07095
52	94,222	409	.99566	.00434	.21762	.07609
53	93,813	446	.99525	.00475	.22732	.08151
54	93,367	486	.99479	.00521	.23734	.08724
55	92,881	526	.99434	.00566	.24766	.09331
56	92,355	571	.99382	.00618	.25832	.09974
57	91,784	621	.99323	.00677	.26930	.10655
58	91,163	680	.99254	.00746	.28059	.11372
59	90,483	741	.99181	.00819	.29215	.12122
60	89,742	803	.99105	.00895	.30398	.12907
61	88,939	864	.99029	.00971	.31610	.13730
62	88,075	929	.98945	.01055	.32854	.14598
63	87,146	999	.98854	.01146	.34130	.15511
64	86,147	1,072	.98756	.01244	.35438	.16471
65	85,075	1,146	.98653	.01347	.36778	.17480
66	83,929	1,222	.98544	.01456	.38151	.18543
67	82,707	1,302	.98426	.01574	.39560	.19665
68	81,405	1,391	.98291	.01709	.41005	.20850
69	80,014	1,492	.98135	.01865	.42483	.22095
70	78,522	1,603	.97959	.02041	.43987	.23398
71	76,919	1,722	.97761	.02239	.45514	.24754
72	75,197	1,847	.97544	.02456	.47060	.26160
73	73,350	1,972	.97312	.02688	.48621	.27616
74	71,378	2,091	.97071	.02929	.50200	.29124
75	69,287	2,205	.96818	.03182	.51800	.30693
76	67,082	2,318	.96545	.03455	.53425	.32333
77	64,764	2,443	.96228	.03772	.55079	.34051
78	62,321	2,588	.95847	.04153	.56752	.35839
79	59,733	2,747	.95401	.04599	.58431	.37681
80	56,986	2,909	.94895	.05105	.60102	.39559

1989-91 U.S. Life Table (for female lives)						
x	ℓ_x	d_x	p_x	q_x	A_x	^2A_x
81	54,077	3,061	.94340	.05660	.61756	.41460
82	51,016	3,196	.93735	.06265	.63389	.43379
83	47,820	3,308	.93082	.06918	.64999	.45315
84	44,512	3,397	.92368	.07632	.66588	.47268
85	41,115	3,472	.91555	.08445	.68153	.49236
86	37,643	3,530	.90622	.09378	.69682	.51201
87	34,113	3,540	.89623	.10377	.71158	.53135
88	30,573	3,498	.88559	.11441	.72582	.55036
89	27,075	3,409	.87409	.12591	.73957	.56909
90	23,666	3,294	.86081	.13919	.75282	.58749
91	20,372	3,141	.84582	.15418	.76533	.60514
92	17,231	2,921	.83048	.16952	.77684	.62159
93	14,310	2,638	.81565	.18435	.78742	.63686
94	11,672	2,326	.80072	.19928	.79729	.65129
95	9,346	2,007	.78526	.21474	.80659	.66504
96	7,339	1,698	.76863	.23137	.81533	.67812
97	5,641	1,398	.75217	.24783	.82338	.69028
98	4,243	1,119	.73627	.26373	.83087	.70166
99	3,124	873	.72055	.27945	.83799	.71258
100	2,251	667	.70369	.29631	.84494	.72335
101	1,584	498	.68561	.31439	.85170	.73391
102	1,086	361	.66759	.33241	.85823	.74420
103	725	256	.64690	.35310	.86476	.75461
104	469	176	.62473	.37527	.87115	.76485
105	293	116	.60410	.39590	.87743	.77493
106	177	74	.58192	.41808	.88424	.78597
107	103	46	.55340	.44660	.89225	.79915
108	57	27	.52632	.47368	.90203	.81554
109	30	15	.50000	.50000	.91670	.84105
110	15	15	.00000	1.00000	.94340	.89000

APPENDIX B

DERIVATION OF THE KOLMOGOROV FORWARD EQUATION

As in Section 3.2, we assume a Markov model with $m+1$ states, denoted $0,1,\cdots,m$. Consider a process known to be in State i at time $t=0$, for a person age x at that time.

Figure B.1

Recall that ${}_{t+s}p_x^{ij}$ denotes the probability that a person known to be in State i at time 0 at age x will be in State j at time $t+s$. Referring to Figure B.1, the process must be in some state, say, State k, at time t, where k can be any state including State i or State j. The probability of being in State k at time t, given in State i at time 0, is ${}_tp_x^{ik}$. The probability of being in State j at time $t+s$, given in State k at time t, is ${}_sp_{x+t}^{kj}$. Then it follows from the law of total probability that

$$ {}_{t+s}p_x^{ij} = \sum_{k=0}^{m} {}_tp_x^{ik} \cdot {}_sp_{x+t}^{kj}.[1] \tag{B.1} $$

Now we use Equation (B.1) to write

$$ \begin{aligned} {}_{t+h}p_x^{ij} - {}_tp_x^{ij} &= \left(\sum_{k=0}^{m} {}_tp_x^{ik} \cdot {}_hp_{x+t}^{kj} \right) - {}_tp_x^{ij} \\ &= \left(\sum_{k \neq j} {}_tp_x^{ik} \cdot {}_hp_{x+t}^{kj} \right) + {}_tp_x^{ij} \cdot {}_hp_{x+t}^{jj} - {}_tp_x^{ij} \\ &= \left(\sum_{k \neq j} {}_tp_x^{ik} \cdot {}_hp_{x+t}^{kj} \right) - \left(1 - {}_hp_{x+t}^{jj}\right) \cdot {}_tp_x^{ij}, \end{aligned} \tag{B.2} $$

[1] Equation (B.1) is known as the Chapman-Kolmogorov equation.

by removing the summand at $k = j$ from the summation term. We then divide both sides of Equation (B.2) by h and take the limit as $h \to 0$, giving us

$$\lim_{h\to 0}\left(\frac{{}_{t+h}p_x^{ij} - {}_tp_x^{ij}}{h}\right) = \lim_{h\to 0}\left\{\left(\sum_{k\neq j} {}_tp_x^{ik} \cdot \frac{{}_hp_{x+t}^{kj}}{h}\right) - \left(\frac{1-{}_hp_{x+t}^{jj}}{h}\right) \cdot {}_tp_x^{ij}\right\}. \tag{B.3}$$

The left side of Equation (B.3) is, by definition, the derivative of ${}_tp_x^{ij}$. To find the limit of $\frac{{}_hp_{x+t}^{kj}}{h}$, we recall that ${}_hp_{x+t}^{kj}$ is the probability of transitioning from State k to State j within a time interval of length h. As demonstrated in Example 6.3, the limit of this probability value, divided by the interval length h, as $h \to 0$, is the force of transitioning from State k to State j at time t, which we denote by μ_{x+t}^{kj}.

The limit of $\frac{1-{}_hp_{x+t}^{jj}}{h}$ is similarly found. Since ${}_hp_{x+t}^{jj}$ is the probability of remaining in State j over an interval of length h, then $1 - {}_hp_{x+t}^{jj}$ is the probability of leaving State j over that interval. When we divide by h, and take the limit as $h \to 0$, we obtain the total force of leaving State j at time t, which we denote by μ_{x+t}^{j}. Equation (B.3) therefore becomes

$$\frac{d}{dt}\,{}_tp_x^{ij} = \left(\sum_{k\neq j} {}_tp_x^{ik} \cdot \mu_{x+t}^{kj}\right) - \mu_{x+t}^{j} \cdot {}_tp_x^{ij}, \tag{B.4}$$

which is Equation (3.14b). If we recall from Equation (3.12) that

$$\mu_{x+t}^{j} = \sum_{k\neq j} \mu_{x+t}^{jk},$$

then we can write

$$\frac{d}{dt}\,{}_tp_x^{ij} = \sum_{k\neq j}\left({}_tp_x^{ik} \cdot \mu_{x+t}^{kj} - {}_tp_x^{ij} \cdot \mu_{x+t}^{jk}\right), \tag{B.5}$$

which is Equation (3.14a).

APPENDIX C

THE MATHEMATICS OF RISK DIVERSIFICATION

In Chapter 15 we discussed diversifiable and non-diversifiable risks. Insurance companies take on large numbers of insurance contracts, and generally assume that these contracts are mutually independent. The financial cost to the insurer of the ith individual contract can be represented as a random variable X_i.

Let $X_1, X_2, \cdots, X_n$ be independent random variables such that each X_i has expected value μ and variance σ^2. Let $S_n = X_1 + X_2 + \cdots + X_n$. Then

$$E[S_n] = n \cdot E[X_i] = n\mu$$

and

$$Var(S_n) = n \cdot Var(X_i) = n\sigma^2.$$

The standard deviation of S_n is $\sqrt{n}\sigma$, and the coefficient of variation, which is the ratio of the standard deviation to the mean, is

$$c_v = \frac{\sqrt{n}\sigma}{n\mu} = \frac{\sigma}{\sqrt{n}\mu},$$

so as n increases the coefficient of variation of S_n tends to zero.

In this case, S_n represents the net financial cost to the insurance company, and c_v represents the risk to the insurance company of variation in their expected results. As the relative magnitude of variation decreases, the risk to the insurance company decreases.

A risk, then, is considered diversifiable if

$$\lim_{n \to \infty} \frac{Var(S_n)}{n} = 0, \tag{C.1}$$

and a risk is considered non-diversifiable if this is not true. This is true if the random variables are independent. Risks that affect every contract, such as interest rate changes and changes in underlying mortality, are non-diversifiable.

If our interest rate or mortality changes, this would change the underlying distribution of X. This changes the value of our mean μ which, in turn, changes the expected financial cost to the insurance company. This risk cannot be diversified.

Refer back to Example 9.6 in the text. Here we see an increase in the expected loss on a single contract due to an increase in the first-year mortality rate. If this increase in mortality rates extended to the entire insured population, the insurer would expect losses on the entire portfolio. This risk is not reduced or diversified with an increase in the number of policies.

ANSWERS TO THE EXERCISES

CHAPTER 3

3-1 (a) .25

(b) $.3\dot{3}$

(c) $.63\dot{3}$

(d) Non-homegenous

3-2 (a) No

(b) More

(c) .489

3-3 (a) Homogeneous

(b) $e^{-1.50r}$

(c) .25896

3-4 (a) 2.548

(b) 2.352

CHAPTER 4

Note: The exercises in Chapter 4 are all of the discussion type, without numerical or symbolic answers. Model solutions are found in the solutions manual that accompanies this text.

CHAPTER 5

5-1 (a) $e^{-(at+bt^2/2)}$

(b) $(a+bt)\cdot e^{-(at+bt^2/2)}$

(c) $b^{-1/2}-ab^{-1}$

5-2 $45\sqrt{2}$

5-3 Because $\lim_{t\to\infty} S_0(t) = e^{-1/r} \neq 0$

5-4 $.20\omega$

5-5 $\frac{1}{3}$

5-7 .60199

5-8 (a) Constant

(b) Decreasing

(c) Increasing

5-9 38.99

5-11 588

5-12 $\frac{1}{6000}$

5-13 .59049

5-14 7

5-15 5.249

5-16 40

5-17 15.4822

5-18 (a) .60

(b) 5

(c) $\frac{1}{20-t}$

5-20 $\max[t \ni X(t)=0]$ or $\min[t \ni X(t)=1]$

5-21 $\max[t \ni X(t)=0]$ or $\min[t \ni X(t)=1]$

5-22 (a) $\int_0^n {}_tp_x^{00} \cdot \mu_{x+t}^{01}\, dt$

(b) $\int_0^n {}_rp_x \mu_{x+r}\, dr$

5-23 $\int_0^\infty {}_tp_x^{00}\,dt$

5-24 $e^{-n\lambda}$

5-25 $1-e^{-n\lambda}$

CHAPTER 6

6-1 (a) 5680
(b) .52
(c) .144
(d) 1.00

6-2 (a) $S_0(x)-S_0(x+1) = \frac{\ell_x - \ell_{x+1}}{\ell_0} = \frac{d_x}{\ell_0}$

6-3 1.80938

6-4 (a) 90
(b) .20
(c) $\frac{5}{24}$

6-5 2081.61

6-6 (a) $-\,{}_tp_x\mu_{x+t}$
(b) ${}_tp_x(\mu_x-\mu_{x+t})$

6-7 .001275

6-8 .20094

6-9 (a) $(64-.80x)^{-2/3}/15$
(b) 60
(c) 514.286

6-10 133.33

6-11 .15

6-12 7.50; 8.03572

6-13 108

6-14 15.59852

6-20 (a) $1-p$

(b) $\begin{vmatrix} p & 1-p \\ 0 & 1 \end{vmatrix}$

(c) $(p^n, 1-p^n)$

6-21 $\dfrac{p}{1-p}$

6-22 All are correct

6-23 .80

6-24 1.4547

6-25 .0782

6-27 .0078431; .0078905; .0079061; .0079218

6-28 2.78084

6-29 (a) 25.10

(b) 25.09682

6-30 278.85

6-31 .56767

6-36 150,000

6-37 .01029

6-38 .45886

6-39 to 6-42 (See Solutions Manual.)

CHAPTER 7

7-3 −.19686

7-4 .54

7-7 .05486

7-8 5.188

7-9 831.84

7-10 555.27

7-13 .81014

7-14 .30

7-15 .99950

7-16 (a) $\bar{Z}^{1}_{x:\overline{n|}} = \begin{cases} v^{T_x} & \text{for } T_x \leq n \\ 0 & \text{for } T_x > n \end{cases}$

(b) $E[\bar{Z}^{1}_{x:\overline{n|}}] = \bar{A}^{1}_{x:\overline{n|}} = \int_0^n v^t \cdot {}_tp_x\mu_{x+t}\,dt$

$E[\bar{Z}^{1\;2}_{x:\overline{n|}}] = {}^2\bar{A}^{1}_{x:\overline{n|}} = \int_0^n (v')^t \cdot {}_tp_x\mu_{x+t}\,dt$

7-17 (a) ${}_{n|}\bar{Z}_x = \begin{cases} 0 & \text{for } T_x \leq n \\ v^{T_x} & \text{for } T_x > n \end{cases}$

(b) $E[{}_{n|}\bar{Z}_x] = {}_{n|}\bar{A}_x = \int_n^\infty v^t \cdot {}_tp_x\mu_{x+t}\,dt$

$E[{}_{n|}\bar{Z}_x^{\;2}] = {}^2_{n|}\bar{A}_x = \int_n^\infty (v')^t \cdot {}_tp_x\mu_{x+t}\,dt$

7-18 Probability mass of $\frac{2}{7}$ at 0

7-19 .044

7-20 $\frac{\lambda}{\lambda+2\delta} - \left(\frac{\lambda}{\lambda+\delta}\right)^2$

7-21 $\frac{\lambda}{\lambda+\delta} \cdot e^{-(\lambda+\delta)n}$

7-22 .35714

7-24 .03825

7-25 (b) 3.80957

7-26 837.24

7-27 (a) $\frac{1}{7}$

(b) .61339

(c) .01816

7-28 .17973

7-29 .11359

7-30 .21787

7-32 (a) $v^n \cdot {}_np_x^{00}$

(b) $\sum_{t=0}^{n-1} v^{t+1} \cdot {}_tp_x^{00} \cdot p_{x+t}^{01}$

(c) $\sum_{t=n}^{\infty} v^{t+1} \cdot {}_tp_x^{00} \cdot p_{x+t}^{01}$

7-33 (a) $\int_0^n v^t \cdot {}_tp_x^{00} \cdot \mu_{x+t}^{01}\, dt$

(b) $\int_n^\infty v^t \cdot {}_tp_x^{00} \cdot \mu_{x+t}^{01}\, dt$

7-34 (a) $\sum_{k=1}^{\infty} k \cdot v^k \cdot {}_{k-1}p_x^{00} \cdot p_{x+k-1}^{01}$

(b) $\sum_{k=1}^{n} k \cdot v^k \cdot {}_{k-1}p_x^{00} \cdot p_{x+k-1}^{01}$

(c) $\int_0^\infty t \cdot v^t \cdot {}_tp_x^{00} \cdot \mu_{x+t}^{01}\, dt$

(d) $\int_0^n (n-t) \cdot v^t \cdot {}_tp_x^{00} \cdot \mu_{x+t}^{01}\, dt$

CHAPTER 8

8-4 106

8-7 .17719

8-8 150,000

8-13 .65

8-14 .02

8-15 .46600

8-18 4.59

8-26 2.2186

8-27 .26039

8-32 .81058

8-33 1.49032

8-47 .60

8-48 5.78534

8-50 (a) $\sum_{k=1}^{\infty} v^k \cdot {}_k p_x^{00}$

(b) $\sum_{k=0}^{n-1} v^k \cdot {}_k p_x^{00}$, where ${}_0 p_x^{00} = 1$

(c) $\sum_{k=n+1}^{\infty} v^k \cdot {}_k p_x^{00}$

(d) $\int_0^n v^t \cdot {}_t p_x^{00} \, dt$

8-51 1.01432

8-52 .002433

CHAPTER 9

9-4 33.06

9-5 434.71

9-6 154.62

9-7 7272.73

9-10 −.25449

9-11 .43200

9-12 36.77077

9-13 .02188

9-14 .01877

9-15 .00360

9-16 12.77

9-19 .70215

9-20 1.1025

9-21 .04

9-22 .22787

9-24 $\left(\frac{P+\delta l}{P+\delta}\right)^{\lambda/\delta}$

9-25 .20130

9-26 955.07

9-27 .06701

CHAPTER 10

10-1 (a) $_t^hV^1_{x:\overline{n}|} = \begin{cases} A^{\;1}_{x+t:\overline{n-t}|} - {}_hP^1_{x:\overline{n}|} \cdot \ddot{a}_{x+t:\overline{h-t}|} & \text{for } t<h \\ A^{\;1}_{x+t:\overline{n-t}|} & \text{for } t \ge h \end{cases}$

(b) $_t^hV_{x:\overline{n}|} = \begin{cases} A_{x+t:\overline{n-t}|} - {}_hP_{x:\overline{n}|} \cdot \ddot{a}_{x+t:\overline{h-t}|} & \text{for } t<h \\ A_{x+t:\overline{n-t}|} & \text{for } t \ge h \end{cases}$

10-2 $_t^hV({}_n|A_x) = \begin{cases} {}_{n-t}|A_{x+t} - {}_hP({}_n|A_x)\cdot \ddot{a}_{x+t:\overline{h-t}|} & \text{for } t<h \\ {}_{n-t}|A_{x+t} & \text{for } h \le t < n \\ A_{x+t} & \text{for } t \ge n \end{cases}$

10-3 .27273

10-4 (a) $P^1_{x:\overline{n}|} \cdot \ddot{s}_{x:\overline{t}|} - {}_tk_x$ (b) $P_{x:\overline{n}|} \cdot \ddot{s}_{x:\overline{t}|} - {}_tk_x$

(c) $P_{x:\overline{n}|}^{\;\;1} \cdot \ddot{s}_{x:\overline{t}|}$ (There is no accumulated cost of insurance because there is no benefit payable in $(x, x+t]$.)

(d) ${}_hP_x \cdot \ddot{s}_{x:\overline{h}|} \cdot \frac{1}{{}_{t-h}E_{x+h}} - {}_tk_x$

10-6 330.38

10-7 1180.00

10-8 (a) ${}_tL_{x:\overline{n}|} = Z_{x+t:\overline{n-t}|} - P_{x:\overline{n}|} \cdot \ddot{Y}_{x+t:\overline{n-t}|}$, where

$$Z_{x+t:\overline{n-t}|} = \begin{cases} v^{K_x-t} & \text{for } K_x \le n \\ v^{n-t} & \text{for } K_x > n \end{cases}$$

and

$$\ddot{Y}_{x+t:\overline{n-t}|} = \begin{cases} \ddot{a}_{\overline{K_x-t}|} & \text{for } K_x \le n \\ \ddot{a}_{\overline{n-t}|} & \text{for } K_x > n \end{cases}$$

(b) $A_{x+t:\overline{n-t}|} - P_{x:\overline{n}|} \cdot \ddot{a}_{x+t:\overline{n-t}|}$ (c) $\left(1+\frac{P_{x:\overline{n}|}}{d}\right)^2 \cdot \left({}^2A_{x+t:\overline{n-t}|} - A_{x+t:\overline{n-t}|}{}^2\right)$

10-9 .83

10-12 1.39730

10-13 .025

10-14 .979

10-15 .03312

10-16 9.82254

10-17 8.75630

10-20 .40

10-21 22.22

10-22 .07516

10-23 0; all continuous contingent functions based on the exponential distribution are constants with respect to age, so future premiums are always adequate to fund future benefits and no reserve is ever needed (prospective view) and no reserve ever accumulates (retrospective view).

10-25 .17352

10-26 .06036

10-27 $\sum_{k=0}^{\infty} v^{k+1} \cdot {}_kp_{50}^{00} \cdot p_{50+k}^{01} - \frac{\sum_{k=0}^{\infty} v^{k+1} \cdot {}_kp_{30}^{00} \cdot p_{30+k}^{01}}{\sum_{k=0}^{\infty} v^k \cdot {}_kp_{30}^{00}} \cdot \sum_{k=0}^{\infty} v^k \cdot {}_kp_{50}^{00}$

10-28 $\sum_{k=0}^{9} v^{k+1} \cdot {}_kp_{40}^{00} \cdot p_{40+k}^{01} - \frac{\sum_{k=0}^{19} v^{k+1} \cdot {}_kp_{30}^{00} \cdot p_{30+k}^{01}}{\sum_{k=0}^{19} v^k \cdot {}_kp_{30}^{00}} \cdot \sum_{k=0}^{9} v^k \cdot {}_kp_{40}^{00}$

CHAPTER 11

11-7 $\sum_{k=0}^{t-1} P_{k+1} \cdot \frac{1}{{}_{t-k}E_{x+k}} - \sum_{k=1}^{t} b_k \cdot \frac{(1+i)^{t-k} \cdot {}_{k-1|}q_x}{{}_tp_x}$

11-8 9.41107

11-9 528.14

11-10 .50152

11-11 799.00

11-14 (a) .21500 (b) .75000

11-17 $\frac{d}{dt}\,{}_t\bar{V} = \bar{G}_t(1-r_t) - \bar{e}_t + \delta \cdot {}_t\bar{V} - \mu_{x+t}(b_t - {}_t\bar{V})$

11-19 (a) −1824.77 (b) 9741.60 (c) 463.32

11-20 (a) 463.62 (b) −467.02

CHAPTER 12

12-2 .08384

12-3 .51017

12-4 3.54167

12-5 100

12-6 $\frac{1}{12}$

12-7 (b) and (c)

12-9 .99725

12-10 100

12-11 .54545

12-12 1.07692

12-13 10.10

12-14 .05

12-15 .18000

12-16 .02222

12-17 14

12-18 (a) $\int_0^n v^t \cdot {}_tp_{xy}^{00}\, dt$

(b) $\dfrac{\sum\limits_{k=0}^{\infty} v^{k+1} \cdot {}_kp_{xy}^{00}\left(p_{x+k:y+k}^{01} + p_{x+k:y+k}^{02}\right)}{\sum\limits_{k=0}^{\infty} v^k \cdot {}_kp_{xy}^{00}}$

(c) $\sum\limits_{k=0}^{n-1} v^{k+1} \cdot {}_kp_{xy}^{00}\left(p_{x+k:y+k}^{01} + p_{x+k:y+k}^{02}\right) + v^n \cdot {}_np_{xy}^{00}$

(d) $\dfrac{\int_0^n v^t \cdot {}_tp_{xy}^{00}\left(\mu_{x+t:y+t}^{01} + \mu_{x+t:y+t}^{02}\right) dt}{\int_0^n v^t \cdot {}_tp_{xy}^{00}\, dt}$

12-19 $\sum\limits_{k=1}^{\infty} v^k \cdot {}_kp_{xy}^{02}$

12-20 (a) $\int_0^\infty v^t \cdot {}_tp_{xy}^{00} \cdot \mu_{x+t:y+t}^{02}\, dt$

(b) $\int_0^\infty v^t \cdot {}_tp_{xy}^{00} \cdot \mu_{x+t:y+t}^{01}\, dt$

(c) $\int_0^\infty v^t \cdot {}_tp_{xy}^{01} \cdot \mu_{x+t}^{13}\, dt$

(d) $\int_0^\infty v^t \cdot {}_tp_{xy}^{02} \cdot \mu_{y+t}^{23}\, dt$

12-21 (a) $\int_0^\infty v^t\left({}_tp_{xy}^{00} + {}_tp_{xy}^{01} + {}_tp_{xy}^{02}\right)dt$

(b) $\sum_{k=0}^{n-1} v^k\left({}_kp_{xy}^{00} + {}_kp_{xy}^{01} + {}_kp_{xy}^{02}\right)$

(c) $\sum_{k=0}^{n-1} v^{k+1}\left({}_kp_{xy}^{01}\cdot p_{x+k}^{13} + {}_kp_{xy}^{02}\cdot p_{y+k}^{23}\right)$

(d) $\int_n^\infty v^t\left({}_tp_{xy}^{01}\cdot \mu_{x+t}^{13} + {}_tp_{xy}^{02}\cdot \mu_{y+t}^{23}\right)dt$

12-22 ${}_np_{xy}$

12-23 (a) ${}_np_x$

(b) ${}_nq_x$

12-24 (a) $\bar{P} + {}_t\bar{V}^{(0)}\cdot(\delta + \mu_{x+t:y+t}^{01} + \mu_{x+t:y+t}^{02}) - {}_t\bar{V}^{(2)}\cdot \mu_{x+t:y+t}^{02}$

(b) Does not exist

(c) $\delta\cdot{}_t\bar{V}^{(2)} - \mu_{y+t}^{23}\cdot(B - {}_t\bar{V}^{(2)})$

12-25 (a) $\delta\cdot{}_t\bar{V}^{(1)} - \mu_{x+t}^{13}\cdot(B - {}_t\bar{V}^{(1)})$

(b) $\delta\cdot{}_t\bar{V}^{(2)} - \mu_{y+t}^{23}\cdot(B - {}_t\bar{V}^{(2)})$

(c) Does not exist

12-27 $(1+t)^{-1}$

12-28 .46667

12-29 .16667

12-30 $(1+3n)^{-1}$

12-31 $\dfrac{2n^2(2+3n)}{(1+n)(1+2n)(1+3n)}$

12-32 .03922

12-33 .73609

CHAPTER 13

13-1 .38

13-2 802.56

13-3 .2157

13-4 (b) $\frac{1}{1+t+t^2}$

13-5 (a) $\frac{75-t}{75}$, for $0 \leq t < 75$

$\left(\frac{50-t}{50}\right)^2$, for $0 \leq t < 50$

$\frac{(75-t)(50-t)^2}{187{,}500}$, for $0 \leq t < 50$; 0 for $t \geq 50$

(b) $\frac{(50-t)^2}{187{,}500}$; $\frac{(50-t)(75-t)}{93{,}750}$

(c) .01307; .03934; .05241

(d) .01333; .03960

(e) $\frac{2}{9}$; $\frac{7}{9}$

(f) .24873; .75127

13-6 7.7373

13-8 .19020

13-9 14.775; 29.775

13-10 .20

13-12 20.625

13-13

x	$q_x^{(1)}$	$q_x^{(2)}$
0	.0875	.2375
1	.1800	.1800
2	.1900	.0900

13-14 (a) .29108; .39788 (b) .32500; .24300; .12096

13-15 (a) .67857 (b) .30160

13-16 .09405

13-17 .11625

CHAPTER 14

14-1 (a) $20{,}000\left(v^{40}\cdot {}_{40}p_{25}^{(\tau)}\cdot \bar{a}_{65}\right)$ (b) $200{,}000\int_0^{40} v^t \cdot {}_tp_{25}^{(\tau)}\cdot \mu_{25+t}^{(1)}\,dt$

(c) $400\int_0^{40} t\cdot v^t \cdot {}_tp_{25}^{(\tau)}\cdot \mu_{25+t}^{(2)}\cdot \bar{a}_{\overline{40-t|}25+t}\,dt$

14-3 7,013.63

14-4 35,230.21

14-7 82,711.91

14-8 (a) $\int_0^n {}_tp_x^{00}\cdot \mu_{x+t}^{02}\,dt = \int_0^n {}_tp_x^{(\tau)}\cdot \mu_{x+t}^{(2)}\,dt$ (b) .54072

14-9 (a) 27 (b) 64

14-10 (a) $\exp\left\{-\int_0^n \left[\mu_{x+t}^{01}+\mu_{x+t}^{02}\right]dt\right\}$

(b) ${}_np_x^{(\tau)} = \exp\left(-\int_0^n \mu_{x+t}^{(\tau)}\,dt\right)$

14-11 (a) $\int_0^n \left[{}_tp_x^{00}\cdot \mu_{x+t}^{02} + {}_tp_x^{01}\cdot \mu_{x+t}^{12}\right]dt$

(b) ${}_nq_x^{(f)} = \int_0^n \left({}_tp_x^{(\tau)}\cdot \mu_{x+t}^{(f)} + \mu_{x+t}^{d}\int_0^t {}_sp_x^{(\tau)}\cdot \mu_{x+s}^{(d)}\,ds\right)dt$

14-12 (a) $\int_0^n {}_tp_x^{11}\cdot \mu_{x+t}^{12}\,dt$ (b) ${}_nq_x^d = \int_0^n {}_tp_x^d\cdot \mu_{x+t}^d\,dt$

14-13 .47645

14-14 (a) The diagram is the same as in Figure 14.6.

(b)

t	${}_tp_x^{00}$	${}_tp_x^{01}$	t	${}_tp_x^{00}$	${}_tp_x^{01}$
1	.750	.200	11	.374	.195
2	.714	.188	12	.341	.199
3	.671	.187	13	.310	.203
4	.629	.186	14	.279	.209
5	.588	.185	15	.248	.215
6	.550	.186	16	.218	.222
7	.512	.186	17	.188	.230
8	.476	.188	18	.158	.240
9	.441	.189	19	.127	.250
10	.407	.192	20	.096	.262

(c) .409; .193
These results are closer to the true solution than those of part (a).

(d) .412; .194

14-15 (a) $h = \frac{1}{12}$

(b) 43,825

14-16 58,415

14-17 543.90

14-18 6507

14-19 .863283

14-20 .064472

14-21 $\frac{d}{dt}\,{}_t\bar{V}^{(0)} = \bar{G}_t(1-r_t) - \bar{e}_t + \delta_t \cdot {}_t\bar{V}^{(0)} - \mu_{x+t}^{02}\left(B - {}_t\bar{V}^{(0)}\right) - \mu_{x+t}^{01}\left({}_t\bar{V}^{(1)} - {}_t\bar{V}^{(0)}\right)$

and $\frac{d}{dt}\,{}_t\bar{V}^{(1)} = \delta_t \cdot {}_t\bar{V}^{(1)} - R - \mu_{x+t}^{12}\left(B - {}_t\bar{V}^{(1)}\right) - \mu_{x+t}^{10}\left({}_t\bar{V}^{(0)} - {}_t\bar{V}^{(1)}\right)$, where R is the rate of continuous disability income and B is the amount of failure (death) benefit at time t, assumed to be the same whether healthy or disabled.

14-22 $\frac{d}{dt}\,{}_t\bar{V}^{(i)} = \bar{G}_t^{(i)}\left(1-r_t^{(i)}\right) - \bar{e}_t^{(i)} + \delta_t \cdot {}_t\bar{V}^{(i)} - \bar{b}_t^{(i)} - \sum_{j \neq i} \mu_{x+t}^{ij} \cdot \left(b_t^{(ij)} + {}_t\bar{V}^{(j)} - {}_t\bar{V}^{(i)}\right)$

14-23 (a) $\begin{bmatrix} .826 & .168 & .006 \\ .345 & .617 & .038 \\ .111 & .500 & .389 \end{bmatrix}$

(b) 4,117.50

(c) (.665, .311, .004); (.659, .316, .025)

(d) 5,486.56

14-24 (a) 418,458.16

(b) 146,460.46

(c) 32.41%

(d) 59.62%

14-25 (a) .42981

(b) .50

14-26 (a) $APV_{51}^{NR} = PAB_{65} \cdot v^{14} \cdot {}_{14}p_{51}^{(\tau)} \cdot {}^{r}\ddot{a}_{65}^{(12)}$, where $PAB_{65} = 22{,}425.92$

(b) $APV_{51}^{ER} = \sum_{y=61}^{64} \left[1-.03\left(65-y-\tfrac{1}{2}\right)\right] \cdot PAB_{y+1/2} \cdot v^{y+1/2-51} \cdot {}_{y-51}p_{51}^{(\tau)} \cdot q_y^{(r)} \cdot {}^{r}\ddot{a}_{y+1/2}^{(12)},$

where

$$PAB_{y+1/2} = .01\left(y+\tfrac{1}{2}-51\right)(100{,}000) \cdot \frac{1}{3}\left(\frac{\frac{1}{2}S_{y-3}+S_{y-2}+S_{y-1}+\frac{1}{2}S_y}{S_{51}}\right)$$

(c) $APV_{51}^{W} = \sum_{y=56}^{60} PAB_{y+1/2} \cdot v^{14} \cdot {}_{y-51}p_{51}^{(\tau)} \cdot q_y^{(w)} \; {}_{65-y-1/2}^{\;\;w}p_{y+1/2} \cdot {}^{r}\ddot{a}_{65}^{(12)}$

(d) $APV_{51}^{I} = \sum_{y=56}^{64} PAB_{y+1/2} \cdot v^{y+1/2-51} \cdot {}_{y-51}p_{51}^{(\tau)} \cdot q_y^{(i)} \cdot {}^{i}\ddot{a}_{y+1/2}^{(12)}$

(e) $APV_{51}^{D} = \sum_{y=61}^{64} .50\left[1-.03\left(65-y-\tfrac{1}{2}\right)\right]$

$\cdot PAB_{y+1/2} \cdot v^{y+1/2-51} \cdot {}_{y-51}p_{51}^{(\tau)} \cdot q_y^{(d)} \cdot {}^{r}\ddot{a}_{y+1/2-3}^{(12)}$

14-27 (a) 1860

(b) The APV for each benefit is calculated the same as in Exercise 14-25, except that PAB_{65} in part (a) and $PAB_{y+1/2}$ in parts (b)-(e) are all replaced by the benefit accrual 1860. The unit credit normal cost is the sum of these five APVs.

(c) The APV for each benefit is calculated the same as in part (b), except that the 1860 benefit accrual is replaced by the 7500 accrued benefit. The accrued liability is the sum of these five APVs.

14-29 (a) −4362.80 (b) 28.25

CHAPTER 15

15-1 577.93; 635.97

15-2 .1875; .1958

15-3 (a) 3.8461

(b) .6155

15-4 (a)

Interest Rate Scenario	Annuity Certain	Life Annuity	Term Insurance
Increasing	3.97	2.53	.53
Decreasing	4.25	2.65	.57

(b) The life annuity

15-5 (a) 289.84; 46.73

(b) Increasing: 23.74; 6.10
Decreasing: –29.25; –7.96

(c) The annual premium product

15-7 2.0%; 4.020%; 6.082%; 8.211%

15-8 2.0%; 4.041%; 6.169%; 8.447%

15-9 2.0%; 3.960%; 5.844%; 7.615%

15-10 2.0%; 3.980%; 5.921%; 7.804%

15-11 74,020

15-14

n	1	2	3	4	5
z_n	4.000%	4.499%	4.997%	5.494%	5.991%

15-15

n	$f_{n,1}$	$f_{n,2}$	$f_{n,3}$	$f_{n,4}$	$f_{n,5}$
0	4.00%	4.499%	4.997%	5.494%	5.991%
1	5.00	5.499	5.997	6.494	--
2	6.00	6.499	6.997	--	--
3	7.00	7.499	--	--	--
4	8.00	--	--	--	--

15-16 (a) 6.997%

(b) Sell a 2-year zero-coupon bond and buy a 5-year zero-coupon bond, each of face amount 274,724.24.

15-17 (a) 5.499%

(b) Sell a 1-year zero-coupon bond and buy a 3-year zero-coupon bond, each of face amount 24,038.46.

15-18

n	$f_{n,1}$	$f_{n,2}$	$f_{n,3}$
1	6.12%	8.32%	10.685%
2	10.56	13.04	--
3	15.58	--	--

15-19, 15-20, 15-21 (See Solutions Manual.)

CHAPTER 16

16-1 2,489.89; 2,479.75; 2,469.59

16-2 1,107.20; 5,676.06; 10,382.10; 15,229.06; 20,221.79

16-3 (b) 44,125.63

16-4 (a) 4,928.54

(b) 3,928.54

(c) 3,928.54

16-5 (a) 5411.49

(b) 4411.49

(c) 3711.49

16-6 (c) 118.66

(d) 119.86; −21.20; 20.00

16-7 (a) 24; 9

(b) 12,000,000; 4,500,000

(c) 6300

16-8 (a) 8.0%; 10.0%; 1.0%

(b) 268.87; 1122.47; 1762.82

16-9 (a) 103,588.72

(b) 65,576.44

16-10 49,027.33

16-11 (a) 5926.20

(b) 14,678.57

(c) .40373

16-12 (a) 5.096%

(b) 3.640%

16-13 93,000

CHAPTER 17

17-1 (a) −26.79

(c) Does not exist

(d) −.00831

17-2 (a) $(-3{,}000.00, 2{,}482.00, 1{,}323.60, 110.00)$

(b) $(-3{,}000.00, 2{,}482.00, 1{,}303.75, 106.51)$

(c) 413.86

(d) .2105

(e) 2

(f) .00877

17-3 .08519

17-7 (a)

t	0	1	2	3	4	5
${}_tV^Z$	0.00	0.00	133.63	243.97	209.52	0.00

(b) (−3,000.00, 450.00, 98.24, 0.00, 0.00, 0.00)

17-10 .01005

17-11 5,298.68

17-12 (a) 580.00

(b) 120.16

17.13 (a) .0000025

(b) (−5.74, 4.14, 4.25, 4.31)

(c) (−5.74, 4.13, 4.24, 4.29)

(d) 5.51

(e) .00801

17.14 (a) $\left[{}_tV_{45}^G + 2{,}264.12\,(1-r_{t+1})\right](1.04)$

$$-100{,}000\, q_{45+t}^{(d)} - {}_{t+1}CV_{45} \cdot q_{45+t}^{(w)} - {}_{t+1}V_{45}^G \cdot p_{45+t}^{(\tau)}$$

(b) (−5,000.00, 1,823.40, 1,864.05, 1,830.05, 455.56, 71.52,
70.14, 71.64, 70.08, 69.81, 71.08)

(c) (−5,000.00, 1,823.40, 1,763.76, 1,637.93, 385.54, 57.21,
53.01, 52.21, 49.22, 47.23 46.29)

(d) −237.72

(e) −.01870

BIBLIOGRAPHY

1. Balducci, G., "Costruzione e critica della tavola di mortalita," *Gior. degli Economisti e Riv. Di Statis.*, 55 (1917), 455.

2. _______, Correspondence, *JIA*, LII (1921), 184.

3. Batten, R.W., *Mortality Table Construction.* Englewood Cliffs: Prentice-Hall, Inc., 1978.

4. Bowers, N.L., et al., *Actuarial Mathematics* (Second Edition). Schaumburg: Society of Actuaries, 1997.

5. Broverman, S.A., *Mathematics of Investment and Credit* (Fifth Edition). Winsted: ACTEX Publications, 2010.

6. Brown, R.L., *Introduction to the Mathematics of Demography* (Third Edition). Winsted: ACTEX Publications, 1997.

7. Dickson, D.C.M., M.R. Hardy, and H.R. Waters, *Actuarial Mathematics for Life Contingent Risks* (Second Edition). Cambridge: Cambridge University Press, 2013.

8. Dobson, R.H., "Mortality and Morbidity Tables," Society of Actuaries Study Note 7BA-111-83, 1983.

9. Gompertz, B., "On the Nature of the Function Expressive of the Law of Human Mortality," *Phil. Trans.*, Royal Society of London, 1825.

10. Halley, E., "An Estimate of the Degrees of the Mortality of Mankind, Drawn from Various Tables of Births and Funerals at the City of Breslau," 1693.

11. Hare, D.J.P. and W.F. Scott, "The Scottish Ministers' Widow's Fund of 1744," in *The Scottish Ministers' Widow's Fund, 1743-1993.* Edinburgh: St. Andrews Press, 1992.

12. Hassett, M.J. and D.G. Stewart, *Probability for Risk Management* (Second Edition). Winsted: ACTEX Publications, 2006.

13. Jones, B.L., "A Stochastic Model for CCRC's," *ARCH*, 1955.1.

14. Jordan, C.W., *Life Contingencies* (Second Edition). Chicago: Society of Actuaries, 1967.

15. Kellison, S.G., *The Theory of Interest* (Third Edition). New York: McGraw Hill Irwin, 2009.

16. Kellison, S.G. and R.L. London, *Risk Models and Their Estimation*. Winsted: ACTEX Publications, 2011.

17. Klugman, S.A., H.H. Panjer, and G.E. Willmot, *Loss Models: From Data to Decisions* (Fourth Edition). Hoboken: John Wiley & Sons, 2012.

18. London, D., *Survival Models and Their Estimation* (Third Edition). Winsted: ACTEX Publications, 1997.

19. Makeham, W.M., "On the Law of Mortality, and the Construction of Annuity Tables," *JIA*, VIII (1860).

20. Mereu, J.A., "Some Observations on Actuarial Approximations," *TSA*, XIII (1961), 87.

21. Ross, S.M., *A First Course in Probability* (Sixth Edition). Old Tappen: Prentice-Hall, 2001.

22. _______, *Introduction to Probability Models* (Eighth Edition). San Diego: Academic Press, 2003.

23. Trenerry, C.F., E.L. Gover, and A.S. Paul, Editors, *The Origin and Early History of Insurance Including the Contract of Bottomry*. London: P.S. King & Son, 1926. (Reprinted 2009, 2010 by The Lawbook Exchange, Ltd.)

24. Woolhouse, W.S.B., "On an Improved Theory of Annuities and Assurances," *JIA*, XV (1869).

INDEX